UPCO'S Living Environment

AN ACTIVITY ORIENTED BIOLOGY COURSE

LORRAINE GODLEWSKI

UPCO – United Publishing Co., Inc.
Albany, New York

Author

LORRAINE GODLEWSKI, New Hartford, New York
Former Science Department Chairperson, Utica Free Academy, Utica, New York
Science Writer and Editor

Acknowledgements

Science Editor

PETER BRUSOE, Albany, New York
Earth Science Teacher, Albany High School, Albany, New York

ISBN 978-937323-16-8

TABLE OF CONTENTS

UNIT ONE: INTRODUCTION TO THE STUDY OF THE ENVIRONMENT

UNIT TWO: SIMILARITIES AMONG LIVING THINGS

UNIT THREE: HUMAN BIOLOGY

UNIT FOUR: DIVERSITY AMONG LIVING THINGS

UNIT FIVE: REPRODUCTION AND DEVELOPMENT

UNIT SIX: GENETICS AND HEREDITY

UNIT SEVEN: EVOLUTION OF LIVING THINGS

UNIT EIGHT: LIVING THINGS AND THEIR ENVIRONMENT

Name__________ Class__________ Date__________

UNIT ONE

INTRODUCTION TO THE STUDY OF THE LIVING ENVIRONMENT

LEARNING OUTCOMES: Upon completion of the study of this unit, you should be able to:

- State several reasons why everyone should study science.
- Define biology as the science that deals with living things.
- Describe the steps of the scientific method.
- Name some safety suggestions for the biology laboratory and recognize common biology laboratory apparatus.
- Be able to use and read instruments such as metric rulers, Celsius thermometers, and graduated cylinders.
- Interpret and produce bar and linear graphs.

Chapter 1: Biology and Science

A. BIOLOGY AND THE LIVING ENVIRONMENT. Biology is the name of the science that studies living things and their relationship to their environment. You should have a basic scientific knowledge, called **scientific literacy**, of your living and nonliving environment because scientific literacy involves internalizing a scientific critical attitude that can be applied to your life. It will help you to be better informed when making important decisions about your everyday life, particularly in relation to your health, and to issues concerning commercial and technological claims concerning the environment. Understanding the scientific view of the natural world is an essential part your personal, societal, and ethical decision making. The study of the living environment will also help you understand and apply scientific concepts, principles, and theories pertaining to the physical setting and the living environment, and to recognize the historical development of ideas in science.

REVIEW QUESTION

1. Biology studies ____________________

B. WHAT IS SCIENCE? Science is both a body of knowledge and a way of knowing and explaining how the world works. It relies on logic and creativity and comes from the study of nature and the universe and the forces that affect them. Science is made up of facts and theories. **Facts** are based on experiments and careful observations and **theories** are scientific guesses— possible answers to complex problems. Theories are changed as new evidence arises and can eventually become scientific laws. A **scientific law** results only when many scientists repeatedly reach the same conclusions. Scientific explanations or theories are developed by using both observations (evidence) and what people already know about the world (scientific knowledge). All scientific explanations are tentative and subject to change. Good science involves questioning, observing and inferring, experimenting, finding evidence, collecting and organizing data, drawing valid conclusions, and undergoing peer review. (Peer review involves the reviewing of experimental results by other scientists.) The sciences that deal with nonliving things are known as **physical sciences** and those that deal with living things are called **biological sciences**.

REVIEW QUESTIONS

1. Science is defined as the body of knowledge that results from ______________________
____
2. Facts are based on ______________________ and ______________________.
3. Theories are ____.
4. State the difference between physical science and biological science.
____
____
5. A scientific law results from ____

C. SCIENTIFIC INQUIRY. The technique used by scientists to solve problems is known as the **scientific method**. The scientific method (scientific inquiry) solves problems in a logical and organized way (Figure 1-1). There is no "mystery" to the scientific method. It is just a matter of logical thinking and common sense and involves asking questions and locating, interpreting, and processing information from a variety of sources. It also involves making judgements about the reliability of the source and the relevance of information. You have probably used it yourself to solve your own everyday problems. The steps in inquiry using the scientific method are listed on the next page.

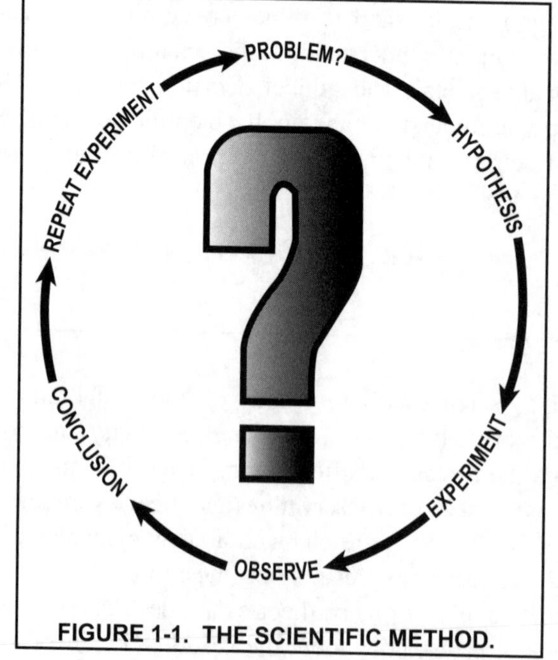

FIGURE 1-1. THE SCIENTIFIC METHOD.

Name________________________ Class____________________ Date__________

Steps of the Scientific Method

(1) State the Problem. The **problem** is a question for which the scientist is trying to find an answer.

(2) Propose a Hypothesis. A **hypothesis** is a prediction about the possible answer to a problem based upon research, previous knowledge of the problem, and observations and information gained from studying a problem. Hypotheses are widely used in science for determining what data to collect and as a guide for interpreting the data. They are valuable, even if they turn out not to be true, because they may lead to further investigation.

(3) Test the Hypothesis. The scientist must design an experiment, called a controlled experiment, that will test the hypothesis. It must involve repeated trials, large sample size, and objective data collection techniques. A **controlled experiment** tests only one factor called the **variable**. The parts of the experiment that remain the same are the **controls.**

(4) Make Observations. The scientist now makes **observations,** called **data,** that are recorded in an organized manner. These observations may include careful measurements as well as observations made with the senses and with instruments. Observations are represented and organized by diagrams, tables, charts, graphs, equations, and matrices. From these observations a conclusion about the problem is reached or the interpretation of the data can lead to the development of additional hypotheses, the formulation of generalizations, or explanations of natural phenomena (a rare scientific fact or event).

(5) State a Conclusion. The answer to the problem is called the **conclusion**. To be valid or true the conclusion must be supported. Conclusions are questioned if the data are based on samples that are very small, biased, inadequately controlled, or if the conclusions are based on the faulty, incomplete, or misleading use of numbers. They are also questioned if fact and opinion are intermingled, if adequate evidence is not cited, or if the conclusions do not follow logically from the evidence given.

(6) Repeat the Experiment. Scientists make the results of their investigations public so that the experiment can be repeated many times by other scientists in order to test the conclusions. When, after repeated testing, many scientists reach the same conclusion the conclusion can be called a scientific law.

Review Question

1. List the steps of the scientific method. ______________________________

____

____

Name____________________ **Class**________________ **Date**________

2. Define the term hypothesis. ____________________________________

____

____

3. State the difference between a variable and a control. ____________________

____

____

4. __________________________ are made with the senses and with instruments.

5. The conclusion is the ________________________ .

6. The experiment should be ____________________ many times to check the conclusions.

7. When many scientists reach the same conclusion the conclusion may be called a

____________________.

D. BRANCHES OF BIOLOGY. Our knowledge of living things is so great that it necessary to divide biology into many branches. Each branch deals with a special area as described in the following chart.

SOME BRANCHES OF BIOLOGY

Anatomy	The study of the structure of organisms.
Bacteriology	The study of bacteria.
Botany	The study of plants.
Cytology	The study of cells.
Ecology	The study of the interactions of organisms with their environment.
Embryology	The study of the development of embryos.
Endocrinology	The study of the endocrine glands.
Genetics	The study of heredity.
Histology	The study of tissues of living things.
Hygiene	The study of conditions and practices that help maintain good health.
Zoology	The study of animals.

REVIEW QUESTIONS

1. Zoology is the study of ______________ while the study of plants is called ______________ .

2. Name and describe two branches of biology.

____

____

Name______________________ Class______________________ Date__________

LAB INVESTIGATON: A CONTROLLED EXPERIMENT

OBJECTIVE

Upon completion of this activity you should be able to set up a controlled experiment.

LABORATORY PROCEDURE

Materials: Two plants of the same species (e.g. ivy plants) that are identical in size and shape and planted in the same kind of soil. Water, labels, and marking pencils.

1. In this lab you will set up a controlled experiment to determine whether green plants need water to survive.

2. Your teacher has provided you with two identical plants. Label one plant the **CONTROL PLANT (WATER EVERY DAY)** and the other plant the **EXPERIMENTAL PLANT (DO NOT WATER).**

3. Place your plants near a window or in a lighted area. Water the control plant with a small amount of water every day. **Do not** water the experimental plant.

4. Observe your plants every other day for 20 days and write your observations in the **Observation Table** in the following section.

OBSERVATIONS

DAY	OBSERVATIONS
2	
4	
6	
8	
10	
12	
14	
16	
18	
20	

Name______________________ Class______________________ Date______________

Conclusion

1. State the problem for your experiment. ______________________

____

2. What was the variable in your experiment? ______________________
3. What was the control in your experiment? ______________________
4. In a controlled experiment you should test only ______________ factor.
5. State in one sentence your observations about your experimental plant after a 20 day period.

____

____

6. What is your conclusion in this experiment? ______________________

____

____

7. In the space below, describe a controlled experiment that you could perform to test whether plants need light energy to live.

____

____

____

____

____

____

____

____

____

____

____

____

____

____

____

Name ____________________ Class ____________________ Date __________

REVIEW ACTIVITIES

Important Terms

***DIRECTIONS:** Define the following terms in the spaces provided.*

anatomy ____________________

____

bacteriology ____________________

____

biological sciences ____________________

____

biology ____________________

____

botany ____________________

____

conclusion ____________________

____

controls ____________________

____

controlled experiment ____________________

____

cytology ____________________

____

data ____________________

____

ecology ____________________

____

embryology ____________________

____

endocrinology ____________________

____

Name________________ Class________________ Date__________

genetics ____

____

histology ____

____

hygiene ____

____

hypothesis ____

____

physical sciences ____

____

physiology ____

____

problem ____

____

science ____

____

theory ____

____

variable ____

____

zoology ____

____

Name______________________ Class______________________ Date__________

Skill Practice

Defining Vocabulary Words

Do you get "turned off" by the vocabulary in science books? So do most students until they learn that all those long words are just small words joined together.

The following activity will teach you how to look for "hints" in long words so that it will be easier for you to figure out what they mean. For example, when you see the word **"zoology"** you will find two hints. **Zoo** means something to do with animals and **logy** refers to science. Put both hints together and what do you get? Right! Zoology is the science that studies animals. Let's try another word. What is the meaning of **cytology**? There's that hint **logy** again. You now know "logy" means science. Check the list below and find **cyto**. When you put the two hints together you get cell science, therefore, cytology must be the science that studies cells.

The list below contains some common word hints called prefixes and suffixes.[1] Use this list to help you define the words in the following activity. You can also refer to this list when you find a word in your reading that is unfamiliar to you.

Some Common Science Prefixes and Suffixes

a-	not, without	*di-*	double, twice
ab-	from, away, off	*diplo-*	double
aero-	air, atmosphere	*dorso-*	back
an-	not, withou	*ec-, eco*	environment
anti-	opposed, against	*ecto-*	outside, external
auto-	self	*endo-*	within, inside
bi-	two	*exo-*	outside, outer
bio-	life	*extra-*	outside
botane-	pasture, herbs	*gastro-*	stomach
cardi-	heart	*geo-*	earth ground
carn-	flesh	*graph*	written
centi-	hundred, hundredth	*hemi-*	half
cerebro-	brain	*hemo-*	blood
chemo-	chemical, chemistry	*herb-*	plant
-cide	killer	*homo-*	same, similar, alike
cranio-	cranium (skull)	*hydro-*	water
cyto-,-cyte	cell	*hyper-*	above, beyond
deca-	ten	*hypo-*	under, down
deci-	tenth part	*in-*	within, into
dermato-	skin	*inter-*	between, among

[1]Definitions were taken from *Webster's Ninth New Collegiate Dictionary*, Merriam-Webster Inc., 1988.

Name______________________________ Class______________________ Date____________

intra-	within, between	*photo-*	light
-itis	desease, inflammation	*-plasm*	formed material
kilo-	thousand	*-pod*	foot
-lateral	side	*pro-*	before
-logy	science	*pseudo-*	false
macro-	large	*pulmo-*	lung
meso-	in the middle	*reni-*	kidney
meta-	among, with	*-scope*	viewing instrument
-meter	measuring instrument	*semi-*	half
micro-	small, minute	*spermato*	seed
milli-	thousandth	*sub-*	under, below
mono-	one, single	*-synthesis*	to combine
nephro-	kidney	*therm-*	heat
neuro-	nerve	*trans-*	across, beyond
non-	not, other than	*tri-*	three
osteo	bone	*uni-*	one, single
ovi-	egg	*-vore*	eating, feeding
-phage	one that eats	*zoo-*	animal

DIRECTIONS: Define the following words using the prefixes and suffixes in the preceding list and your knowledge of the English language.

dermatitis ______________________________

herbivore ______________________________

geology ______________________________

nephrology ______________________________

bilateral ______________________________

abnormal ______________________________

cardiology ______________________________

ecology ______________________________

biology ______________________________

endosperm ______________________________

hypothermic ______________________________

intercellular ______________________________

antibody ______________________________

insecticide ______________________________

thermometer ______________________________

neurosurgeon ______________________________

decimeter ______________________________

cytoplasm ______________________________

mesoderm ______________________________

hypoactive ______________________________

gastroscope ______________________________

prophases ______________________________

intramuscular ______________________________

exoskeleton ______________________________

extracellular ______________________________

photosynthesis ______________________________

millimeter ______________________________

carnivorous ______________________________

hemisphere ______________________________

cranial ______________________________

asexual ______________________________

dorsal ______________________________

Name________________________ Class________________________ Date____________

CHAPTER 1: QUIZ

A. FILL-IN QUESTIONS

DIRECTIONS: Complete each of the following statements by writing the correct word or phrase in the space provided.

1. The body of knowledge that results from the study of things in nature and the universe is called ________________________.
2. Facts are based on ________________________.
3. The first step in the scientific method is to ________________________.
4. The sciences that deal with nonliving things are known as ________________________.
5. The sciences that deal with living things are called ________________________.
6. Careers are ________________ that are available for people.
7. The study of animals is known as ________________________.
8. The planned study and methods used by scientists to gain information is the ________________________.
9. A question for which the scientist is trying to find an answer is the ________________________.
10. A hypothesis is a/an ________________________.
11. An experiment that tests only one factor is a ________________________.
12. The factor to be tested is called the ________________________.
13. Another experiment that is the same in every way but does not contain the variable is called the ________________________.
14. The conclusion is the ________________________.
15. Facts are also called ________________________.
16. A conclusion can be called a scientific law when ________________________.
17. Possible answers to very complex problems are called ________________________.
18. Your senses provide you with ________________________.
19. Theories are changed as ________________________.
20. In order to check conclusions the experiment must be ________________________.

Name______________________ Class____________________ Date__________

B. MULTIPLE-CHOICE QUESTIONS

DIRECTIONS: Circle the number of the expression that best completes each of the following statements.

1. The first step in the scientific method is
   (1) state the problem (3) state the hypothesis
   (2) do an experiment (4) make an observation.
2. Facts gained from experimentation and observation are known as
   (1) theories (3) data
   (2) laws (4) hypothesis
3. The study of cells is called
   (1) botany (3) biology
   (2) zoology (4) cytology
4. The part of an experiment that does not contain the variable is known as the
   (1) conclusion (3) control
   (2) data (4) variable
5. An educated guess about the possible answer to a problem is called the
   (1) variable (3) problem
   (2) scientific method (4) hypothesis
6. Genetics is the study of
   (1) good health (3) insects
   (2) heredity (4) tissues
7. The science that deals with the interactions of organisms with their living and nonliving environments is
   (1) embryology (3) ecology
   (2) entomology (4) endocrinology
8. The factor in the experiment to be tested is known as the
   (1) variable (3) control
   (2) theory (4) conclusion
9. When writing a report of a laboratory investigation the data collected would be included in the part of the investigation known as the
   (1) materials (3) introduction
   (2) purpose (4) observations
10. When many scientists reach the same conclusion, after repeating an experiment many times, the conclusion can be called a(an)
    (1) theory (3) scientific law
    (2) experiment (4) method

C. ESSAY QUESTION

DIRECTIONS: Use complete sentences to answer the question in this part.

1. Give an example of one of your everyday problems that could have been solved by using the scientific method and describe how you would have used this method to find a solution.

____

____

____

Name______________________________ Class__________________________ Date____________

Chapter 2: The Biology Laboratory

A. SAFETY IN THE LABORATORY. The laboratory is as safe as its least safe person. It is the **responsibility of each student to avoid accidents.** Some safety suggestions for the biology laboratory are listed below.

Safety in the Biology Laboratory

- ✓ **Read, understand,** and **follow** your laboratory directions exactly.
- ✓ **Work quietly, thoughtfully,** and **efficiently**. **Do not** "fool around" in the laboratory.
- ✓ Work in the laboratory room **only when a teacher is present**.
- ✓ **Do not** handle chemicals or equipment until you have been given specific instructions.
- ✓ **Never** directly **taste** or **inhale** laboratory chemicals.
- ✓ **Do not pour** reagents back into stock bottles or exchange stoppers.
- ✓ **Never point** the **open end** of a heated test tube toward anyone.
- ✓ Any reactions that appear to be proceeding in an **abnormal** way should be reported.
- ✓ Be **very** careful when handling **hot glassware** or other equipment.
- ✓ **Report at once** any equipment in the laboratory that appears to be unusual or improper such as **broken, cracked, or jagged apparatus**.
- ✓ **Prevent loose clothing and hair** from coming in contact with any science apparatus, chemicals, or sources of heat or flame.
- ✓ **Tell your teacher immediately** if you have any personal injury or damage to your clothing.
- ✓ **Wear safety goggles** when heating substances, dissecting, or working with acids or bases that can cause burns.
- ✓ **Do not** use dissection instruments until you have been given proper instructions.
- ✓ **Tell your teacher** if you see any electrical wiring that is frayed, exposed or loosely connected.
- ✓ **Make sure you know** where the fire blanket, fire extinguisher, and eye baths are located.
- ✓ Laboratory materials **should not be moved** through hallways by unsupervised students.

REVIEW QUESTIONS

1. The laboratory is as safe as its ________________ safe person.

2. List **five** rules for laboratory safety.____

____

____

____

Name____________________ Class________________ Date__________

B. IDENTIFYING LABORATORY APPARATUS. When you work in the laboratory, you will be required to know the names of your laboratory apparatus (equipment) and how they are used. Some common biology laboratory apparatus and their uses are shown in Figure 2-1.

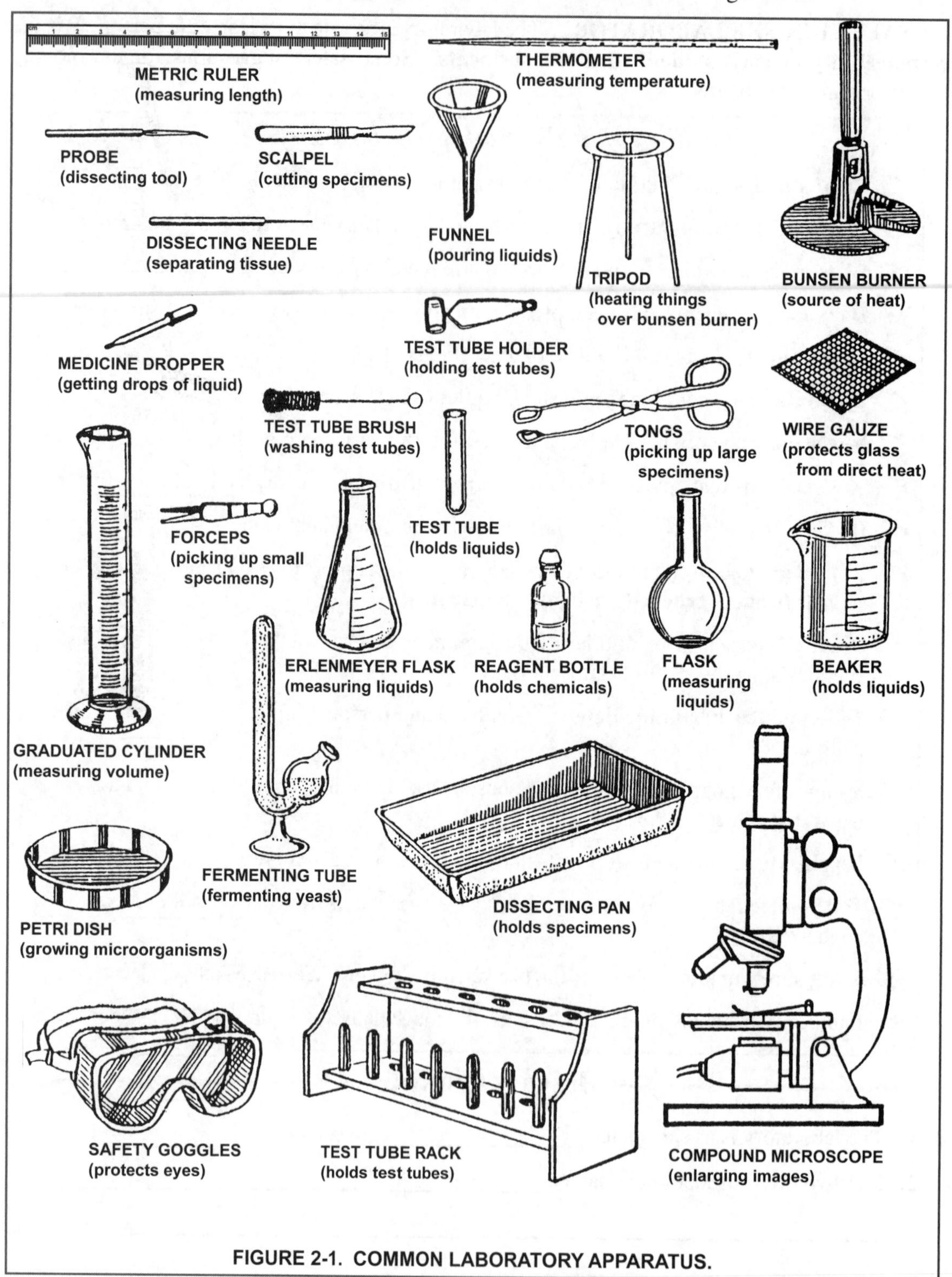

FIGURE 2-1. COMMON LABORATORY APPARATUS.

Name________________________ Class________________ Date__________

REVIEW QUESTION

1. On the line provided, identify the following laboratory equipment.

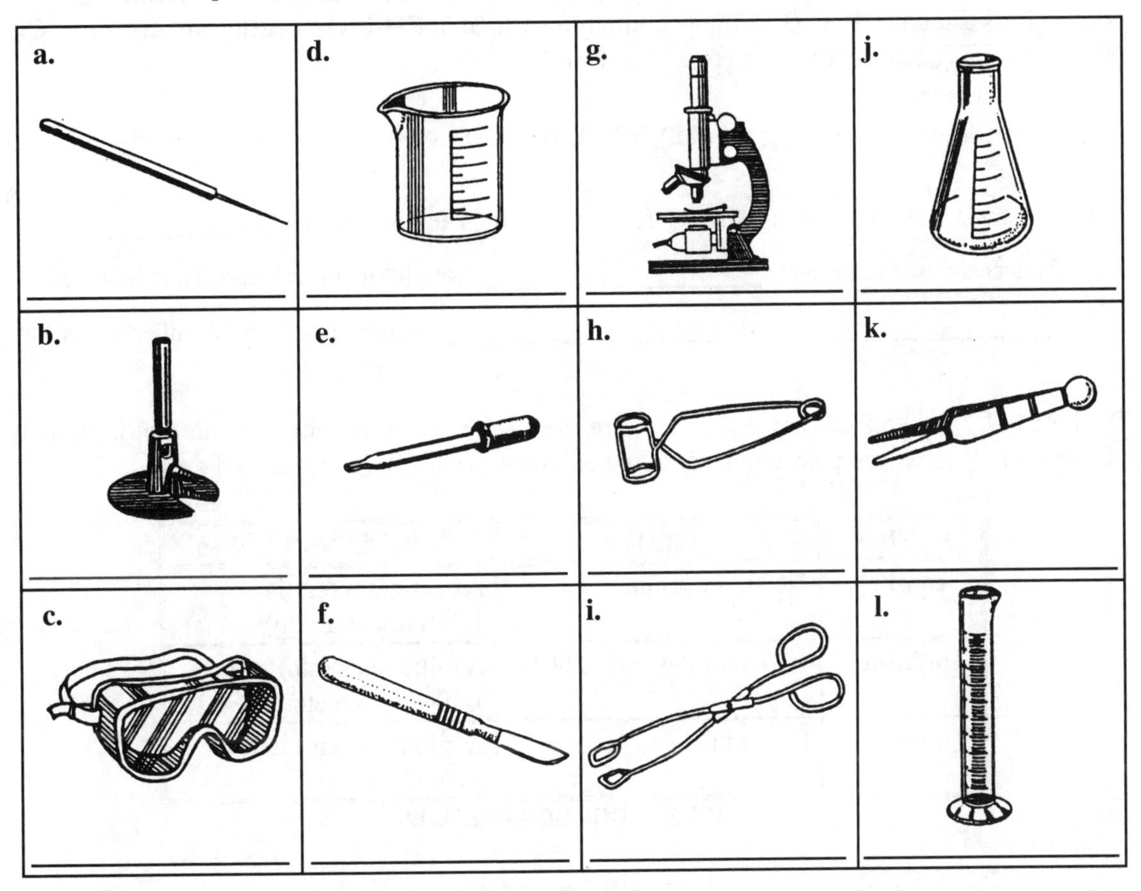

2. On the line provided, name the piece of laboratory equipment you would use to perform each the following tasks.

a. measure length ______________

b. measure temperature ______________

c. observe a cell ______________

d. pick up a beaker ______________

e. protect your eyes ______________

f. pick up an earthworm ______________

g. measure volume ______________

h. hold liquids ______________

i. heat a test tube ______________

j. cut open a frog ______________

k. place water on a slide ______________

l. wash out a test tube ______________

Name ____________ Class ____________ Date ____________

C. MEASUREMENT IN THE LABORATORY. The most common system of measurement used by scientists is the metric system. The metric system is based on multiples of ten. Distance (length) is measured in units called **meters (m)**, weight (mass) is measured in **grams (g)**, and volume is measured in **liters (L)**. Temperature is measured in **Celsius or centigrade degrees (°C)**. (Microscope measurement will be covered in Unit 2.)

REVIEW QUESTIONS

1. The most common system of measurement used by scientist is called the ____________
2. Meters are used to measure ____________, weight (mass) is measured in units called ____________, and ____________ is measured in units called liters.

D. PREFIXES. Prefixes are words that are used with the basic units of the metric system (Table 2-1). Prefixes are placed in front of the unit to show how large or small the unit is.

PREFIX	SIZE	EXAMPLE
centi(c)	1/100 of the unit (0.01)	A centigram (cg) is 1/100 of a gram (g)
milli(m)	1/1000 of the unit (0.001)	A millimeter(mm) is 1/1000 of a meter(m)
kilo(k)	1000 of the unit	A kilometer(km) is 1000 meters(m)

TABLE 2-1. COMMON PREFIXES.

REVIEW QUESTIONS

1. ____________ are words that are placed in front of the basic units of the metric system.
2. Centi means ________ of the unit, milli means ________ of the unit, and 1000 of a unit has the prefix ________
3. Complete the following equations:

   (1) 1 kilogram = ________ grams

   (2) 1000 meters ________ kilometer

   (3) 1 milliliter = ________ liter

   (4) 1 gram = ________ kilogram

4. A centimeter is equal to

   (1) 1/100th of a meter

   (2) 100 meters

   (3) 1/1000th of a meter

   (4) 1000 meters

Name______________________ Class______________________ Date__________

E. MEASURING VOLUME. The volume of a liquid is measured with a **graduated cylinder**. When liquid is poured into the cylinder a curved surface called the **meniscus** is formed. Volume readings are made at the bottom of the meniscus (Figure 2-2).

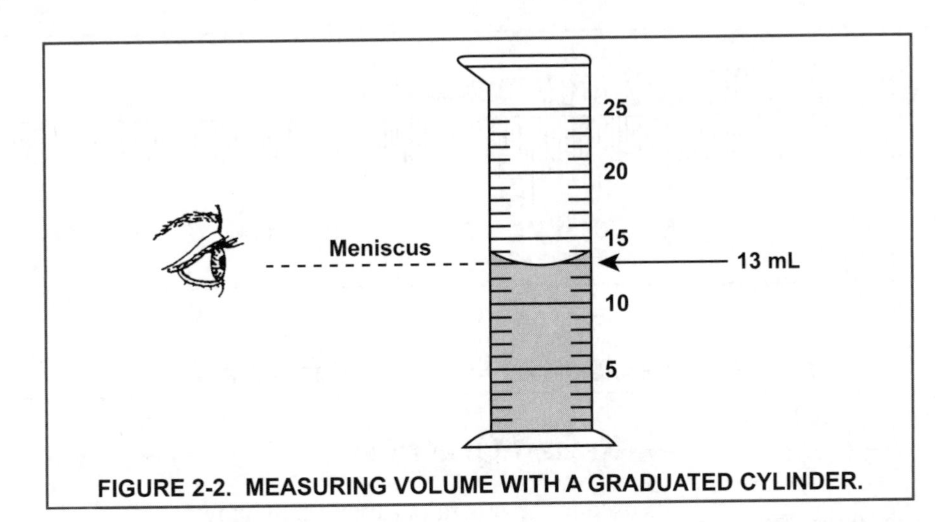

FIGURE 2-2. MEASURING VOLUME WITH A GRADUATED CYLINDER.

REVIEW QUESTION

1. In the diagram above the volume of water is ______________ mL.
2. A ______________ is used to measure liquids in the laboratory.
3. A meniscus is a ______________ surface.
4. Volume readings are made at the ______________ of the meniscus.
5. Find the amount of liquid (to the nearest milliliter) in each of the graduated cylinder sections shown below.

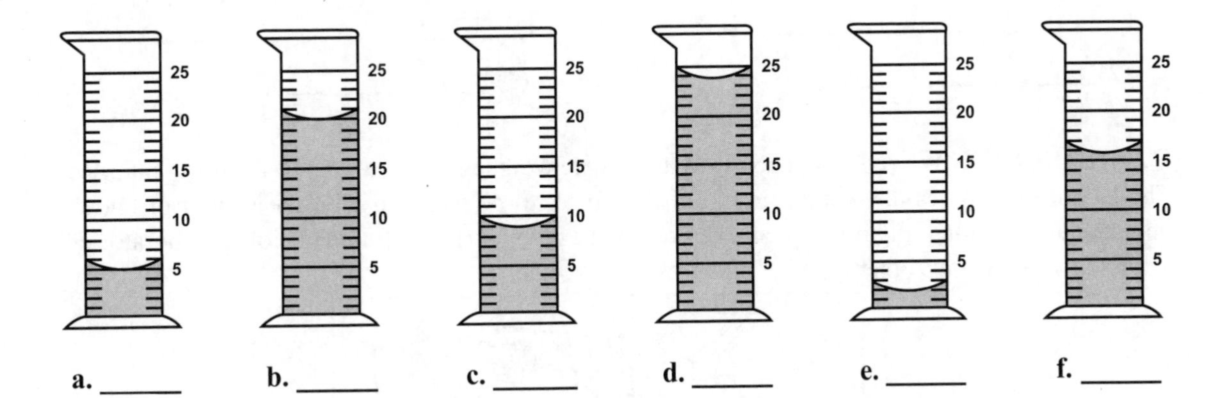

a. ______ b. ______ c. ______ d. ______ e. ______ f. ______

Name______________________ Class ______________________ Date __________

F. MEASURING LENGTH. The **metric ruler** is used in the laboratory to measure length. The most common units used to measure length are the centimeter and millimeter. The worm in Figure 2-3 measures 9 centimeters or 90 millimeters.

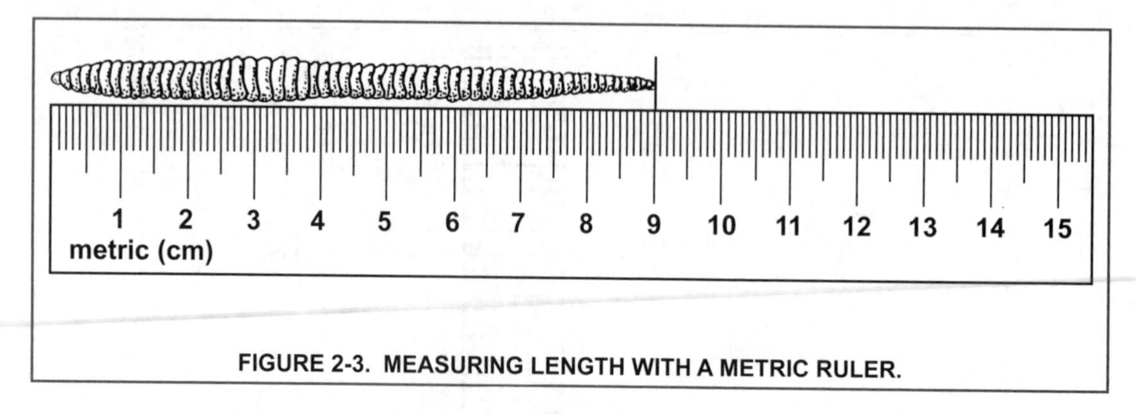

FIGURE 2-3. MEASURING LENGTH WITH A METRIC RULER.

REVIEW QUESTIONS

1. The ______________________ is used in the laboratory to measure length.

2. Below are drawings of metric rulers. Write the length of each object in the space provided.

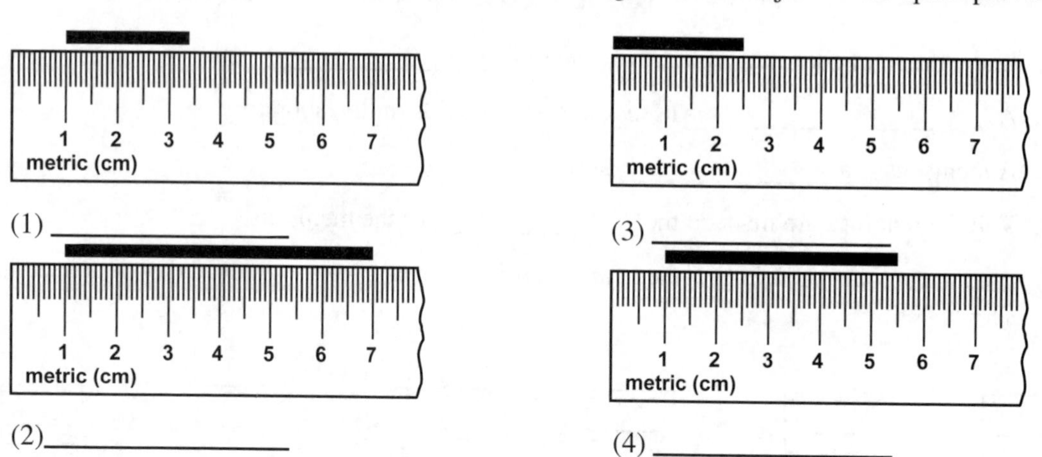

G. MEASURING WEIGHT (MASS). Materials are weighed in the laboratory by using **balance.** The balance compares the weight (mass) of the object to be weighed with the weight of known objects called weights. Figure 2-4 is an example of one type of balance found in biology laboratories. Your school may have other types of balances.

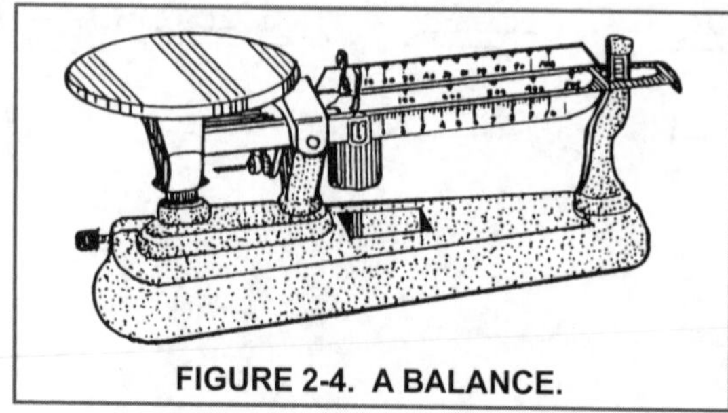

FIGURE 2-4. A BALANCE.

Name________________________ Class____________________ Date__________

REVIEW QUESTIONS

1. A balance is used in the laboratory to measure ____________________
2. The balance compares the weight(mass) of ______________________ with the weight of ____________________

H. MEASURING TEMPERATURE. A **Celsius or centigrade thermometer** is used to measure temperature (Figure 2-5). On the Celsius or centigrade scale 0 degrees is the freezing point of water and 100 degrees is the boiling point of water. The divisions on the thermometer are called centigrade degrees or °C.

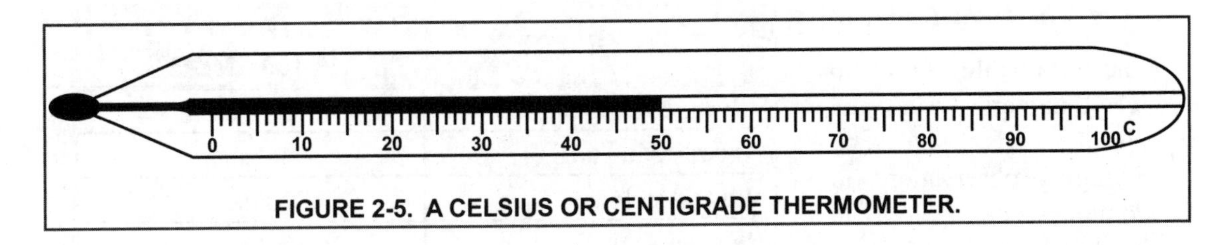

FIGURE 2-5. A CELSIUS OR CENTIGRADE THERMOMETER.

REVIEW QUESTIONS

1. A ______________ or ______________ thermometer is used to measure temperature in the laboratory. _____ is the freezing point of water and _____ degrees is the boiling point.
2. What is the temperature in degrees Celsius indicated on the thermometer in Figure 2-5?

   ____

3. In the spaces provided write the Celsius temperatures shown in each of the following diagrams.

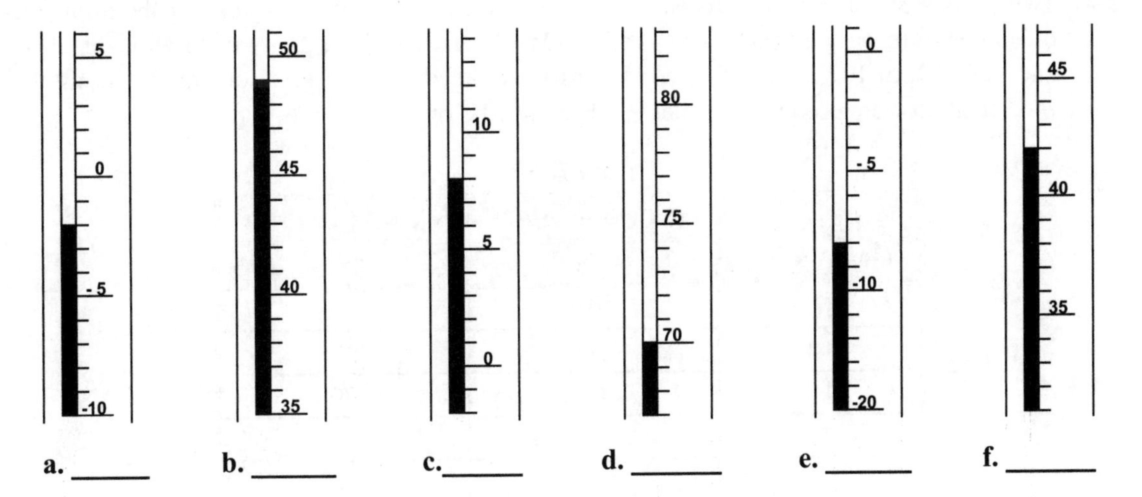

a. _____ b. _____ c._____ d. _____ e. _____ f. _____

Name________________________ Class__________________ Date__________

I. ORGANIZATION AND INTERPRETATION OF DATA. Scientists record laboratory observations and measurements in an orderly manner. This careful method of organization helps the scientist reach more accurate conclusions. Three common methods used to record observations are the data table, the bar graph, and the line graph.

REVIEW QUESTION

1. Name three methods used to record data. ______________________________

____

♦ *The Data Table.*

The **data table** is used to record numerical data. The information is organized by arranging observations in columns with appropriate headings. Table 2-2 is an example of a data table.

TYPE OF TREE	AVERAGE FALL TIME OF 100 FRUITS
Silver Maple (A)	3.2 sec.
Norway Maple (B)	4.9 sec.
White Ash (C)	1.5 sec.
Red Oak (D)	0.8 sec.
Shagbark Hickory (E)	0.8 sec.

TABLE 2-2. A DATA TABLE.

REVIEW QUESTIONS

1. Based on the information in the Data Table above, the fruit of which type of tree(s) had the longest fall time? ______________________

2. Which type(s) had the shortest fall time? ______________________________

3-4. Two groups of 100 carrot seeds each were used in an investigation to test for the influence of temperature on germination of seeds. One group was kept at a temperature of 20°C and the other at 10°C. All other conditions were the same. Observations made during the investigation were used to construct the data table below.

Data Table

Day Of Observation	Total Number of Seeds That Germinate	
	10°C	20°C
7	0	5
10	20	35
15	40	70
20	45	80
25	45	80

3. According to this investigation, what is the difference in the number of seeds germinated at the two temperatures on day 10?

(1) 15 (3) 30
(2) 20 (4) 35

4. Which is a correct conclusion based on the results of this investigation?

(1) The only variable in this experiment was the amount of germination time.
(2) The experiment was a failure since not all of the carrot seeds germinated.
(3) At a temperature of 20°C fewer seeds germinated that at 10°C.
(4) At a temperature of 20°C more seeds germinated that at 10°C.

♦ *The Bar Graph.*

A **bar graph** allows the scientist to compare data. The bar graph shown in Figure 2-6 represents the same data as Table 2-2. Notice how easy it is for you to compare data when you use a bar graph.

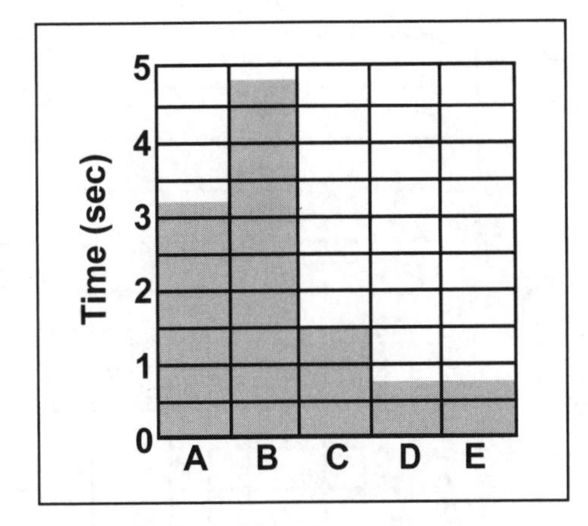

FIGURE 2-6. A BAR GRAPH.

REVIEW QUESTIONS

1. Which fruit type took the longest time to fall? __________

2. Which fruit type fell in 1.5 seconds? __________

3. The graph to the right represents the percent of variation for a given trait in four different populations of the same species. These populations are of equal size and inhabit similar environments. Which population has the greatest percentage of variations for the trait?______

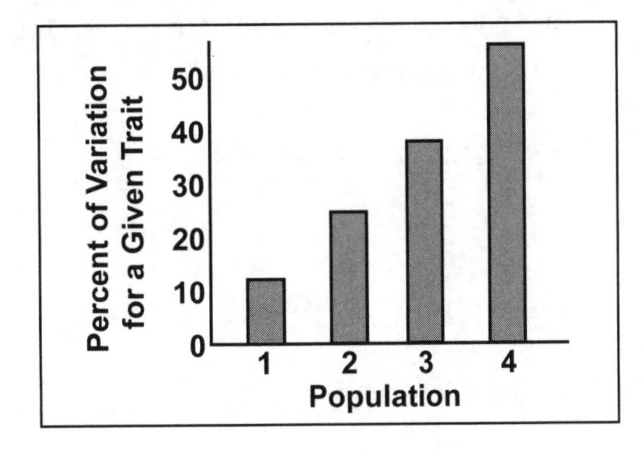

Name________________________ Class__________________ Date__________

♦ ***The Line Graph.*** A **line graph** is used to show relationships between two variables. One variable, called the **independent variable**, is placed along the horizontal (bottom) or **X-axis**. The other variable, the **dependent variable**, is placed on the vertical (side) or **Y-axis**. The data for the dependent variable depends on the changes in the independent variable. The data points are then plotted and the points are connected by a line (Figure 2-7).

Data Table

Light Intensity (footcandles)	Number of Bubbles Per 5 Minutes
100	2
200	4
300	6
400	9
500	10
600	13
700	17

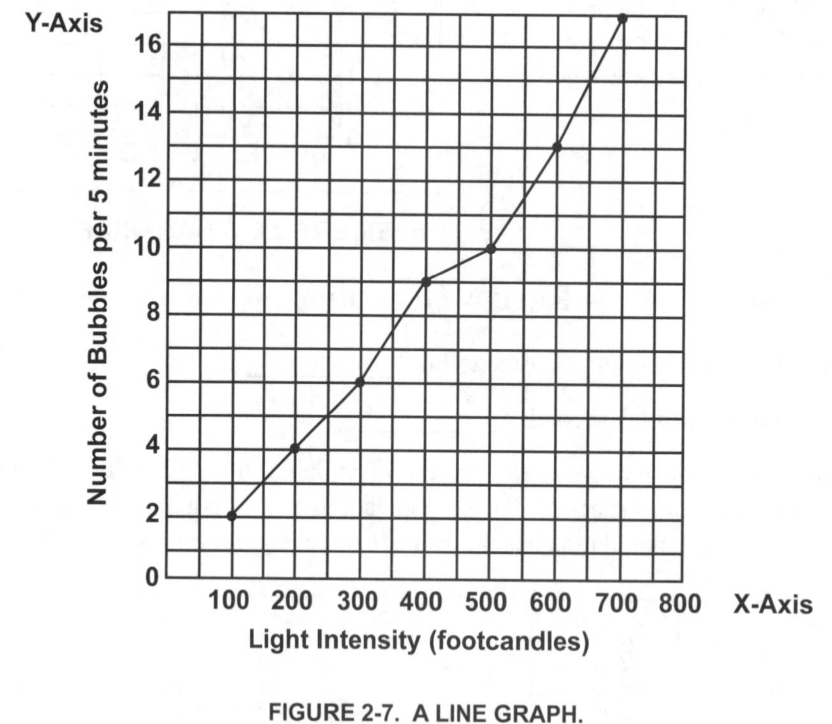

FIGURE 2-7. A LINE GRAPH.

REVIEW QUESTION

1. A line graph is used to show relationships between ________________.

Name________________ Class________________ Date__________

2. Name the independent variable in the line graph shown in Figure 2-7.

____

3. As the light intensity increases, does the number of bubbles increase or decrease?

____

DIRECTIONS (4-6): Base your answers to questions 4 through 6 on the information below that shows the average amount of grain in bushels per acre produced by a farm each year from 1979 to 1985. The table also shows the amount of rainfall received during the early growing season of each year.

Data Table

YEAR	AMOUNT OF RAIN (INCHES)	BUSHELS OF GRAIN PER ACRE
1979	13	60
1980	7	50
1981	10	65
1982	9	60
1983	11	70
1984	15	20
1985	12	65

4. Rearrange the above data by completing both columns of the data table provided, so that values of **Amount of Rain (Inches)** are ***increasing*** from the top of the table to the bottom.

Data Table

AMOUNT OF RAIN (INCHES)	BUSHELS OF GRAIN PER ACRE

Name________________________ Class ____________________ Date __________

5. Using the information in the preceding data table, construct a line graph on the grid that follows. Then: *Mark an appropriate scale on each labeled axis and plot the data for bushels of grain per acre. Surround each point with a small circle and connect the points.*

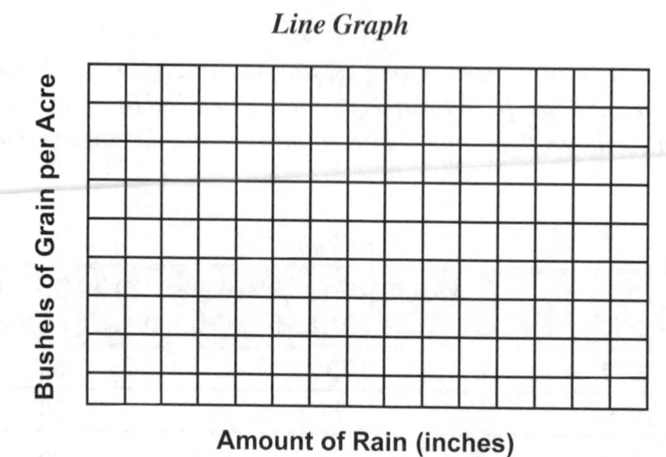

6. Based on the data presented, what amount of rain will produce the most bushels of grain?

____

CAREER OPPORTUNITIES

MEDICAL LABORATORY TECHNICIAN: If you like working with laboratory equipment, you might be interested in a career in medical laboratory technology. The **medical laboratory technician** helps doctors and other medical people perform many medical laboratory tests that help in the diagnosis and treatment of disease. Some of these tests include preparing samples of patients' tissues, doing blood and urine tests, and performing chemical and biological analysis of body specimens. Some technicians may specialize in one area of testing while others perform many different kinds of medical laboratory work.

A high school diploma and a one or two year training certification program are minimum requirements for a laboratory technician. Many two year schools offer an Associate Degree in Medical Technology. High school courses in biology, chemistry, mathematics, and English will help prepare you for a career in medical technology.

Review Question

1. The ______________________________ helps doctors and other medical people perform laboratory tests.

Name________________________ Class _______________________ Date ____________

LAB INVESTIGATION: LABORATORY MATERIALS

OBJECTIVE

Upon completion of this activity you should be able to identify and state the use for some common laboratory materials.

LABORATORY PROCEDURE

Materials: 20 examples of common laboratory materials labeled by number and placed at stations around the laboratory. Reference books.

1. Your teacher has placed examples of laboratory materials at various locations (stations) around the room. Each example is labeled with a number. You are to observe and identify each example.
2. Write the name of the laboratory material and its use in the laboratory in the **observation table** in the following section.

OBSERVATIONS

Example	Name	Use
1		
2		
3		
4		
5		
6		
7		
8		
9		
10		
11		
12		
13		
14		
15		
16		
17		
18		
19		
20		

Name________________________ Class____________________ Date__________

CONCLUSIONS

1. In the space below discuss why you think it is important to be able to correctly identify laboratory materials.

____

____

____

____

____

____

____

____

____

2. Which materials probably were used to dissect a frog? Circle the correct answer.

(1)

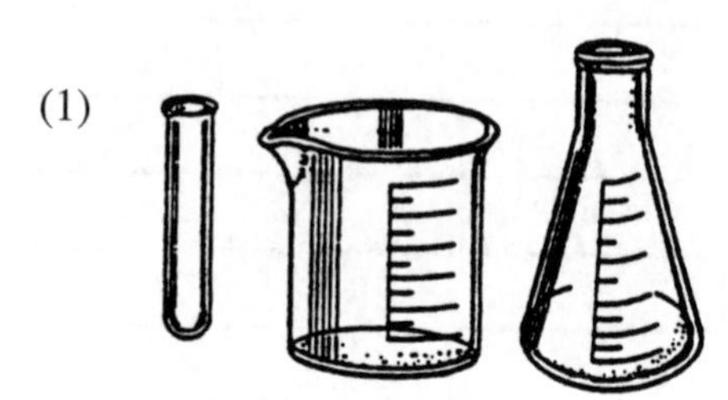

(3)

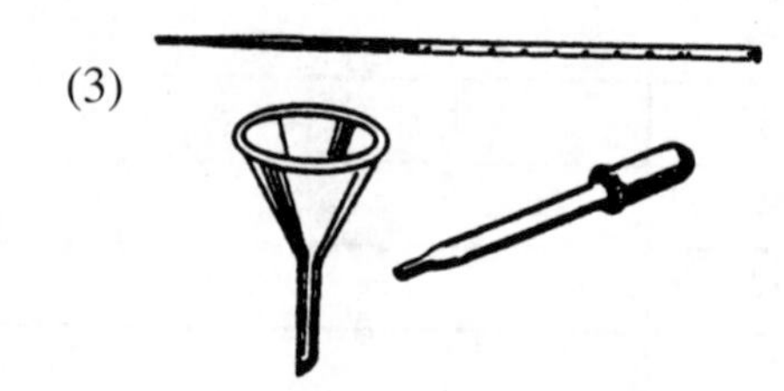

(2)

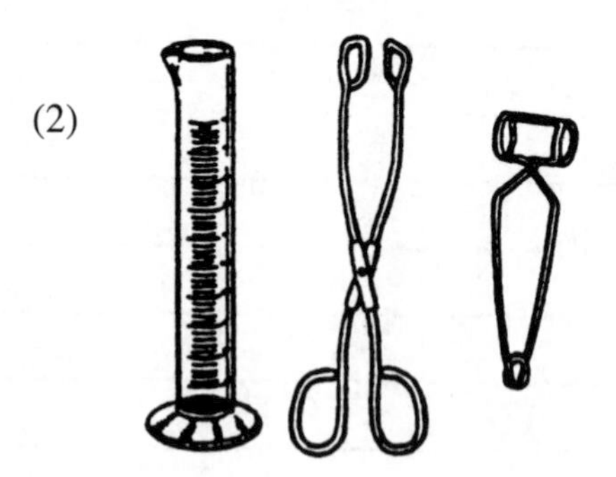

(4)

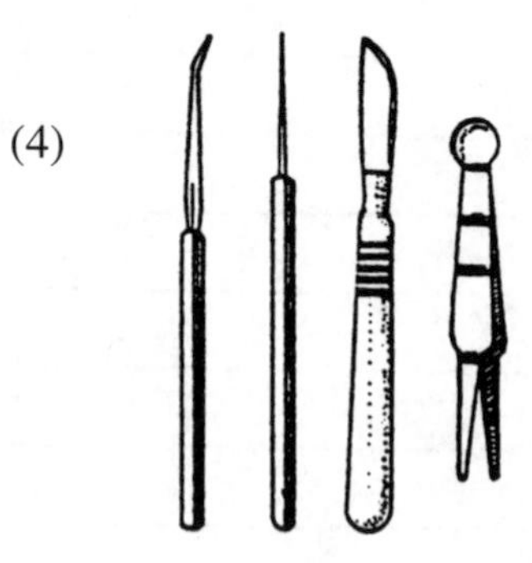

Name____________________ Class____________________ Date__________

REVIEW ACTIVITIES

Important Terms

DIRECTIONS: Define the following terms in the spaces provided.

balance ____

____

Celsius (centigrade) thermometer ____

____

centi ____

____

data table ____

____

graduted cylinder ____

____

meniscus ____

____

gram ____

____

kilo ____

____

liter ____

____

meter ____

____

metric ruler ____

____

metric system ____

____

milli ____

____

prefix ____

____

Name________________________ Class________________ Date__________

Skill Practice

The following information was obtained by a student testing the effect of temperature on the rate of the digestion of starch by an enzyme. Study the information and data table and answer questions 1 through 3.

Data Table

TEST TUBE NUMBER	TEMPERATURE IN °C	AMOUNT OF STARCH DIGESTED PER MINUTE
1	0°	0 grams
2	10°	2 grams
3	20°	4 grams
4	30°	8 grams
5	40°	10 grams
6	50°	3 grams

1. According to the data in the table, which statement provides the most accurate summary of the results of the experiment?

(1) Increasing temperature always increases digestion.

(2) As the temperature increases, the rate of digestion increases and then decreases.

(3) Rising temperature does not affect digestion.

(4) A decrease in digestion takes place between 30°C and 40°C.

2. For the written report on this laboratory investigation, the data collected would be included in the part of the investigation known as the

(1) materials (2) introduction (3) purpose (4) observations

3. When the student graphs these data for a lab report, how should the student label the graph to show the effect of temperature on starch digestion?

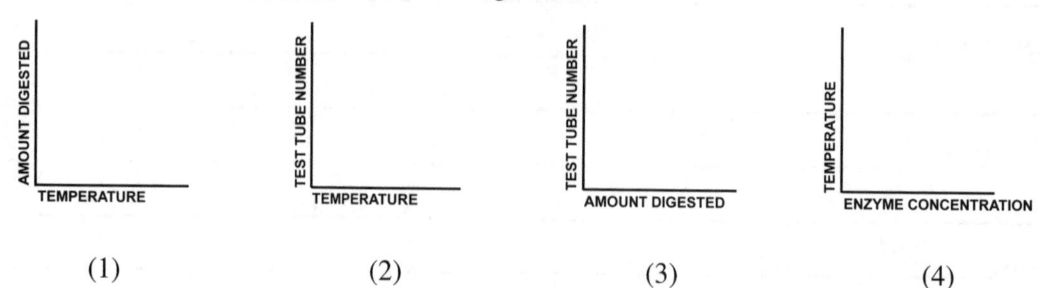

(1) (2) (3) (4)

Name______________________ Class______________________ Date__________

CHAPTER 2: QUIZ

A. FILL-IN QUESTIONS

DIRECTIONS: Complete each of the following statements by writing the correct word or phrase in the space provided.

1. Volume is measured in units called ______________________.
2. Temperature is measured in units called ______________________.
3. Grams are used to measure ______________________.
4. The most common system of measurement used by scientists is called the ______________.
5. Volume readings are made at the bottom of a curved surface called the ______________.
6. The ______________________ thermometer is used to measure temperature in the laboratory.
7. The ______________ axis is found along the bottom of a line graph.
8. A graduated cylinder is used to measure the volume of ______________________.
9. Meters are used to measure ______________________.
10. The prefix centi means ______________________ of the unit.
11. Numerical data is recorded on a ______________________.
12. In the laboratory the ______________________ is used to measure length.
13. The prefix milli means ______________________ of the unit.
14. Materials are weighed in the laboratory by using a ______________________.
15. The meniscus is a ______________________ surface.
16. The independent variable is placed along the ______________________ of a graph.
17. The bar graph helps the scientist to compare ______________________.
18. A ______________________ is used to show relationships between two variables.
19. The dependent variable is placed along the ______________________of a graph.
20. A millimeter is ______________________of a meter.

B. MULTIPLE-CHOICE QUESTIONS

DIRECTIONS: Circle the number of the expression that best completes each of the following statements.

1. Which of the following statements concerning laboratory safety is true?

   (1) Students should fool around in the laboratory.

   (2) Students should work in the lab only when a teacher is present.

   (3) Students should not follow the directions.

   (4) Students should never read the procedures before starting work in the lab.

Name________________________________ Class________________________ Date____________

2. In the metric system, the height of a building would be given in units called
(1) centimeters (3) millimeters
(2) meters (4) milliliter

3. Which group of measurement units is correctly arranged in order of increasing size?
(1) millimeter, centimeter, meter, kilometer
(2) kilometer, centimeter, millimeter, meter
(3) meter, kilometer, centimeter, millimeter
(4) millimeter, kilometer, centimeter, meter

4. Which of the following measurements is the smallest?
(1) meter (3) centimeter
(2) millimeter (4) inch

DIRECTIONS (5-6): Base your answers to questions 5 and 6 on the diagrams of the laboratory equipment below and on your knowledge of biology.

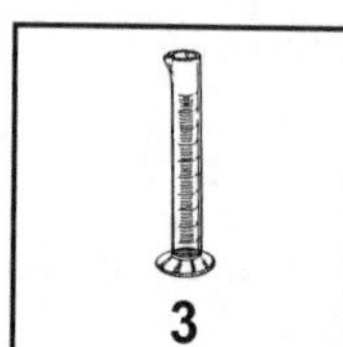

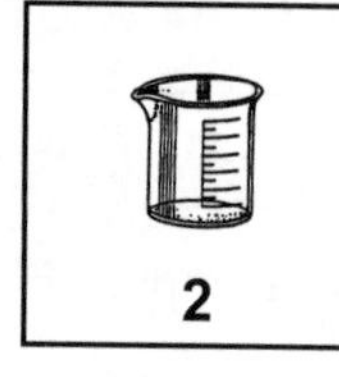

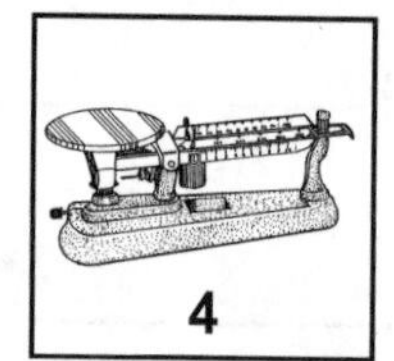

5. Which piece of laboratory equipment would be used to obtain the most accurate measure of the volume of a glucose solution?
(1) 1 (2) 3 (3) 2 (4) 4

6. Which piece of equipment could be used to determine the weight of a frog?
(1) 1 (2) 3 (3) 2 (4) 4

7. The diagram below shows a moss plant and a metric ruler. How tall is the moss plant in centimeters?

(1) 1.5cm

(2) 2cm

(3) 15cm

(4) 4cm

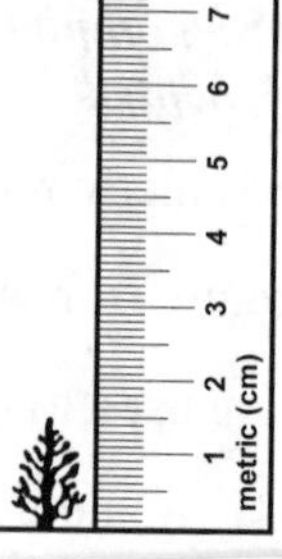

8. What is the total volume of water indicated in the graduated cylinder illustrated below?

(1) 9mL

(2) 12mL

(3) 11mL

(4) 10mL

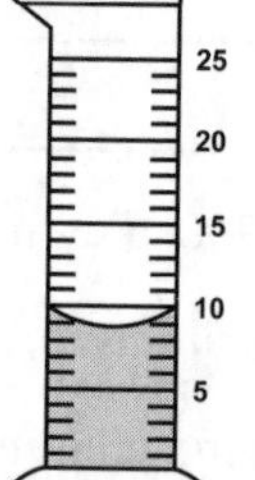

9. Which procedure should not be used during the heating of substances in a test tube?
(1) Point the test tube away from you.
(2) Stopper the test tube to prevent spills.
(3) Wear safety goggles.
(4) Use a test tube holder to avoid burns.

10. What is the length of the object represented in the diagram below?

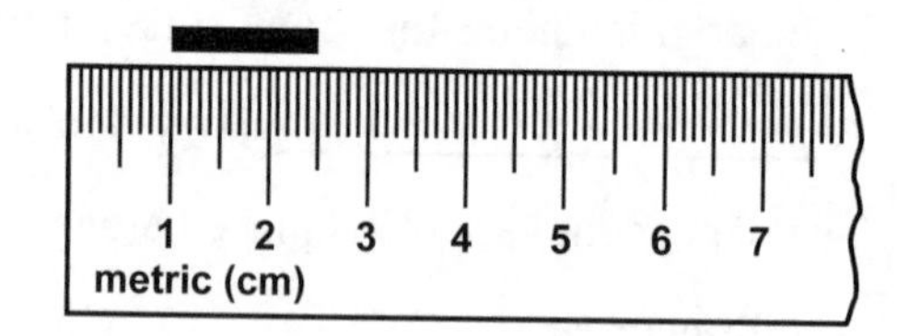

(1) 1.0cm (3) 2.0cm
(2) 1.5cm (4) 2.5cm

C. ESSAY QUESTIONS

DIRECTIONS: Use complete sentences to answer the questions in this part.

1. What is one safety practice that should be used in a biology laboratory?

____

____

____

Name_________________________ Class_____________________ Date___________

UNIT ONE TEST

Matching Questions

***DIRECTIONS:** In the space at the left of each item in Column A, place the letter of the term or phrase in Column B that is most closely related to that item.*

Column A	Column B
_______ **1.** Answer to a problem	**a.** Millimeter
_______ **2.** Measures weight in the laboratory	**b.** Hypothesis
_______ **3.** Records numerical data	**c.** Graduated cylinder
_______ **4.** 1/1000 of a meter	**d.** Variable
_______ **5.** Facts	**e.** Conclusion
_______ **6.** 1/100 of a meter	**f.** Bar graph
_______ **7.** An educated guess	**g.** Data
_______ **8.** Compares data	**h.** Balance
_______ **9.** Measures volume in the laboratory	**i.** Centimeter
_______ **10.** The factor to be tested in an experiment	**j.** Data table
	k. Metric ruler

True-False Questions

***DIRECTIONS:** Write TRUE before each statement that is true and FALSE before each statement that is false.*

_______ **1.** Scientists use the scientific method to solve problems.

_______ **2.** It is safe to inhale chemicals in the laboratory.

_______ **3.** Volume readings are made at the top of the meniscus.

_______ **4.** Distance is measured in units called grams.

_______ **5.** A kilometer is equal to 10 meters.

_______ **6.** A line graph is used to show relationships between two variables.

_______ **7.** The freezing point on a Celsius (centigrade) thermometer is 0 degrees.

_______ **8.** The dependent variable is placed at the bottom of a graph.

_______ **9.** An experiment is repeated many times to check conclusions.

_______ **10.** The science that deals with nonliving things is called biology.

Name ______________________ Class ________________ Date __________

Fill-In Questions

DIRECTIONS: Complete each of the following statements by writing the correct word or phrase in the space provided.

1. The scientist must design an experiment that will test the ________________.
2. An example of a career that requires the study of biology is ________________.
3. Measurements, odors, and colors, are examples of ________________.
4. When many scientists reach the same conclusion, the conclusion can be called a ________.
5. An experiment that tests only one factor is called a ____________ experiment.
6. The independent variable is placed along the ______________ of a graph.
7. The ______________ is used in the laboratory to measure length.
8. The part of an experiment that does not contain the variable is called the _________.
9. The prefix centi means ________________ of the unit.
10. A line graph is used to show ________________ between two variables.

Multiple-Choice Questions

DIRECTIONS: Circle the number of the expression that best completes each of the following statements.

1. A millimeter is equal to
   (1) 1/100 of a meter
   (2) 10 meters
   (3) 1/1000 of a meter
   (4) 1 gram
2. Which piece of equipment should be used to accurately measure a certain volume of water?
   (1) a meter stick
   (2) a beaker
   (3) a graduated cylinder
   (4) a test tube
3. Information gained from experimentation and observation is known as
   (1) theory
   (2) laws
   (3) data
   (4) hypothesis
4. Which represents an unsafe action in the laboratory?
   (1) smelling unknown chemicals
   (2) warming liquids in beakers on hot plates
   (3) heating liquids in unstoppered test tubes
   (4) wearing safety goggles
5. The first step in the scientific method is
   (1) to state the problem
   (2) experimentation
   (3) to state the hypothesis
   (4) observation
6. The study of animals is known as
   (1) botany
   (2) biology
   (3) zoology
   (4) bacteriology
7. To measure and pour 10 milliliters of a liquid into a test tube, which of the following is the best procedure to insure the accuracy of the measurement?
   (1) Use a graduated cylinder.
   (2) Fill a medicine dropper ten times.
   (3) Use a metric ruler.
   (4) Use a metric balance.

Name________________ Class________________ Date__________

8. When a student graphs the data in the table for a laboratory report, how should she label the graph if she wishes to show the effect of temperature on protein digestion?

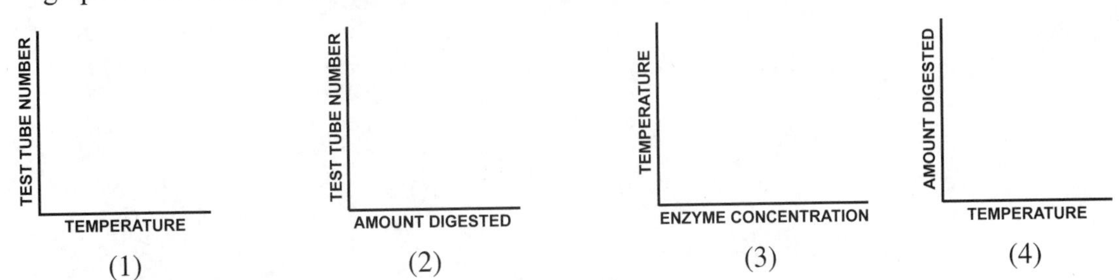

9. The graph below shows two hormone levels in the blood. Based on the data shown in the graph, which statement is true?

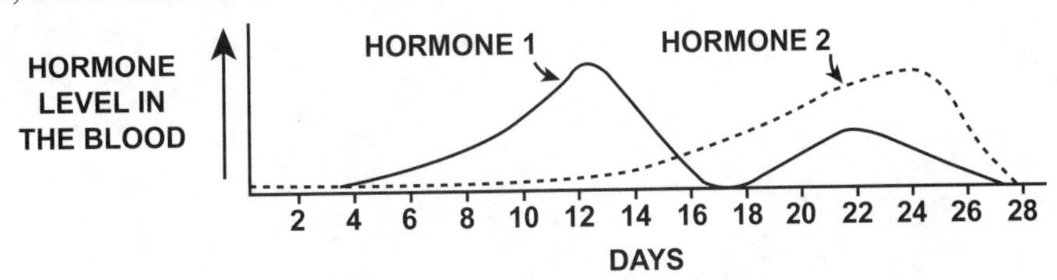

(1) Hormone 1 increases during the first 20 days.
(2) Hormone 2 remains the same throughout the 28 days.
(3) Hormone 1 decreases on the 20th day.
(4) Hormone 2 is highest on the 24th day.

10. A student placed ten radish seeds of the same variety on moist paper in each of three petri dishes and placed the dishes in the following environments:

Dish No. 1: Refrigerator, 5°C

Dish No. 2: Room Temperature, 20°C

Dish No. 3: Incubator, 37°C

Which factor is the variable in the investigation described above?

(1) temperature
(2) moisture
(3) kind of seeds
(4) number of seeds

Essay Question

DIRECTIONS: Use complete sentences to answer the question in this part.

1. State ***three*** reasons why everyone should study biology.

____

____

____

____

____

Class Notes

Name______________________ Class______________________ Date__________

UNIT TWO

SIMILARITIES AMONG LIVING THINGS

LEARNING OUTCOMES: Upon completion of the study of this unit, you should be able to:

- Identify the cell as the unit common to living things.
- Describe several functions carried on by cells that promote their survival.
- Identify several cell organelles and describe their functions.
- Describe ways cells can be studied in the laboratory.
- Describe the levels of organization in living things.
- List the major elements found in living things.
- Name the main types of organic compounds in living cells.

Chapter 3: Characteristics of Living Things

A. DEFINING LIFE. The science of biology studies life and living things. Do you know what is meant by the term "*life*"? Scientists do not agree on one definition of life. They do agree, however, that the cells of living things (**organisms**) carry on certain processes that are necessary for life. These processes or activities, common to all living things, are known as **life functions.** An organism is considered to be alive as long as its cells perform certain life functions. Nutrition, transport, respiration, excretion, regulation, growth, reproduction, synthesis, and metabolism are the life functions or characteristics shared by living things.

REVIEW QUESTIONS

1. The science of biology studies ________________ and ____________________.

2. How do scientists define life? ____

____

3. The term "organism" is another word for ______________________.

4. Life functions are ______________ or ______________ that are common to all living things.

5. An organism is considered alive as long as its ____________________________________.

Name________________ Class________________ Date__________

6. Name nine life functions. ____

____

____

7. Complete the following chart with examples of things that you think are living and nonliving. For example, a horse is living and a rock is nonliving.

LIVING THINGS	NONLIVING THINGS

B. NUTRITION. Living things need food to supply energy for life activities and materials for the growth and repair of cells. During the life process of **nutrition** organisms obtain (get) and process food. Some organisms, such as green plants, can make their own food while other living things must obtain their food already formed. Organisms that are able to make their own food are called **autotrophs. Heterotrophs** are organisms that are not able to make their own food.

Nutrition involves ingestion and digestion. Food is taken in from the environment by **ingestion**. Ingested food is not usually in a form that can be used by body cells and must be changed into a usable form. **Digestion** is the process that changes food into a form that can be used by the cell. During digestion large complex molecules are broken down into small simple molecules.

REVIEW QUESTIONS

1. The life activity responsible for obtaining and processing food is called ________________.
2. During ingestion food is ____.

Name____________________ Class____________________ Date__________

3. Digestion is a process that ____
4. Explain why living things need food. ____

____

C. TRANSPORT. After digestion is completed **nutrients**, the parts of food that can be used by the cell, are carried to the cell. **Transport** is the life process that includes the absorption and circulation of materials throughout an organism. **Absorption** is the process by which the usable materials from food called the end products of digestion, as well as other dissolved materials, are taken into the cells and fluids of the body. **Circulation** involves the movement of materials to and from the cells, within cells, and/or throughout an organism. Along with nutrients, oxygen, water, and wastes are also transported throughout a cell or organism.

REVIEW QUESTIONS

1. The usable parts of food are called ______________________________.
2. ________________________ is the life process that includes the absorption and circulation of materials throughout an organism.
3. Circulation is the ____,

   ____.
4. Absorption occurs when ____.

D. RESPIRATION. Living things need a constant supply of energy for their life activities. **Respiration** is a complex series of chemical reactions that release energy for life activities. An organism's energy is stored in food nutrients. Most organisms need oxygen for respiration—they are called **aerobic organisms.** A few organisms, known as **anaerobic organism,** do not need oxygen for their respiratory processes.

REVIEW QUESTIONS

1. Living things need ____ for their life activities.
2. Respiration is defined as ____

   ____
3. What is the difference between aerobic and anaerobic organisms?

   ____

   ____

   ____

   ____

Name______________________________ Class__________________________ Date____________

E. EXCRETION. Life processes result in the formation of cellular wastes. These wastes are harmful to the organism and must be removed. **Excretion** is the removal of waste materials produced in the cells as a result of life activities. Products commonly excreted from cells are carbon dioxide and water.

Egestion is the process that removes undigested materials from the body. Do not confuse the process of egestion, which means to get rid of solid wastes, with excretion. Excretion is the elimination of the gaseous or liquid wastes of cellular respiration.

REVIEW QUESTIONS

1. What is excretion? ____

   ____

2. Why is it necessary for an organism to remove wastes? ____________________

   ____

3. Egestion is the removal of ______________________________________

F. REGULATION. The life activity responsible for the control and coordination of all the various activities of an organism is called **regulation.** The nervous and endocrine systems are responsible for regulation. Regulation allows organisms to respond to changes in the environment. This means they can find food, avoid danger, respond to light, and perform other tasks important to their survival. A change in the internal or external environment is known as a **stimulus**. Some examples of stimuli are light and temperature.

REVIEW QUESTIONS

1. Regulation is the life activity responsible for ______________ and ______________ in an organism.
2. The ______________ system and the ______________ system carry on regulation.
3. A stimulus is ____.
4. Some examples of stimuli are ____________________ and ______________.

G. SYNTHESIS. Living things are able to produce complex substances from simpler substances by the process of **synthesis.** During this process the simpler food molecules produced during digestion are put together to make the complex materials needed by the organism. These complex materials become part of the structure of the organism. For example, during photosynthesis green plants "make" complex compounds (sugar) from simpler materials.

REVIEW QUESTIONS

1. The process of synthesis makes ______________ materials from ______________ food molecules.

Name______________________ Class______________________ Date______________

2. What happens to the materials that are synthesized by an organism? ____________

____

____.

H. GROWTH. Growth results from synthesis. **Growth** is an increase in the size and/or number of cells of an organism. The complex materials produced during synthesis are used for growth. When cells grow, the size of the cytoplasm changes but not the size of the nucleus (Figure 3-1).

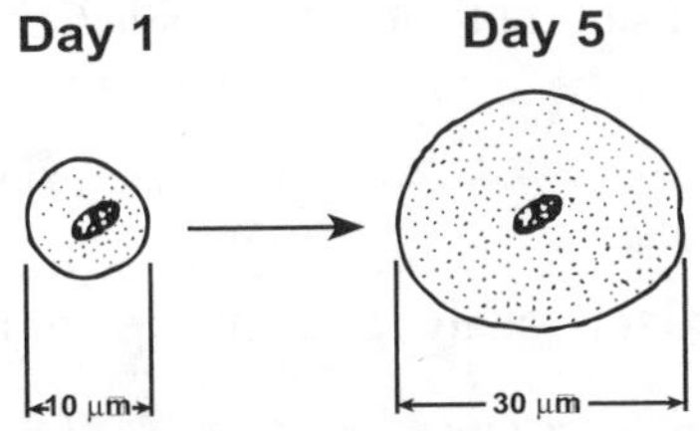

FIGURE 3-1. CELL GROWTH.

REVIEW QUESTIONS

1. Growth results from the complex materials produced during ____________.
2. Compare the changes in the size of the cytoplasm and the size of the nucleus that occur as a result of growth. ____________

____

3. An increase in the size or number of cells in an organism is called ____________.

I. LOCOMOTION. The ability to move from place to place is called **locomotion**. Organisms that are able to move from place to place are said to be **motile.** Most animals are motile. There are a few animals that are nonmotile (sessile) during their adult form. **Sessile** animals attach themselves to an object and stay there all their lives. Many small aquatic organisms cannot move around on their own. These organisms must be carried around by water currents or blown around in the air. Locomotion is important because the ability of an organism to move around on its own increases its probability of survival. It also increases its opportunity to find food, seek shelter, avoid predators, move away from toxic wastes, and find a mate.

REVIEW QUESTIONS

1. What are the meanings of the terms *sessile* and *motile*? ____________

____

____

2. List 2 reasons why the ability to move around is advantageous for organisms. ____________

____

____

J. REPRODUCTION. Reproduction is the production (making) of new organisms. This is the only life process that is not necessary for the life of an individual organism. It is, however, necessary for the continued existence of a particular group of organisms. For example, one cat can live a normal life without reproducing, but if all cats stopped reproducing, the group of organisms called *cats* would become extinct.

Cells reproduce by cell division—one cell divides into two cells. Cell division involves a series of changes in the cell leading to the production of two new cells. In organisms made up of many cells the production of new cells also results in the growth and repair of damaged tissues. You will learn more about reproduction in Unit 5.

REVIEW QUESTIONS

1. Do individual organisms need to reproduce to stay alive? ____________________

2. Cells reproduce by a process called ______________________________.

K. METABOLISM AND HOMEOSTASIS. The sum total of all the life processes taking place in an organism is known as **metabolism**. It includes the chemical reactions essential to the organism as well as the conversion of energy into forms needed by the cells. Metabolic activities occur all the time in every living system.

The parts of the human body and those of all multicellular organisms, from organ systems to cell organelles, interact to maintain a balanced internal environment. The structures present in some single-celled organisms act in a manner similar to the tissues and systems found in multicellular organisms. This enables them to perform all of the life processes needed to maintain a balanced internal environment. To successfully accomplish this organisms possess a diversity of control mechanisms that detect deviations and make corrective actions.

The maintenance of a stable internal (inside) environment in spite of changes in the external (outside) environment is called **homeostasis** or **dynamic equilibrium.** When the organism is in homeostasis it is in a balanced or "steady" state. If there is a disruption in any organ system there may be a corresponding imbalance in homeostasis. Homeostasis in an organism is constantly threatened—if the organism's body fails to respond effectively, disease and/or death can occur. As a result of regulation the metabolic reactions of an organism are constantly adjusted in the direction necessary to maintain a constant internal environment. These activities are self-regulated so as to maintain a balanced state within the organism.

The mechanisms for self-regulation are known as **feedback mechanisms**. An example of a feedback mechanism is maintenance of body temperature. When body temperature rises above normal the increase is sensed by a part of the brain. A message is sent by the nervous system to the sweat glands of the skin to produce sweat. As sweat evaporates from the body its temperature is lowered because evaporation is a cooling process. If the body temperature of the body is low the nervous system sends a message to the sweat glands to constrict (get smaller). This action causes the body temperature to rise. Other examples include changes in heart rate or respiratory rate in response to increased activity in muscle cell, maintenance of blood sugar levels by insulin from the pancreas, and changes in openings in the leaves of plants by guard cells to regulate water loss and gas exchange.

REVIEW QUESTIONS

1. Define metabolism and homeostasis. ______________________________________

____

____

Name________________________ Class________________________ Date__________

LAB INVESTIGATION: LIVING AND NONLIVING THINGS

OBJECTIVE

Upon completion of this activity you should be able to identify living things, nonliving things, and products of living things.

LABORATORY PROCEDURE

Materials: An assortment of 20 specimens that are living things, nonliving things, and products of living things, such as coal, wood, iron, plants, animals, rocks, etc., labeled by number and placed at stations around the laboratory. Reference books.

1. Your teacher has placed examples of living, nonliving, and products of living things at various locations (stations) around the room. Each example is labeled with a number. You are to observe and identify each example and decide whether it is a living thing, a nonliving thing, or a product of a living thing.

2. Place a check (√) in the appropriate box in the **observation table** in the following section.

OBSERVATIONS

Example	Living Thing	Nonliving Thing	Product of Living Thing
1			
2			
3			
4			
5			
6			
7			
8			
9			
10			
11			
12			
13			
14			
15			
16			
17			
18			
19			
20			

Name________________________ Class________________ Date__________

Conclusions

1. How do you distinguish living things from nonliving things?

2. List and describe eight life functions that are characteristic to all living things.

Name________________________ Class________________________ Date______________

REVIEW ACTIVITIES

Important Terms

DIRECTIONS: Define the following terms in the spaces provided.

absorption ____

____

aerobic organisms ____

____

anaerobic organisms ____

____

autotroph ____

____

circulation ____

____

digestion ____

____

egestion ____

____

excretion ____

____

growth ____

____

heterotroph ____

____

ingestion ____

____

life functions ____

____

metabolism ____

____

Name______________________ Class__________________ Date__________

nutrients ____

____

nutrition ____

____

organisms ____

____

regulation ____

____

reproduction ____

____

respiration ____

____

synthesis ____

____

transport ____

____

Name ____________________ Class ____________________ Date __________

Skill Practice

Part A. Complete the following chart.

LIFE ACTIVITY	DEFINITION
Transport	
	The release of energy from food.
Nutrition	
Regulation	
	The removal of harmful cellular wastes.
Growth	
	The production of new individuals.
Synthesis	
	The total of all life activities.

Name________________________ Class__________________ Date__________

Part B. Complete the following crossword puzzle.

Crossword Puzzle

Clues

ACROSS

2. Movement of materials to cells
5. Removal of undigested materials
6. Increase in size of organism
9. Study of living things
11. Living things carry on ______functions
12. Process that releases energy from food

DOWN

1. Changes food into a usable form
3. Usable parts of food
4. Obtaining and processing food
7. Ingestion is the taking in of _____
8. Making complex materials from simple materials
10. Organisms that use oxygen

Name________________________ Class________________________ Date__________

CHAPTER 3: QUIZ

A. FILL-IN QUESTIONS

DIRECTIONS: Complete each of the following statements by writing the correct word or phrase in the space provided.

1. Individual organisms ________________ need reproduction to stay alive.
2. The study of living things is called ________________.
3. The materials formed from synthesis become a part of the ______________ of an organism.
4. Living things are known as ___________________
5. The characteristics that all living things have in common are referred to as ______________ functions or activities.
6. __________________ is the life activity by which organisms obtain and process food.
7. The endocrine and nervous systems are responsible for the life activity of _______________.
8. Taking in food from the environment is called ________________.
9. Circulation and absorption are both parts of the life process called ________________.
10. All the life processes together are its ________________.
11. ___________________ are organisms that can make their own food.
12. Respiration is the series of chemical reactions that releases ________________.
13. The removal of cellular wastes is ________________.
14. Nutrients are the _________________ parts of food.
15. A stimulus is defined as ____.
16. Living things produce complex substances from simple substances by ________________.
17. ________________ is the process that changes food into a form that can be used by the cell.
18. An increase in size and/or number of cells of an organism is ________________.
19. The life process that is not necessary for the life of a single organism is ______________.
20. Control and coordination of life activities is carried on by the _________________ system.

B. MULTIPLE-CHOICE QUESTIONS

DIRECTIONS: Circle the number of the expression that best completes each of the following statements.

1. The process by which a cell gets rid of wastes is known as
   (1) synthesis
   (2) excretion
   (3) growth
   (4) digestion

2. By which life process does a plant produce energy?
   (1) respiration
   (2) excretion
   (3) digestion
   (4) photosynthesis

3. Which of the following processes changes complex molecules into simple molecules?
   (1) excretion
   (2) ingestion
   (3) digestion
   (4) egestion

Name______________________ Class____________________ Date__________

4. The energy stored in food molecules is released during

(1) digestion (3) circulation
(2) excretion (4) respiration

DIRECTIONS (5-7): For each phrase in questions 5 through 7, select the life process, chosen from the list below, that is most closely associated with that phrase. Then write its number in the space next to the question.

Life Processes
(1) Digestion
(2) Excretion
(3) Reproduction
(4) Respiration

5. The removal of metabolic wastes. ______

6. The release of energy from foods. ______

7. The production of new organisms that are essentially the same as their parents. ______

8. Before being transported in the body, food must be

(1) digested by enzymes
(2) absorbed by alveoli
(3) moved by cilia
(4) egested by the large intestine

9. The manufacture of insulin in the pancreas is an example of the life function called

(1) excretion (3) synthesis
(2) respiration (4) reproduction

10. Which process takes place during digestion?

(1) Large molecules are broken into small molecules.
(2) Small molecules join to form large molecules.
(3) Large molecules are changed into different large molecules.
(4) Small molecules are changed into different small molecules.

C. ESSAY QUESTION

DIRECTIONS: Use complete sentences to answer the question in this part.

1. State one difference between the processes of egestion and excretion.

____

____

____

____

____

Name________________________ Class____________________ Date____________

Chapter 4: Cell Theory and Cell Study

A. THE CELL THEORY. The **cell** is the basic unit of structure and function of living things. Hundreds of years of cell study have given us information about the cell known as the cell theory. The **cell theory** states that:

The Cell Theory

- The cell is the basic unit of structure of all living things. This means that all living things are made up of cells. The smallest living things are one-celled or **unicellular**. Large organisms contain millions of cells. They are many-celled or **multicellular.**
- The cell is the basic unit of function of all living things. Therefore, all of the organism's life functions are carried out by cells or parts of cells.
- Cells arise (come) from other living cells—not from nonliving matter.

REVIEW QUESTIONS

1. The cell is the basic unit of ____________________ and ____________________ of living things.

2. List the three parts of the cell theory.

____

____

____

B. EXCEPTIONS TO THE CELL THEORY. As scientists continued to study the cell they discovered facts that could not be explained by the cell theory. These unexplained facts are called exceptions to the cell theory. Two exceptions to the cell theory are:

Exceptions To The Cell Theory

- **Viruses** are not made up of cells. They do contain genetic material. Viruses reproduce inside another cell called the **host cell**.
- The first cell could not have arisen from a previously existing cell. Scientists do not know the origin (beginning) of the first cell.

Name________________________ Class ____________________ Date ___________

REVIEW QUESTIONS

1. State two exceptions to the cell theory.

____

____

____

C. HISTORY OF CELL STUDY. Scientists did not know much about cells until the discovery of the microscope. Cells are so small they cannot be seen without a microscope. Once the microscope was developed many scientists made important contributions to our knowledge of the cellular nature of living things. Some of the most important contributions to the cell theory are listed in Table 2-1.

SCIENTIST	CONTRIBUTION
Anton van Leeuwenhoek	A Dutch naturalist who worked in the 1600's. He is credited with the development of the first simple microscope. This microscope was just a single lens but it enabled him to examine drops of pond water. He drew pictures of the organisms he saw. These observations were thought to be the first drawings of microscopic light.
Robert Hooke	An Englishman who, in 1665, put two lenses together and made a crude compound microscope. Through this microscope he observed thin slices of cork. He saw tiny box-like structures that reminded him of rooms, or cells, in a monastery. He called them "cells." What he really saw were cell walls.
Robert Brown	A very important discovery was made in England in 1831. Robert Brown noticed a small round structure inside a plant cell. He named this structure the nucleus.
Matthias Schleiden	About the same time that Brown was working in England Scleiden, a botanist, was studing plant tissue in Germany. He concluded that all plants were made up of cells.
Theodor Schwann	A German scientist who was studing animal cells at the same time that Scleiden was working with plant cells. Schwann reported that all animals were made up of cells.
Rudolf Virchow	In 1858 he formulated the idea that all new cells must come from other previously existing cells.

TABLE 2-1. THE HISTORY OF CELL STUDY.

Name ____________________ Class ____________________ Date ____________

REVIEW QUESTIONS

1. What instrument had to be developed before cells could be studied? ______________.
2. The first simple microscope was developed by ______________________.
3. The first compound microscope was made by ______________________.
4. Why did Hooke name the box-like structures "cells"? ______________________

   ____
5. What part of the cell was Hooke actually observing? ______________________.
6. The nucleus was named by ______________________.
7. State Schleiden's contribution to the cell theory.

   ____

   ____
8. What was Schwann's contribution to the cell theory?

   ____

   ____
9. What was Virchow's contribution to the cell theory?

   ____

   ____

D. THE COMPOUND LIGHT MICROSCOPE. Because the cell is so small various tools and techniques (procedures) are needed so that the cell can be seen. The microscope used most commonly for cell study is called the **compound light microscope.** It increases the apparent size of materials making them easier to study. For study with this microscope the **specimen** (material being viewed) must be thin enough for light to pass through it easily. Compound microscopes have two lenses or systems of lenses. Light passing through a specimen then passes through the **objective lens**. The enlarged **image** (picture) produced by the objective lens is magnified again by the **ocular or eyepiece lens**. The final image appears enlarged (made bigger) and upside down and backward (Figure 4-1).

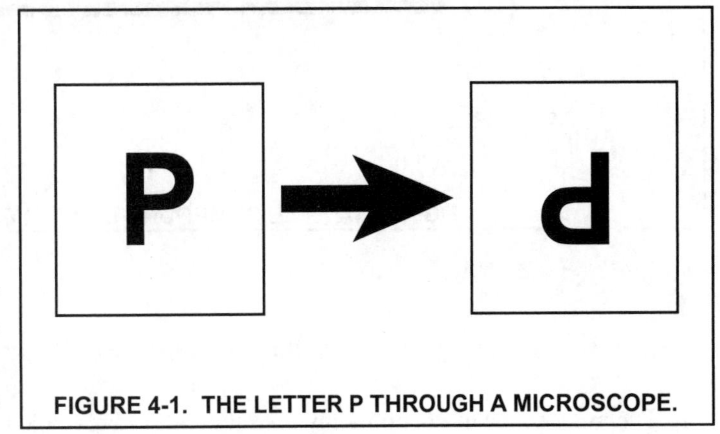

FIGURE 4-1. THE LETTER P THROUGH A MICROSCOPE.

Name____________________ Class________________ Date__________

The parts and the functions of each part of the compound microscope are shown in Figure 4-2.

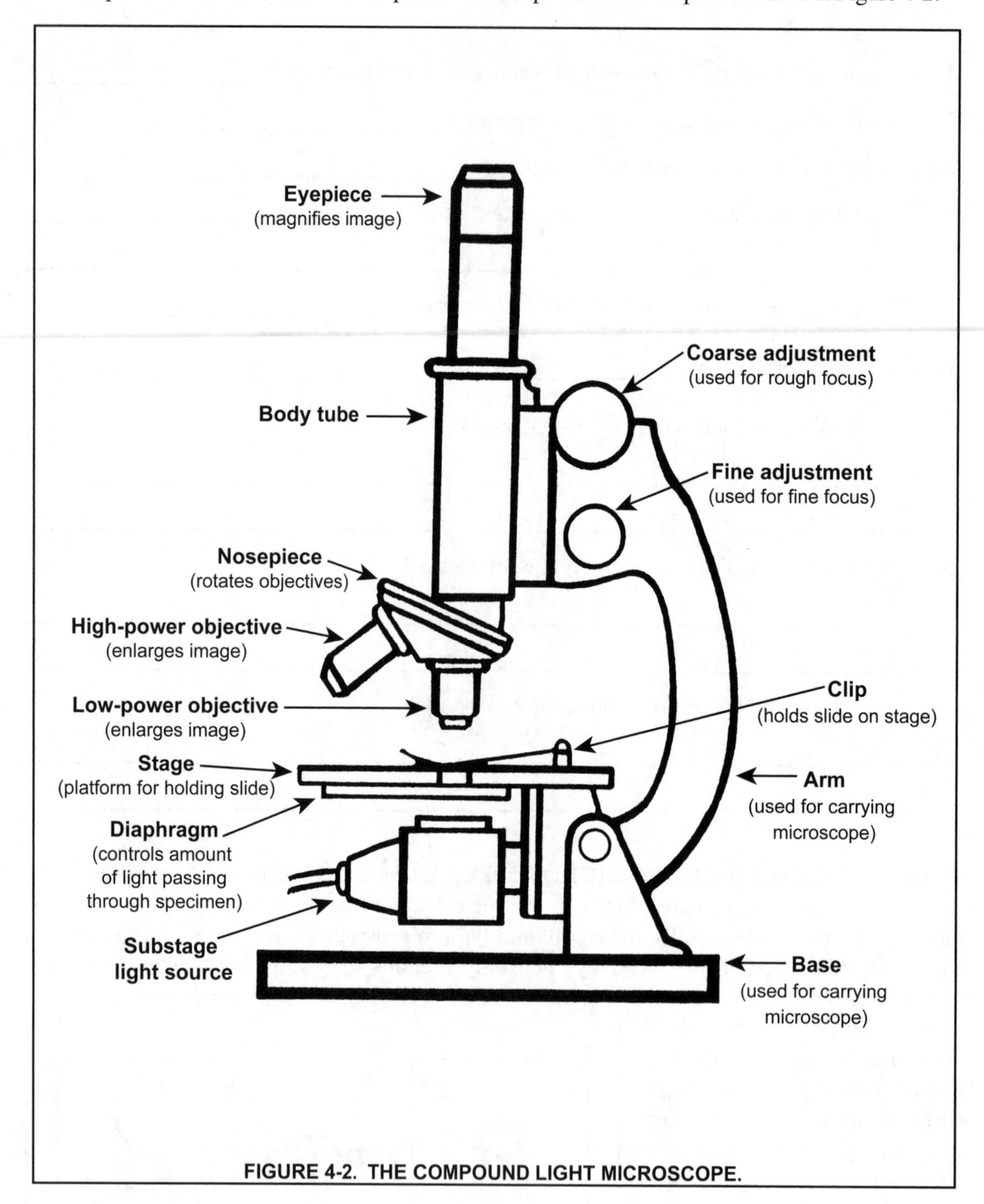

FIGURE 4-2. THE COMPOUND LIGHT MICROSCOPE.

REVIEW QUESTIONS

1. The microscope most commonly used for cell study is called the ____________________

Name____________________ Class ____________________ Date ____________

2. The compound light microscope increases the ________________________________

______________________________.

3. The material being viewed is called the ____________________.

4. Name the two lenses of the compound microscope. ____________________________

____

5. Describe the final image of the compound microscope. __________________________

____

6. Complete the following chart.

PART	FUNCTION
Eyepiece	
Objectives	
Diaphragm	
Coarse Adjustment	
Fine Adjustment	
Arm	
Clips	

E. STAINING TECHNIQUES. Many parts of the cell are almost colorless and are hard to distinguish from other cell parts. **Staining techniques** have been developed to "color" certain cell parts so that they are more easily studied with the compound light microscope. The most commonly used stains are iodine and methylene blue.

REVIEW QUESTIONS

1. Staining techniques have been developed to add ____________________ to certain cell parts.

2. Name two commonly used laboratory stains. ______________________________

Name____________________________ Class______________________ Date____________

F. THE DISSECTING MICROSCOPE. The **dissecting microscope** (Figure 4-3) allows you to study large specimens that cannot be easily seen with the compound light microscope. It has two eyepieces and two objective lenses. The lower magnification, usually from 5X to 50X, and three-dimensional quality are useful in performing dissections. This microscope is used to examine specimens that are small, but can be seen by the unaided eye. This microscope is also called the stereo-microscope.

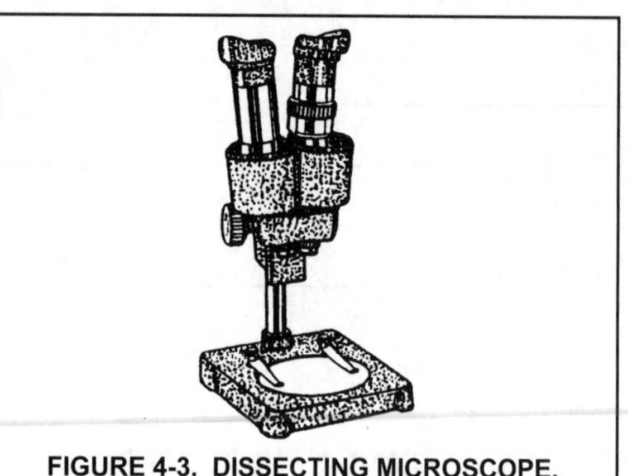

FIGURE 4-3. DISSECTING MICROSCOPE.

REVIEW QUESTIONS

1. When would you use a dissecting microscope?

____

____

2. Compare the number of lenses and eyepieces of the dissecting microscope and the compound microscope.

____

____

____

____

3. Why is the dissecting microscope useful in performing dissections?

____

____

G. THE ELECTRON MICROSCOPE. Electron microscopes can produce magnifications of more than 100,000X. These microscopes use a narrow beam of electrons instead of light. The electron beam is focused by sets of magnets instead of lenses. Specimens to be viewed in an electron microscope must be embedded in plastic and cut into very thin slices. This special preparation is a disadvantage because live specimens cannot be viewed. However, because of its high magnification, the electron microscope allows biologists to see the internal structure of the cell.

REVIEW QUESTIONS

1. The magnification of the electron microscope is __________________________.
2. Instead of light the electron microscope uses __________________________.

3. Name one disadvantage of the electron microscope.

____

H. THE ULTRACENTRIFUGE. The **ultracentrifuge** is an instrument that is used to separate cell parts according to density (Figure 4-4). The material to be separated is whirled around in a test tube at very high speeds. The heaviest parts settle to the bottom of the test tube, the next to heaviest form the next layer, and so on. The lightest material collects as the top layer.

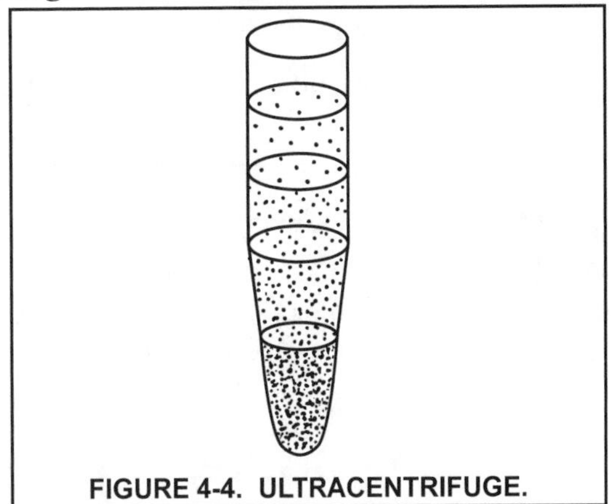

FIGURE 4-4. ULTRACENTRIFUGE.

REVIEW QUESTIONS

1. The centrifuge is an instrument used to ____

____

I. MAGNIFICATION IN CELL STUDY. When you use the microscope it is important to understand how it magnifies and its use as a measuring tool for small objects. In a compound microscope each lens **magnifies**, or enlarges, the image. To determine the total magnification produced by the microscope the magnifying power of the objective lens is multiplied by the magnifying power of the eyepiece lens. For example, if the eyepiece lens has a magnifying power of 10X, or 10 times, and the objective lens has a magnifying power of 10X the total magnifying power of the microscope is 100X. If the magnifying power of the eyepiece is 10X and the magnifying power of the objective is 40X the total magnifying power of the microscope is 400X. The maximum magnification possible with a compound light microscope is about 2,000X. **Total magnification** refers to the total amount that the image is enlarged.

EYEPIECE POWER	×	OBJECTIVE POWER	=	TOTAL MAGNIFICATION
10X	×	40X	=	400X

REVIEW QUESTIONS

1. Total magnification is ____

____

2. To find the total magnification of a microscope, multiply the ____________________ of the ____________________ by the ____________________ of the ____________________.

3. A 10X eyepiece and a 50X objective would produce an image that is ____________.

4. If the total magnification is 100X, and the eyepiece power is 5X, what is the power of the objective? ____________.

J. MEASUREMENT IN CELL STUDY. Objects viewed through the microscope are very small and cannot be measured with the standard units of length used to measure larger objects. The unit of length used to measure microscopic specimens is the **micrometer (μ m)** or the **micron (μ).** One thousand microns (micrometers) is equal to one millimeter.

REVIEW QUESTIONS

1. The unit of length used for microscopic measurement is the

____________________.

2. One thousand microns equals ____________________.

CAREER OPPORTUNITIES

MICROBIOLOGIST: A **microbiologist** is a life scientist who works with organisms that are so tiny that they must be seen under a microscope. These scientists do research on bacteria, yeasts, and other microorganisms. They isolate and make cultures of microorganisms, identify their characteristics, and observe their reactions to chemicals and other kinds of stimuli. They use special methods and equipment such as compound microscopes, electron microscopes, centrifuges, glass tubes, and slides.

Education and training requirements differ according to the type of job. Laboratory technicians in microbiology need a high school diploma and at least a two year associate degree. Other jobs require a bachelor's, master's or doctoral degree.

REVIEW QUESTIONS

1. Name one career opportunity for people who like to work with microscopes.

____

Name________________ Class________________ Date__________

LAB INVESTIGATION: THE COMPOUND MICROSCOPE

OBJECTIVE

Upon completion of this activity, you should be able to identify the parts, state the function of each part, and know how to use the compound microscope.

LABORATORY PROCEDURE

Materials: Compound microscope, lens paper, and a prepared slide of the letter **e**.

1. Carry the microscope to your lab area by placing one hand under the microscope under the **base** and the other hand holding the **arm.** The diagram at the right will help you identify microscope parts.

2. The **eyepiece** is at the top of the **body tube** of your microscope. It contains a lens that magnifies or enlarges images (figures). Look at the number stamped on the eyepiece. This tells you how many times the lens enlarges an image. It is called the ***magnification power***. Write the magnification power of your eyepiece in the observation section next to **Observation (1)** on the next page.

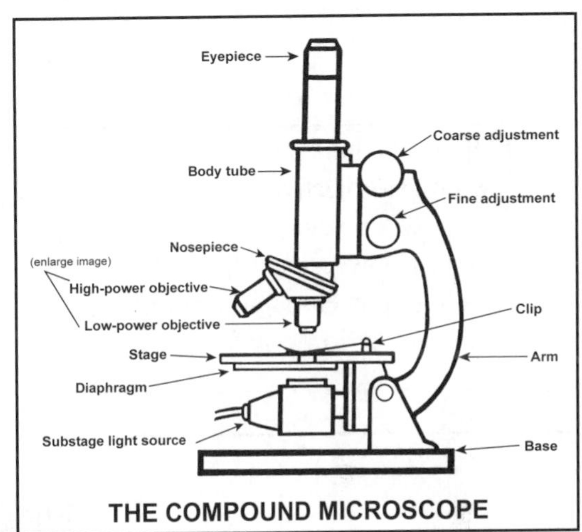

THE COMPOUND MICROSCOPE

3. At the bottom of your body tube is the **nosepiece**. The nosepiece holds two **objective lenses** that further enlarge the image. The longer objective is the **high power objective** and the shorter objective is the **low power objective**. The magnification power is stamped on each objective. Write the magnification power of the low power lens in **Observation (2)** in the observation section. Write the magnification of the high power lens in **Observation (3)**.

4. To figure out the total magnification of your microscope when using low power, multiply the eyepiece magnification by the magnification of the low power objective. Write your answer in **Observation (4)**. Now figure out the total high power magnification of your microscope and write that number in **Observation (5)**.

5. Turn the nosepiece so that the low power objective is in line with the body tube. Carefully clean both objectives and the eyepiece with lens tissue. Place the prepared slide on the **stage** so that the letter **e** is upright on the stage. Make sure that it is in the center of the hole. Fasten the slide on the stage with the **stage clips**. Plug in and turn on the **light** (or tilt the **mirror**) so that light is directed through the stage. Use the **diaphragm** to adjust the amount of light coming through the stage. *(If your microscope has a mirror DO NOT USE DIRECT SUNLIGHT because it will injure your eyes.)*

6. While looking through the eyepiece slowly turn the **coarse adjustment** upwards to roughly focus the image. (You may have to readjust your slide so that the letter e is in the center of the hole.) Now turn the **fine adjustment** upwards to sharpen the focus. *Always move objectives upwards while looking through the eyepiece*. Draw what you actually see in **Observation (6)**.

Name_________________________ Class_____________________ Date___________

7. Write a sentence in **Observation (7)** to describe how the letter **e** "appears" through the microscope Does it look the same as it does on the stage?

8. While looking through the eyepiece move the prepared slide to the right. Does the letter **e** move to the right or to the left? Write your answer in **Observation (8)**. Slowly move the slide toward the front of the stage. Does the letter **e** move toward you or away from you? Write your answer in **Observation (9)**.

9. With the letter **e** in the center of the stage slowly turn the nosepiece until the **high power objective** is in line with the body tube. Use only the fine adjustment to focus the high power objective. *Never use the coarse adjustment with the high power objective.* After you have focused your letter **e** draw your observation in **Observation (10)**.

10. When you are finished unplug the light, clean the lenses and the slide with your lens tissue, and carefully carry your microscope back to its storage area. Return your materials.

OBSERVATIONS

(1) eyepiece magnification: ____________	(7) ______________________
(2) low power objective: ____________	______________________
(3) high power objective: ____________	(8) ____________
(4) total low power magnification: ________	(9) ____________
(5) total high power magnification: ________	(10) letter **e** under high power ____________
(6) letter **e** under low power: ____________	______________________
______________________	

CONCLUSIONS

1. Complete the following chart.

MICROSCOPE PART	FUNCTION
Arm and Base	
Body Tube	
Eyepiece	
Coarse Adjustment	
Fine Adjustment	
Stage Clip	
Light (Mirror)	
Diaphragm	
Objectives	
Nosepiece	

Name ______________________ Class ______________________ Date __________

REVIEW ACTIVITIES

Important Terms

DIRECTIONS: Define the following terms in the spaces provided.

cell ____

centrifuge ____

coarse adjustment ____

diaphragm ____

dissecting microscope ____

electron microscope ____

fine adjustment ____

high power objective ____

Hooke ____

image ____

Leeuwenhoek ____

low power objective ____

magnify ____

Name______________________ Class__________________ Date__________

micron ____

____

multicellular ____

____

Schleiden ____

____

Schwann ____

____

specimen ____

____

stage ____

____

stage clips ____

____

staining techniques ____

____

total magnification ____

____

unicellular ____

____

Virchow ____

____

Name_______________ Class_______________ Date_______________

Skill Practice

Part A. Base your answers to questions 1 through 4 on the diagram below of a microscope and on your knowledge of biology.

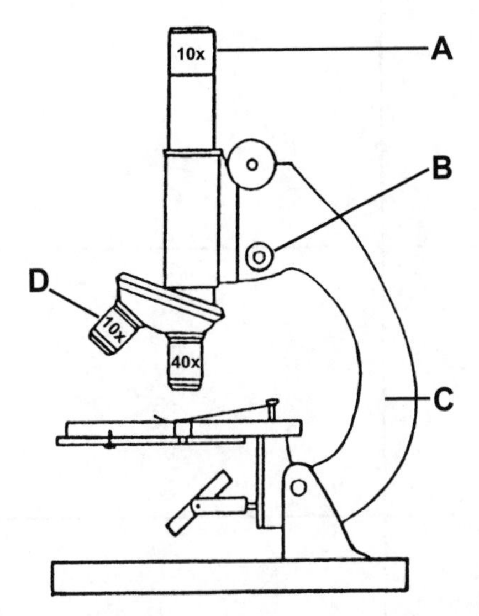

1. While viewing a specimen under high power, a student noticed that the specimen was out of focus. Which part of the microscope should the student use to obtain a clearer image?

(1) A (3) C

(2) B (4) D

2. The highest possible magnification that can be obtained when using this microscope is

(1) 40X (3) 400X

(2) 100X (4) 4,000X

3. The diagram at the right represents a strand of a one-celled plant viewed under the low power objective of this microscope. Under the high power objective, how would this same slide appear?

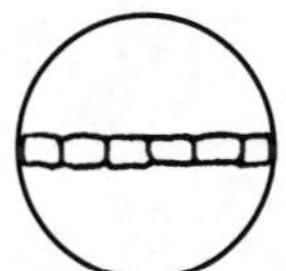

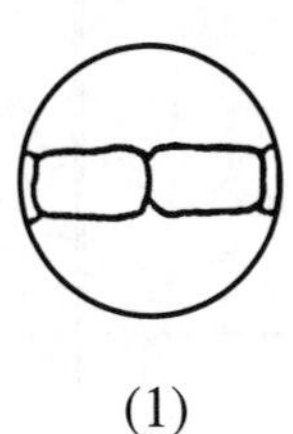

(1)

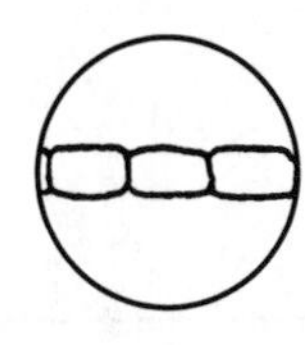

(2)

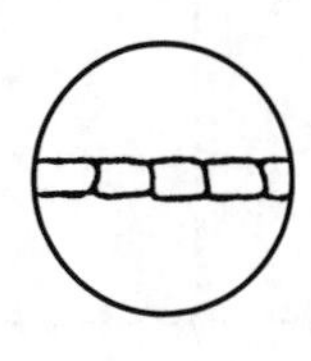

(3)

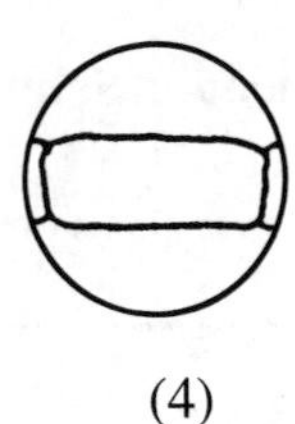

(4)

4. Label the parts of the microscope in the diagram in the spaces provided.

A _______________ C _______________

B _______________ D _______________

Name________________________ Class____________________ Date__________

Part B. Complete the following table

SCIENTIST	CONTRIBUTION
Anton van Leeuwenhoek	
Robert Hooke	
Robert Brown	
Matthias Schleiden	
Theodor Schwann	
Rudolf Virchow	

Name________________________ Class________________________ Date____________

CHAPTER 4: QUIZ

A. FILL-IN QUESTIONS

DIRECTIONS: Complete each of the following statements by writing the correct word or phrase in the space provided.

1. The basic unit of structure and function of living things is called the ____________________.
2. Cells come from other living cells not from ____________________ matter.
3. Viruses contain genetic material and can ____________________.
4. Leeuwenhoek developed the first ____________________.
5. The cell was named by ____________________.
6. Robert Brown named the ____________________.
7. The microscope used most commonly for cell study is called the ____________________.
8. The material to be seen under to microscope is called the ____________________.
9. Light passing through a specimen first passes through the ____________________ lens.
10. The position of the final microscope image is enlarged, upside down, and ____________________.
11. The ______________ of the microscope controls the amount of light that enters the microscope.
12. The microscope used to study large specimens is called the ____________________.
13. The electron microscope uses ____________________ instead of lenses.
14. The instrument used to separate cell parts according to density is the ____________________.
15. In the compound microscope, images are enlarged by the ____________________.
16. The total amount that the image has been enlarged is called ____________________.
17. Microscopic specimens are measured in units called ____________________.
18. The microscope lens located at the top of the microscope is the ____________________.
19. The concept that all animals are made up of cells was reported by ____________________.
20. The word unicellular means ____________________.

B. MULTIPLE-CHOICE QUESTIONS

DIRECTIONS: Circle the number of the expression that best completes each of the following statements.

1. If a wet-mounted specimen is to be viewed with a compound microscope the specimen should be
   (1) taken from an aquatic environment
   (2) placed on top of the eyepiece
   (3) glued to the slide
   (4) thin enough to let light pass through it

2. Which statement is not a part of the cell theory?
   (1) Cells are the basic unit of structure of living things.
   (2) All cells are multicellular.
   (3) Cells are the basic unit of function of living things.
   (4) Cells come from other living cells.

Name____________________ Class____________________ Date__________

3. A laboratory project required students to estimate the width of a piece of human hair with the microscope. Which unit of measurement would be most appropriate?
   (1) inches (3) feet
   (2) millimeters (4) meters
4. In a compound microscope, the lens located closest to the slide is the
   (1) objective (3) eyepiece
   (2) nosepiece (4) mirror
5. In the diagram at the right, which part of the microscope would a student have to adjust to change from low power to high power?

A
B
C
D

   (1) A (3) C
   (2) B (4) D
6. Which of the following scientists first observed and named the cell?
   (1) Robert Brown (3) Robert Hooke
   (2) Matthias Schleiden (4) Theodor Schwann
7. Which part of the microscope controls the amount of light that passes through a specimen?
   (1) eyepiece (3) diaphragm
   (2) objective lens (4) fine-adjustment knob
8. Adding stain to a specimen on a slide helps to
   (1) cause cells to absorb water.
   (2) make cell structures easier to see.
   (3) make the cover glass stick to the slide.
   (4) cause more light to pass through the specimen.
9. Which organisms are noncellular?
   (1) protozoans (3) trees
   (2) algae (4) viruses
10. Which of the following instruments will produce the greatest enlargement of a specimen?
   (1) compound light microscope (3) electron microscope
   (2) dissecting microscope (4) centrifuge

C. ESSAY QUESTION

DIRECTIONS: Use complete sentences to answer the question in this part.

1. State one way that the microscope is used in the field of medicine.

____

____

____

____

Name ______________ Class ______________ Date ______________

Chapter 5: Cell Structure and Function

A. ORGANELLES. There are many small structures located inside the cell. These structures are called **organelles**, which means "little organs". These tiny structures perform certain functions that keep the cell (and the organism) alive. Some organelles are found only in animal cells and others are located only in plant cells. Most organelles, however, are found in both plant and animal cells (Figure 5-1).

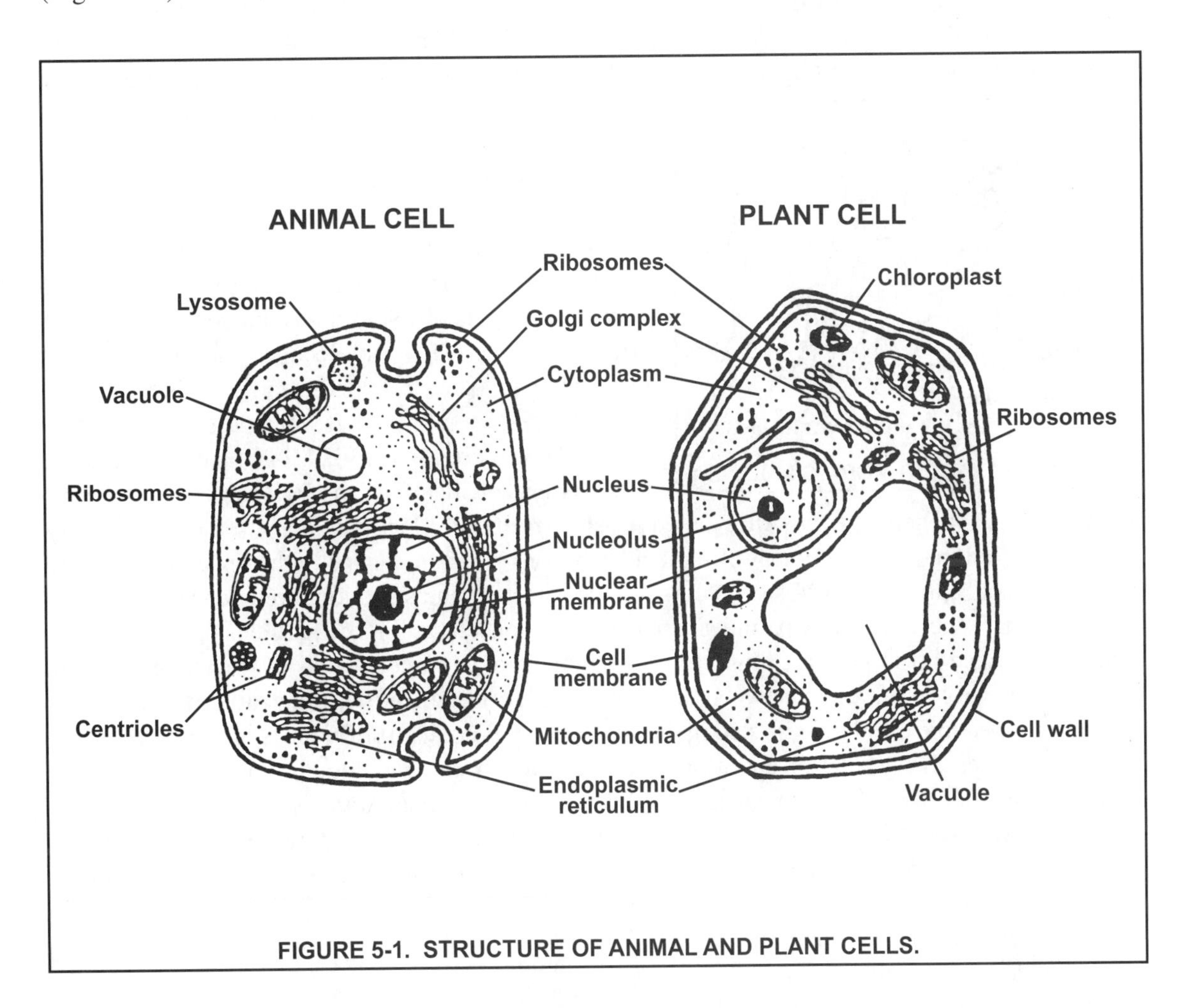

FIGURE 5-1. STRUCTURE OF ANIMAL AND PLANT CELLS.

REVIEW QUESTIONS

1. The small structures located inside the cell are called ______________.
2. List six organelles found in both plant and animal cells.

____

____

Name____________________ Class__________________ Date__________

B. CELL MEMBRANE. The **cell membrane** (or **plasma membrane**) is a double-layered structure that surrounds the cell. It provides a boundary between the cell and its environment. In animal cells it is the outside cell border and in plant cells it is located inside the cell wall (Figure 5-1). The function (job) of the membrane is to regulate or control the passage of materials into and out of the cell and to help maintain cell shape. The cell membrane is **semi-permeable,** that is, some substances can pass through it and others cannot. Because it is involved with the passage of materials into and out of the cell the cell membrane is part of the transport system. The selectivity of the cell membrane allows particular substances to pass through some of the time but not other times. The selective permeability of cell membranes aids cells in maintaining homeostasis.

The currently accepted model (representation) of cell membrane structure is called the **fluid-mosaic model.** According to this model the cell membrane is made up of a double lipid layer containing large floating protein molecules (Figure 5-2). Various kinds of small molecules, such as water and carbon dioxide, can easily pass through the cell membrane. Most large molecules, such as proteins and starch, cannot pass through the membrane. These substances must be digested before they can enter or leave a cell. In addition to molecular size, factors that affect the passage of molecules through the cell membrane are electrical charge and solubility in fats.

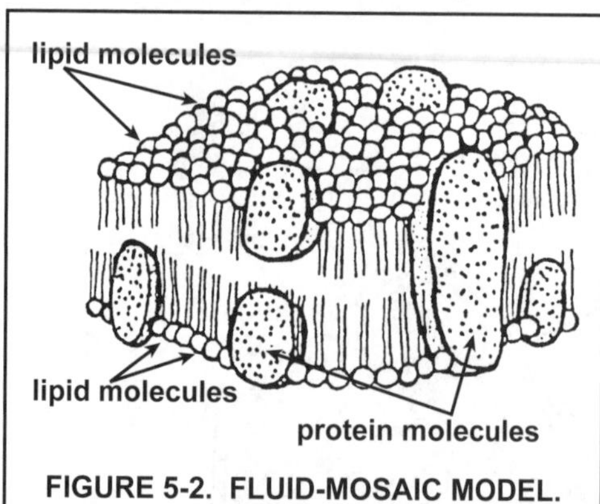

FIGURE 5-2. FLUID-MOSAIC MODEL.

The cell membrane has both passive and active roles in transporting materials into and out of cells. The passage of materials through the cell membrane without the use of energy by the cell is called **passive transport.** Passive transport most commonly involves **diffusion**—the movement of molecules or ions from an area of high concentration to an area of low concentration. Diffusion occurs because the molecules and ions are in constant random motion. Where there are many particles (areas of high concentration) the particles bump into each other and bounce off in all directions. In this way they spread out to areas of low concentration. The difference in concentration between two areas is called the **concentration gradient.** Eventually the particles become evenly distributed in the space. At that point **equilibrium** is reached and there is no further net change in concentration. Equilibrium occurs when equal numbers of particles move into and out of an area. The diffusion of water through a membrane is called **osmosis.**

Active transport is a process in which cellular energy is used to move particles through a membrane. This movement occurs from a region of lower concentration toward a region of higher concentration. The movement is against the concentration gradient. Carrier proteins that are embedded in the cell membrane help in the transport of materials. **Pinocytosis** and **phagocytosis** are two types of active transport processes. In pinocytosis large *dissolved* molecules are taken into the cell by the formation of vacuoles. The cell membrane forms an indentation containing

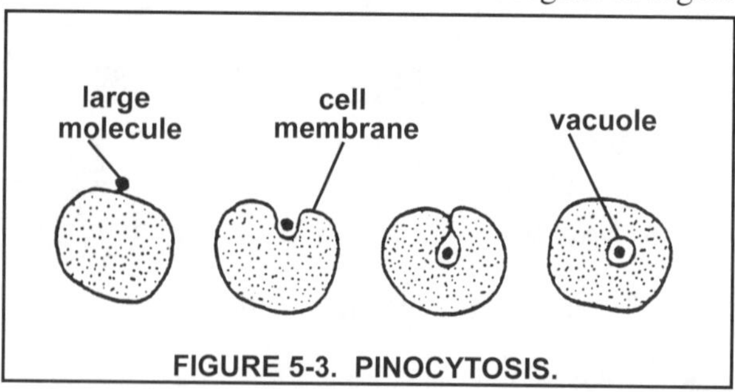

FIGURE 5-3. PINOCYTOSIS.

Name ____________________ Class ____________________ Date __________

the molecule to be taken in (Figure 5-3). This folded in section of the cell membrane then pinches off inside the cell forming a vacuole. In phagocytosis the cell surrounds and engulfs large *undissolved* particles by flowing around them and enclosing them in a vacuole.

REVIEW QUESTIONS

1. Describe the cell membrane. ____________________

2. Explain the following terms:

passive transport ____________________

diffusion ____________________

equilibrium ____________________

osmosis ____________________

active transport ____________________

pinocytosis ____________________

phagocytosis ____________________

C. CYTOPLASM. The watery cell fluid that contains the cell organelles is called the **cytoplasm**. The cytoplasm is located between the cell membrane and the nucleus. Many life processes take place in the cytoplasm. The cytoplasm exists in two different phases–a watery (**sol**) phase and a thicker (**gel**) phase

REVIEW QUESTIONS

1. Cytoplasm is the watery cell fluid that contains ____________________.
2. Where is the cytoplasm located? ____________________
3. Describe the two phases of cytoplasm. ____________________

Name_____________________________ Class________________________ Date____________

D. NUCLEUS. The **nucleus** is a large round structure located inside the cytoplasm of the cell (Figure 5-4). It is surrounded by its own membrane, called the **nuclear membrane,** and it contains other organelles (chromosomes and nucleoli). Cell activities are controlled by the nucleus. The **nucleolus** is located in the nucleus. It is involved in the production of ribosomes.

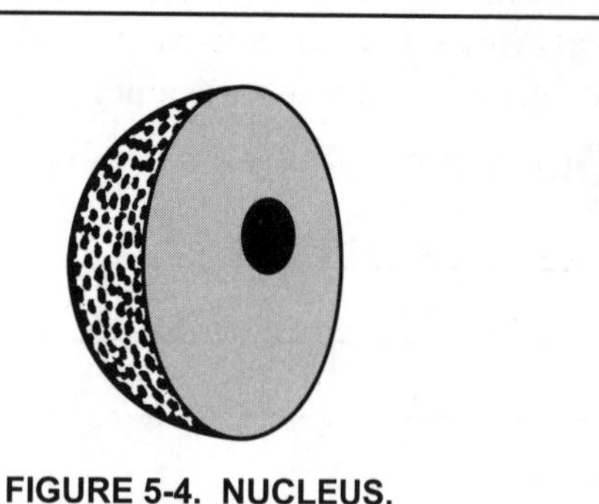

FIGURE 5-4. NUCLEUS.

REVIEW QUESTIONS

1. Where is the nucleus located? ______________________________

2. The function of the nucleus is to ______________________________.

3. What is the function of the nucleolus? ______________________________

____

E. CHROMOSOMES. The **chromosomes** are long threadlike structures located in the nucleus of the cell. They contain heredity information organized as genes. **Genes** are hereditary units made up of **DNA** that control cell activities and may be passed on to the next generation.

REVIEW QUESTIONS

1. The chromosomes contain __________________ information.

2. What is a gene? ______________________________

____

F. MITOCHONDRIA. Mitochondria are the organelles involved in cellular respiration (Figure 5-5). They are called the "powerhouses" of the cell. Mitochondria contain materials necessary for respiratory reactions. It is here that energy is released in the cell. Without the constant supply of energy produced by respiration the cell would die.

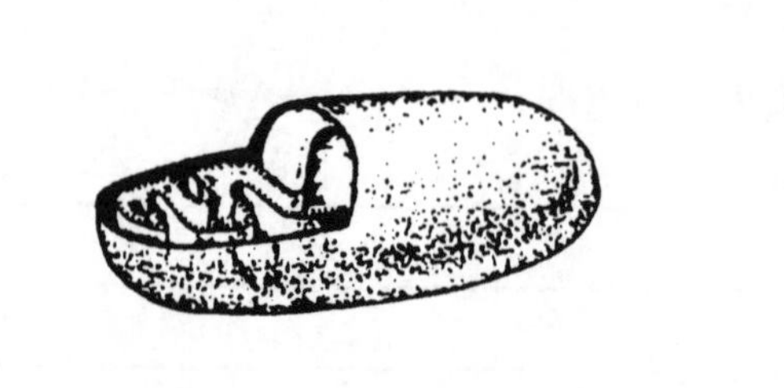

FIGURE 5-5. MITOCHONDRION.

There are two types of respiration carried out by living cell known as aerobic respiration and anaerobic respiration. **Aerobic respiration** *requires oxygen* to aid in the release of energy. Aerobic respiration releases more energy per molecule of food than anaerobic respiration.

Name ____________________ Class ____________________ Date ____________

Cells of most complex animals and plants carry on aerobic respiration. The word equation for aerobic respiration is:

SUGAR + OXYGEN —enzymes→ ENERGY + CARBON DIOXIDE + WATER

This equation tells you that during aerobic respiration the organism combines sugar (food) and oxygen, in the presence of enzymes, to make energy that the organism uses for its life processes. In addition to energy the organism makes carbon dioxide and water that are either used by the organism or excreted from the cells into the environment.

Anaerobic respiration or **fermentation** does not require oxygen. A small amount of energy is produced along with carbon dioxide and either alcohol or lactic acid. The word equation for anaerobic respiration is:

SUGAR —enzymes→ ENERGY + CARBON DIOXIDE + ALCOHOL or LACTIC ACID

Review Questions

1. What is the function of the mitochondria? ____________________
2. Mitochondria are called the ____________________ of the cell.
3. The two types of respiration are ____________________ and ____________________.
4. Another name for anaerobic respiration is ____________________.
5. Which type of respiration releases more energy? ____________________.
6. Write the word equation for aerobic respiration.

____

7. Write the word equation for anaerobic respiration.

____

8. Fermentation produces energy and ____________________.

Name______________________ Class__________________ Date__________

G. ENDOPLASMIC RETICULUM. Materials are transported throughout the cell by a system of channels or canals called the **endoplasmic reticulum (ER).** Chemical reactions take place on the surface of the endoplasmic reticulum. In some places it has a rough surface and in other places it is smooth. The rough surface is due to the presence of ribosomes. Cells making proteins contain a large amount of rough endoplasmic reticulum (Figure 5-6).

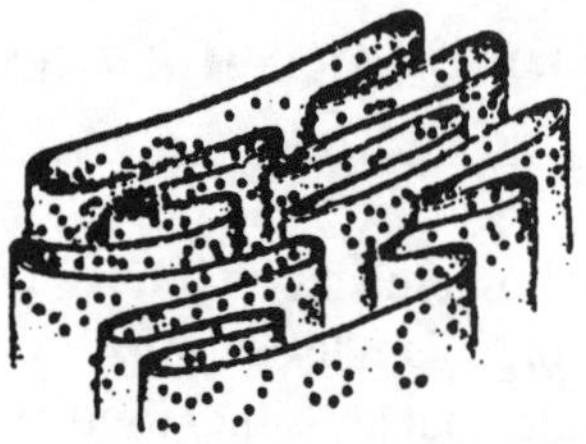

FIGURE 5-6. ENDOPLASMIC RETICULUM.

REVIEW QUESTIONS

1. The function of the endoplasmic reticulum is ________________________.

2. Name the two kinds of endoplasmic reticulum. ________________________________

____

H. RIBOSOMES. Proteins are synthesized (made) at the **ribosomes.** They may be attached to the endoplasmic reticulum or free in the cytoplasm .

REVIEW QUESTIONS

1. The ribosomes synthesize ___________________.

2. Ribosomes are located on the _______________________ and in the _______________.

I. GOLGI COMPLEX. The **Golgi complex** or apparatus is a stack of membrane-bounded channels and vacuoles. They synthesize (make), package, and secrete cell products (Figure 5-7).

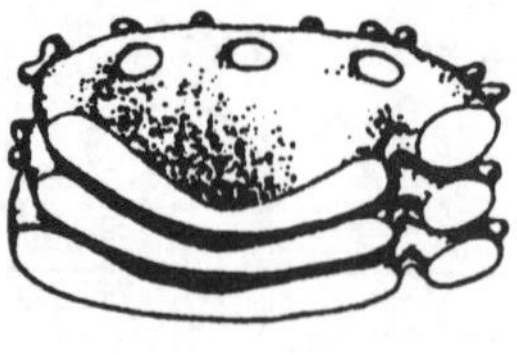

FIGURE 5-7. GOLGI COMPLEX

REVIEW QUESTIONS

1. The Golgi complex ________________________, ________________________ and

_____________________ cell products.

Name________________________ Class________________________ Date____________

J. VACUOLES. **Vacuoles** are sac-like structures used by the cell to store various materials including water, wastes, and food. They are located in the cytoplasm. Plant cell vacuoles are bigger than those found in animal cells.

REVIEW QUESTIONS

1. Vacuoles are located in the ______________ and are used by the cell for ______________
____

K. LYSOSOMES. Membrane-bounded sacs, called **lysosomes**, contain digestive enzymes. They are involved in food digestion in one-celled animals. Lysosomes destroy damaged or old cell parts or cells in multicellular animals. Although they have been seen only in animal cells, plant cells are now thought to have a similar organelle.

REVIEW QUESTIONS

1. Digestive enzymes are found in the ______________________ of the cell.

L. CHLOROPLASTS. The organelles involved in the manufacture of food (photosynthesis) are called **chloroplasts** (Figure 5-8). They are located in the cytoplasm and contain the green pigment **chlorophyll.** Also present are **enzymes** (organic catalysts) that are necessary for food-making reactions. Inside the chloroplasts are stacked disks called **grana.** It is in the grana that chlorophyll is held and light energy for photosynthesis is trapped. The spaces inside the chloroplasts contain a protein-containing fluid called **stroma**.

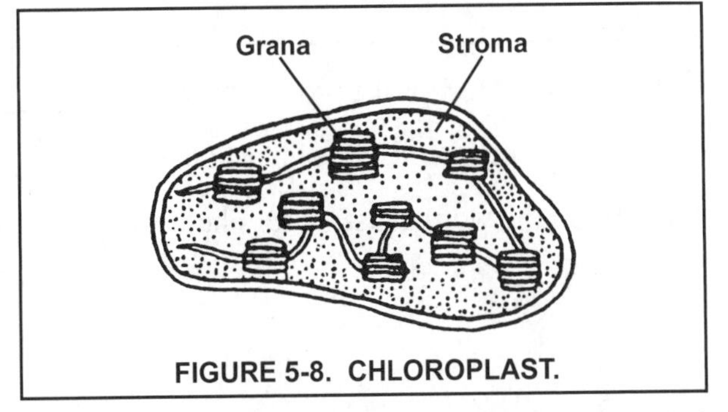

FIGURE 5-8. CHLOROPLAST.

The pigments in chloroplasts can be separated and identified by a laboratory technique called **paper chromatography.** This process involves putting a drop of plant extract along one edge of a square of absorbent paper. The paper is then dipped into a solvent. The solvent moves up the sheet because of capillary attraction. As the solvent moves the substances in the drop of plant extract are carried along at different rates that are unique to each substance. Because of this movement the different substances separate at distinct places on the sheet of paper thus forming what is called a **chromatogram.** Each substance can then be identified by comparing its position with the positions occupied by known substances under the same conditions.

Chloroplasts are also found in one-celled organisms called **algae.** Because algae are not multicellular they are not classified as plants but as protists. Green plant cells and algae make their own food by the process of **photosynthesis.** This process involves a series of complex chemical reactions that use light as an energy source. Photosynthesis provides food for green plants and algae. The food that is manufactured by photosynthesis is also used by other living things.

Name______________________ Class__________________ Date__________

Photosynthesis involves chemical reactions in which carbon dioxide and water are converted into sugar. Energy for cell activities is stored in sugar. Oxygen gas is a by-product of this reaction. In addition to light, photosynthesis needs chlorophyll and enzymes (organic catalysts) which aid the reaction. Enzymes are necessary for all cell reactions. The word equation for photosynthesis is:

$$\text{CARBON DIOXIDE + WATER} \xrightarrow[\text{chlorophyll}]{\text{enzymes and light}} \text{SUGAR + OXYGEN + WATER}$$

This equation tells you that the plant combines carbon dioxide and water in the presence of enzymes, light, and chlorophyll to produce sugar (food), oxygen, and water. The sugar is used by the organism as a source of energy and the oxygen is used for its respiration. Excess oxygen is released into the air and is used by animals for respiration. Water is released into the environment.

REVIEW QUESTIONS

1. What is the function of the chloroplast? ______________________________

____

2. The green pigment in chloroplasts is called ______________________.

3. Why aren't algae classified as plants? ______________________________

____

4. Photosynthesis is the process by which ______________________________.

5. The energy source for photosynthesis is ____________________

6. Write the word equation for photosynthesis.

7. Why do scientists use chromatography? ______________________________

____

M. CENTRIOLES. These structures are found mainly in animal cells. They look like cylinders and are located in pairs near the nucleus. Centrioles are involved in cell division.

REVIEW QUESTIONS

1. The centrioles are ________________ in shape and are located near the ____________ in ____________ cells. They are involved in the process of ____________________

Name ____________ Class ____________ Date ____________

N. CELL WALL. The **cell wall** is the stiff outer layer of plant cells. It surrounds the cell membrane and its contents. Cell walls are composed of a nonliving material called **cellulose.** The stiffness of the cell wall limits the plant's growth and movement. The cell wall gives the plant its shape (Figure 5-9).

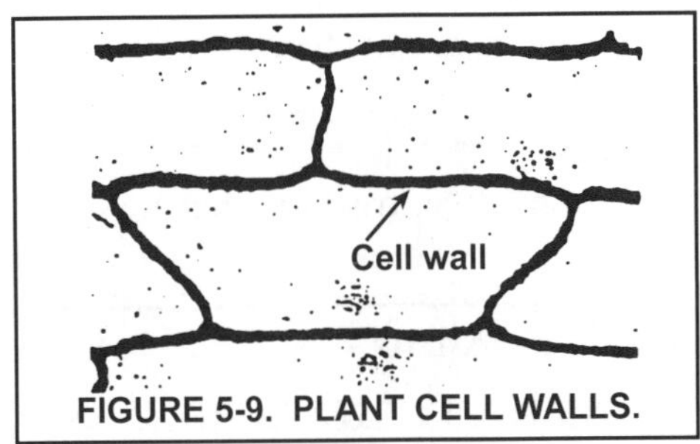

FIGURE 5-9. PLANT CELL WALLS.

REVIEW QUESTIONS

1. Describe the cell wall. ____________

____

____

2. Cellulose is a ____________ material.

O. COMPARISON OF PLANT AND ANIMAL CELLS. Most cell organelles are found in both plant and animal cells. However, there are some structural differences between a typical animal cell and a typical green plant cell. Table 5-1 compares the structural similarities and differences between the two types of cells.

ORGANELLE	GREEN PLANT	ANIMAL
Plasma Membrane	present	present
Cytoplasm	present	present
Nucleus	present	present
Chromosomes	present	present
Mitochondria	present	present
ER	present	present
Ribosomes	present	present
Golgi Complex	present	present
Vacuoles	large	small
Lysosomes	present	present
Centrioles	absent	present
Chloroplasts	present	absent
Cell Wall	present	absent

TABLE 5-1. COMPARISON AND ANIMAL CELLS.

REVIEW QUESTIONS

1. Name two structures that are found only in plant cells. ____________

____

Name ____________________ Class ________________ Date __________

2. Name one structure that is found only in animal cells.

____

3. Name five structures that are found in both plant and animal cells.

____

P. CELL SPECIALIZATION. Certain cells in multicellular organisms do certain jobs. This is called cell specialization. Examples of specialized cells are shown in Table 5-2.

CELL TYPE	FUNCTION
Cell Blood Cells	Carry oxygen to body cells.
Muscle Cells	Move parts of organism.
Nerve Cells	Carry impulses (messages) throughout organism.
Xylem and Phloem Cells	Transport materials throughout plants.

TABLE 5-2. SPECIALIZED CELLS.

REVIEW QUESTIONS

1. Name two specialized cells and state the function of each. ____________________

____

Name________________________ Class________________________ Date____________

Q. CELL ORGANIZATION. In multicellular organisms cells are grouped together into units or levels. These specialized units perform similar functions. Groups of cells make up tissues and groups of tissues form organs. Organs working together make systems and systems make up organisms. Plants and animals are examples of organisms.

- ♦ **Cells.** The **cell** is the basic unit of structure and function of all living things.
- ♦ **Tissues.** Groups of similar cells performing the same function are called **tissues**. Muscle tissue and blood tissue are examples of tissues.
- ♦ **Organs.** A group of specialized tissues performing one main function is known as an **organ.** Examples of organs are the stomach and kidney.
- ♦ **Systems.** A group of organs that carry on one of the major body function is known as a **system.** Examples of some major body systems are digestive and nervous systems
- ♦ **Organism.** An **organism** is made up of systems that perform its life functions. Plants and animals are examples of organisms.

REVIEW QUESTIONS

1. A group of cells performing the same function is known as a ________________.

2. A group of organs working together to perform the same function is called a ____________.

3. Systems make up units called ________________.

4. List and define the levels organization of living systems beginning with the simplest unit and ending with the most complex unit.

____

____

____

____

____

____

____

Name________________________ Class__________________ Date__________

CAREER OPPORTUNITIES

CYTOTECHNICIAN: A **cytotechnician** is a medical laboratory technician who specializes in cytology (cell study). They prepare and stain body cell samples and then mount them on slides. After staining and mounting the cells, the cytotechnician uses a microscope with very high magnification—some cells are enlarged over 1,000 times. The cytotechnician's job is to separate normal cells from abnormal cells. Abnormal cell structure indicates the possibility that a disease is present. Pathologists, doctors who specialize in the study of abnormal cell structure, then look at the abnormal cells.

To be a cytotechnician you must complete at least a two-year degree program in medical technology with a specialization in cytology. Most states require that you also pass a certification exam. There is job advancement in this field if you continue to study and complete a four-year bachelor's degree. You could then become a cytotechnologist. Cytotechnologists differ from cytotechnicians in the amount of responsibility they have and in the salary they earn. Cytotechnicians perform mostly routine work in the laboratory and are closely supervised. Their salary is less because they lack the necessary education and skills required in more advanced jobs.

REVIEW QUESTIONS

1. Describe the job of a cytotechnician.

Name____________________ Class____________________ Date__________

LAB INVESTIGATION: OBSERVING CELL STRUCTURE

Objective

Upon completion of this activity you should be able to prepare a temporary wet mount slide and identify several cell organelles.

Laboratory Procedure

Materials: Compound microscope, lens paper, glass slides, cover slips, water, medicine dropper, dissecting needle, pieces of onion, forceps, iodine solution,and paper towels.

1. Pick up your laboratory materials at the supply table and carry them to your lab area. Use lens paper to clean your microscope lenses, glass slides, and cover slips.

2. Use the medicine dropper to place a drop of water in the center of a glass slide **(Figure 1).**

3. With forceps, gently peel off the *very thin* tissue from the *inside curve* of a piece of onion **(Figure 2).**

4. Carefully place the onion tissue in the drop of water on the slide. Cover it with a cover slip. Use a dissecting needle to *slowly* lower the cover slip over the onion specimen **(Figure3).** This method forces out air bubbles. If any air bubbles are left push them out by gently pressing on the cover slip with the dissecting needle. You have now made a temporary wet mount slide.

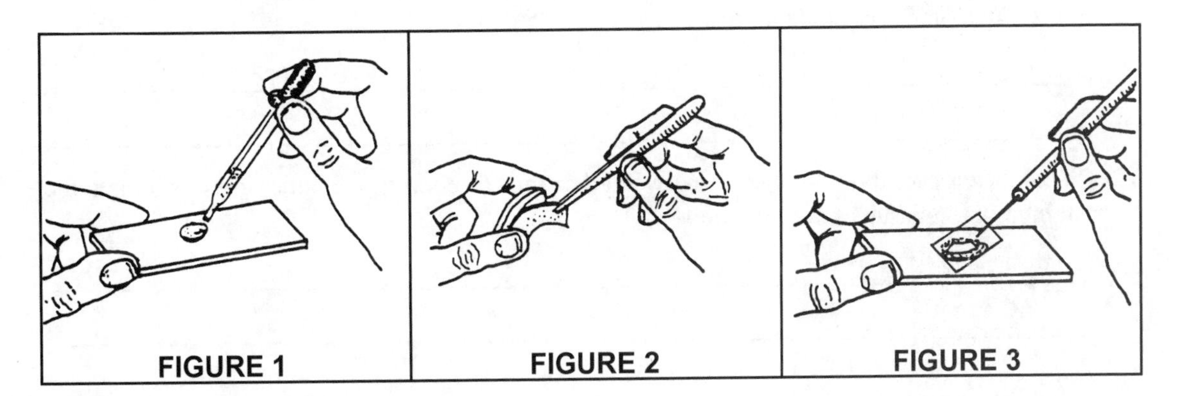

FIGURE 1 FIGURE 2 FIGURE 3

5. Place your slide on the microscope stage and focus the onion tissue under low power. You should see brick-shaped cells outlined in pale gray. You may or may not see the nucleus in the center of the cells.

6. Place a small drop of iodine solution at the edge of the cover slip. Touch a piece of paper towel to the opposite edge of the cover slip. The paper towel will absorb the water thereby pulling the stain through the onion tissue.

7. Observe your cells again under low power. The cell structures should now be clear because staining colors cell parts so that they are more easily seen. Draw your observations of the stained onion tissue under low power in the space provided in **Observation (1)** on the next page.

Name________________________ Class __________________ Date __________

8. Change your microscope to high power. Use ***only the fine adjustment*** to focus under high power. ***Do not focus downwards under high power while looking through the eyepiece.*** Focus your specimen by *slowly* turning the fine adjustment knob to move the body tube upwards.

9. Draw your observations of the stained onion tissue under high power in the space provided in **Observation (2)** below. Label the *cell wall* and the *nucleus*.

10. When you are finished clean your lenses, slide, and cover slip, and throw away your used piece of onion. Clean your lab area and return your materials to the supply table.

Observations

(1) STAINED ONION TISSUE (Low Power)	(2) STAINED ONION TISSUE (High Power)

Conclusions

1. What differences did you observe between the unstained onion tissue under low power and the stained onion tissue under low power?

   ____

   ____

2. What differences did you observe between the stained onion tissue under low power and the stained onion tissue under high power?

   ____

   ____

3. **Diagrams A** represents the appearance of plant tissue as seen through compound light microscope. **Diagram B** represents the appearance of the same field of view after the fine adjustment knob was turned. What do you think is the best conclusion to be made from these observations

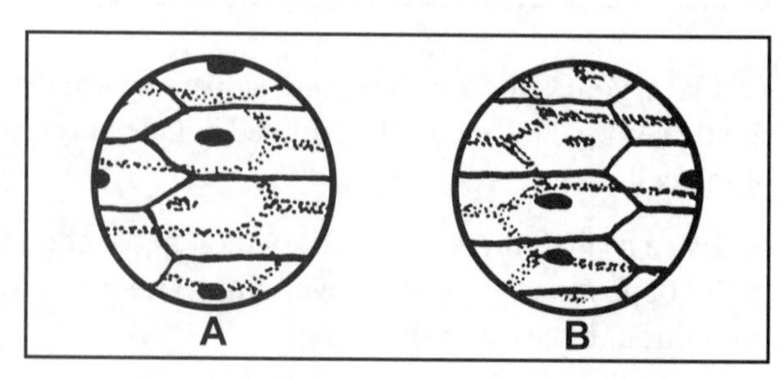

   ____

Name________________ Class________________ Date________

REVIEW ACTIVITIES

Important Terms

***DIRECTIONS:** Define the following terms in the spaces provided.*

active transport ________________________________

aerobic respiration ________________________________

anaerobic respiration ________________________________

cell wall ________________________________

centrioles ________________________________

chlorophyll ________________________________

chloroplasts ________________________________

chromosomes ________________________________

cytoplasm ________________________________

diffusion ________________________________

endoplasmic reticulum ________________________________

fermentation ________________________________

lysosome ________________________________

Name ______________________ Class ____________________ Date ____________

mitochondria ____

____

nuclear membrane ____

____

nucleolus ____

____

nucleus ____

____

organelles ____

____

organs ____

____

osmosis ____

____

passive transport ____

____

photosynthesis ____

____

plasma membrane ____

____

ribosomes ____

____

selectively permeable ____

____

systems ____

____

tissues ____

____

vacuoles ____

____

Name ______________________ Class ______________________ Date ____________

Skill Practice

Part A. Complete the following table.

ORGANELLE	FUNCTION
Plasma Membrane	
Cytoplasm	
Nucleus	
Nucleolus	
Ribosomes	
Endoplasmic Reticulum	
Mitochondria	
Golgi Complex	
Lysosomes	
Vacuoles	
Centrioles	
Chloroplasts	
Cell Wall	

Name______________________________ Class________________________ Date ____________

Part B. In the space below draw a typical animal cell and a typical plant cell. Label the organelles.

STRUCTURE OF A TYPICAL PLANT CELL AND A TYPICAL ANIMAL CELL

Name________________________ Class________________________ Date____________

CHAPTER 5: QUIZ

A. FILL-IN QUESTIONS

DIRECTIONS: Complete each of the following statements by writing the correct word or phrase in the space provided.

1. Cell activities are controlled by the ____________________ of the cell.
2. The double-layered structure surrounding all cells is called the ______________________.
3. The ______________________ synthesizes and secretes cell products.
4. The part of the cell where life processes take place is the ______________________.
5. Similar cells are grouped together to form ____________________.
6. ____________________ are hereditary units made up of DNA.
7. The organelles involved in the manufacture of food are called ______________________.
8. The cell stores wastes in structures called ______________________.
9. Oxygen is needed during ______________________ respiration.
10. Materials are transported around the plant by ________________ and ______________ cells.
11. ____________________ are small structures located inside the cell.
12. Nerve cells carry ______________________.
13. Osmosis involves the movement of ________________ across a semipermeable membrane.
14. Materials are moved across cell membranes by the process of ____________________.
15. One-celled green organisms are called ______________________.
16. ______________________ is the nonliving material found in cell walls.
17. Plants make food during the process of ____________________________.
18. Cell respiration takes place at the ____________________________.
19. The pair of structures involved in animal cell division are called ______________________.
20. Proteins are made at the ______________________.

B. MULTIPLE-CHOICE QUESTIONS

DIRECTIONS: Circle the number of the expression that best completes each of the following statements.

1. Which organisms contain chlorophyll in their cells?
   (1) algae
   (2) earthworms
   (3) grasshoppers
   (4) tapeworms

2. The stiff outer part of a plant cell is the
   (1) nucleus
   (2) cytoplasm
   (3) cell membrane
   (4) cell wall

3. By which life process does a leaf produce sugar?
   (1) respiration
   (2) excretion
   (3) transpiration
   (4) photosynthesis

Name______________________________ Class________________________ Date____________

4. Which structure controls the movement of materials into and out of the cell?

   (1) cell wall (3) chloroplast
   (2) cell membrane (4) vacuole

5. What process is taking place if an organism produces alcohol from a sugar solution?

   (1) fermentation (3) growth
   (2) locomotion (4) reproduction

6. A group of specialized tissues performing one main function is known as

   (1) an organ (3) a cell
   (2) an organism (4) a system

7. The movement of perfume molecules throughout a room is an example of the process of

   (1) respiration (3) diffusion
   (2) synthesis (4) fermentation

Directions (8-9): Base your answers to questions 8 and 9 on the diagrams below that represent two cells observed under a microscope.

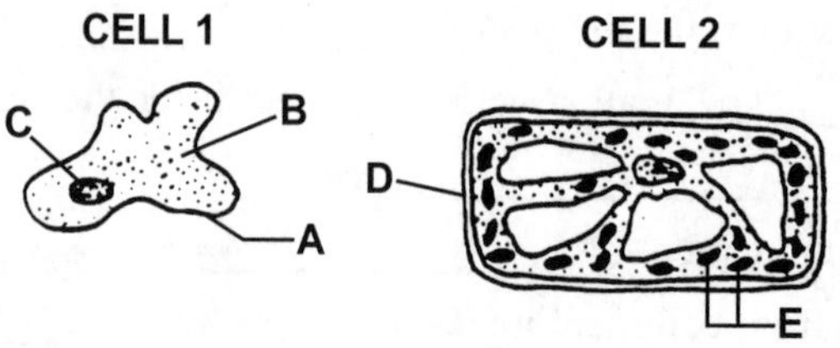

CELL 1 CELL 2

C B A D E

8. Which cell structure is involved with the production of food?

   (1) A (3) C
   (2) B (4) E

9. Which cell structure directs the function of the other cell parts?

   (1) A (3) C
   (2) B (4) E

10. Which process is represented by the following equation?

CARBON DIOXIDE + WATER —— light / chlorophyll and enzymes ——→ SUGAR + OXYGEN + WATER

   (1) reproduction (3) respiration
   (2) photosynthesis (4) digestion

C. ESSAY QUESTION

DIRECTIONS: Use complete sentences to answer the question in this part.

1. Describe one occupation where a knowledge of the cell would be useful.

____

____

____

Name________________________ Class____________________ Date__________

Chapter 6: Chemistry of Living Things

A. BASICS OF CHEMISTRY. The cell is a complex "chemical factory". It is made up of atoms, elements, compounds, and molecules. The chemical processes of the organism take place inside the organism's cells. To understand life processes you need a basic knowledge of chemistry. This chapter will give you a background in basic chemistry that will help you understand the chemistry of living things.

REVIEW QUESTIONS

1. The cell is a complex ____________________ factory.

2. Where do the chemical processes of the organism take place? ____________________

____

B. THE ATOM. Living and nonliving things are made up of tiny units called **atoms**. The center core is called the **nucleus.** The nucleus is made up of particles called **protons** and **neutrons.** **Protons** have a positive charge (+1) and **neutrons** have no electrical charge (0). Negatively charged particles, called **electrons** (-1), revolve around the nucleus at different distances from the nucleus. The electrons move in paths called shells or **energy levels** (Figure 6-1).

Atoms have the same number of electrons and protons. This makes them electrically neutral (have no electrical charge).

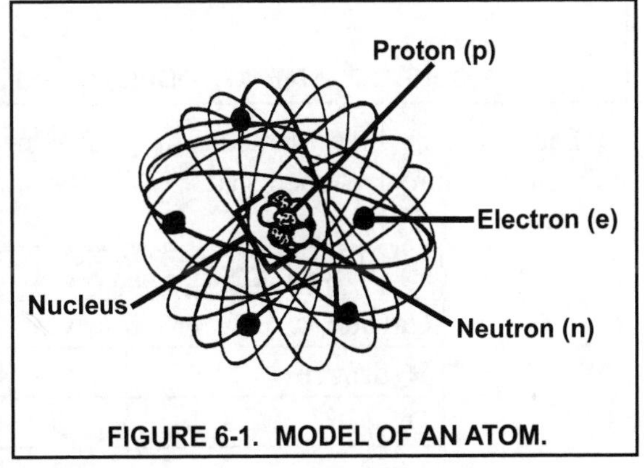

FIGURE 6-1. MODEL OF AN ATOM.

REVIEW QUESTIONS

1. Living things are composed of tiny units called ____________________.

2. The nucleus is the ____________________ of an atom.

3. Complete the following chart that compares electrons, proton, and neutrons.

PARTICLE	CHARGE	LOCATION
Electron		
Proton		
Neutron		

Name______________________________ Class ________________________ Date ____________

4. Why are atoms electrically neutral? ____

____

____

C. ELEMENTS. There are about 100 different kinds of atoms known to scientists today. A substance made up entirely of one kind of atom is called an **element.** Ninety-two elements occur naturally and the others were made in a laboratory. Elements differ from one another in their proton, neutron, and electron number (Figure 6-2). An element cannot be broken down into any other substance or matter. For example, pure silver is an element. It is made up only of silver atoms. When you break down a silver atom you get electrons, protons, and neutrons.

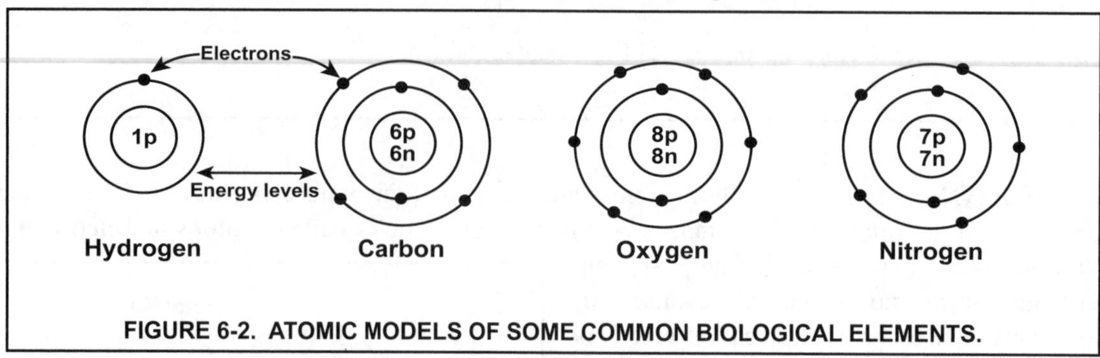

FIGURE 6-2. ATOMIC MODELS OF SOME COMMON BIOLOGICAL ELEMENTS.

Each element is represented by a **symbol** made up of one or two letters. The symbols of some of the most common elements are:

ELEMENT	SYM.	ELEMENT	SYM.
Carbon	C	Iodine	I
Hydrogen	H	Iron	Fe
Oxygen	O	Calcium	Ca
Nitrogen	N	Sodium	Na
Sulfur	S	Chlorine	Cl
Phosphorus	P	Potassium	K
Magnesium	Mg	Zinc	Zn

REVIEW QUESTIONS

1. A substance made up entirely of one kind of atom is called an ____________________.
2. A symbol represents an ____________________________.
3. How do elements differ from one another? ______________________________________

____

4. In the space below, draw and label the atomic models of carbon and oxygen.

Name________________ Class________________ Date__________

5. Complete the following table.

ELEMENT	SYMBOL	ELEMENT	SYMBOL
Phosphorus		Calcium	
	O		S
	Mg		H
Iron		Carbon	
Nitrogen			I
	K	Chlorine	

D. COMPOUNDS. A **compound** is formed when two or more elements combine chemically. The **properties** (characteristics) of compounds are quite different from the properties of the elements of which they are composed. For example, table sugar is made up of the elements carbon, hydrogen, and oxygen. Carbon is a black solid and hydrogen and oxygen are colorless gases. However, when they combine chemically they form a white granular substance.

Elements combine to form compounds by a process called **chemical bonding.** The formation of a chemical bond involves either the transfer of electrons from one atom to another or the sharing of electrons between atoms. For example, when sodium combines with chlorine one molecule of sodium chloride (table salt) is formed. During this process the sodium atom loses (transfers) an electron to the chlorine atom (Figure 6-3).

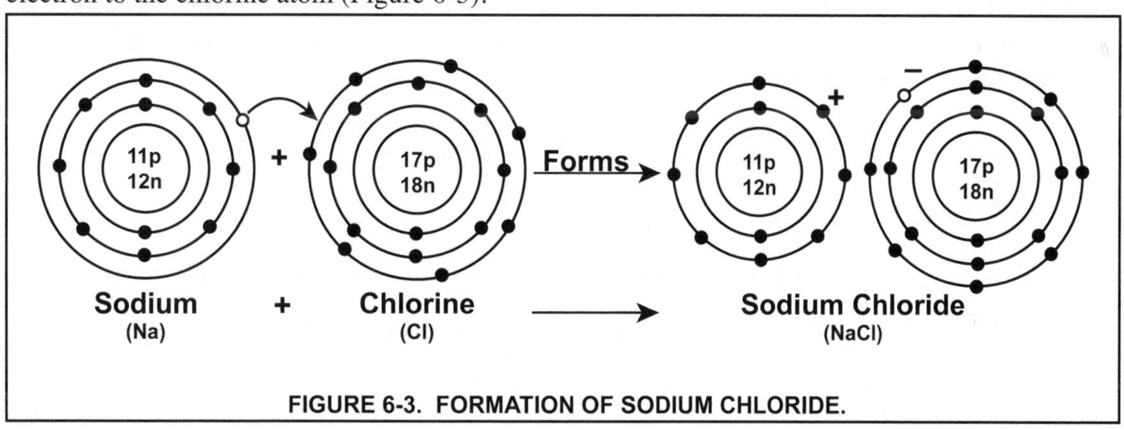

FIGURE 6-3. FORMATION OF SODIUM CHLORIDE.

REVIEW QUESTIONS

1. What is a compound? ________________________________

2. Compounds are made up of ______________________.

3. How do elements combine to form compounds? ______________________

____

____

____

____

Name________________________Class____________________Date__________

E. MOLECULES. The smallest particle of an element or compound capable of independent motion is a **molecule.** A molecule of a particular compound is made up of definite numbers and kinds of atoms bonded (joined) together. A molecule of water contains two hydrogen atoms and one oxygen atom bonded together. Two atoms of hydrogen bonded together form a molecule of hydrogen.

REVIEW QUESTIONS

1. Molecules are defined as ____

____

2. A molecule of water is composed of ___________________________________ and

____

F. IONS. An **ion** is an atom that has gained or lost an electron. Ions are formed during a type of chemical bonding that involves the transfer of electrons. When electrons are transferred from one atom to another both atoms become electrically charged. The atom that loses electrons becomes positively charged and the atom that gains electrons becomes negatively charged. The ions with opposite electrical charges are attracted to one another. A chemical bond that is formed when atoms lose or gain electrons is called an **ionic bond.**

In the formation of sodium chloride (refer back to Figure 6-3), the sodium atom lost an electron and became a sodium ion with an electrical charge of +1. The chlorine atom gained an electron and became a chloride ion with a charge of –1.

REVIEW QUESTIONS

1. What is an ion? ____

____

2. When is an ionic bond formed? ______________________________________

____

G. COVALENT BONDS. Covalent bonds are formed when atoms produce compounds by sharing electrons. A simple example is the formation of hydrogen gas (Figure 6-4). One molecule of hydrogen gas is formed when two hydrogen atoms join by sharing electrons.

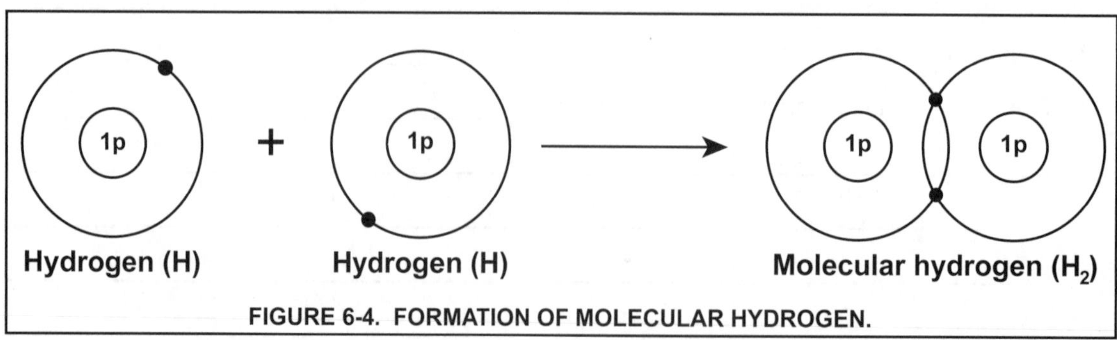

FIGURE 6-4. FORMATION OF MOLECULAR HYDROGEN.

Name________________________ Class________________________ Date____________

REVIEW QUESTIONS

1. Covalent bonds are formed when atoms ______________ electrons.

H. FORMULAS. A **chemical formula** represents the chemical makeup of a compound. It shows the numbers and kinds of atoms present in a compound. It is a kind of "shorthand" that scientists use. For example, the chemical formula for a simple sugar molecule is $C_6H_{12}O_6$. This means that in one molecule of sugar there are six carbon atoms, twelve hydrogen atoms, and six oxygen atoms. Other examples of chemical formulas are: H_2O (water), SO_2 (sulfur dioxide), and CO_2 (carbon dioxide).

O=C=O

FIGURE 6-5. CARBON DIOXIDE.

A formula can also show the kinds, numbers, and arrangement of atoms. This is called a **structural formula**. The structural formula for carbon dioxide is shown in Figure 6-5. You will see more structural formulas later in this chapter.

REVIEW QUESTIONS

1. A chemical formula represents the ______________________________.

2. The chemical formula for simple sugar is ______________.

3. How many atoms of oxygen are in the compound H_2O? ________

4. Draw the structural formula of carbon dioxide.

5. A structural formula shows the ______________, ______________, and ______________ of atoms present in a compound.

I. EQUATIONS. Equations are used to describe chemical reactions. The substances that start the reaction are called the **reactants.** They are placed on the left side of the equation. The substances formed by the reaction are called the **products.** The products are placed on the right side of the equation. The arrow means "to make" or "to form". Reactions may be represented either by words or formulas. For example, the **word equation** for aerobic respiration is:

$$\text{SUGAR + OXYGEN} \xrightarrow{\text{enzymes}} \text{ENERGY + CARBON DIOXIDE + WATER}$$

Name______________________ Class__________________ Date__________

An equation using formulas instead of words is called a **chemical equation.** For example, the chemical equation for aerobic respiration is:

$$C_6H_{12}O_6 + O_2 \longrightarrow 6H_2O + 6CO_2$$

REVIEW QUESTIONS

1. Why are equations used in chemistry? ______________________________

____

2. Define reactants and products. ______________________________

____

3. Reactants are placed on the ________________ side of an equation and products are placed on the ________________ side of an equation.

4. Write the word equation for aerobic respiration.

5. Write the chemical equation for aerobic respiration.

J. ORGANIC AND INORGANIC COMPOUNDS. Living things are made up of inorganic and organic compounds. Compounds that do not contain both carbon and hydrogen are called **inorganic compounds.** The principal inorganic compounds found in living things are water, salts, and inorganic acids and bases. **Organic compounds** are compounds that contain both carbon and hydrogen. The classes of organic compounds found in living things are carbohydrates, proteins, lipids, and nucleic acids.

REVIEW QUESTIONS

1. Living things are made up of ________________ and ________________ compounds.

2. What is the difference between an inorganic compound and an organic compound?

____

____

____

3. Name the four classes of organic compounds. ______________________________

____

Name_______________ Class_______________ Date___________

K. CARBOHYDRATES. **Carbohydrates** are the main source of energy for cell activities. Starch and sugars are examples of carbohydrates. Carbohydrates are formed from the elements carbon, oxygen, and hydrogen. The ratio (comparison) of hydrogen to oxygen in a molecule of a carbohydrate generally is 2:1. This means that there are twice as many hydrogen atoms as oxygen atoms.

REVIEW QUESTIONS

1. Carbohydrates are the main source of ____________________ for cell activities.

2. Name two examples of carbohydrates. ____________________

____

3. What elements are present in carbohydrates? ____________________

____

4. What is the ratio of hydrogen to oxygen in carbohydrates? ____________________

____

L. MONOSACCHARIDES. The simplest carbohydrates are called **monosaccharides** or simple sugars. They are called the "building blocks" of carbohydrates. A common monosaccharide is **glucose** ($C_6H_{12}O_6$). Glucose is formed during photosynthesis. The structural formula for glucose is shown in Figure 6-6.

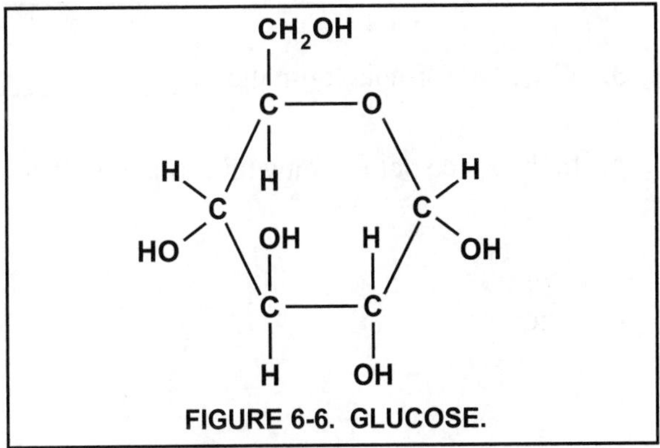

FIGURE 6-6. GLUCOSE.

REVIEW QUESTIONS

1. Simple sugars are classified as ____________________.

2. An example of a simple sugar is ____________________.

3. Write the chemical formula of glucose. ______________.

4. In the space below, draw the structural formula for glucose.

Name______________________________ Class______________________ Date____________

M. DISACCHARIDES. When two simple sugars combine they form a **disaccharide** or double sugar. **Maltose** (C_{12} H_{22} O_{11}) is an example of common disaccharide. Maltose is formed when two glucose molecules chemically combine. The structural equation for maltose is shown in Figure 6-7.

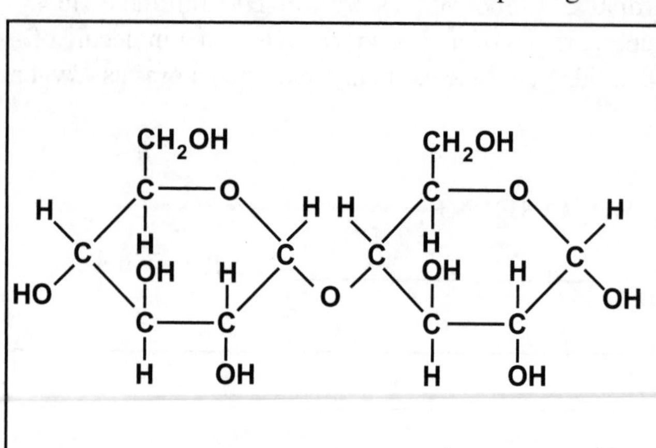

FIGURE 6-7. MALTOSE.

REVIEW QUESTIONS

1. Double sugars are formed by combining ______________________________.

2. Name a common disaccharide. ______________________________.

3. Write the formula for maltose. ______________________________.

4. In the space below, draw the structural formula for maltose.

N. POLYSACCHARIDES. Long chains of monosaccharides (sugar molecules) bonded together form **polysaccharides.** Important polysaccharides found in living things are starch and cellulose.

REVIEW QUESTIONS

1. Long chains of monosaccharides form ______________________________.

2. Two important polysaccharides are ____________________ and ____________________.

Name________________________ Class____________________ Date__________

O. LIPIDS. **Lipids** include fats and oils. **Fats** are lipids that are solid at room temperature. **Oils** are lipids that are liquid at room temperature. In living organisms lipids form part of the structure of cell membranes. Extra food that is not immediately needed as a source of energy is changed to fat and stored. Thus lipids are a source of stored energy in living organisms.

Lipids, like carbohydrates, contain the elements carbon, hydrogen, and oxygen (Figure 6-8). However, the ratio of hydrogen to oxygen in lipids is much greater than 2:1 and varies from one lipid to another. The building blocks of lipids are **fatty acids** and **glycerol.**

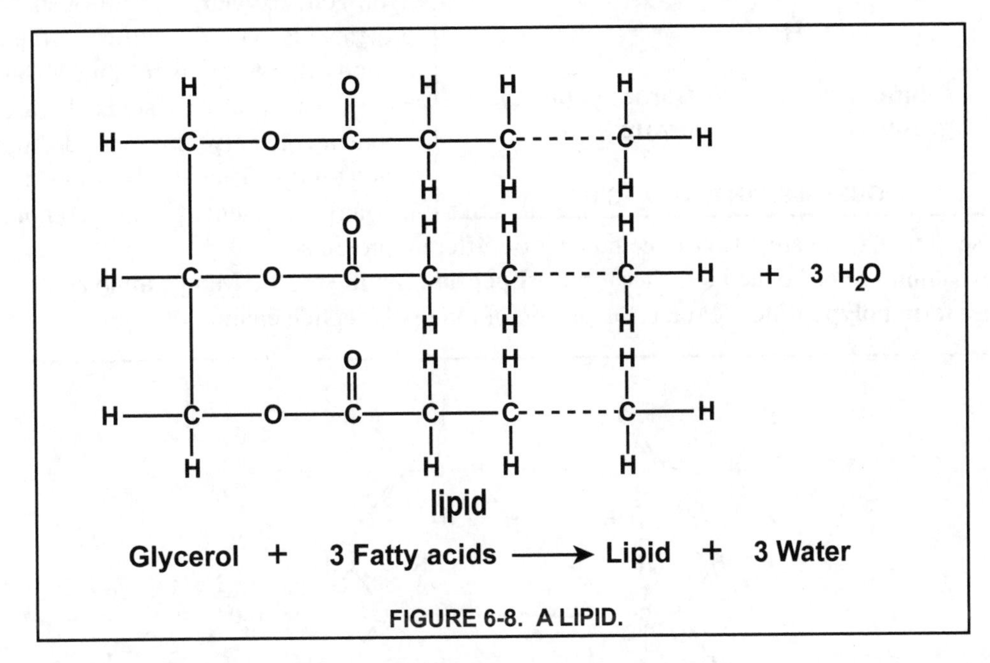

FIGURE 6-8. A LIPID.

REVIEW QUESTIONS

1. Two examples of lipids are ______________ and ______________.

2. Lipids are a source of ______________________________ in living organisms.

3. Name the elements found in lipids and the ratio in which they are found. ______________

____

____

4. In the space below, draw the structural formula of a lipid.

Name______________________ Class__________________ Date__________

P. PROTEINS. Many different kinds of structures in living things are composed of **proteins**. They form important cell products such as enzymes, many hormones, antibodies, and hemoglobin. They also play an important role in cell repair and growth.

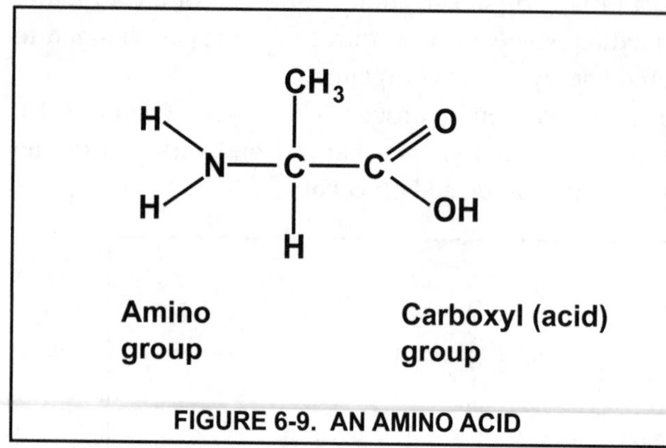

FIGURE 6-9. AN AMINO ACID

Proteins are made up of carbon, hydrogen, oxygen, and nitrogen. Some proteins also contain sulfur. Proteins are composed of simpler units (building blocks) called **amino acids** (Figure 6-9). There are twenty amino acids found in living things. They can be joined together in any sequence and combination. Because of this, there are a very large number of different proteins.

Two amino acids bonded together form a **dipeptide** (Figure 6-10). Many amino acids bonded together form **polypeptides**. Proteins are made of long polypeptide chains .

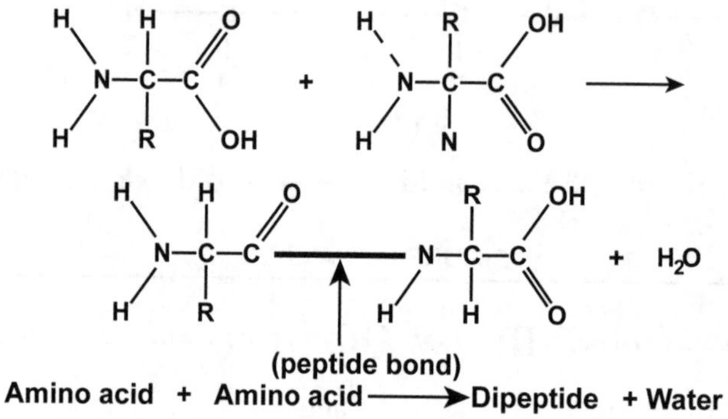

(peptide bond)

Amino acid + Amino acid ⟶ Dipeptide + Water

FIGURE 6-10. FORMATION OF A DIPEPTIDE.

REVIEW QUESTIONS

1. The building blocks of proteins are ______________________.

2. List the elements that are found in proteins. ______________________

____

3. In the space below draw an amino acid molecule.

Name________________________ Class________________________ Date____________

Q. ENZYMES. Each chemical reaction that occurs in a living thing is controlled by an enzyme. **Enzymes** are large complex protein molecules that control the rate of chemical reactions. Enzymes are the organic catalysts in cellular chemical reactions. In chemistry a **catalyst** is something that speeds up or slows down a chemical reaction. Catalysts are neither permanently changed nor used up by the reaction they catalyze. In organisms enzymes allow the chemical reactions of metabolism to take place more efficiently than they otherwise would at body temperature. For example, amino acids are produced from protein digestion. The enzymes needed for this reaction are not changed but must be present for the reaction to occur (Figure 6-11).

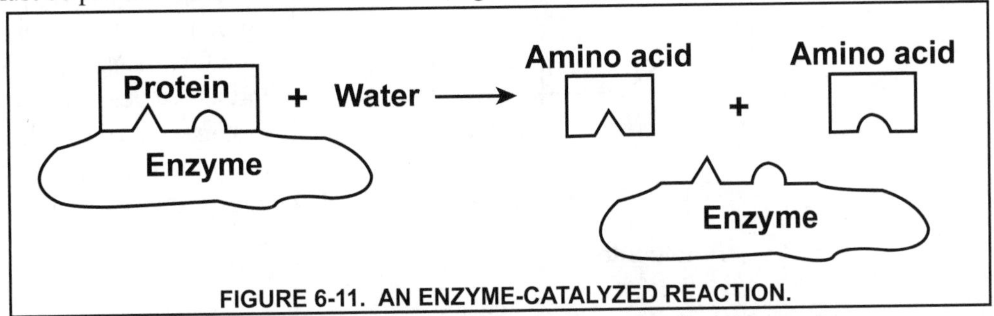

FIGURE 6-11. AN ENZYME-CATALYZED REACTION.

Some enzymes have a nonprotein part called a **coenzyme**. Many coenzymes are vitamins. If a vitamin is missing from the human body, a certain enzyme cannot function. When an enzyme doesn't function properly, one or more metabolic reactions cannot occur. This is one of the reasons why it is important that you eat a well balanced diet every day. Without the coenzymes (vitamins) needed by the body the chemical processes necessary for proper metabolism cannot take place.

The rate of enzyme action is influenced by several factors such as temperature, relative concentrations of enzyme and substrate, and pH. Each enzyme has a optimum temperature–a temperature at which it functions most efficiently and its rate of action is the greatest. At temperatures below the optimum, the rate of enzyme action is low. It increases, with increasing temperature, up to the optimum temperature. Above the optimum temperature the rate of enzyme action decreases.

REVIEW QUESTIONS

1. What is an enzyme? ____

____

____

2. Something that speeds up or slows down a chemical reaction is called a/an ____________

____

3. What is the relationship between coenzymes and vitamins? ____________________

____

4. How do coenzymes get into your body? ______________________________

____

5. Name three factors that influence the rate of enzyme action. ____________________

____

Name_______________________ Class_______________________ Date ___________

R. NUCLEIC ACIDS. Nucleic acids are very large molecules made up of carbon, oxygen, nitrogen, and phosphorus. The simplest unit (or building block) of nucleic acids is the **nucleotide.** It is composed of a sugar molecule, a nitrogen base, and a phosphate group. Figure 6-12 is a model of a nucleotide.

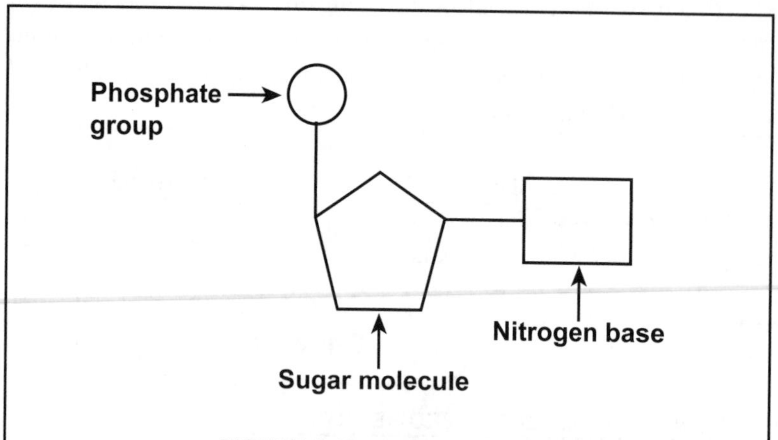

DNA and RNA are two kinds of nucleic acids found in living things. **DNA** makes up genes and is involved in heredity. **RNA** is involved in the synthesis (making) of proteins. You will learn more about these compounds when you study genetics in Unit 6.

Phosphate group

Nitrogen base

Sugar molecule

FIGURE 6-12. A NUCLEOTIDE.

REVIEW QUESTIONS

1. Nucleic acids are composed of ____________________________________.

2. Two kinds of nucleic acids are _______________ and _______________.

3. The simplest unit or building block of nucleic acids is the _______________.

S. THE pH SCALE. The pH scale measures whether a solution is acid, basic, or neutral. The scale runs from 0 to 14. A pH of 7 indicates that the solution is neutral. This means that the solution is neither an acid nor a base. The lower the pH number the stronger the acid solution. A pH above 7 indicates that the solution is basic. As the pH number increases above seven the solution becomes more basic (Figure 6-13).

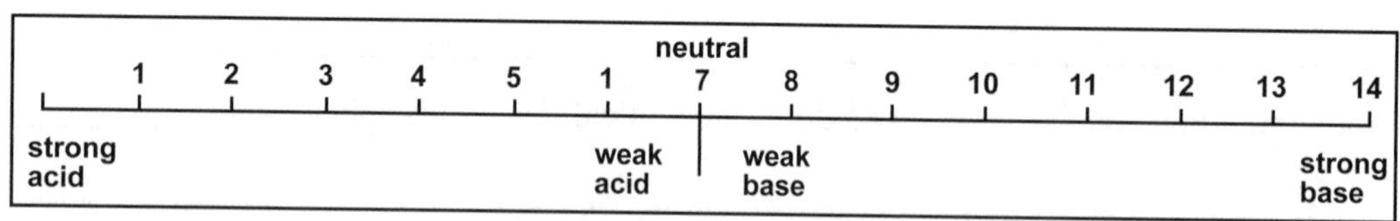

FIGURE 6-13. THE pH SCALE.

REVIEW QUESTIONS

1. The pH scale measures whether a solution is _______________, _______________, or _______________.

Name________________ Class________________ Date__________

LAB INVESTIGATION: MOLECULAR MODELS

OBJECTIVE

Upon completion of this activity you should be able to list the major elements found in living things and identify the molecular structure of several compounds.

LABORATORY PROCEDURE

Materials: Molecular model kit and colored pencils.

1. Pick up your laboratory materials at the supply table and carry them to your lab area. Check your molecular model kit to be sure that it contains the following: *10 black balls, 2 blue balls, 28 yellow balls, 6 red balls, 40 wooden sticks and 10 springs.* The sticks and springs represent chemical bonds. The colored balls represent the major elements in living things and are color coded as follows:

[BLACK=CARBON, BLUE=NITROGEN, YELLOW=HYDROGEN, RED=OXYGEN]
(Important: If your kit contains a different color coding, ask your teacher for help.)

2. You will use your molecular model kit to make *ball-and-stick-models* of some common chemical molecules. This will help you visualize (picture) the three-dimensional structures of molecules. A *molecule* is the smallest part of an element or compound capable of independent motion. It is made up of definite numbers and kinds of atoms bonded (joined) together. A *chemical bond* or *bond* holds the atoms together either by transferring or sharing of electrons.

3. A molecule of hydrogen gas (H_2) is formed when two atoms of hydrogen (H) combine. To make a model of hydrogen gas join (bond) two yellow balls *(yellow=hydrogen)* with one wooden stick *(sticks=bonds)* from your molecular model kit as shown in **Figure 1** in the diagram below. Figure 1 shows both the structural formula and the ball-and-stick model of one molecule of hydrogen gas. A *structural formula* shows the kinds, numbers, and arrangement of atoms.

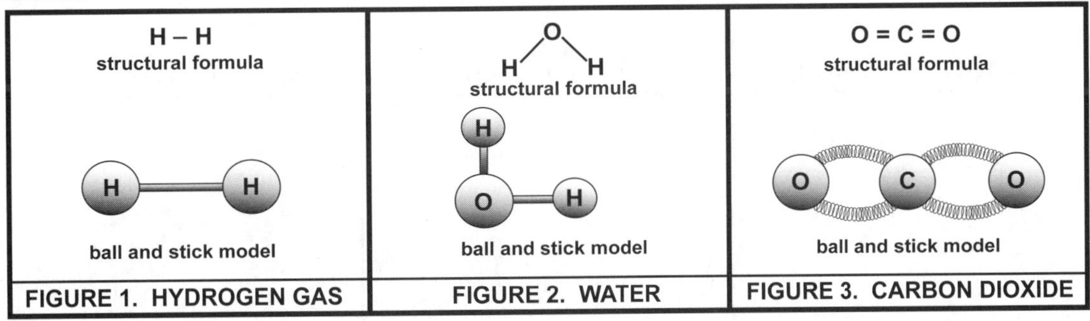

FIGURE 1. HYDROGEN GAS | FIGURE 2. WATER | FIGURE 3. CARBON DIOXIDE

4. Have your teacher check your hydrogen gas model, then draw your *ball and stick model* in the space provided in **Observation (1)** on the next page. Color the elements using the color coding method in **Procedure 1**.

5. Repeat **Procedure 3** to make a model of one molecule of water as shown above in **Figure 2.** ***(Important: Use the correct colored balls.)*** Have your teacher check your water molecule model, then draw your model in the space provided in **Observation (2)** on the next page. Color the elements using the color coding method in **Procedure 1**.

6. Repeat **Procedure 3** to make a model of one molecule of carbon dioxide as shown in **Figure 3.** (***Important: Use the correct colored balls and use springs instead of sticks to form double bonds.***) Have your teacher check your carbon dioxide model, then draw your model in the space provided in **Observation (3)** below. Color the elements using the color coding method in **Procedure 1**.

7. Below are the structural formulas for **ethylene** (a hydrocarbon gas used to help fruits ripen), **an amino acid** (a building block of proteins), and **glucose** (a simple sugar). Repeat **Procedure 3** and make models of each of the compounds shown below. (***Important: Use springs for double bonds and ring bonds. Use sticks for single bonds***).

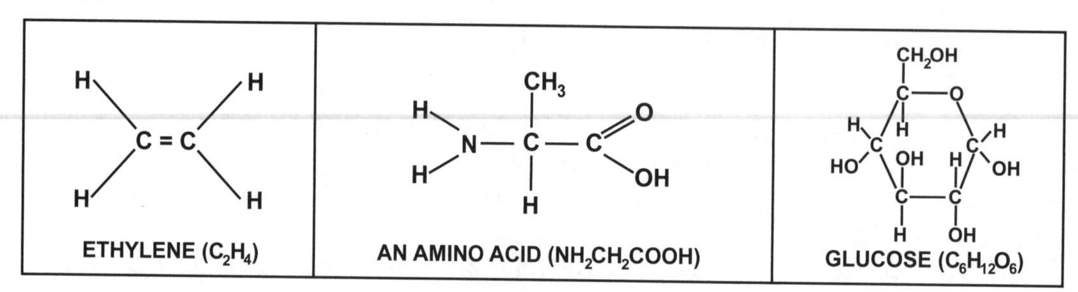

ETHYLENE (C_2H_4) | AN AMINO ACID (NH_2CH_2COOH) | GLUCOSE ($C_6H_{12}O_6$)

8. Have your teacher check your models, then draw them in the spaces provided in **Observations (4, 5, and 6)** below. Color the elements using the color coding method in **Procedure 1**.

9. When you are finished with your lab put your model-making materials back in your kit. Clean your lab area and return your materials to the supply table.

OBSERVATIONS

(1) HYDROGEN GAS (H_2)	(2) WATER (H_2O)	(3) CARBON DIOXIDE (CO_2)
(4) ETHYLENE (C_2H_4)	(5) AMINO ACID (NH_2CH_2COOH)	(6) GLUCOSE ($C_6H_{12}O_6$)

CONCLUSIONS

1. List the four major elements found in living things. ______________________________

____

Name________________________ Class_______________ Date__________

REVIEW ACTIVITIES

Important Terms

DIRECTIONS: Define the following terms in the spaces provided.

amino acid ____

____

atom ____

____

carbohydrates ____

____

catalyst ____

____

compound ____

____

dissaccharide ____

____

electron ____

____

element ____

____

enzyme ____

____

fats ____

____

fatty acids ____

____

glucose ____

____

glycerol ____

____

inorganic compound ____

____

Name____________________ Class________________ Date__________

ion ____

____

lipid ____

____

maltose ____

____

molecule ____

____

monosaccharide ____

____

neutron ____

____

nucleic acid ____

____

nucleus ____

____

oils ____

____

organic compound ____

____

polysaccharide ____

____

pH scale ____

____

protein ____

____

proton ____

____

Name________________ Class________________ Date________

Skill Practice

Part A. Base your answers to questions 1 and 2 on the diagram below and on your knowledge of biology.

1. In the reaction illustrated in the diagram below, which structure represents the enzyme?

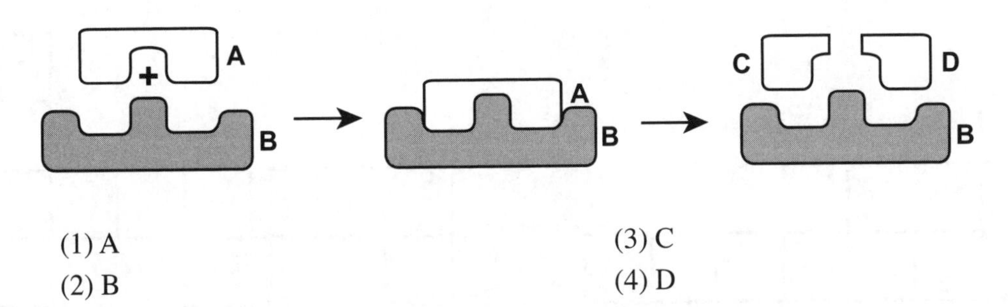

(1) A
(2) B
(3) C
(4) D

2. Enzymes are composed of which of the following organic compounds?

(1) carbohydrates
(2) lipids
(3) proteins
(4) nucleic acids

Part B. Base your answers to questions 3 and 4 on the graph below which shows the relative rates of action of four enzymes, A, B, C, and D, and on your knowledge of biology.

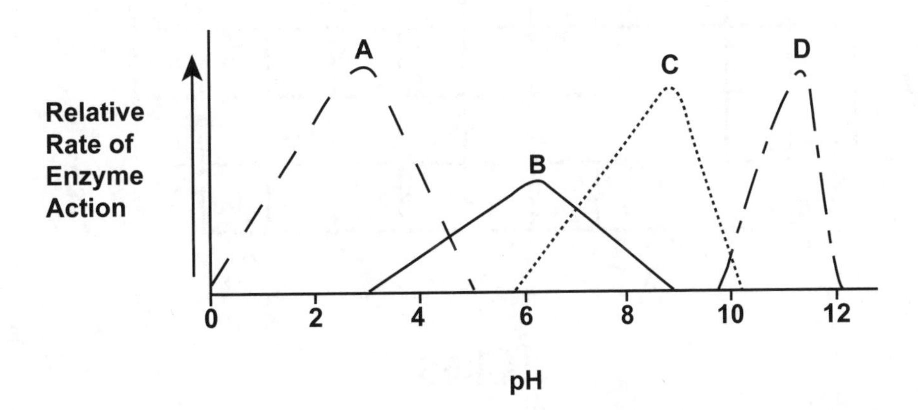

3. Which enzyme shows the greatest change in its rate of action with the least change in pH?

(1) A
(2) B
(3) C
(4) D

4. Which enzymes would function in a region of the human body having a neutral pH?

(1) A and B
(2) B and C
(3) A and D
(4) C and D

Name ____________________ Class ________________ Date __________

Part C. Complete the following crossword puzzle.

Crossword Puzzle

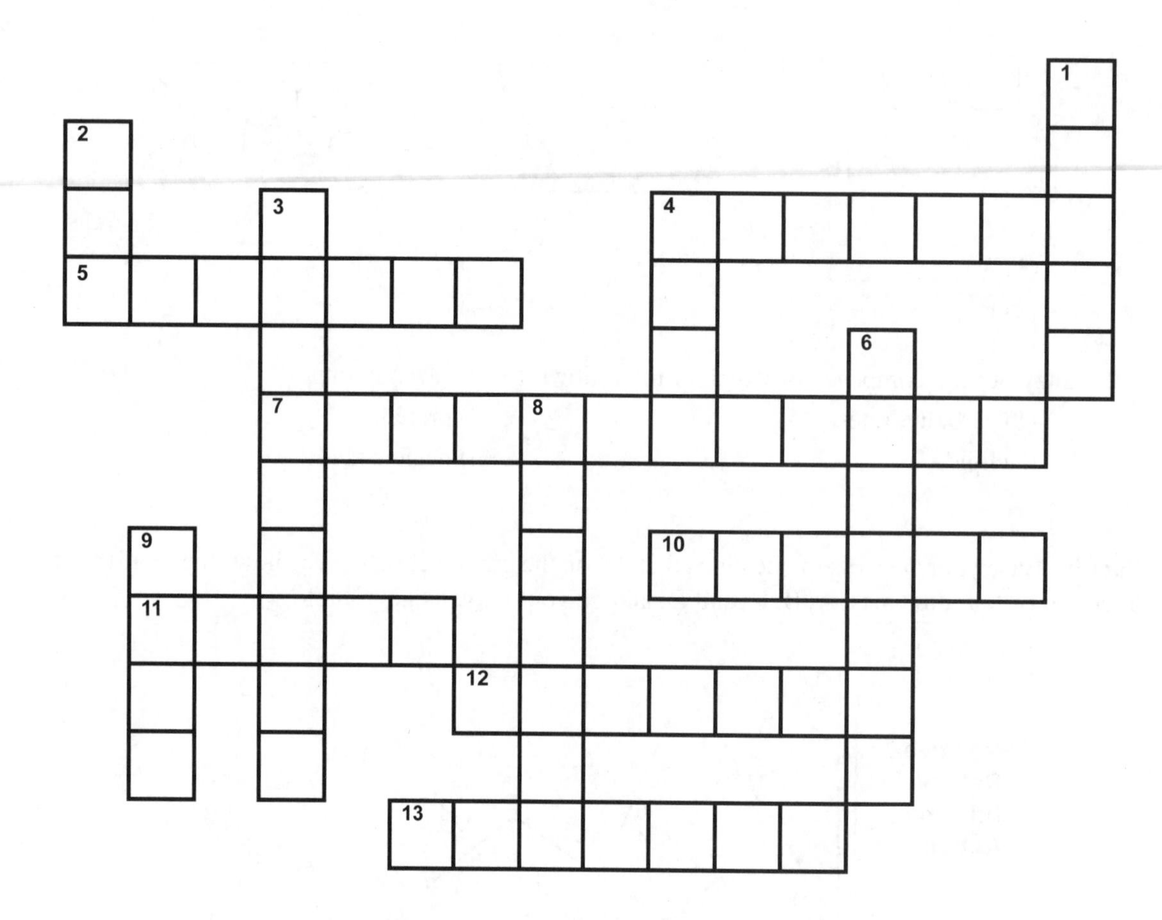

Clues

ACROSS

4. Compound important in cell repair
5. Center core of atom
7. Main source of energy for cell activities
10. Has a positive electrical charge
11. Tiny units
12. Control speed of chemical reactions
13. _____ acids make up DNA

DOWN

1. Holds elements together chemically
2. Electrically charged atom
3. Negatively charged particles
4. ______ saccharides are long chains
6. A double sugar
8. Compounds containing carbon and hydrogen
9. Solid lipids at room temperature

Name______________________ Class______________________ Date__________

CHAPTER 6: QUIZ

A. FILL-IN QUESTIONS

DIRECTIONS: Complete each of the following statements by writing the correct word or phrase in the space provided.

1. ______________________ are the main source of energy for cell activities.
2. A chemical equation uses ______________________ instead of words.
3. Each different kind of atom is called a/an ______________________.
4. ______________________ compounds do not contain both carbon and hydrogen.
5. Fats and oils are classified as ______________________.
6. Living and nonliving things are made up of tiny units called ______________________.
7. Maltose is a ______________________ sugar.
8. A ______________________ formula shows the arrangement of atoms in a molecule.
9. An example of a simple sugar is ______________________.
10. The substances formed by a reaction are called the ______________________.
11. A proton is a ______________________ charged particle.
12. Lipids provide ______________________ energy for the cell.
13. Sugars and starch are examples of ______________________.
14. A ______________________ speeds up or slows down a chemical reaction.
15. Two or more elements chemically combined is called a ______________________.
16. The ratio of hydrogen to oxygen in carbohydrates is ______________________.
17. Proteins contain carbon, oxygen, hydrogen, and ______________________.
18. ______________________ are large complex protein molecules that modify chemical reactions.
19. The symbol for the element carbon is ______________________.
20. ______________________ compounds contain both carbon and hydrogen.

B. MULTIPLE-CHOICE QUESTIONS

DIRECTIONS: Circle the number of the expression that best completes each of the following statements.

1. Which substance is a carbohydrate?
   (1) sugar
   (2) cheese
   (3) oil
   (4) meat

2. What is the major use of carbohydrates in the human body?
   (1) for repair of cell walls
   (2) for production of enzymes
   (3) as a source of vitamins
   (4) as a source of energy

Name________________________ Class____________________ Date___________

3. Which molecule is involved in heredity?
   (1) DNA (3) fat
   (2) PTC (4) carbohydrate

4. Which of the following particles have a negative electrical charge?
   (1) proton (3) electron
   (2) neutron (4) atom

5. Energy may be supplied by both
   (1) vitamins and water
   (2) minerals and vitamins
   (3) water and carbohydrates
   (4) fats and carbohydrates

6. Which element is found in proteins, but not in carbohydrates or fats?
   (1) carbon (3) hydrogen
   (2) oxygen (4) nitrogen

7. Which of the following is a coenzyme?
   (1) carbohydrate (3) RNA
   (2) vitamin (4) DNA

8. Which molecule will provide the greatest amount of energy to a living cell.
   (1) water (3) sugar
   (2) oxygen (4) carbon dioxide

9. Which class of organic compounds is used by the body for cell repair and growth?
   (1) carbohydrates (3) minerals
   (2) proteins (4) lipids

10. Which of the following is the simplest unit of carbohydrates?
   (1) glucose (3) amino acids
   (2) fats (4) oils

C. ESSAY QUESTION

DIRECTIONS: Use complete sentences to answer the question in this part.

1. State one difference between organic and inorganic compounds.

____

____

____

____

____

____

____

Name________________________ Class____________________ Date__________

UNIT TWO TEST

Matching Questions

DIRECTIONS: In the space at the left of each item in Column A, place the letter of the term or phrase in Column B that is most closely related to that item.

	Column A	Column B
________	**1.** Organisms requiring oxygen.	**a.** Biology
________	**2.** Positive charge.	**b.** Regulation
________	**3.** Cell respiration organelle.	**c.** Aerobic
________	**4.** The study of living things.	**d.** Diffusion
________	**5.** Makes proteins.	**e.** Unicellular
________	**6.** Making complex compounds	**f.** Mitochondria
________	**7.** Control and coordination	**g.** Anaerobic
________	**8.** One-celled	**h.** Multicellular
________	**9.** Change in environment	**i.** Proton
________	**10.** Process for absorbing materials.	**j.** Stimulus
		k. Synthesis
		l. Ribosome

True-False Questions

DIRECTIONS: Write TRUE before each statement that is true and FALSE before each statement that is false.

________ **1.** Neutrons have a negative charge.

________ **2.** Undigested wastes are removed by the process of egestion.

________ **3.** Energy is released from food by respiration.

________ **4.** Viruses are made up of cells.

________ **5.** The first simple microscope was developed by Robert Hooke.

________ **6.** The enlarged picture produced by the microscope is called the stimulus.

________ **7.** The greatest magnification is produced by the compound microscope.

________ **8.** The chromosomes are made up of DNA.

________ **9.** Water is an element.

________ **10.** Nucleic acids are composed of carbon, oxygen, nitrogen, and phosphorus.

Name________________________ Class____________________ Date___________

Fill–In Questions

DIRECTIONS: Complete each of the following statements by writing the correct word or phrase in the space provided.

1. Organisms are ________________ things.
2. ________________ is the life process involved with the absorption and circulation of materials in an organism.
3. All of the processes required by an organism to maintain life are known as its ______________.
4. The life process that is not necessary to the individual organism is ________________.
5. The ______________ is the basic unit of structure and function of living things.
6. The ______________ microscope magnifies more than 100,000X.
7. Eyepiece power multiplied by objective power equals ________________.
8. The watery cell fluid that contains the other organelles is called the ________________.
9. Groups of tissues performing a similar function are known as ______________.
10. Compounds containing both carbon and hydrogen are called ______________ compounds.

Multiple–Choice Questions

DIRECTIONS: Circle the number of the expression that best completes each of the following statements.

1. Plant cells contain small structures known as
   (1) organelles (3) organs
   (2) tissues (4) organ systems
2. Plants obtain energy from food by the process of
   (1) digestion (3) photosynthesis
   (2) respiration (4) adaptation
3. Plant and animal cells are similar in that they
   (1) carry on fermentation (3) have cell walls
   (2) contain chloroplasts (4) have a plasma membrane
4. In order to release energy from food, an animal cell needs
   (1) mineral salts (3) nitrogen gas
   (2) carbon dioxide (4) oxygen gas
5. Materials move into a cell by
   (1) digestion (3) excretion
   (2) diffusion (4) growth
6. The ability to avoid danger is included in the life process of
   (1) excretion (3) regulation
   (2) reproduction (4) nutrition

Name____________________ Class____________________ Date__________

7. A tissue is composed of specialized
   (1) organisms (3) cells
   (2) systems (4) organs

Directions (8-10): Base your answers to questions 8 through 10 on the diagrams of animal and plant cells shown below.

PLANT CELLS

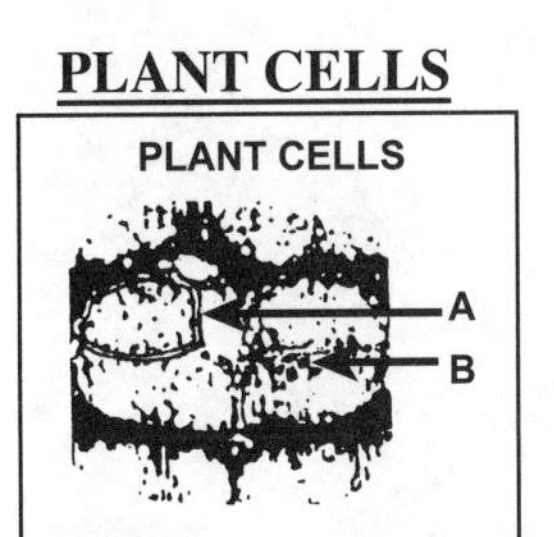

ANIMAL CELLS

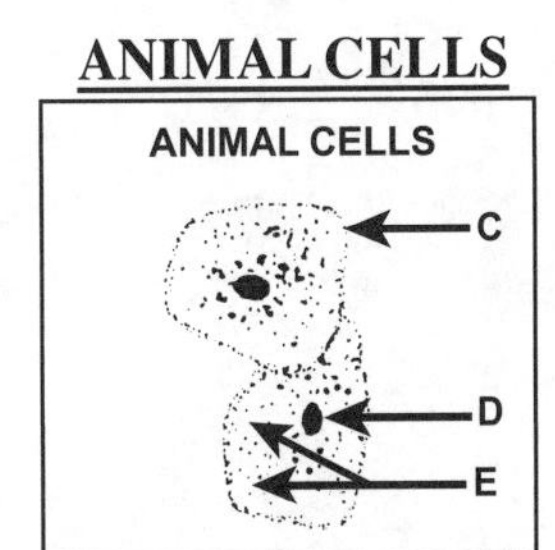

8. Which letter indicates watery cell fluid:
   (1) A (3) C
   (2) E (4) D
9. Which letter indicates the location of chromosomes?
   (1) A (3) E
   (2) B (4) D
10. Which occurs in structure B?
   (1) egestion (3) digestion
   (2) photosynthesis (4) respiration

Essay Question

DIRECTIONS: Use complete sentences to answer the question in this part.

1. State the three parts of the cell theory.

____

____

____

____

____

____

____

____

Class Notes

Name________________________ Class____________________ Date__________

UNIT THREE
HUMAN BIOLOGY

LEARNING OUTCOMES: Upon completion of the study of this unit, you should be able to:

- Identify and describe the roles of the nutrients needed to sustain life.
- Recognize the need for a balanced diet.
- Describe some of the structures associated with the digestive, transport, respiratory, excretory, regulatory, muscle, and skeletal systems.
- Explain some of the functions of the various body systems and their components.
- Identify some of the disorders of the body system.
- Describe the function of the blood as a component of the immune system.

Chapter 7: Nutrition

A. IMPORTANCE OF NUTRITION. The life activity by which your body gets food and changes it into a usable form is called nutrition. Food supplies your body with the chemicals and energy you need to survive. To function properly your body requires the proper amounts and kinds of foods. Good health depends upon good nutrition. Bad nutrition can cause poor health.

REVIEW QUESTIONS

1. The life activity by which your body gets food and changes it into a usable form is called

______________________.

2. Good health depends upon ______________________________.

3. Food supplies your body with the ________________ and ________________ it needs to survive.

B. FOODS AND NUTRIENTS. The usable parts of food are called **nutrients.** Nutrients provide energy and/or chemicals needed by the body to build and repair tissue. They also regulate body processes. The six groups of nutrients are carbohydrates, fats and oils, proteins, vitamins, minerals, and water.

Name ______________________ Class __________________ Date __________

Food Nutrients

Carbohydrates.......... Source of energy for life activities.
Fats and Oils............. Source of stored energy for life activities.
Proteins..................... Build and repair body tissue. Also source of energy.
Vitamins.................... Necessary for a healthy body.
Minerals.................... Important in building body parts. Help regulate body functions.
Water........................ Dissolves and transports materials.

REVIEW QUESTIONS

1. Nutrients are the ______________________ of food.
2. List the six basic nutrients and their uses in the body.

____

____

____

____

____

____

C. CARBOHYDRATES. Sugars and starches are **carbohydrates**. They provide the body with most of the energy it needs for its life activities. When you eat more carbohydrates than your body uses the extra carbohydrates are stored in the liver as **glycogen** (animal starch) and they are also stored in muscle tissue as fat. When you eat fewer carbohydrates than your body requires the stored carbohydrates are changed into simple sugars (glucose). Glucose is then oxidized or burned by the body to release energy. Common foods rich in starch are breads, potatoes, and cereals. Foods rich in sugar include candy, molasses, and most fruits (Figure 7-1).

FIGURE 7-1. SOURCES OF CARBOHYDRATES.

REVIEW QUESTIONS

1. The main kinds of carbohydrates are __________________ and __________________
2. Describe what happens when you eat more carbohydrates than your body needs.

____

____

____

Name__________ Class__________ Date__________

3. Carbohydrates provide ____________________ for the body.
4. List six foods that are good sources of carbohydrates.

____

____

D. FATS AND OILS. Fats and oils, like carbohydrates, provide energy for life activities. Fats and oils, however, yield more energy per gram than carbohydrates and sometimes can be stored in the body as energy reserves. Good sources of fats and oils are butter, lard, peanut butter, bacon, and vegetable oils (Figure 7-2).

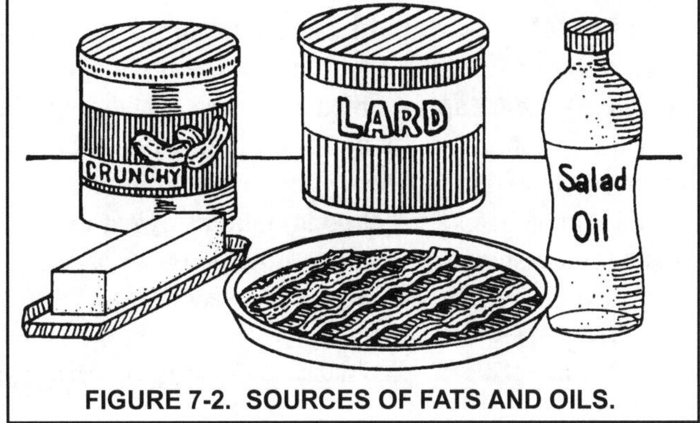

FIGURE 7-2. SOURCES OF FATS AND OILS.

REVIEW QUESTIONS

1. Fats and oils provide ____________________ for life activities.
2. Name three foods that are rich in fats and oils.

____

E. PROTEINS. Proteins provide the organic compounds needed to build and repair body tissue. They also can provide energy when carbohydrates and fats are missing from the diet. Because proteins are the most expensive and least available nutrients, protein malnutrition is one of the world's biggest health problem. The human body requires a daily intake of one gram of protein for every two pounds of ideal body weight. Lean meat, eggs, milk, cheese, and fish are excellent sources of proteins (Figure 7-3).

FIGURE 7-3. SOURCES OF PROTEINS.

Name______________________ Class__________________ Date__________

REVIEW QUESTIONS

1. Why are proteins important nutrients? ______________________________

____

____

2. Two examples of foods rich in proteins are ______________ and ______________.

F. VITAMINS. A **vitamin** is a natural substance found in small quantities in food. Vitamins are necessary for a healthy body. Vitamins are coenzymes. Enzymes cannot function properly without vitamins. Vitamins are identified by the letters of the alphabet, for example, vitamin A, B, C, etc.

Since vitamins are found naturally in foods, a balanced diet provides all the vitamins you need. It is possible to obtain vitamins by taking vitamin pills. Most scientists and doctors agree that it is healthier and cheaper to get your vitamins by eating a well balanced diet. Taking too many vitamin pills can have harmful effects on the body. A lack of vitamins is also harmful and may result in body disorders called **deficiency diseases.**

REVIEW QUESTIONS

1. What is a vitamin? ______________________________

____

2. Explain why vitamins are important. ______________________________

____

3. Lack of vitamins may result in conditions called ______________________.

♦ **Vitamin A.** This vitamin is commonly found in liver, eggs, yellow and green vegetables (Figure 7-4). The body manufactures **vitamin A** from a chemical called carotene**. Carotene** is a yellow or red pigment found in vegetables. Vitamin A is essential for normal vision. It is also important in fighting infections because it keeps body membranes healthy. Some studies suggest vitamin A may protect against cancer and may cut the risks of heart disease and strokes in women. People who don't get enough vitamin A cannot see well in the dark. This condition is known as **night blindness**.

FIGURE 7-4. SOURCES OF VITAMIN A.

REVIEW QUESTIONS

1. Vitamin A is commonly found in ______________________________.

Name________________________ Class__________________ Date__________

2. What is night blindness?

____

♦ **Vitamin B_1 (Thiamine).** Dr. Christiaan Eijkman, a Dutch physician, is credited with the discovery of **vitamin B_1**. During his travels he observed that people living in Java were dying of a disease called **beriberi**. The first symptom of this disease is weak muscles. As the disease progresses, the person becomes paralyzed and eventually dies. The doctor also observed that the chickens in Java were showing the same symptoms. He noticed that both the chickens and the people were eating a diet of polished rice (rice that has had its outer covering removed). Unpolished brown rice was substituted for polished rice and the chickens and the Java people became healthy again. The doctor concluded that something in unpolished rice prevented beriberi. Years later, scientists discovered that the outer covering of rice contained a material called thiamine or vitamin B_1.

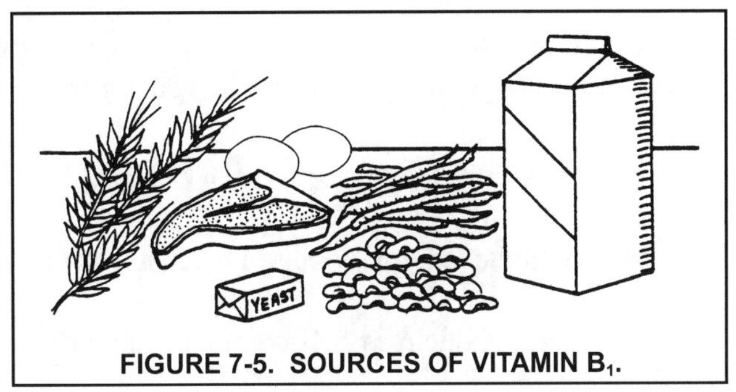

FIGURE 7-5. SOURCES OF VITAMIN B_1.

Thiamine helps oxidize starches and sugars. It also stimulates appetite and vigor (energy). A deficiency of vitamin B_1 results in a lack of appetite, various digestive disorders, nervous upset, and finally beriberi. Beriberi is commonly found in alcoholics. Whole cereals and grains, yeast, pork, eggs, liver, legumes, and milk contain this vitamin (Figure 7-5).

REVIEW QUESTIONS

1. Thiamine is another name for ______________________.

2. Not enough thiamine results in a disease called ______________________.

3. Name some good food sources of vitamin B_1.

____

♦ **Vitamin B_2 (Riboflavin).** Riboflavin is needed for cellular respiration and is found in most of the same foods as vitamin B_1. (Cereals do not contain vitamin B_2.) Skin problems and inflammation and cracking at corners of the mouth result from a deficiency (lack) of this vitamin.

REVIEW QUESTIONS

1. Riboflavin is necessary for ______________________.

2. A deficiency of vitamin B_2 results in ______________________

____.

Name______________________ Class__________________ Date__________

♦ **Vitamin B_6 (Pyridoxine). Vitamin B_6** is needed for the manufacture of amino acids and for the metabolism of proteins. The lack of this vitamin causes skin conditions, digestive tract problems, and convulsions. The sources for this vitamin are the same as for the other B vitamins.

REVIEW QUESTIONS

1. The lack of vitamin B_6 causes ____

____.

♦ **Vitamin B_{12}.** Lack of **vitamin B_{12}** causes a blood condition called **pernicious anemia.** This vitamin is important in nucleic acid metabolism. Vitamin B_{12} is found in liver, meat, and fish.

REVIEW QUESTIONS

1. What blood condition is caused by a lack of vitamin B_{12}?____________________.

♦ **Niacin. Niacin** is a B-complex vitamin necessary for cellular respiration. Niacin is commonly found in liver, meat, fish, cereals, legumes, and whole-grain and enriched breads (Figure 7-6). The lack of this vitamin causes **pellagra.** Pellagra is a deficiency disease characterized by nervous and mental disorders, skin disorders, and diarrhea.

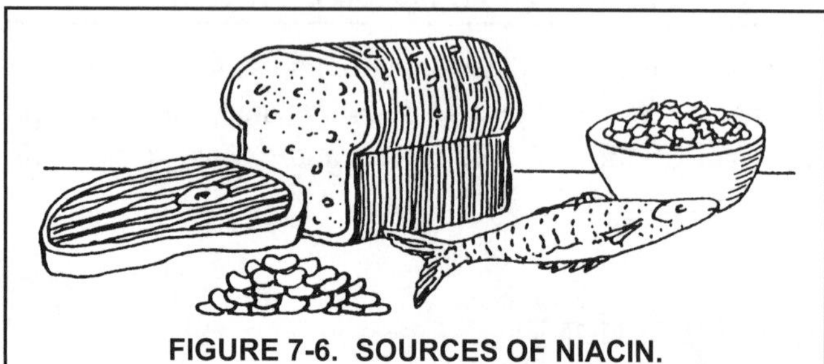

FIGURE 7-6. SOURCES OF NIACIN.

REVIEW QUESTIONS

1. Name three foods that contain niacin.

____

____

2. The deficiency disease caused by a lack of niacin is ____________________.

♦ **Vitamin C (Ascorbic Acid).** The use of citrus fruits to treat the deficiency disease **scurvy** was discovered in 1757 by the English doctor James Lind. Dr. Lind observed that English sailors aboard his ship had **scurvy.** The symptoms of scurvy are bleeding gums, teeth that do not form properly, and stiff and sore joints. The doctor did an experiment that involved feeding half the sailors citrus fruit. The other half did

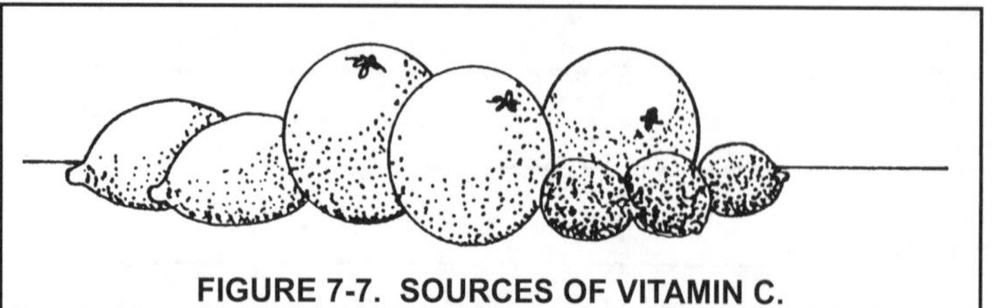

FIGURE 7-7. SOURCES OF VITAMIN C.

Name______________________________ Class______________________ Date______________

not receive the fruit. Citrus fruits (lemons and limes) have large amounts of **vitamin C**. The sailors who ate the citrus fruits recovered from scurvy and the others did not. Lind concluded that something in citrus fruit prevented scurvy. Because of this experiment English sailors have been called "limeys".

Vitamin C is also thought to play an important role in preventing common colds. This vitamin is plentiful in citrus fruits, tomatoes, cabbage, and bananas (Figure 7-7).

REVIEW QUESTIONS

1. Scurvy is caused by ______________________________.

2. List some foods that have a large amount of vitamin C. ______________________________

____

3. Describe how the scientific method was used to find a the cause of scurvy. Use the following terms: **problem, hypothesis, control, variable, observations,** and **conclusion.**

____

____

____

____

____

____

____

♦ **Vitamin D. Vitamin D** is called the "sunshine vitamin" because sunshine helps the body manufacture vitamin D. Liver, fish liver oils, egg yolk, fortified milk, butter, and margarine are good sources of vitamin D (Figure 7-8). Vitamin D helps the body use calcium and phosphorus. These minerals aid in building healthy bones and teeth. Not enough vitamin D in early childhood results in a condition called **rickets.** Rickets causes bowed legs, soft bones, and bad teeth.

FIGURE 7-8. SOURCES OF VITAMIN D.

REVIEW QUESTIONS

1. Vitamin D is sometimes called the ______________________ vitamin.

2. Examples of foods containing vitamin D are ______________________________

____.

Name________________________ Class____________________ Date__________

♦ **Vitamin K. Vitamin K** helps blood to clot. Without enough of this vitamin excessive bleeding occurs. Intestinal bacteria normally supply vitamin K as do green leafy vegetables such as spinach, cabbage, and collard greens.

REVIEW QUESTIONS

1. Vitamin K helps ______________________________.

2. Name three foods that contain vitamin K.

____

G. MINERALS. Minerals are inorganic nutrients usually eaten as salts dissolved in food and water. Essential minerals such as calcium, phosphorus, zinc, sodium, iodine, iron, and potassium, come from compounds found in various foods. They are used for building body parts and are involved in many functions including nerve and muscle action (Table 7-1). There are other elements called **trace elements** that the body requires in very small amounts.

MINERAL	FUNCTIONS	SOURCES
Calcium	Makes up bones and teeth; essential for normal blood clotting; needed for normal muscle and nerve function.	Milk and other dairy products, green leafy vegetables.
Phosphorus	Important in structure of bone; essential in energy transfer and storage and in many other metabolic processes; makes up DNA and RNA.	Milk and other dairy products.
Zinc	Important in protein digestion; may be important in wound healing.	Found in many foods.
Sodium	Important in fluid balance; essential for conduction of nerve impulses.	Occurs naturally in most foods. Sodium chloride (table salt) added to foods as a seasoning is a common source of sodium.
Iodine	Makes up thyroid hormones.	Seafoods, iodized salt, vegetables grown in iodine rich soil.
Iron	Makes up part of hemoglobin, important respiratory enzymes and other enzymes.	Meat (especially liver), nuts, egg yolk, legumes.
Potassium	Influences muscle contraction and nerve action.	Oranges, bananas, Brazil nuts, mushrooms.

TABLE 7-1. FUNCTIONS AND SOURCES OF SOME IMPORTANT MINERALS.

Name________________________________ Class ________________________ Date ____________

REVIEW QUESTIONS

1. List 3 essential minerals, their use in the body, and one source of each.

____

____

____

H. WATER. Water dissolves and transports materials. It makes up the largest percentage of body weight—about 65%. Most foods have a high percentage of water. Most of our daily water requirement is met by eating a normal amount of food each day. The rest of our water supply comes from drinking beverages and water. Water is important in the body because it dissolves most of the other substances in the body. Materials that dissolve other materials are called **solvents.**

REVIEW QUESTIONS

1. Approximately ______________ of the body is water.

2. A solvent is defined as ____.

I. ROUGHAGE. Many of the foods we get from plants contain cellulose. **Cellulose** is an indigestible fiber found in plant cell walls. This part of food is also called **roughage.** It is very important because it helps push food through the digestive tract and exercises stomach and intestine muscles. The lack of roughage (fiber) in the diet causes diseases of the digestive tract. Fiber prevents constipation and helps control the blood sugar levels of diabetics and decreases blood cholesterol. To be sure you are getting enough roughage in your diet you must eat foods high in fiber. Some examples of high fiber foods are fruits, bran cereals, and nuts (Figure 7-9).

FIGURE 7-9. ROUGHAGE FOODS.

REVIEW QUESTIONS

1. The indigestible part of food is called ______________________________.

2. Why is it important for you to eat foods that contain fiber? ______________________

____

____

____

____

J. CALORIES AND FOOD. The power source of the body is food energy. The energy content of food is measured heat units called **Calories.** One **food Calorie** or **Calorie** is the amount of heat that will raise the temperature of 1kg (1000 grams) of water one degree centigrade. Scientists spell the food calorie with a capital **"C"** so that it will not be confused with a smaller calorie used in other branches of science. When reading about nutrition you will often see it spelled with a small **"c"**. Foods contain different numbers of Calories per gram. Fats have more than twice the number of Calories per gram as carbohydrates and proteins.

The energy content (Calories) of food is measured by finding how much heat is given off when food is burned. A machine called the **calorimeter** measures the food energy (Calories) in nutrients. In Table 7-2 you will find the caloric values of some common foods.

FOOD	AMOUNT	CALORIES
MILK AND MILK PRODUCTS		
Milk: Whole; yogurt	1 cup	160
skim	1 cup	90
Milkshake, chocolate	10 ounces	400
Cheeses: cheddar, American, Swiss, processed	1 ounce (1, 1/4" cube)	115
Cheese: cottage creamed	1/2 cup	120
Ice cream (10% fat)	1/2 cup	130
Milk pudding, vanilla	1/2 cup	140
Cream, half-half	1/4 cup	80
VEGETABLES		
Asparagus	1/2 cup, pieces	15
Beans, lima	1/2 cup cooked	95
Beans, green	1/2 cup cooked	15
Beets, onions	1/2 cup cooked	30
Broccoli	1/2 cup cooked	20
Brussels sprouts	1/2 cup cooked	25
Cabbage, cauliflower	2/3 cup cooked	15
Carrots	1/2 cup	30
Celery, cucumber, radishes	1/2 cup sliced	10
Corn	1/2 cup cooked	85
Green pepper	1 medium raw	25
Greens: beet, collards, spinach	1/2 cup cooked	20
Lettuce	1 cup shredded	8
Mushrooms	1/2 cup cooked	20
Peas, green	1/2 cup cooked	65
Potatoes, white	1 medium	85
Potato: white, mashed	1/2 cup, milk, butter	90
Squash, winter: pumpkin	1/2 cup cooked	60
Squash, summer: zucchini, yellow	1/2 cup cooked	15
Tomatoes, raw, canned, juice	1 sm; 1/2 cup	20
Turnips, rutabaga	1/2 cup	20
FRUITS		
Apples: applesauce, (sweetened)	1 med, 1 cup	85/200
Apricots, canned in syrup	1/2 cup	110
Bananas	1 medium	100
Blueberries, raspberries	1/2 cup unsweetened	40

Canned fruit in syrup	1/2 cup	80
Cantaloupe	1/4 medium	40
Grapefruit, white, juice	1/2 med; 1/2 cup	50
Grapes	1/2 cup	60
Orange juice	1 medium, 1/2 cup	65
Peaches, raw	1 medium	40
Pears	1 medium	100
Pineapple, raw	1/2 cup diced	40
Raisins, seedless	1/3 cup	120
Strawberries, raw; frozen	1 cup	60/250
Watermelon	1 cup diced	40
MEAT, FISH, POULTRY, EGGS, LEGUMES		
Beef, veal, lamb	3 ounces lean	180/225
Chicken, fried	1 drumstick, thigh	250
Chicken, turkey	3 ounces, no skin	180
Fish: clams, shrimp,	3 ounces, no fat	100
haddock, perch, cod	3 ounces, no fat	100
tuna, canned	3 ounces, in water; in oil	110/170
Hamburger	3 ounces cooked	250
Hot dogs, bologna, cold cuts	2 ounces	160
Liver	2 ounces	135
Pork, ham	3 ounces, lean	300
Pork sausage, cooked	1 small link	95
Eggs	1 large	80
Legumes: dried beans, peas	1/2 cup cooked	125
Peanut Butter, nuts	2 tbsp; 1 cup	190
CEREAL PRODUCTS, WHOLE GRAIN/ENRICHED		
Bread: toast, bagel	1 slice, 1/2 bagel	70
Cereals: oatmeal, wheat	1 cup cooked	110
ready-to-eat	1 ounce	100
Corn grits, corn meal	1 cup cooked	125
Hamburger roll	1 medium	120
Spaghetti, macaroni, noodles	1 cup cooked	120
Rice	1 cup cooked	120

TABLE 7-2. CALORIC VALUE OF SOME COMMON FOODS
(Source: U.S. Department of Agriculture)

REVIEW QUESTIONS

1. What is meant by the term Calorie? ______________________________________

____

2. Which food group has the greatest amount of Calories? ______________________

3. A calorimeter measures the ______________________________________.

Name__________ Class__________ Date__________

K. CALORIES AND YOU. The number of calories you need each day depends on your body size, age, sex, climate, and mental and physical activity. Generally, younger people need more calories than older people. This is because young people are more active and their bodies are still growing (Table 7-3). A person engaged in heavy labor uses up more calories than a person with a sedentary job. Men require more calories than women because their bodies are less insulated by fat and thus need a greater supply of heat in winter. A heavier person has more cells therefore needs more energy. A person living at the North Pole needs more heat energy to keep his body warm than inhabitants near the equator.

TYPE OF INDIVIDUAL	CALORIE LEVEL*
Children, teen aged girls, active women, most men	about 1,600
Many women, older adults**	about 1,600
Teen aged boys, active men	about 2,800

TABLE 7-3. RECOMMENDED USDA CALORIE ALLOWANCES.

* These are the calorie levels if you choose low fat, lean foods from the 5 major food groups and use foods from the fats, oils, and sweets group sparingly.

** Add 300 calories if you are pregnant, 500 if you are nursing.

The number of calories you take in plays an important part in controlling your weight. Weight control is important because certain diseases are more common in people who are overweight or underweight. Overweight normal people have taken in more food calories than their body needs. Extra food is stored as body fat. With the help of a doctor weight can be safely lost. Losing weight occurs when the number of calories taken into the body is decreased. An underweight condition is usually the result of the opposite situation—not enough calories have been taken into the body. Taking in more calories increases body weight.

REVIEW QUESTIONS

1. How do the calorie needs of a 16 year old female compare with those of a 16 year old male?

____

____

2. How many calories do you require each day? ____________________

3. Use the information in Table 7-2 to count the number of calories that you consumed yesterday. Did you take in more, less, or about the same calories that you needed?

____

Name________________________Class________________________Date____________

L. A BALANCED DIET. A **balanced diet** is made up of a variety of foods that supply the body with the proper amounts of necessary nutrients and energy. In 1992, the United States Department of Agriculture recommended a **Food Guide Pyramid** to educate you about nutrition (Figure 7-10).

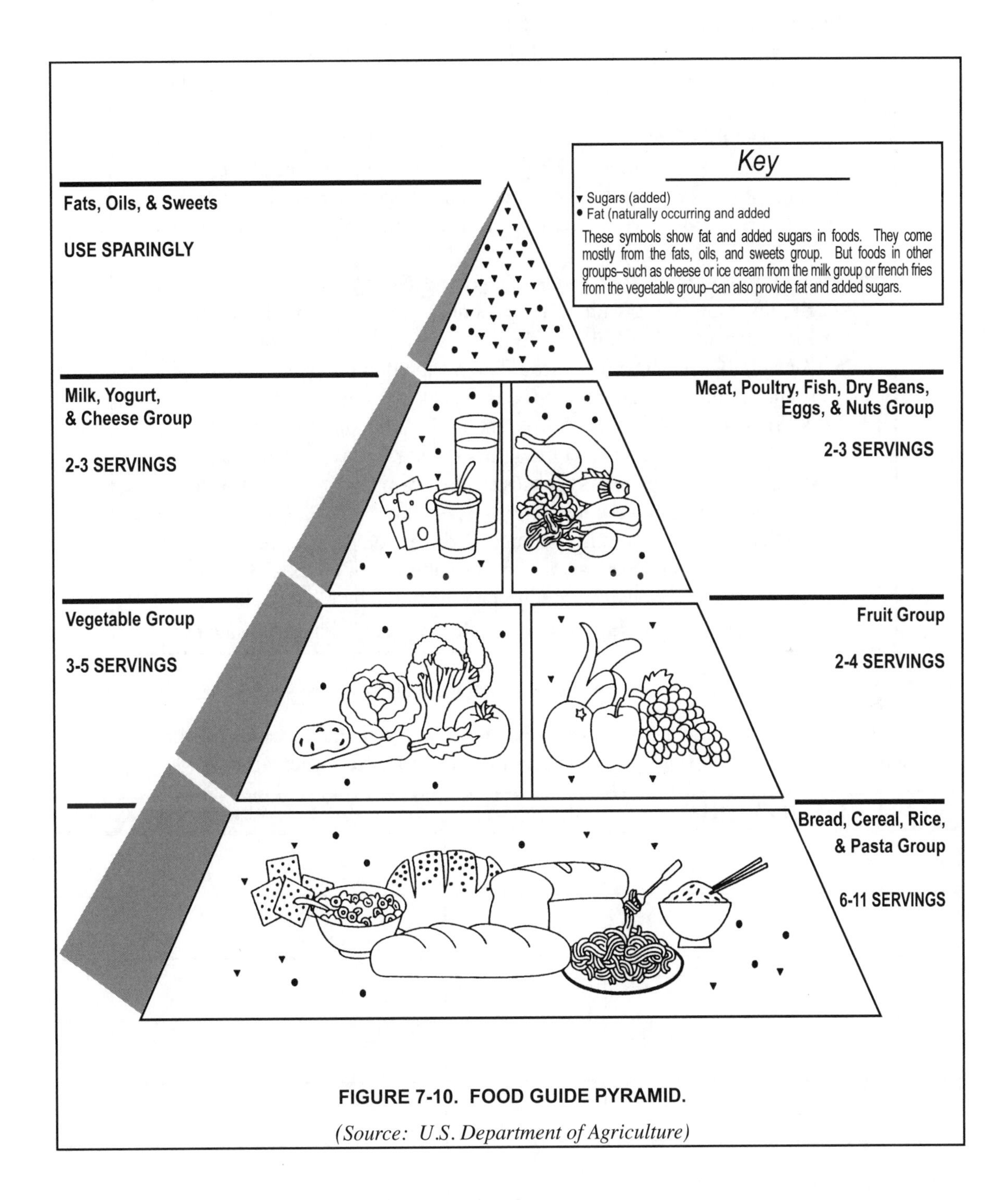

FIGURE 7-10. FOOD GUIDE PYRAMID.

(Source: U.S. Department of Agriculture)

Name ____________________ Class ____________________ Date __________

According to the *Food Guide Pyramid*, a well-balanced diet should contain a variety of the following basic food groups:

Basic Food Groups

- **Bread, Cereal, Rice, and Pasta Group.** This group is a good source of carbohydrates, iron, thiamine, and niacin. It includes breads, pizza, cereals, corn, macaroni, and rice. Six to eleven servings a day are recommended for all age groups.
- **Fruit/Vegetable Group.** Fruits and vegetables are an important source of all vitamins. Two to four servings of a variety of fruits and three to five servings of vegetables are recommended daily. Apples, bananas, pears, and oranges are examples of fruits. Carrots, broccoli, cabbage, and squash are examples of vegetables.
- **Meat, Poultry, Fish, Dry Beans, Eggs, and Nuts Group.** Protein, iron, niacin, thiamine, along with other nutrients, are supplied by this group. A balanced diet should include two to three servings of meat group foods for persons of all ages. The meat group includes red meat, poultry, fish, eggs, nuts, and legumes. Legumes are foods such as dried beans and peas.
- **Milk, Yogurt, and Cheese Group.** The milk group supplies the body with many nutrients including calcium, protein, and riboflavin. Some common foods from this group are milk, cheeses, ice cream, and yogurt. A balanced diet should include two to three servings each day.
- **Fats, Oils, and Sweets.** It is recommended that you eat very few fats, oils, and sweets. This includes fats that occur naturally in foods and those that have been added. Foods with a high fat content include bacon, butter, and sausage. Candy and soda pop are examples of foods with added sugar.

REVIEW QUESTIONS

1. In the chart below, name the five basic food groups and state the recommended daily serving amounts for each group and give examples of three foods from each group.

BASIC FOOD GROUP	SERVINGS	EXAMPLES

2. What is a balanced diet? ____________________

Name______________________ Class__________________ Date__________

M. NUTRITION AND HEALTH. You don't have to be an expert in nutrition to eat for good health. The following *Guide To Good Eating* makes healthy eating easy. All you have to do is follow these simple steps:

Guide To Good Eating

Step 1. Eat Foods From All Five Food Groups Every Day. Foods from the ***Five Food Groups*** can supply the more than 40 nutrients your body needs to stay healthy. Foods in each food group are good sources of different nutrients. That is why it is important to eat foods from all Five Food Groups every day.

Step 2. Include a Wide Variety of Foods. Foods within a food group are usually good sources of the same nutrients. But some foods are better sources of a particular nutrient than others. By eating different foods within each food group, you have a good chance of getting all the nutrients you need.

Explore the dairy case. Try new milks, cheeses, and yogurts from the Milk Group. Experiment with new recipes for beef, chicken, fish, eggs, and dried beans from the Meat Group. Find creative ways to include foods from the Fruit/Vegetable Group. Add spinach, carrots, broccoli, mushrooms, and green pepper to your salads. Enjoy new tastes from the Grain Group. Try bagels, tortillas, or rye, pita, or cracked wheat bread for sandwiches.

Step 3. Practice Moderation. By practicing moderation you can get the nutrients you need without getting too many calories or too much fat or sodium. Eat at least the recommended number of servings from each food group every day.

Step 4. Eat Less Fats. Most health authorities recommend a diet with less fat, saturated fat, and cholesterol**.** **Cholesterol** is a fatty substance found in food that comes from animals. It can cause health problems by building up in blood vessels. *(Source: adapted from National Dairy Council)*

REVIEW QUESTIONS

1. List four steps for good nutritional health.

____

____

____

____

____

____

Name______________________ Class____________________ Date__________

N. EATING DISORDERS. Two eating disorders that may affect today's teenager are anorexia nervosa and bulimia.

Eating Disorders

♦ **Anorexia Nervosa. Anorexia nervosa** is characterized by intense fear of being fat and by severe weight loss. Eventually, in females, monthly periods stop. People with this disorder starve themselves. It mainly affects teenage and young adult women. Sometimes it affects young men. It is difficult to treat and can sometimes be fatal. Doctors do not agree to the causes of anorexia. Most victims are often highly conforming people and want to please. They try to take control over their lives by dieting stubbornly. Starvation upsets the body chemistry. There is also binge eating and induced vomiting along with the use of laxatives to cause weight loss. Doctors recommend individual psychotherapy or family therapy. Relapses are common and some die from starvation or suicide.

♦ **Bulimia.** People with **bulimia** overeat and then vomit secretly once or several times a day. Most patients are girls or women between the ages of 15 and 30. This disease is thought to be caused by an extreme fear of being fat. Dehydration and loss of potassium from the body, weakness and muscle cramps, result from this disease. In addition the gastric acid in the vomit may damage teeth. People with this disorder are often depressed and sometimes suicidal. The treatment is similar to that of anorexia.

REVIEW QUESTIONS

1. Name two eating disorders. ______________________________

CAREER OPPORTUNITIES

DIETITIAN: A **dietitian** is a professional nutritionist — a person who has a special interest in food and health. Some dietitians teach while others conduct research. There are many who speak or write about nutrition. Dietitians may also plan well balanced menus for various types of employers. Hospitals, schools and universities, government agencies, industries, and community agencies all employ dietitians. There are also jobs in private practice and in the military.

A college degree and an internship or equivalent work are both required of dietitians. They must also pass an examination and become registered. Most states require dietitians to continue their education regularly to be sure their nutrition information is current.

REVIEW QUESTIONS

1. What is a dietitian? ______________________________

____

Name________________________ Class________________________ Date____________

LAB INVESTIGATION: NUTRIENT TESTING

OBJECTIVE

Upon completion of this activity you should be able to test different food samples to identify the nutrients they contain.

LABORATORY PROCEDURE

Materials: Pieces of potato, iodine solution, medicine droppers, pieces of bacon fat, brown paper, glucose solution, *Benedict's solution* or *Fehling's solution*, test tubes, test tube holders, test tube rack, bunsen burner, lab apron, safety goggles, hard boiled egg white, and nitric acid. (*Note: Other food samples may be substituted.)*

1. Collect your laboratory materials from the supply table and take them to your lab area. Work in pairs or alone as your teacher directs. ***Important: Wear safety goggles and a lab apron while doing this activity.***

2. To test a food sample for the presence of starches place a drop of iodine solution on a piece of potato. Observe any color change that occurs. In the **Observation Section** on the next page write the name of your food sample and the color change that occurred.

3. To test a food sample for the presence of fats rub a piece of bacon fat on brown paper. Observe any change that occurs to the paper. In the **Observation Section** on the next page write the name of your food sample and a description of the change that occurred.

4. To test a food sample for the presence of simple sugars pour a small amount of glucose solution into a test tube. Add either *Fehling's solution* or *Benedict's solution* to the test tube and carefully bring to a boil. ***Important: Point the test tube away from yourself and other students***. Observe any color change that occurs. In the **Observation Section** on the next page write the name of your food sample and the color change that occurred.

5. To test a food sample for the presence of proteins, place a small piece of hard-boiled egg white in a test tube. Add 6 drops of nitric acid. ***Important: Nitric acid can burn your skin. Wash with water if you spill any on your skin, then tell your teacher.*** Wait a few minutes and observe any color change that occurs. In the **Observation Section** on the next page write the name of your food sample and the color change that occurred.

6. When you are finished with your laboratory activity wash your test tubes and clean your other materials and your lab area. Return your materials to the supply table.

7. Answer the questions in the **Conclusion Section** on the next page.

Name ______________________ Class ____________________ Date ____________

Observations

NUTRIENT TESTED	FOOD SAMPLE	DESCRIPTION OF TEST RESULTS
Starch		
Fat		
Simple Sugar		
Protein		

Conclusions

1. Describe the tests used to identify the following nutrients:

Starch: ____

____

____

Glucose (Simple Sugar): ____

____

____

Fat: ____

____

____

Protein: ____

____

____

2. Name the elements present in each of the following nutrients:

Starch: ____

Glucose (Simple Sugar): ____

Fat: ____

Protein: ____

Name________________ Class________________ Date________

REVIEW ACTIVITIES

Important Terms

DIRECTIONS: Define the following terms in the spaces provided.

anorexia nervosa ____

____

ascorbic acid ____

____

balanced diet ____

____

beriberi ____

____

bulimia ____

____

Calorie ____

____

calorimeter ____

____

carbohydrates ____

____

carotene ____

____

cholesterol ____

____

fats and oils ____

____

glycogen ____

____

Name ______________________ **Class** ____________________ **Date** ___________

minerals ____

____

night blindness ____

____

nutrients ____

____

pernicious anemia ____

____

proteins ____

____

rickets ____

____

roughage ____

____

scurvy ____

____

solvent ____

____

thiamine ____

____

trace elements ____

____

vitamins ____

____

Name____________________ Class ____________________ Date __________

Skill Practice

Part A. Complete the following chart.

NUTRIENT	USE IN BODY	GOOD SOURCES
Carbohydrates		
Fats		
Proteins		

Part B. Menu Planning.

1. Make a list of the foods that you ate yesterday.

BREAKFAST	LUNCH	DINNER	SNACKS

2. Plan balanced diet for one day for a teen-aged person following good nutrition suggestions from the *Food Guide Pyramid*.

BREAKFAST	LUNCH	DINNER	SNACKS

3. Compare your planned menu with the food you actually ate yesterday. Did you eat a balanced diet?

____

Name________________________ Class____________________ Date__________

Part C. Complete the following vitamin chart.

VITAMIN	USES IN BODY	EFFECT OF DEFICIENCY	GOOD SOURCES
A			
B_1 THIAMINE			
B_2 RIBOFLAVIN			
B_6			
B_{12}			
NIACIN			
C			
D			
K			

Name______________________ Class______________________ Date__________

CHAPTER 7: QUIZ

A. FILL-IN QUESTIONS

DIRECTIONS: Complete each of the following statements by writing the correct word or phrase in the space provided.

1. The usable parts of food are called ______________________.
2. Sugars and starches are in the ______________________ food group.
3. ______________________ provide most of the energy required by the body.
4. Butter and lard are included in the food group ______________________.
5. ______________________ are organic compounds used to build and repair body tissue.
6. A ______________________ is a natural substance found in small quantities in food.
7. A lack of vitamins causes ______________________ diseases.
8. Night blindness is caused by a lack of ______________________.
9. Thiamine is another name for ______________________.
10. Citrus fruits contain vitamin ______________________.
11. ______________________ is a B-complex vitamin necessary for cellular respiration.
12. Pernicious anemia occurs when you don't eat foods that contain ______________________.
13. ______________________ is the vitamin that helps blood to clot.
14. Bowed legs, soft bones, and bad teeth are symptoms of ______________________.
15. ______________________ dissolves and transports materials in the body.
16. The energy content of food is measured in units called ______________________.
17. Taking in more calories than the body needs increases ______________________.
18. A ______________________ diet is made up of a selection of foods that supply the body with enough energy and chemicals.
19. Sodium and iodine are examples of ______________________.
20. Scurvy is caused by a lack of ______________________.

B. MULTIPLE-CHOICE QUESTIONS

DIRECTIONS: Circle the number of the expression that best completes each of the following statements.

1. Which nutrient contains the greatest number of calories per gram?
   (1) vitamins (3) water
   (2) fats (4) proteins
2. Muscle tissue is chiefly made up of which substances?
   (1) carbohydrates (3) minerals
   (2) fats (4) proteins

Name____________________________ Class____________________ Date____________

3. Which combination of foods is the best selection for a **balanced diet**?

(1) milk, fish, steak, ice cream
(2) fish, roll, milk, apple
(3) roll, potato, cookie, pie
(4) apple, peach, carrots, lettuce

4. Growth and repair in the human body require building materials provided mostly by

(1) water
(2) enzymes
(3) vitamins
(4) proteins

5. To which of the following does the term "calorie" refer?

(1) food mass
(2) energy content
(3) fat quality
(4) carbohydrate density

6. Which necessary part of a balanced diet usually does **not** enter the body cells?

(1) vitamins
(2) water
(3) minerals
(4) roughage

7. The primary solvent in the body that is essential for most chemical reactions.

(1) fat
(2) water
(3) protein
(4) sugar

8. Which substance is required to prevent the deficiency disease scurvy?

(1) a protein
(2) a fat
(3) a carbohydrate
(4) a vitamin

9. Which is most helpful for the regular elimination of solid wastes from the body?

(1) rice
(2) milk
(3) meat
(4) roughage

10. Which minerals are most needed for proper bone development?

(1) phosphorus and calcium
(2) iron and calcium
(3) sodium and phosphorus
(4) iron and sodium

C. ESSAY QUESTION

DIRECTIONS: Use complete sentences to answer the question in this part.

1. Name two food nutrients and state one use of each nutrient by the body.

____

____

____

____

____

____

Name________________________ Class________________________ Date____________

Chapter 8: Digestion

A. INTRODUCTION. Digestion is the process that changes food into a form that can be used by your body cells. Food is taken in and processed through your digestive system before it can be used by your body. The usable parts of foods (nutrients) supply you with the chemicals and energy you need to survive. The digestive process begins when food is taken into the body. Taking food into the body is called **ingestion**. The teeth and tongue help ingest food. When you eat a hamburger and a milkshake, ingestion takes place when you put the food into your mouth. (Throughout this chapter we will follow the path of your hamburger and milkshake to show how and where digestion takes place.)

Digestion begins with the breakdown of food into smaller pieces. This process is called mechanical digestion and it prepares the food for chemical digestion. During chemical digestion large complex food molecules are chemically changed into smaller simpler molecules. The hamburger and milkshake that you ate for lunch cannot be used by your body until they are chemically digested. In unicellular and other simple organisms digestion is **intracellular.** This means that digestion takes place in vacuoles inside the cell of the organism. In larger complex multicellular organisms digestion is **extracellular** (outside the cell).

REVIEW QUESTIONS

1. The first step in the digestive process is ____________________.

2. What is the difference between ingestion and digestion? ____________________

____

____

____

____

3. In unicellular and other simple organisms, digestion is ____________________. In larger more complex organisms, digestion is ____________________.

B. MECHANICAL AND CHEMICAL DIGESTION. In most organisms food must undergo a mechanical breakdown, called **mechanical digestion**, where food is physically cut, ground, and torn into smaller pieces. Mechanical digestion increases the surface area of the food particles that prepares them for chemical digestion. During **chemical digestion** large complex molecules are broken down into smaller simpler molecules by the chemical process of hydrolysis. During **hydrolysis** water is added to large complex molecules causing them to split into simpler molecules that can be used by the cells. Each reaction in digestion is catalyzed by a specific enzyme. These digestive enzymes help to chemically break down foods and must be present for digestion to occur. The complete chemical digestion of large molecules produces the end products shown in Table 8-1.

Name________________________ Class____________________ Date__________

LARGE MOLECULES	ENZYMES	END PRODUCTS
Carbohydrates	Maltase and Amylase	Simple sugars
Lipids	Lipases	Fatty acids and glycerol
Proteins	Proteases	Amino acids

TABLE 8-1. END PRODUCTS OF CHEMICAL DIGESTION.

Chemical digestion does not completely break down all food molecules. An organism may lack enzymes to digest some types of food molecules or there may not be enough time for enzymes to digest the food completely. When this happens the organism must eliminate indigestible or undigested materials. **Egestion** is the process by which heterotrophs (organisms that cannot make their own food) eliminate or remove food wastes from the body.

REVIEW QUESTIONS

1. Explain the difference between mechanical and chemical digestion.

____

____

____

____

2. Compounds that help cause the chemical breakdown of foods are called

____

3. Complete the following chart.

LARGE MOLECULES	ENZYMES	END PRODUCTS
Carbohydrates	Amylase and Maltase	
Lipids		fatty acids and glycerol
	Proteases	

4. The process by which food wastes are eliminated from the body is ________________

C. THE ALIMENTARY CANAL. The digestive system is made up of a continuous one-way tube that begins in the mouth and ends with the anus. This tube is commonly called the **alimentary canal** or **gastrointestinal (GI) tract**. As food passes through the tube special areas of the tube mechanically and chemically change food. Food is moved in one direction through the alimentary canal by slow rhythmic muscular contractions called **peristalsis** (Figure 8-1). After chemical digestion is completed nutrients pass from the alimentary canal (Figure 8-2) into all the cells of the body.

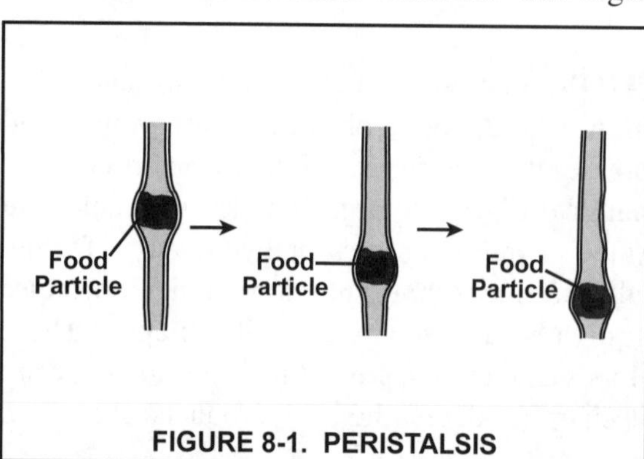

FIGURE 8-1. PERISTALSIS

Name________________________ Class____________________ Date__________

Food is ingested through the mouth. The mouth is also called the **oral cavity.** When you chew your hamburger your teeth and tongue break up the hamburger into small pieces. This process begins mechanical digestion by increasing the surface area of the food. Chemical digestion also begins in the mouth. The **salivary glands,** located in the oral cavity, secrete saliva. **Saliva** has mucus that moistens food making it easier to swallow. Saliva also contains the enzyme **ptyalin** or salivary amylase. Ptyalin starts the chemical digestion of starches. The starch in the bread of the hamburger bun is changed into maltose. Maltose is a disaccharide (double sugar). You can check this for yourself by chewing a piece of bread for a few minutes. When the starch in the bread is changed to sugar you will notice a sweet taste.

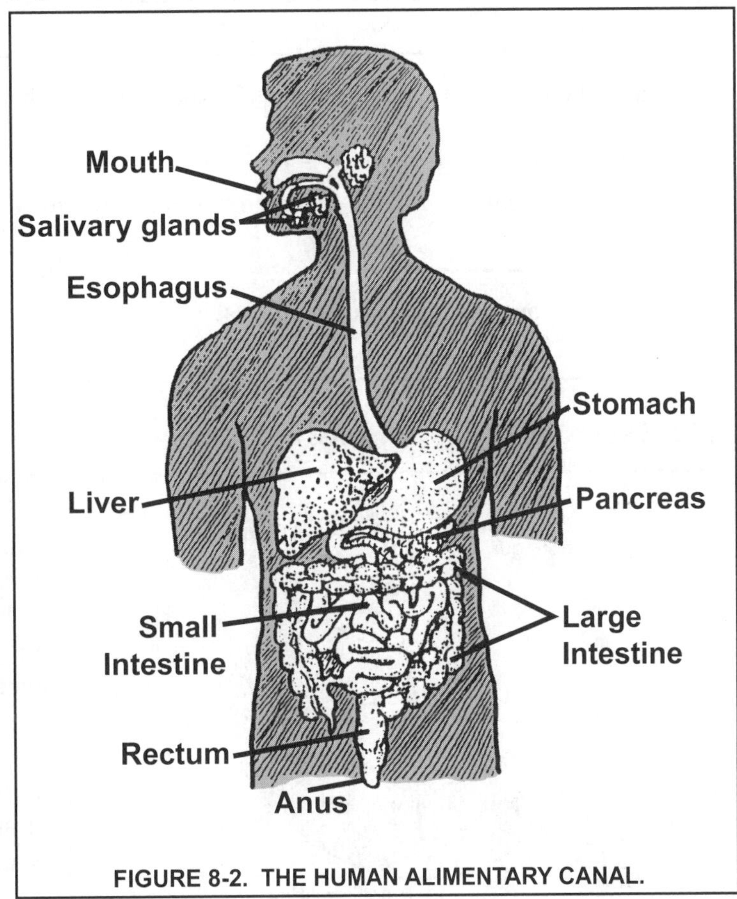

FIGURE 8-2. THE HUMAN ALIMENTARY CANAL.

Besides aiding in mechanical digestion the **tongue** is important during the swallowing and tasting of food. There are little groups of cells located in the tongue and roof of the mouth called **taste buds**. Four basic kinds of taste are sweet, sour, salty, and bitter. After food is swallowed it goes into the esophagus. The **esophagus** or **gullet** is a tube that moves food from the mouth to the stomach by peristalsis. No additional chemical digestion *begins* in the esophagus. The chemical action of saliva continues in the esophagus until food reaches the stomach. The esophagus produces a slimy material called **mucus.** Mucus lubricates (moistens) food so that it slides down the esophagus more easily.

Review Questions

1. Two common names for the digestive tube are ______________________

and ______________________.

2. Name and describe the process by which food moves through the digestive tract.

____

____.

3. Oral cavity is another name for the ______________.

Name ______________________ Class ____________________ Date ____________

4. Explain why breaking up food is important for the digestive process. ______________________

____

5. What is ptyalin? ____

____

6. Name the four main types of teeth and a function of each. ______________________

____.

7. Food is transported from the mouth to the stomach through a tube called the

____________________.

8. Why does the esophagus secrete mucus? ______________________________

____

D. THE STOMACH. The **stomach** is a muscular J-shaped organ (Figure 8-3). Mechanical digestion occurs when stomach muscles churn and mash food. The food becomes a thick soupy mixture called **chyme**. Some chemical digestion also occurs in the stomach. Glands in the stomach lining secrete gastric juice and hydrochloric acid. The **gastric juice** contains **pepsin** an enzyme that begins the chemical digestion of protein. This means the chemical digestion of the meat (protein) in your hamburger has begun.

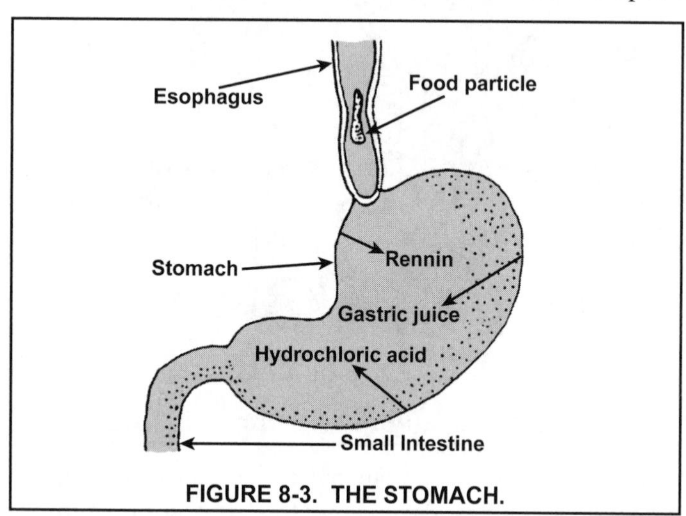

FIGURE 8-3. THE STOMACH.

The digestion of your milkshake will be started by rennin. **Rennin** is an enzyme that begins the chemical digestion of milk protein. Also located in the stomach is hydrocholoric acid. **Hydrochloric acid** (HCl) destroys bacteria normally present in food and provides the proper pH for enzyme action.

REVIEW QUESTIONS

1. Describe mechanical digestion in the stomach. ______________________________

____

2. What chemical digestion occurs in the stomach? ______________________________

____

____

____

____

Name________________________ Class____________________ Date__________

E. THE SMALL INTESTINE. After three or four hours partly digested food leaves the stomach and enters the **small intestine** where food digestion is completed and digested nutrients are absorbed into the bloodstream.

Most chemical digestion takes place and is completed in the small intestine as a result of the action of enzymes produced by **intestinal glands** and the **pancreas**. The pancreas secretes several enzymes including intestinal protease, lipase, and amylase. Intestinal glands that line the intestinal wall secrete the enzymes protease, lipase, and maltase. Protease completes protein digestion, lipase works on lipids, and amylase changes polysaccharides into disaccharies. Maltase then completes carbohydrate digestion by changing maltose (a disaccharide) into the simple sugars (monosaccharide).

Bile is made by the **liver**, stored in the **gall bladder**, and enters the small intestine through the **bile duct**. Bile prepares fats and oils for enzyme digestion by physically breaking them down into smaller pieces. This process greatly increases the surface area of fat particles thereby speeding up fat digestion by **lipases**. The action of bile on fats is referred to as a "detergent effect" because detergent also breaks up fats.

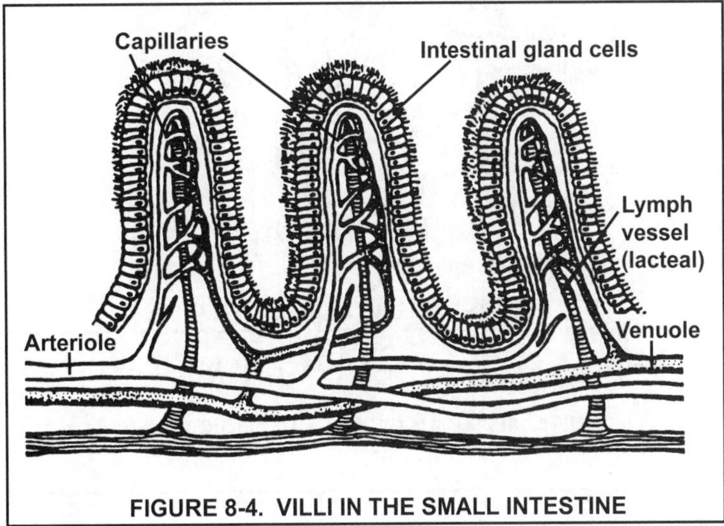

FIGURE 8-4. VILLI IN THE SMALL INTESTINE

Lining the inside of the small intestine are tiny finger-like projections of the intestinal wall called **villi** (Figure 8-4). Villi increase the surface area of the small intestine for the absorption of the end products of digestion. End products are absorbed by the process of diffusion.

What has become of your hamburger and milkshake? The starch in the roll was changed into simple sugars. Proteins in the meat and milk were changed into amino acids. Fats from the meat and milk became fatty acids and glycerol. These end products of digestion (review Table 8-1) were absorbed by the villi of the small intestine.

REVIEW QUESTIONS

1. Food digestion is completed in the ____________________.

2. Where does most chemical digestion take place? ________________.

3. Bile is made in the ______________________ and stored in the __________________.

4. Enzymes that digest fat are called ______________.

5. Describe the villi. ____

Name______________________ Class____________________ Date___________

F. THE LARGE INTESTINE. Undigested foods (wastes) pass from the small intestine into the **large intestine** (Figure 8-5). The large intestine is also called the **colon.** In the large intestine water, some vitamins, and minerals are absorbed into the blood stream. The remaining undigested substances, called **feces,** are stored in the lower end of the large intestine called the **rectum**. Feces are eliminated from the body (egestion) through the **anus.**

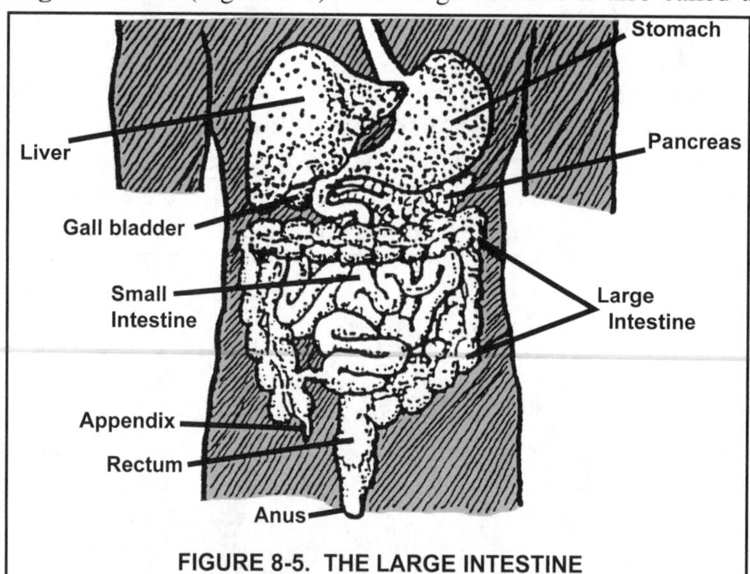

FIGURE 8-5. THE LARGE INTESTINE

Located near the beginning of the large intestine is a small finger-like projection called the **appendix.** The appendix has no known function in humans.

REVIEW QUESTIONS

1. What materials are absorbed by the large intestine? ______________________

____

2. The large intestine is also called the ____________________.

3. Egestion occurs through the ____________________.

G. END PRODUCTS OF DIGESTION. We are now at the end of the digestion of your hamburger and milkshake. The final compounds formed by digestion are called end products. These molecules are small and chemically simple so that they can be absorbed and used by the body's cells. The end products of the complete digestion of the carbohydrates in your hamburger bun and in your milkshake are now called simple sugars. Fatty acids and glycerol were produced from the complete digestion of the fats and oils in your meal and amino acids were formed by protein digestion. Simple sugars and amino acids pass into blood capillaries. Fatty acids and glycerol move into the lymph system.

Once these end products enter a cell, the cell will use them as building blocks in the synthesis (making) of complex compounds (nutrients) necessary for life. This is done by the chemical process of dehydration synthesis. Dehydration synthesis is the opposite of hydrolysis. Simple sugars are made into complex carbohydrates, fatty acids and glycerol are made into fats, and amino acids become complex proteins. Excess water is absorbed by the large intestine and undigested wastes are egested through the anus.

REVIEW QUESTIONS

1. End products of digestion are called ______________________ when they are used by the body to form the complex compounds needed by the body.

Name________________________ Class__________________ Date__________

2. Complete the following chart.

NUTRIENT	BUILDING BLOCKS
Carbohydrates	
Fats	
Proteins	

H. DIGESTIVE SYSTEM DISORDERS. When the digestive system does not function properly problems may occur. These problems are referred to as digestive disorders.

Digestive System Disorders

♦ **Ulcers.** An **ulcer** is an open painful sore in the stomach lining. **Mucus**, secreted by cells lining the surface of the stomach, helps to protect the stomach lining from hydrochloric acid. Open sores occur when there is too little mucus or too much acid in the stomach. Ulcers can bleed and can sometimes eat completely through the stomach wall. Ulcers are treated with diet and medication.

♦ **Tooth Decay.** Mouth bacteria cause **tooth decay**. Brushing and flossing your teeth at least once a day will help slow down the action of bacteria on food caught between your teeth. Regular visits to your dentist are also very important in preventing tooth decay and gum disease.

♦ **Appendicitis.** An infection of the appendix is called **appendicitis.** Treatment for this very painful condition is surgical removal of the appendix. If the appendix is not removed it may burst and infect the surrounding membranes and organs possibly leading to death.

♦ **Diarrhea.** The condition in which the feces do not remain in the large intestine long enough for the water to be absorbed is called **diarrhea.** Diarrhea can be caused by bacteria or viruses, emotional stress, or eating certain foods. If diarrhea lasts for a long time the body becomes dehydrated (loss of water) resulting in weakness. Severe diarrhea can result in death.

♦ **Constipation.** The opposite of diarrhea is called **constipation.** Constipation is a condition where the feces remain in the colon too long. Constipation can be caused by too little fiber or water in the diet.

REVIEW QUESTIONS

1. Name three digestive disorders and state one cause of each disorder.

____

Name ______________________ Class __________________ Date __________

CAREER OPPORTUNITIES

DENTAL HYGIENISTS: Dental hygienists work with dentists to help patients have healthy teeth. They clean teeth, take X-rays, and teach patients how to care for their teeth. This career requires at least two years of training after high school.

GASTROENTEROLOGIST: A **gastroenterologist** is a medical doctor who specializes in the human digestive system and the diseases that affect it. They study and treat disorders of the entire digestive (gastrointestinal) tract. This includes all the organs of the digestive tract and other organs involved in digestion such as the liver and gallbladder.

Gastroenterologists must first earn a medical degree, then complete a three-year residency program and a two year specialized study in gastroenterology. They must then pass a certification exam.

REVIEW QUESTIONS

1. Describe the job of a dental hygienist.

____

____

____

____

____

____

2. Doctors who treat the digestive system are called ____________________.

Name____________________________ Class_______________________ Date____________

LAB INVESTIGATION: DIGESTIVE ORGANS

OBJECTIVE

Upon completion of this activity you should be able to identify and state the functions of several frog digestive organs.

LABORATORY PROCEDURE

Materials: Preserved frog, dissecting pan, dissecting pins, dissecting scissors, scalpel, safety goggles, disposable rubber gloves, forceps, lab apron, and paper towels.

1. Collect your laboratory materials from the supply table and take them to your lab area. Work in pairs or alone as your teacher directs. ***Important: Wear safety goggles, rubber gloves, and laboratory apron while doing this activity.***

2. Cover your dissecting pan with a paper towel. Place the frog in the dissecting pan with its ventral (under) side facing upward and its feet pointing toward you. Refer to the *frog dissection diagram* on this page to see how to pin the frog to the dissecting pan.

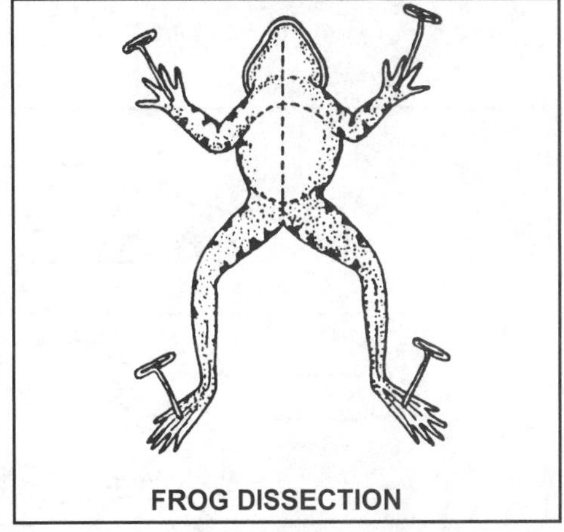

FROG DISSECTION

3. Pinch the skin to pull it away from the muscle layer. Use the dissecting scissors to carefully cut the skin as shown in the diagram on this page. ***Important: Make a very shallow cut.*** Now pin the two skin flaps to the dissecting pan to expose the muscle layer.

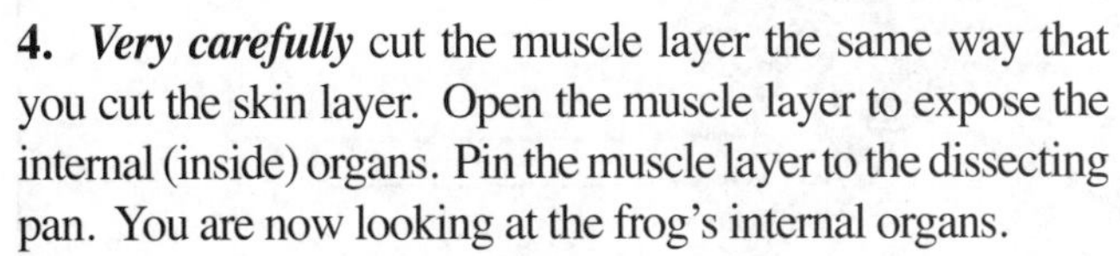

4. ***Very carefully*** cut the muscle layer the same way that you cut the skin layer. Open the muscle layer to expose the internal (inside) organs. Pin the muscle layer to the dissecting pan. You are now looking at the frog's internal organs.

5. If you see a mass of black eggs, your frog is a female. Remove the eggs and the attached ovaries. Also remove the triangular-shaped heart. You are now ready to locate the digestive organs of the frog. ***Note: The digestive system of the frog is similar to the human digestive system both in structure and function.***

6. Find the large reddish-brown *liver*. It has three lobes and covers most of the other digestive organs. The liver stores digested food products, secretes bile, and performs digestive gland functions. Label the liver on the diagram in the **Observation Section** on the next page.

7. Lift the liver and find the small, round, sac-like, green-colored *gall bladder*. The gall bladder stores bile. Look for the *bile duct* that runs from the gall bladder to the upper part of the small intestine. Label the gall bladder on the diagram in the **Observation Section** on the next page. Now carefully cut out the liver using your scissors.

8. You should now be able to see the *esophagus* and *stomach*. The esophagus is the tube that connects the *mouth* and *gullet* to the curved, white, sac-like stomach located on the right side of the frog's abdominal cavity. The stomach contains *gastric glands* that secrete gastric fluid into the stomach. Gastric fluids chemically digest some foods. Label the mouth, gullet, esophagus, and stomach on the diagram in the **Observation Section** on the next page.

Name______________________________ Class________________________ Date____________

9. In the inside curve of the stomach is a grayish white organ that looks like a feather. It is attached to the bile duct by a small tube. This is the *pancreas*. The pancreas secretes digestive fluids through the bile duct into the small intestine. Label the pancreas on the diagram in the **Observation Section** on this page.

10. Now find the *small intestine* and *large intestine*. The small intestine is a looped tube that is connected to the end of the stomach. The lower end of the small intestine leads into the large intestine. The large intestine is thicker and shorter than the small intestine. At the end of the large intestine is the *cloaca*. Find the cloaca on your frog. The small intestine completes food digestion. The large intestine collects waste materials and passes them into the cloaca. The cloaca passes the wastes out of the body. Label the small intestine, large intestine and cloaca on the diagram in the **Observation Section** on this page.

11. When you are finished with your laboratory activity, wrap the frog in the paper towel and throw it away. Clean your materials and lab area and return your materials to the supply table. Then answer the question in the **Conclusion Section**.

OBSERVATIONS

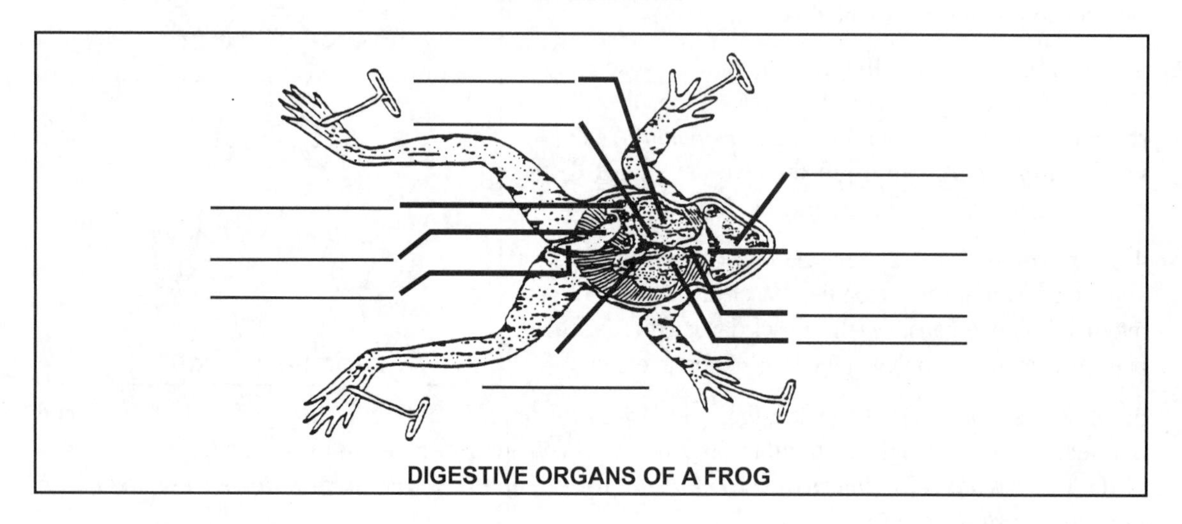

DIGESTIVE ORGANS OF A FROG

CONCLUSIONS

1. State the functions of the following digestive structures:

Liver: ____

Gall Bladder: ____

Stomach: ____

Pancreas: ____

Small Intestine: ____

Large Intestine: ____

Name______________ Class______________ Date______________

REVIEW ACTIVITIES

Important Terms

DIRECTIONS: Define the following terms in the spaces provided.

alimentary canal ______________________________

____

anus ______________________________

____

appendicitis ______________________________

____

appendix ______________________________

____

bile ______________________________

____

chemical digestion ______________________________

____

chyme ______________________________

____

colon ______________________________

____

constipation ______________________________

____

diarrhea ______________________________

____

esophagus ______________________________

____

feces ______________________________

____

gall bladder ______________________________

____

gastric juice ______________________________

____

hydrochloric acid ______________________________

____

Name ____________________ Class ________________ Date __________

large intestine ____

____

lipases ____

____

liver ____

____

mechanical digestion ____

____

mucus ____

____

oral cavity ____

____

pancreas ____

____

pepsin ____

____

peristalsis ____

____

ptyalin ____

____

rectum ____

____

rennin ____

____

saliva ____

____

salivary glands ____

____

small intestine ____

____

stomach ____

____

ulcer ____

____

villi ____

____

Name______________________________ Class______________________ Date____________

Skill Practice

Part A. Label the parts of the digestive system on the diagram below with the following terms: **stomach, small intestine, large intestine, oral cavity, esophagus, liver, rectum, appendix, gall bladder.**

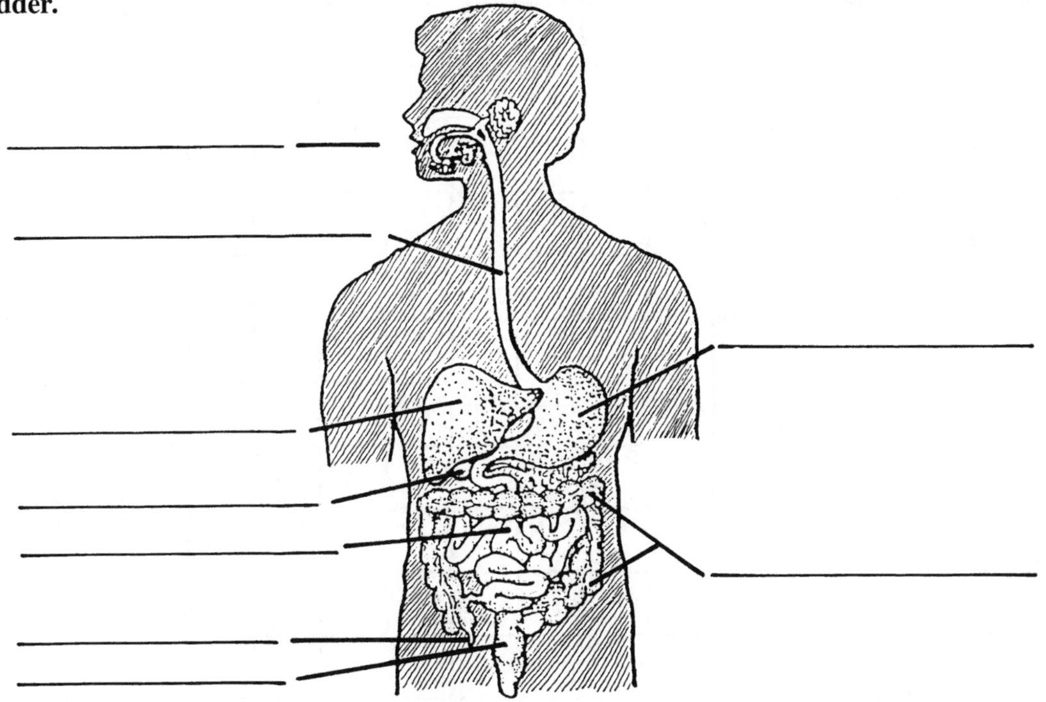

Part B. In the space at the left of each item in Column A, place the letter of the term or phrase in Column B that is most closely related to that item.

Column A	Column B
_______ **1.** Absorbs water.	**a.** Peristalsis
_______ **2.** End product of protein digestion.	**b.** Stomach
_______ **3.** Absorbs end products of digestion.	**c.** Gall Bladder
_______ **4.** Enzyme that begins starch digestion.	**d.** Villi
_______ **5.** Lower end of large intestine.	**e.** Oral Cavity
_______ **6.** Muscular action that moves food.	**f.** Ptyalin
_______ **7.** Secretion that moistens food.	**g.** Saliva
_______ **8.** Most chemical digestion occurs here.	**h.** Small Intestine
_______ **9.** Connects mouth with stomach.	**i.** Large Intestine
_______ **10.** Another name for the mouth.	**j.** Amino Acid
	k. Rectum
	l. Simple Sugar
	m. Esophagus

Name______________________ Class __________________ Date __________

Part C. Complete the following crossword puzzle.

Crossword Puzzle

Clues

ACROSS

1. Food is egested here
2. Organ that makes bile
5. Connects mouth and stomach
7. Secretes enzymes into small intestine
9. Thick soupy food mixture
12. Secretion in mouth
13. Breaks down fats
14. Peristalsis moves food in _____ direction
15. Bacteria causes _____ decay
16. Digestion begins in this cavity
17. Undigested food

DOWN

1. Infection in digestive tract
2. Water is absorbed in the _____ intestine
3. Enzyme that begins milk digestion
4. Open sore in stomach lining
6. Acid found in stomach
7. Enzyme found in saliva
8. J-shaped digestive organ
10. _____ acids are end products of protein digestion
11. Type of bud located in the mouth

Name________________________________ Class ________________________ Date ____________

CHAPTER 8: QUIZ

A. FILL-IN QUESTIONS

DIRECTIONS: Complete each of the following statements by writing the correct word or phrase in the space provided.

1. Food is broken down physically by a process called ______________________.
2. Simple sugars are the end product of ______________________ digestion.
3. Tooth decay is caused by ______________________.
4. Food moves in ______________________ direction through the alimentary canal.
5. An open sore in the stomach is a/an ______________________.
6. Undigested wastes are called ______________________.
7. ______________________ glands are located in the mouth.
8. Hydrochloric acid is secreted in the ______________________.
9. ______________________ are tiny finger like projections lining the intestinal wall.
10. The tube that connects the mouth and the stomach is called the ______________________.
11. Too little fiber or water in the diet causes a condition called ______________________.
12. Most chemical digestion takes place in the ______________________.
13. The rectum is the lower part of the ______________________ intestine.
14. The stomach lining secretes ______________________ juice.
15. Rennin helps digest ______________________.
16. The ______________________ in the digestive tract moistens food.
17. ______________________ is a thick soupy food mixture produced by the stomach.
18. Incisors are used for ______________________ food.
19. Bile is stored in the ______________________.
20. The slow, rhythmic, muscular contractions of the digestive tract are called

    ____

B. MULTIPLE-CHOICE QUESTIONS

DIRECTIONS: Circle the number of the expression that best completes each of the following statements.

1. In humans, food passes from the mouth into the stomach through the
   - (1) esophagus
   - (2) large intestine
   - (3) small intestine
   - (4) liver
2. A body structure that aids in the process of ingestion is the
   - (1) intestine
   - (2) stomach
   - (3) esophagus
   - (4) tongue

Name______________________ Class__________________ Date__________

3. The main function of the human digestive system is to
   (1) break down large molecules into smaller molecules
   (2) add necessary vitamins to food
   (3) synthesize minerals
   (4) excrete oxygen and carbon dioxide

4. In humans, most digested food is absorbed by the
   (1) stomach (3) small intestine
   (2) esophagus (4) large intestine

5. Ulcers, a disorder of the digestive system, are most closely associated with which of the following?
   (1) the inability to chew food thoroughly
   (2) the excessive production of gastric juice
   (3) excess water in the large intestine
   (4) the inability of the liver to produce bile

6. Digested nutrients are absorbed into the blood through structures called
   (1) alveoli (3) glands
   (2) bladders (4) villi

7. The end products of protein digestion are
   (1) lactic acid molecules (3) hydrochloric acid molecules
   (2) amino acids (4) fatty acids

Directions(8-10): For *each* statement in questions 8 through 10 select the structure, shown in the diagram at the right, that is most closely associated with that statement. Write the *number* of the correct answer in the space next to the question.

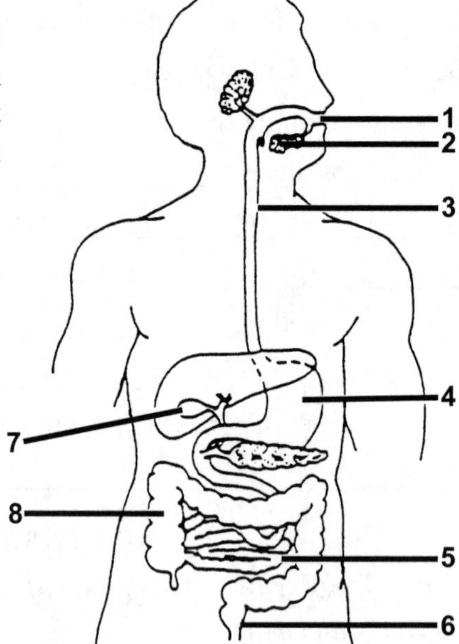

8. This structure produces saliva. __________

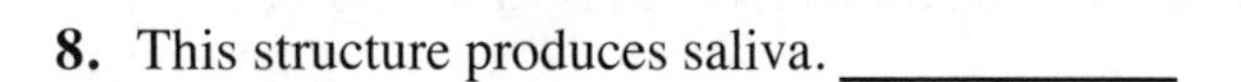

9. Acid is produced in this organ. __________

10. Undigested food materials are eliminated from this structure. __________

C. ESSAY QUESTION

DIRECTIONS: Use complete sentences to answer the question in this part.

1. Name two digestive system disorders.

____

____

____

Name________________________ Class________________________ Date____________

Chapter 9: Transport

A. INTRODUCTION. After digestion is completed nutrients go into the blood stream and are transported to the cells of the body. In the cells, nutrients are chemically combined with oxygen and energy is released. **Transport** is the process of absorption and circulation of materials throughout the body. **Absorption** involves the passage of materials into and out of the bloodstream. Oxygen diffusing into blood capillaries of the lungs, food entering blood in villi, and carbon dioxide diffusing into the blood capillaries of body tissues are all examples of absorption. (In Chapter 5 you learned that diffusion is the movement of materials from an area of high concentration to an area of low concentration.) **Circulation** is the distribution of materials to all parts of the body. The transport system is also called the circulatory system. The **circulatory system** is made up of the heart, blood vessels, blood, lymph and lymph vessels.

REVIEW QUESTIONS

1. The absorption and distribution of materials throughout the body is called ______________.

2. ______________________________ is the distribution of materials throughout the body.

3. The passage of materials into and out of the bloodstream is known as ________________.

4. The transport system is also called the ______________________________ system.

5. State two examples of diffusion in the body. ______________________________

____

____

6. Name four parts of the circulatory system. ______________________________

____

B. CIRCULATION. The circulation of blood was discovered by **William Harvey**. Harvey, an English doctor, did not believe what he had been taught about the movement of blood in the body. He did many experiments on different animals. From his experiments and observations, he concluded that the blood flowed in a circle throughout the body and was used over and over.

Blood moves through the body in a continuous pathway of blood vessels. The two basic pathways of circulation are pulmonary circulation and systemic circulation (Figure 9-1). **Pulmonary circulation** involves blood flow from the right ventricle to the lungs where it picks up oxygen and loses carbon dioxide and water vapor. The blood then returns to the heart by way of veins. During **systemic circulation** blood flows from the left ventricle to all body parts and then returns to the heart.

Name________________________ Class____________________ Date__________

This system provides the body cells with needed substances and carries away cellular excretions.

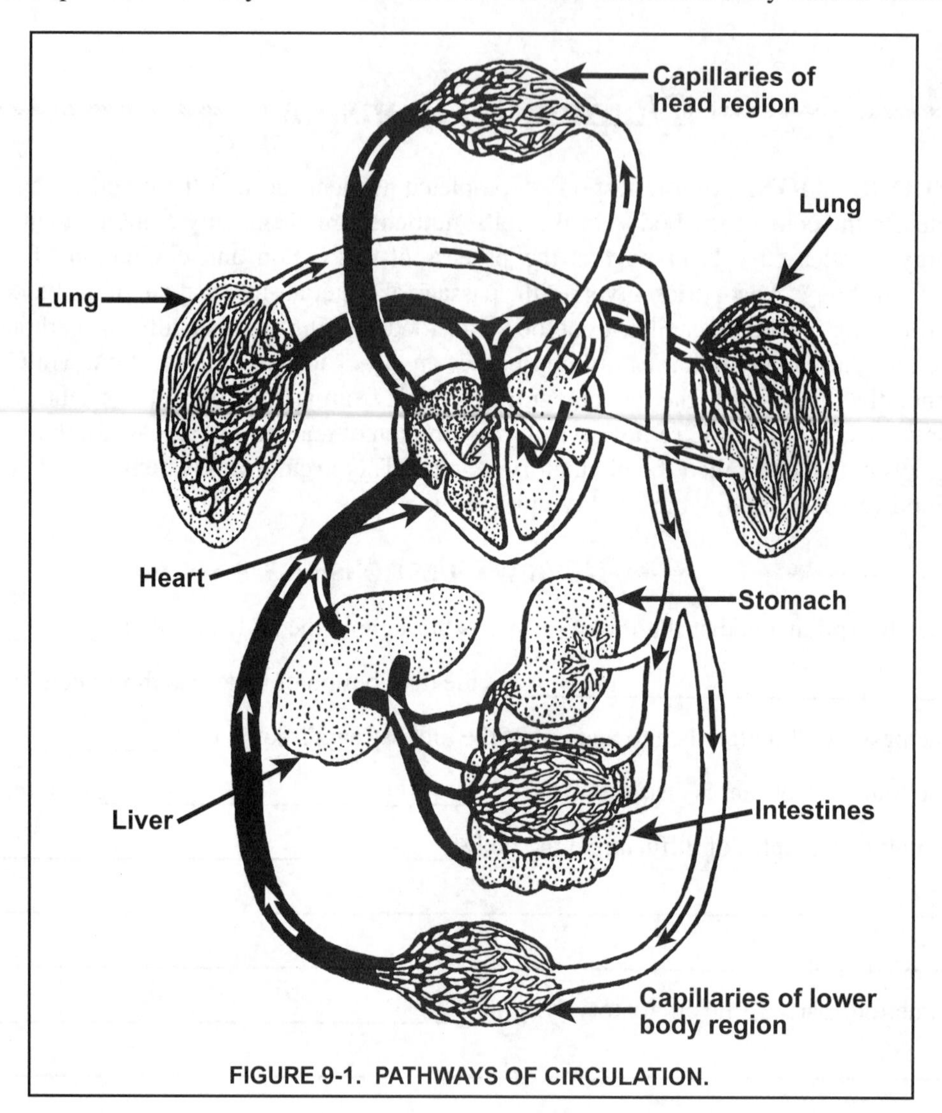

FIGURE 9-1. PATHWAYS OF CIRCULATION.

REVIEW QUESTIONS

1. ______________________________ discovered the circulation of blood.
2. Blood circulates in a __________________________ throughout the body.
3. Explain the difference between pulmonary circulation and systemic circulation.

____

____

____

____

____

____

Name________________________ Class____________________ Date__________

C. THE HEART. The **heart** is a muscular four-chambered organ (Figure 9-2). It pumps blood through blood vessels adjusting the rate of flow and pressure to changing body requirements. The two upper chambers are the **atria** (singular **atrium**). The two lower chambers are the **ventricles.** The ventricles have thicker walls than the atria. The atria receive blood returning in the veins from the lungs and other body tissues and pump it to the ventricles. The ventricles pump blood into the arteries, which carry it to the lungs and other body tissues. The chambers are separated by **valves** that regulate the direction of blood flow in and out of the heart. Valves prevent blood from flowing backward. The heart is covered by a thin tough sac called the **pericardium.**

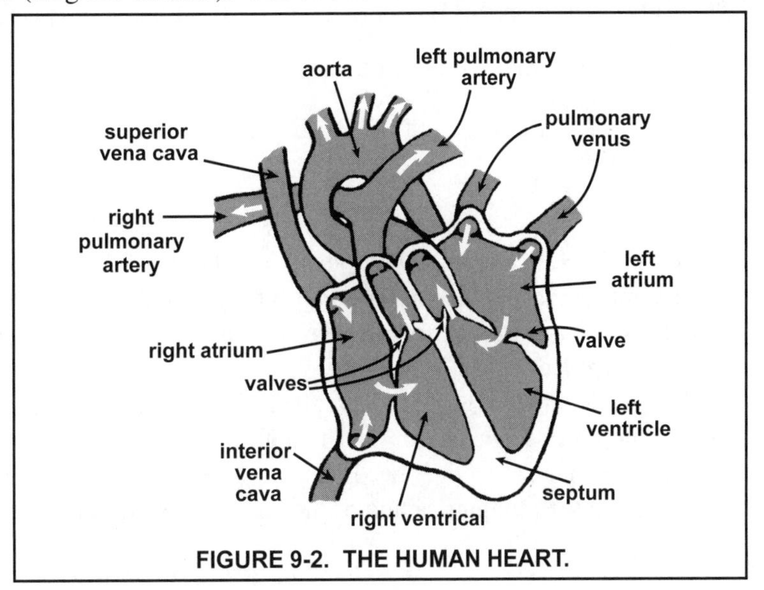

FIGURE 9-2. THE HUMAN HEART.

REVIEW QUESTIONS

1. Fill in the blank spaces in the following sentences.

   a. The ____________________ is a muscular, four-chambered organ.

   b. The upper chambers of the heart are called the ____________________.

   c. The lower chambers of the heart are called the ____________________.

   d. The ____________________ is the membrane covering the heart.

   e. ____________ separate the heart chambers and prevent the back flow of ____________.

D. BLOOD VESSELS. Blood vessels are tubes that transport blood to and away from body parts. The three major types of blood vessels are arteries, capillaries, and veins (Figure 9-3).

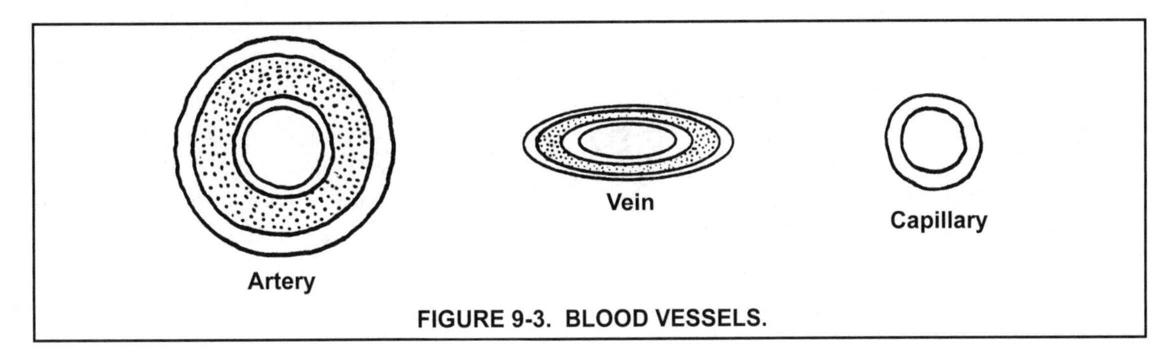

FIGURE 9-3. BLOOD VESSELS.

Name ______________________ Class ____________________ Date __________

REVIEW QUESTIONS

1. Tubes that transport blood to and away from body parts are called ________________.
2. Name three major types of blood vessels.

____

E. ARTERIES. Arteries are blood vessels that carry blood away from the heart. Because they are very muscular and elastic they help pump blood through the body. In order to do this they expand and then snap back to normal size. This expansion and snapping back of the arterial walls is called the **pulse.**

Arteries located in the heart are called **coronary arteries.** The largest artery in the body is the **aorta.** The aorta carries blood that is high in oxygen. Arteries branch and become smaller and smaller in diameter until they become tiny vessels called **arterioles**. Blood in the arteries is under pressure from the pumping action of the heart. This pressure is called **blood pressure.**

REVIEW QUESTIONS

1. Arteries carry blood ______________________________ from the heart.
2. Describe the structure of an artery. ______________________________

____

3. The largest artery in the body is the ______________________________.
4. What is meant by the term blood pressure? ______________________________

____

F. CAPILLARIES. The **capillaries** are the smallest blood vessels. They are one-celled microscopic blood vessels that connect arteries to veins. Exchange of oxygen and carbon dioxide between the blood and body parts takes place through capillary walls (Figure 9-4). This material exchange takes place by diffusion. Plasma is also filtered out at the capillaries. The filtered plasma becomes tissue fluid.

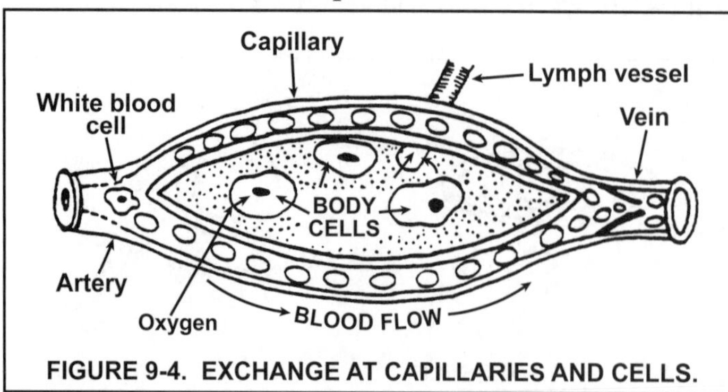

FIGURE 9-4. EXCHANGE AT CAPILLARIES AND CELLS.

Name________________________ Class________________ Date__________

REVIEW QUESTIONS

1. Describe the structure of a capillary. ____

____

2. What materials are exchanged at the capillaries? ________________________________

____

____

G. VEINS. Veins are blood vessels that transport blood under low pressure from the capillaries back to the heart. The muscular walls of veins are thinner than the walls of arteries. Veins have valves that prevent the backflow of blood (Figure 9-5). The **vena cavae** (singular **vena cava**) are two large veins that return blood to the heart.

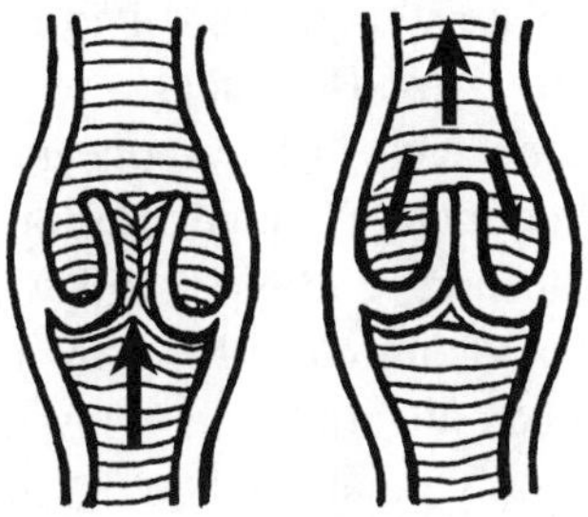

FIGURE 9-5. VALVES IN VEINS.

REVIEW QUESTIONS

1. Veins carry blood ______________________ heart.

2. Veins have ______________________ to prevent the backflow of blood.

H. COMPOSITION OF BLOOD. The average adult has about 5 liters of blood. **Blood** is the liquid medium that transports materials throughout the body within the blood vessels. Plasma, red blood cells, white blood cells, and platelets make up blood (Figure 9-6).

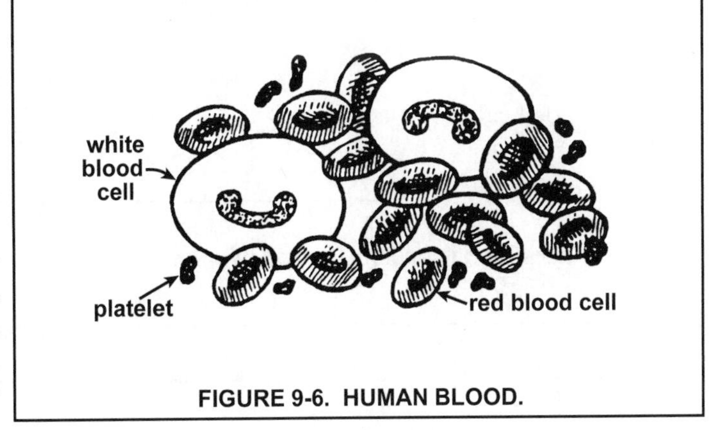

FIGURE 9-6. HUMAN BLOOD.

Plasma is the straw colored nonliving part of blood. It is 90 percent water. Plasma transports blood cells, end products of digestion, hormones, cellular excretions, and antibodies throughout the body. Plasma also helps to regulate body temperature.

REVIEW QUESTIONS

1. The average adult has about ______________________ of blood.

Name ____________________ Class ________________ Date __________

2. List the 4 materials that make up blood. ____________________

____

3. Describe plasma. ____________________

____

4. Name two materials carried by plasma. ____________________

____

____

I. RED BLOOD CELLS. Red blood cells are the most abundant blood cells and are shaped like round plates that are indented in the center. Red blood cells are produced in special tissue called **bone marrow**. Bone marrow is located inside certain long bones Mature red blood cells do not have a nucleus. Blood appears to be red because red blood cells contain the iron rich pigment (coloring material) **hemoglobin**. Hemoglobin carries oxygen from the lungs to the body cells. It also transports carbon dioxide from the body cells to the lungs. Blood high in oxygen content is called **oxygenated**. Blood low in oxygen content is called **deoxygenated**.

You could not live if your blood was unable to carry oxygen. This could happen if you were to accidentally inhale carbon monoxide. (Carbon monoxide is a gas that is given off by the exhaust fumes from cars.) Your hemoglobin would permanently combine with the carbon monoxide molecules and would not be able to combine with oxygen. When this happens your cells cannot get oxygen for respiration. If enough carbon monoxide is combined with your hemoglobin you suffocate and die. This is called **carbon monoxide poisoning**.

REVIEW QUESTIONS

1. In the space below, draw two red blood cells.

2. Red blood cells are made in ____________________.

3. Red blood cells carry ____________________.

4. Why does blood appear to be red in color?

____

____

5. When does carbon monoxide poisoning occur?

____

____

Name______________________________ Class______________________ Date____________

J. PLATELETS. **Platelets** are smaller than either red or white blood cells and do not contain a nucleus. They are cell fragments produced by bone marrow cells and are very numerous. Platelets are involved in the clotting of blood.

REVIEW QUESTIONS

1. What is the function of platelets? ____

____

2. Describe blood platelets. ____

____

K. WHITE BLOOD CELLS. **White blood cells** fight infections and are part of the body's defense or immune system. White blood cells are produced in bone marrow and in tissue called lymph tissue. They are irregular in shape and have no color. White blood cells are larger than red blood cells and have a nucleus. There are fewer white cells than red cells unless they are fighting infection. When they are fighting infection they increase in number.

There are several different types of white blood cells (Figure 9-7). Some white blood cells, called **phagocytes,** aid in fighting disease by **engulfing** (ingesting) bacteria, viruses, and other foreign organisms. Phagocytes engulf bacteria the same way amoebas engulf food. Other white blood cells (**lymphocytes**) produce proteins known as **antibodies.** Antibodies are produced when foreign particles (**antigens**) enter the body. Some common antigens are bacteria and foreign tissues. When a disease virus (an antigen) enters your body white blood cells produce antibodies to fight the disease.

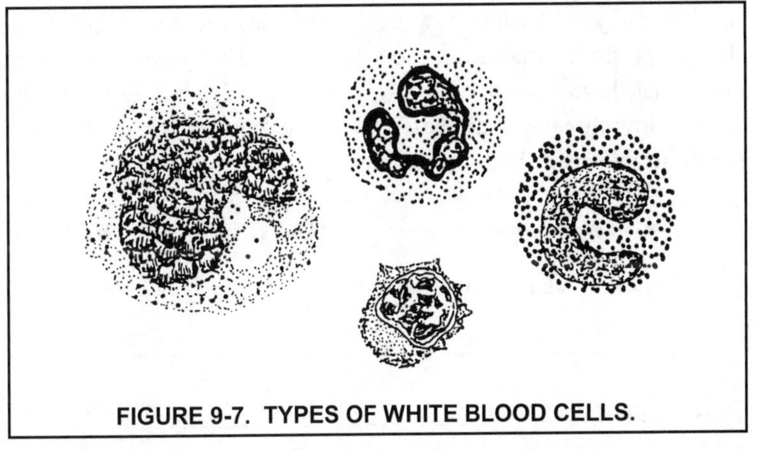

FIGURE 9-7. TYPES OF WHITE BLOOD CELLS.

REVIEW QUESTIONS

1. Describe a white blood cell. ____

____

2. White blood cells take in bacteria by a process called ______________________.

3. What do lymphocytes produce to help fight disease? ________________________

____

Name________________________ Class____________________ Date___________

L. LYMPH AND LYMPH VESSELS. Lymph comes from the portion of the blood plasma that diffuses out of the capillaries. It surrounds the body cells as intercellular fluid (Figure 9-8). Intercellular fluid helps transport dissolved materials between capillaries and cells. Intercellular fluid is also called tissue fluid.

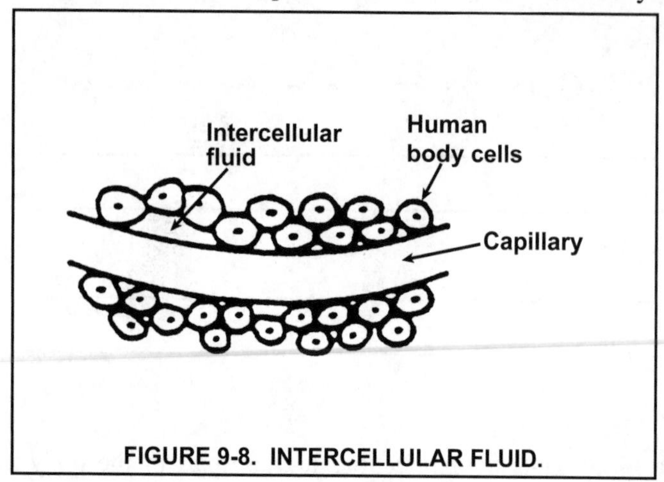

FIGURE 9-8. INTERCELLULAR FLUID.

Excess intercellular fluid enters **lymph vessels** and is circulated through these vessels as lymph. Lymph vessels transport the lymph to veins where it enters the blood and becomes part of the plasma again.

The lymph system also helps protect the body against infection. The armpits, neck, and groin contain groups of tiny bean-shaped organs called **lymph nodes.** These structures filter out bacteria and viruses from lymph. Lymph tissue also produces a type of white blood cell that helps the body fight disease. When you have an infection, the lymph nodes that drain the affected area may become enlarged. These swollen lymph nodes show that there is an infection in your body. Lymph tissue is also located in the tonsils, adenoids, spleen, thymus gland, digestive tract, and bone marrow. Lymph is circulated in lymph vessels by the contractions of body muscles.

REVIEW QUESTIONS

1. Where does lymph come from? ____

____

2. Lymph is carried by ____________________.

3. Where are lymph nodes located? ____

____

4. What do swollen lymph nodes tell you about your health? ____________________

____

M. IMMUNITY. The ability of the body to resist certain disease causing organisms (**pathogens**) is known as **immunity.** To resist disease the body has certain body defenses (Figure 9-9). One body defense is the presence of barriers such as skin, nose hairs, and mucus coated linings in the digestive and respiratory tracts. Another is hydrochloric acid in the stomach. A third defense is the ability of white blood cells to engulf bacteria. The body's final defense is the production of antibodies to fight foreign substances that enter the body. These antibodies are carried by the blood.

Name________________________________ Class________________________ Date______________

Immune reactions occur between antibodies and antigens when the body defends itself against invading organisms. Along with antibody production there are other types of immune responses such as skin graft rejection, organ transplant rejection, and allergic reactions.

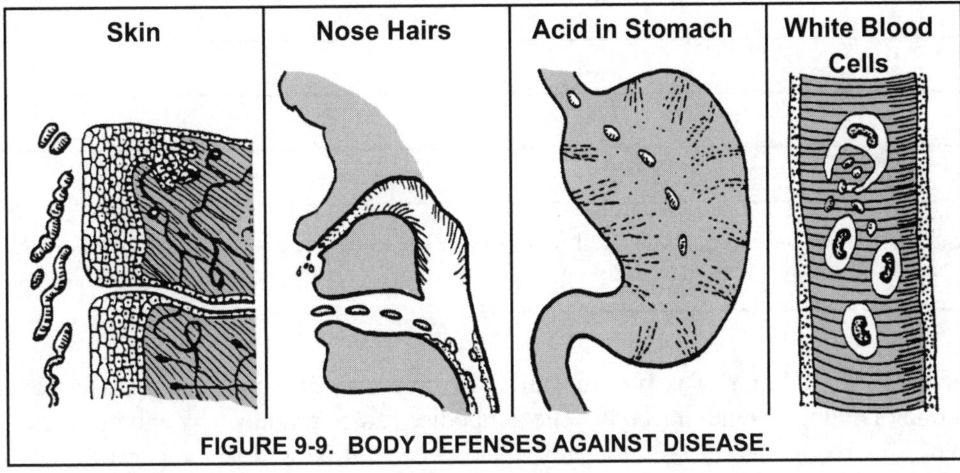

FIGURE 9-9. BODY DEFENSES AGAINST DISEASE.

REVIEW QUESTIONS

1. What is immunity? ____

____

2. A disease-producing organism is called a ______________________.

3. List three body defenses.

____

____

____

____

4. Name two immune reactions. ______________________________________

____

N. ACTIVE IMMUNITY. **Active immunity** occurs when the body makes its own antibodies against a particular antigen. This can occur as a result of having a particular disease and recovering from it or by having a vaccination for a particular disease. If you had chicken pox, you now have active immunity against this disease. Young children are vaccinated against small pox to provide active immunity. A **vaccination** consists of an injection of a dead or weakened form of a disease causing microorganism that can no longer cause the disease but can still stimulate antibody production by white blood cells. This type of immunity lasts a long time. Diphtheria-Tetanus, Oral Polio (Sabin), Measles, Mumps, and Rubella (German measles) are immunizations required for public school attendance.

Name________________________ Class________________ Date__________

REVIEW QUESTIONS

1. Describe how a person gets active immunity. ______________________________

____

____

____

____

2. An injection of a dead or weakened form of a disease-causing microorganism is called a

______________________________.

O. PASSIVE IMMUNITY. Passive immunity is a temporary immunity to a disease produced by the injection of antibodies into the body. The antibodies can be produced by another person or by an animal. Passive immunity lasts for only a short time. It is used to temporarily increase the body's defense against a particular disease. People who have been exposed to hepatitis are given injections of gamma globulin containing antibodies to hepatitis.

REVIEW QUESTIONS

1. What is passive immunity? ______________________________

____

____

2. How long does passive immunity last? ______________________________

P. BLOOD TYPING AND TRANSFUSIONS. Some time in your life you may need a blood transfusion. Knowing how immunity works have made it possible to type blood and give safe blood transfusions. There are four blood types known as A, B, AB and O. The typing of blood in the ABO blood group system is based on the presence or absence of antigens on the surface of the red blood cells. There are two types of antigens: A and B. In addition, the blood plasma may contain anti-A and/or anti-B antibodies.

Blood type is important when giving transfusions. If the blood types of the donor and receiver are not agreeable an antigen-antibody reaction occurs. This reaction results in the clumping of blood. When this happens the blood cells clog the capillaries and cause death (Table 9-1).

Blood Type	Anitigens On Red Cells	Antibodies in Plasma	May Donate To	May Receive
A	A	anti-B	A, AB	A, O
B	B	anti-A	B, AB	B, O
AB	A and B	none	AB	A, B, AB, O
O	none	anti-A & anti-B	A, B, AB, O	O only

TABLE 9-1. BLOOD TYPES AND SAFE TRANSFUSIONS.

Name________________ Class________________ Date________

REVIEW QUESTIONS

1. Blood type is important when giving or receiving ________________.

Q. TRANSPORT SYSTEM DISORDERS. Problems or diseases of the transport system can involve the heart and blood vessels **(cardiovascular diseases)**, the blood, or the immune system. The following are some common transport system disorders.

Transport System Disorders

♦ **High Blood Pressure.** The most common form of cardiovascular disease is **high blood pressure.** High blood pressure occurs when the blood pressure in the arteries is increased. This can be caused by stress, diet, heredity, cigarette smoking, and aging. High blood pressure can damage the lining of arteries and weaken heart muscle. Some ways of controlling high blood pressure are by decreasing stress, losing weight, and taking medication.

♦ **Coronary Thrombosis.** A **coronary thrombosis** is a type of heart attack caused by a blockage in one of the arteries that carries blood to the heart muscle. The blockage stops the flow of blood to some of the heart muscle. The heart muscle is then usually damaged from lack of oxygen. Treatment includes anti-thrombotic drugs, which are administered in the emergency room, balloon angioplasty, where they stick a catheter in and inflate a balloon inside the artery, or bypass surgery. Some doctors recommend aspirin once a day as a means of prevention.

♦ **Leukemia. Leukemia** is a form of cancer in which the bone marrow makes too many white blood cells. The large numbers of white cells crowd out developing red blood cells and platelets. There is no cure for leukemia but treatment with radiation and drugs can cause partial or complete remissions lasting many years in some patients.

♦ **Anemia. Anemia** occurs when blood does not have enough hemoglobin or red blood cells. When this happens the body cells do not receive enough oxygen. This results in low levels of energy. Anemia can be treated by eating iron rich foods or taking pills containing iron.

♦ **AIDS.** The **acquired immune deficiency syndrome (AIDS)** is a disease for which there is no cure at this time. It is caused by a virus that scientists call HIV (human immunodeficiency virus). The virus destroys the body's immune system so that it is unable to fight off even small infections. Current evidence indicates that the disease is transmitted by body secretions during sexual contact or by direct exposure to infected blood. AIDS is not spread by casual contact such as shaking hands or sitting next to someone who has the disease. AIDS can be prevented by not having sex, not injecting drugs, and not receiving contaminated blood. A female with the AIDS virus can give it to her unborn baby. Drugs, such as AZT, DDI, and others, have been developed to treat the disease. These drugs prolong the patient's life but do not cure the disease.

Name ____________________ Class ____________________ Date ____________

Review Questions

1. What are cardiovascular diseases? ____

____

2. Complete the following table.

DISORDER	CAUSE	TREATMENT
High Blood Pressure		
Leukemia		
Coronary Thrombosis		
Anemia		
AIDS		

Name______________________ Class ________________ Date ________

LAB INVESTIGATION: OBSERVING BLOOD CELLS

Objective

Upon completion of this activity you should be able to identify and state the functions of red blood cells, white blood cells, and platelets.

Laboratory Procedure

Materials: Prepared slide of stained human blood cells, lens paper, and compound microscope.

1. Collect your laboratory materials from the supply table and take them to your lab area. Clean your microscope lenses and prepared slide with the lens paper.

2. Place the prepared slide on the microscope stage. Focus the slide using the low power objective. Refer to the diagram on this page to be sure you have located the blood cells.

3. Once you have located and focused the blood cells under low power, carefully switch your microscope to high power. If your cells are not clearly focused under high power, refocus by ***using only the fine adjustment knob to focus upwards.***

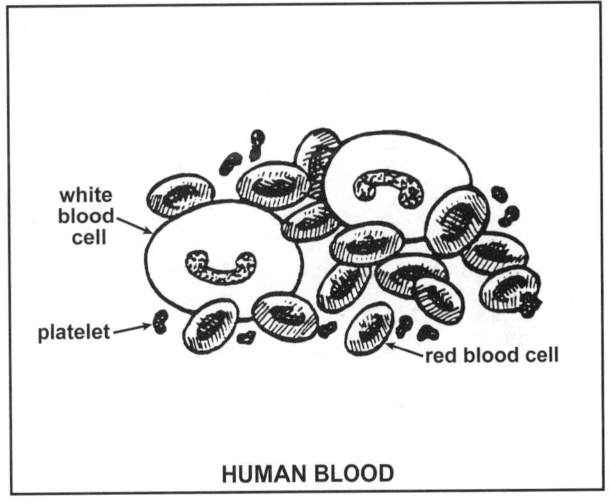

HUMAN BLOOD

4. Scan your slide to locate the *red blood cells*. The red blood cells are more abundant than white blood cells and are stained a pale pink on your prepared slide. They are shaped like a round plate that is indented in the center. Red blood cells carry oxygen to the cells of the body.

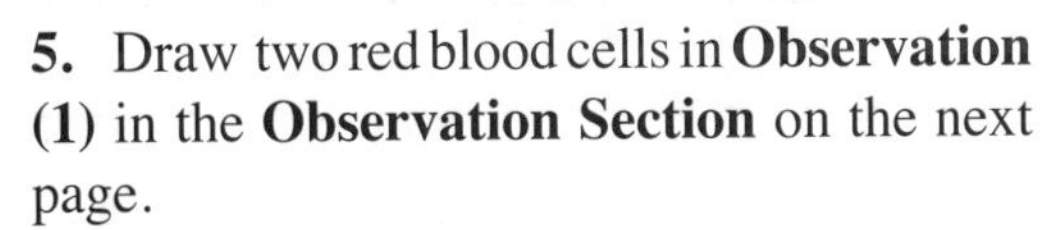

5. Draw two red blood cells in **Observation (1)** in the **Observation Section** on the next page.

6. Now look for the *white blood cells*. White blood cells are larger than red blood cells and have a nucleus. They do not have a regular round shape as do the red cells. Instead, the edges look sort of ragged or torn. The nuclei of white blood cells are stained a dark reddish-purple on your prepared slide. White blood cells fight infections in the body.

7. Draw three white blood cells in **Observation (2)** in the **Observation Section** on the next page.

8. The blood *platelets* are stained blue on your prepared slide. They look like very small particles. Platelets are numerous and do not have a nucleus. They last for only a few days and are involved in blood clotting.

Name______________________________ Class_______________________ Date_____________

9. Draw two blood platelets in **Observation (3)** in the **Observation Section** below.

10. When you are finished with your laboratory activity clean your lab area and return your lab materials and microscope to the supply table.

11. Answer the questions in the **Conclusion Section**.

OBSERVATIONS

(1) RED BLOOD CELLS.	**(2) WHITE BLOOD CELLS.**	**(3) PLATELETS.**

CONCLUSIONS

1. Describe the structure and state the functions of the following blood cells:

Red Blood Cells. ____

____

____

White Blood Cells. ____

____

____

Platelets. ____

____

____

2. Which blood cells are the most numerous? ____________________.

Name______________________ Class______________________ Date__________

REVIEW ACTIVITIES

Important Terms

DIRECTIONS: Define the following terms in the spaces provided.

absorption ____

____

active immunity ____

____

AIDS ____

____

anemia ____

____

arteries ____

____

arterioles ____

____

atria ____

____

blood ____

____

blood pressure ____

____

capillaries ____

____

circulation ____

____

coronary arteries ____

____

coronary thrombosis ____

____

Name ____________________ Class ____________________ Date ____________

heart ____________________

____

hemoglobin ____________________

____

immunity ____________________

____

leukemia ____________________

____

lymph ____________________

____

passive immunity ____________________

____

pathogens ____________________

____

pericardium ____________________

____

plasma ____________________

____

platelets ____________________

____

red blood cells ____________________

____

transport ____________________

____

vaccination ____________________

____

veins ____________________

____

ventricles ____________________

____

white blood cells ____________________

____

Name______________________ Class______________________ Date__________

Skill Practice

Part A. Label the parts of the heart diagram below by placing the correct term on the line.

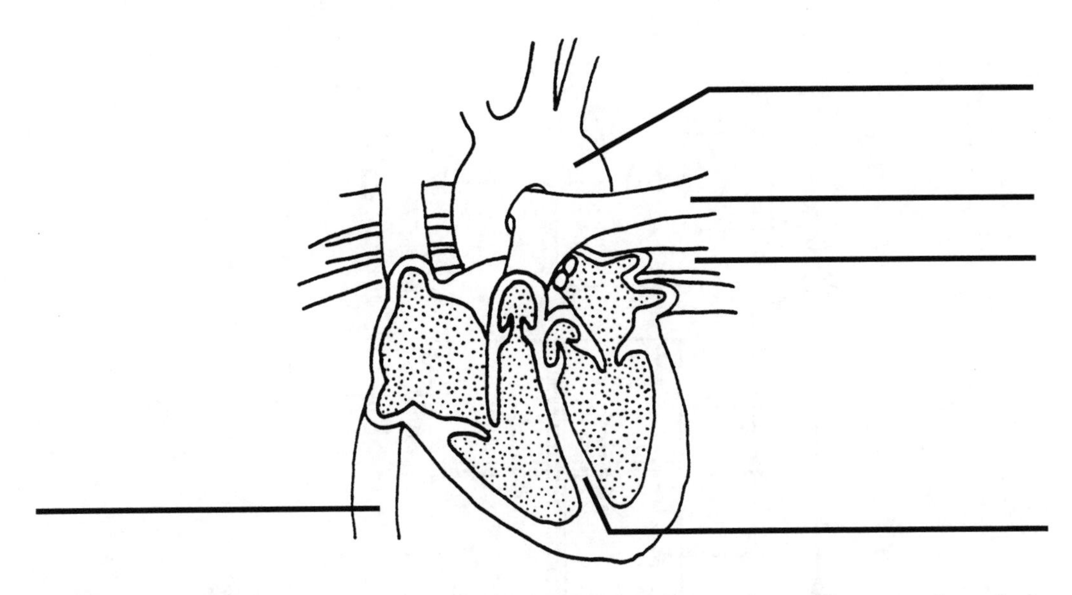

Part B. Base your answers to questions 1 and 2 on the diagram below and on your knowledge of biology.

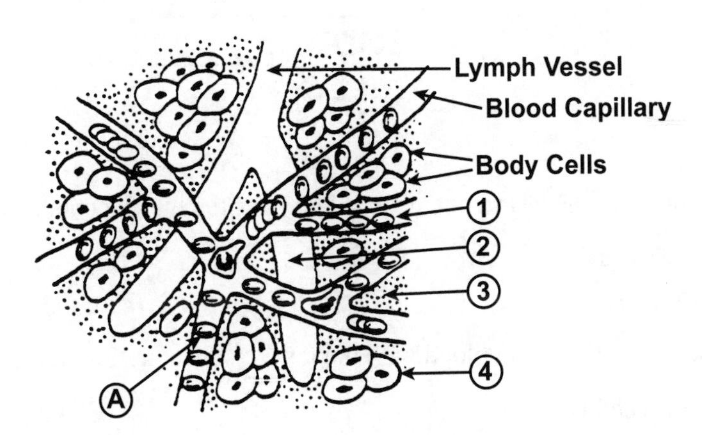

1. The major function of cell A is to

(1) start blood clot formation
(2) produce antibodies
(3) engulf invading bacteria
(4) transport oxygen

2. Materials passing between body cells and blood must pass through intercellular fluid which is located in area

(1) 1
(2) 2
(3) 3
(4) 4

Name____________________ Class____________________ Date__________

Part C. Base your answers to questions 1 through 3 on the schematic diagram below of blood flow throughout the human body and on your knowledge of biology.

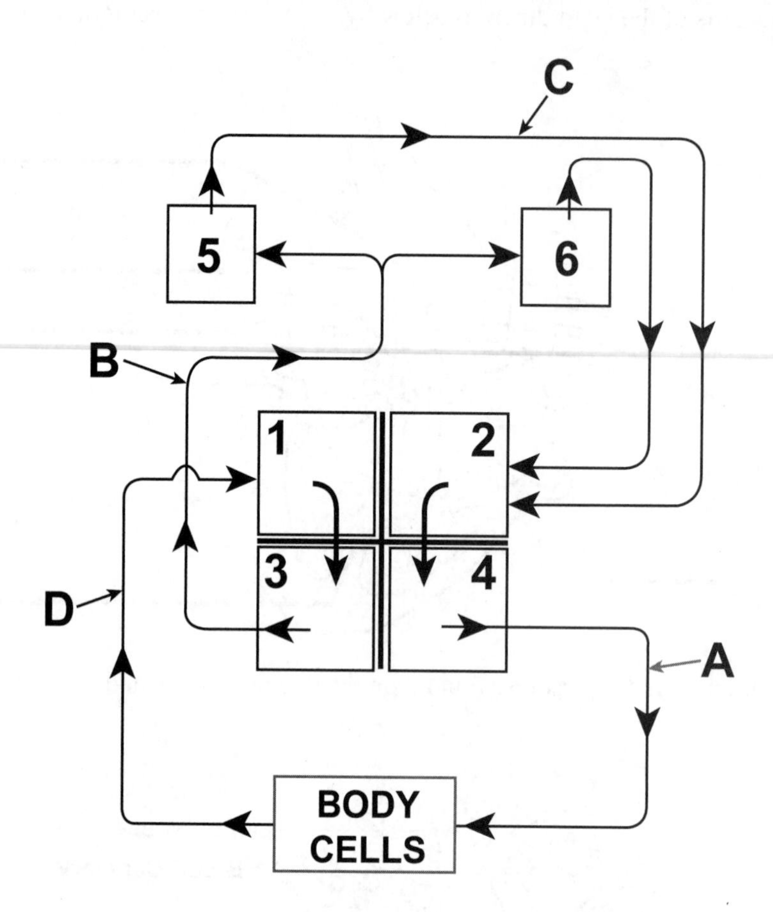

1. Which chambers of the heart contain blood that has the highest concentration of oxygen?

(1) 1 and 2
(2) 2 and 4
(3) 3 and 4
(4) 1 and 3

2. Which blood vessels contain blood with the lowest concentration of oxygen?

(1) A and D
(2) B and C
(3) C and A
(4) D and B

3. Microscopic structural units known as the alveoli of lungs are located in structures

(1) 1 and 3
(2) B and C
(3) 5 and 6
(4) D and A

Name________________________ Class________________________ Date__________

CHAPTER 9: QUIZ

A. FILL-IN QUESTIONS

DIRECTIONS: Complete each of the following statements by writing the correct word or phrase in the space provided.

1. The circulation of blood was discovered by ________________________.
2. The non-living part of blood is the ________________________.
3. The average adult has about liters ____________ of blood.
4. ________________________ is the process of absorption and distribution of materials.
5. ________________________ are thin, one-celled, microscopic blood vessels.
6. Absorption involves the passage of materials into and out of the ________________.
7. The heart has ____________ chambers.
8. The ________________________ carry blood back to the heart.
9. Coronary arteries are located in the ________________________.
10. Red blood cells are shaped like a/an ________________________.
11. The covering of the heart is called the ________________________.
12. ________________________ are involved in the clotting of blood.
13. The iron-rich material in blood is ________________________.
14. When antigens enter the body, ________________________ are produced.
15. The upper chambers of the heart are called the ________________________.
16. ________________is the ability of the body to resist certain disease causing organisms.
17. ________________________ carry blood away from the heart.
18. In ________________________ immunity body makes its own antibodies.
19. The part of blood plasma that diffuses out of the capillaries is the ________________.
20. The ________________________ is the largest artery in the body.

B. MULTIPLE-CHOICE QUESTIONS

DIRECTIONS: Circle the number of the expression that best completes each of the following statements.

1. Blood clot formation is started by

   (1) red blood cells
   (2) white blood cells
   (3) platelets
   (4) vitamins

2. In the diagram below, which chambers of the heart pump blood to the lungs and all other body areas?

   (1) A and B
   (2) B and D
   (3) C and B
   (4) C and D

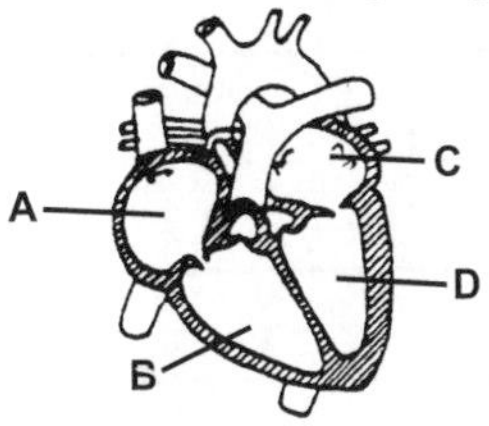

Name________________________ Class____________________ Date__________

3. A sudden increase in the number of white blood cells in a human may be an indication of

   (1) growth
   (2) color blindness
   (3) mental retardation
   (4) infection

4. Special proteins produced by the blood that protect against disease causing organisms are known as

   (1) vaccines
   (2) toxins
   (3) red blood cells
   (4) antibodies

Directions (5-9): For **each** statement in questions 5 through 9 select the structure in the diagram shown at the right that is most closely associated with that statement. Then, record its **number** in the space at the end of each statement. (A number may be used more than once or not at all.)

GENERAL PATTERN OF HUMAN CIRCULATION

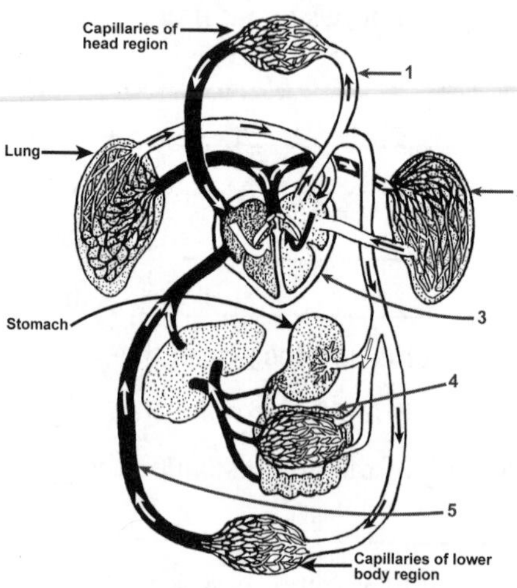

Capillaries of head region
1
Lung
2
Stomach
3
4
5
Capillaries of lower body region

5. This organ pumps blood to all body regions. ________

6. Capillaries exchange gases with the external environment in this organ. ________

7. Blood clots in the coronary arteries of this organ may interfere with nerve transmission and can lead to sudden death. ________

8. This blood vessel carries blood that is rich in oxygen. ________

9. Digested foods pass into the blood from this organ. ________

10. Arteries transport blood from

   (1) the heart to capillaries
   (2) capillaries to veins
   (3) capillaries to the heart
   (4) organs to the heart

C. ESSAY QUESTION

DIRECTIONS: Use complete sentences to answer the question in this part.

1. Name and describe one type of immunity.

____

____

____

____

Name________________________ Class ____________________ Date __________

Chapter 10: Respiration

A. INTRODUCTION. The transport system delivers the nutrients prepared in the digestive system to the body cells where some of the nutrients combine with oxygen to release energy needed to carry out the life processes of the organism. The life process responsible for releasing energy from nutrients is **respiration.** This process occurs continuously in all plant and animal cells. In most organisms respiration requires oxygen and produces carbon dioxide and involves an exchange of gases between the organism and its environment.

Respiration in humans is external, internal, and cellular. **External respiration** occurs outside the cells and involves the exchange of gases between the lungs and the blood. **Internal respiration** takes place when gases are exchanged between the blood and the body cells. **Cellular respiration** is the energy releasing process that takes place inside the cells.

Review Questions

1. Respiration is the process that releases ____________________ from nutrients.

2. What is the difference between external respiration, internal respiration, and cellular respiration?

____

____

____

____

B. THE HUMAN RESPIRATORY SYSTEM. The **respiratory system** transports gases between the external environment and the internal surfaces where gas exchange occurs. In humans, air from the environment moves through a series of passageways to the lungs where gas exchange occurs (Figure 10-1).

Air first enters the respiratory system through the **nostrils** and **mouth.** From the nostrils air moves through hollow cavities, called **nasal passages,** to the throat. The nasal passages are lined with mucous membranes and hair-like structures called **cilia.** Air is filtered by the cilia where it is moistened and warmed by the mucous membranes before it enters the pharynx. From the nasal cavity air passes into the pharynx. The back of the throat is called the **pharynx.** Located in the pharynx is the **glottis**–the opening to the windpipe. A flap of tissue called the **epiglottis** covers the glottis during swallowing. This prevents food from entering the glottis and trachea. When food enters the windpipe choking occurs.

The **trachea** (windpipe) transports air to the bronchial tubes. It is kept open by rings of cartilage. The trachea is lined with cilia that beat constantly in one direction. The cilia move foreign material such as dust, pollen, and smoke, out of the trachea and back to the nasal passages. The cilia can be damaged by smoking and air pollution. At the upper end of the trachea is the **larynx** (voice box). The larynx contains the vocal cords. Different sounds are produced in the larynx by vibration of the vocal cords. The pitch of sounds are determined by the amount of tension in the vocal cords. The trachea divides into two bronchial tubes called **bronchi.** The bronchi branch into the lungs. Bronchial tubes are also lined with cilia. The bronchi further divide into smaller tubes called **bronchioles.** The bronchioles are lined with mucous membranes. The bronchioles continue to divide ending in air sacs in the lungs called alveoli.

Name________________________ Class__________________ Date__________

The **lung** is a large spongy organ made up of a bronchus with its bronchioles and alveoli. Humans have two lungs located in the left and right chest cavity. The right lung is divided into three parts called **lobes.** The left lung is divided into two lobes. Each lung is covered with a membrane called the **pleural membrane.** The membrane secretes moisture that allows the lungs to move smoothly. Gas exchange takes place in the **alveoli.** The alveoli are also called **air sacs.** They are moist and thin and are surrounded by a network of blood capillaries. [*In all organisms, the surface through which gas exchange occurs is a thin moist membrane*.] As blood passes through the capillaries oxygen, carried by inhaled air, is absorbed from the alveoli. Carbon dioxide and water vapor are released from the bloodstream into the alveoli.

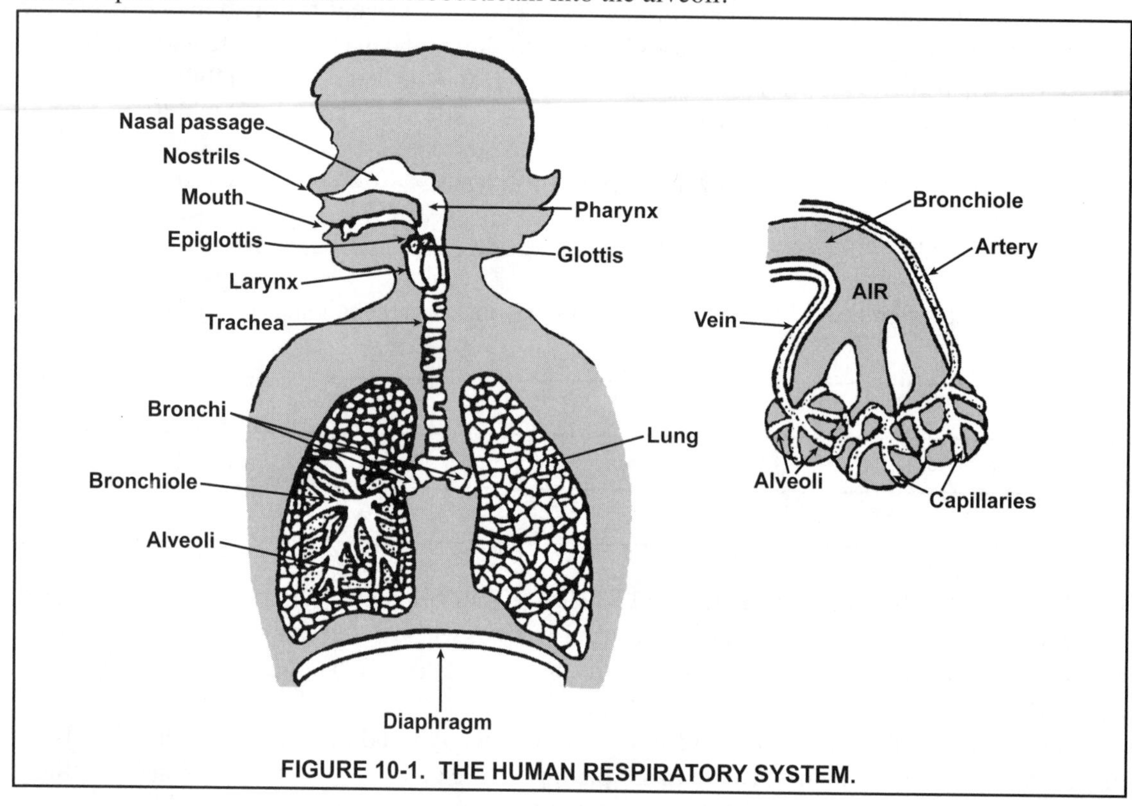

FIGURE 10-1. THE HUMAN RESPIRATORY SYSTEM.

REVIEW QUESTIONS

1. The respiratory system transports ______________ between the ________________ environment and the ______________ surfaces where ____________ exchange occurs.
2. Air enters the respiratory system through the ____________________.
3. Describe the functions of the cilia and mucous membranes of the nasal passage.

____

____

4. What is the function of the epiglottis?

____

____

Name________________________________ Class________________________ Date____________

5. Gas exchange takes place in the ______________________ of the lungs.

6. During gas exchange in the lungs, ______________________ enters the bloodstream and ____________________ and ______________________ leave the bloodstream.

7. What is the pleural membrane? ____

____

C. BREATHING. Breathing, a part of external respiration, is the movement of gases between the atmosphere and the lungs. Air is moved into the lungs by a process called **inhalation** and moves out of the lungs by the process of **exhalation.** The oxygen present in air is brought into the body and carbon dioxide is given off into the air. Air moves into and out of the lungs because of differences in air pressure between the chest cavity and the outside environment. Lungs have no muscle tissue to help inhalation or exhalation. Air enters and leaves the lungs because of air pressure changes in the chest cavity.

The pressure changes are caused by the contraction and relaxation of the diaphragm and rib muscles during inhalation and exhalation (Figure 10-2). The **diaphragm** is a dome-shaped muscle located at the bottom of the chest cavity. When you inhale the diaphragm moves *down* and the ribs move *upward* and *outward*. This movement enlarges your chest cavity and air is forced into your lungs because of unequal air pressure. When you exhale the diaphragm moves up to its original *curved* position and the ribs move *in* making your chest cavity smaller and forcing air out of the lungs.

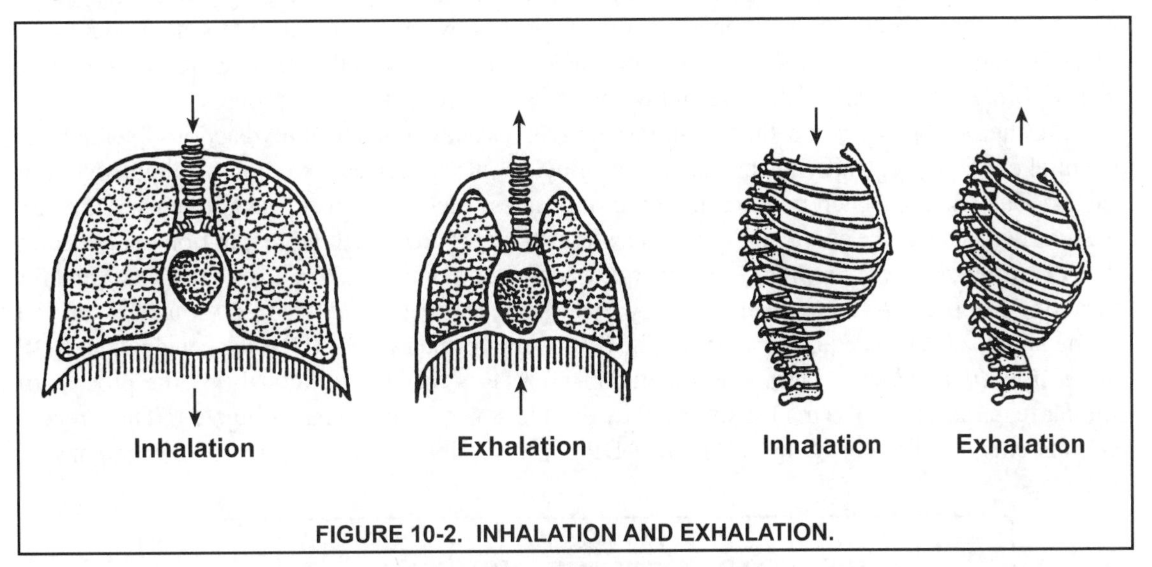

FIGURE 10-2. INHALATION AND EXHALATION.

Breathing rate is affected by foreign particles from smoking or air pollution and the oxygen, carbon monoxide, and carbon dioxide levels in the blood. The most important factor in controlling breathing rate is the concentration of carbon dioxide (CO_2) in the blood. An increase in blood CO_2 concentration increases breathing rate. When the CO_2 level decreases breathing rate decreases. Exercise also increases breathing rate. The next time you exercise notice that you inhale and exhale much faster when you exercise than when you are not exercising.

Name ______________________ Class ____________________ Date ____________

REVIEW QUESTIONS

1. What is breathing?

____

2. The taking in of air is called ______________________ and the giving off of air is called ______________________.

3. List three factors that affect your breathing rate. ______________________________

____

4. What causes air to enter and leave the lungs? ______________________________

5. The dome-shaped muscle at the bottom of the chest cavity is the ____________________.

6. Describe the movement of the diaphragm and rib muscles during inhalation and exhalation.

____

____

____

____

D. CELLULAR RESPIRATION. Cellular respiration, the energy-releasing process that takes place inside living cells, involves the exchange of gases between the blood and tissue fluid and the cells. During cellular respiration, oxygen combines chemically with the sugar (glucose) to release energy. Molecules of carbon dioxide and water are waste products of this process.

The chemical process of cellular respiration involves enzyme-controlled reactions in which the potential energy of organic molecules, such as glucose, is transferred to a more available form of energy. The chemical energy in organic food molecules, such as glucose, cannot be used directly by the cells. Instead, the energy in food molecules is transferred by cellular respiration to molecules of **ATP** (*adenosine triphosphate*), an energy-transfer compound. When energy is needed for metabolic reactions, ATP is broken down by hydrolysis, and energy is released for use by the cell for metabolic activities requiring energy. The compound formed when ATP is broken down is **ADP** (*adenosine diphosphate*). During cell metabolism, ATP is made continuously by the process of cellular respiration. ATP is made from ADP by the addition of a phosphate group (P). This process requires energy. The changing of ATP to ADP is a reversible reaction catalyzed by the enzyme ATPase.

$$\mathbf{H_2O + ATP \underset{\text{(enzyme)}}{\overset{\text{(ATPase)}}{\rightleftharpoons}} ADP + P + energy}$$

In most organisms, cellular respiration requires molecular oxygen. This process is known as **aerobic cellular respiration.** In aerobic respiration, glucose is broken down completely to carbon dioxide and water. In a series of enzyme-controlled reactions, the chemical energy of the glucose molecule is gradually released and used to make ATP from ADP and phosphates. The chemical reactions for aerobic cellular respiration are summarized on the next page.

Name______________________ Class______________________ Date__________

$$\text{glucose} + \text{oxygen} \xrightarrow{\text{enzymes}} \text{water} + \text{carbon dioxide} + \text{ATP}$$

$$C_6H_{12}O_6 + 6O_2 \xrightarrow{\text{enzymes}} 6\,H_2O + 6CO_2 + 36ATP$$

Some organisms do not require oxygen and they get their energy from **anaerobic cellular respiration.** Anaerobic respiration, or **fermentation,** occurs mainly in yeasts and bacteria. Some of these organisms lack the enzymes needed for aerobic respiration and others can switch from aerobic to anaerobic respiration when oxygen is not available. During anaerobic respiration glucose is partially broken down by a series of enzyme-controlled reactions. Organisms have different end products that result from anaerobic respiration. Lactic acid or alcohol and carbon dioxide are common end products. Lactic acid is produced by some bacteria and is important in the production of cheese, buttermilk, and yogurt. Yeasts and some bacteria produce alcohol and carbon dioxide. Yeasts are used in the baking and brewing industries. The lactic acid or alcohol produced by anaerobic respiration still contains much of the chemical energy of the original glucose molecule. As a result of anaerobic respiration there is a net gain of 2 ATP molecules. Anaerobic cellular respiration reactions are shown below:

$$\text{glucose} \xrightarrow{\text{enzymes}} 2\text{ lactic acid} + 2\text{ ATP}$$

or

$$\text{glucose} \xrightarrow{\text{enzymes}} 2\text{ alcohol} + 2\,CO_2 + 2\text{ ATP}$$

Anaerobic respiration also occurs in human skeletal muscles during prolonged exercise when muscle cells use oxygen faster than the circulatory system can supply it. In this case anaerobic respiration results in the production of lactic acid, which builds up in the muscle tissue, and is associated with **muscle fatigue**. When oxygen again becomes available lactic acid is broken down aerobically. Aerobic respiration, which produces a net gain of 36 ATP, is much more efficient than anaerobic respiration, which produces only 2 ATP.

REVIEW QUESTIONS

1. The waste products of respiration are ______________________ and ______________.
2. What is cellular respiration? ____

   ____

   ____
3. The energy in food molecules is transferred by cellular respiration to molecules of a compound called ______________________________. The compound formed from this transfer is ______________________________.
4. The process of ______________ cellular respiration does *not* require molecular oxygen, while the process of ______________ cellular respiration does require oxygen.

Name____________________________ Class______________________ Date____________

5. In the space below, write the reversible reaction showing the change of ATP to ADP.

6. In the space below, write the word equation for aerobic respiration.

7. Another name for anaerobic respiration is ____________________________.

8. The common end products for anaerobic respiration are ____________________ and ________________________________.

E. RESPIRATORY SYSTEM DISORDERS. Respiratory disorders involve the lungs and the bronchial tubes. Some common respiratory diseases are described below.

Respiratory System Disorders

♦ **Bronchitis** is an inflammation of the lining of the bronchial tubes. The bronchioles secrete too much mucus and become small and irritated. Respiratory cilia cannot clear the passages of the mucus and particles that clog them. Affected persons are short of breath and often cough up mucus.

♦ **Asthma** is caused by unknown substances or by allergic reactions. During an asthma attack the bronchial tubes narrow, which prevents oxygen from entering the lungs. When someone has an asthma attack they feel as though they are suffocating because they have a hard time breathing. In an emergency, adrenaline is given to the person to open up the air passages. Asthma is made worse by air pollution, including pollution of indoor air by nearby smokers.

♦ **Emphysema** is a lung disease in which the alveoli become large and break down. The lungs become less elastic and the amount of air they can hold decreases. A person with emphysema experiences shortness of breath with the slightest activity. Going from one chair to another is a difficult thing for a person with this disease. There is no cure for emphysema, but life can be prolonged with proper treatment. Smoking is thought to be one of the causes of emphysema.

♦ **Lung cancer** is an uncontrollable growth of cells causing the growth of tumors in the lungs. There is a proven relationship between lung cancer and cigarette smoking.

♦ **Pneumonia** is an infection of the lungs that is caused by a bacteria or virus. The alveoli of the lungs fill with fluid preventing proper exchange of gases. This makes breathing difficult. Some types of pneumonia can be treated with antibiotics.

REVIEW QUESTIONS

1. Name three respiratory disorders and the symptoms and causes of each. ____________________

____

Name________________ Class________________ Date__________

LAB INVESTIGATION: SMOKING AND LUNG DISEASE

Objective

Upon completion of this activity you should be able to state the effects of smoking on normal lung tissue.

Laboratory Procedure

Materials: Prepared slides of normal lung tissue (bronchial epithelium) and smoker's lung tissue, lens paper, and a compound microscope.

1. Collect your laboratory materials from the supply table and take them to your lab area. Clean your microscope lenses and prepared slides with the lens paper.

2. Place the prepared slide of normal lung tissue on the microscope stage. Focus the slide using the low power objective. Refer to the diagram on this page to be sure you have located the lung tissue.

3. Once you have located and focused the lung cells under low power, carefully switch your microscope to high power. If your cells are not clearly focused under high power, refocus them by ***using only the fine adjustment knob to focus upwards.***

4. Scan your slide to locate the *cilia* and *columnar epithelium*. They are stained a pale purple-pink on your prepared slide. Cilia are hair-like projections lining the respiratory passageways that sweep foreign particles out of the passageways. Epithelial cells also line respiratory passageways and contain cells that secrete mucus into the passageways. Both the cilia and mucus keep air passages clean. The mucus traps particles and the cilia remove them from the body.

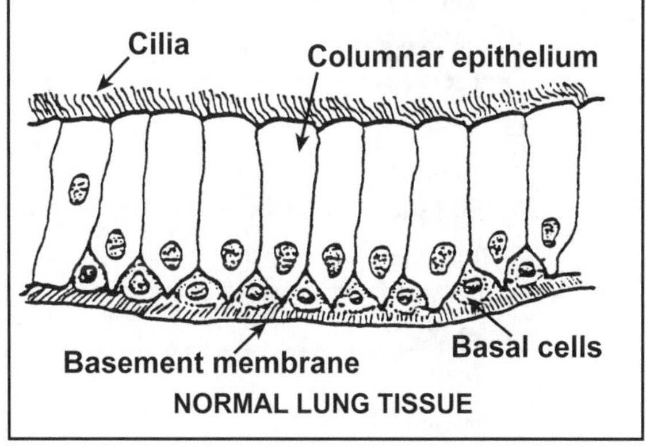

NORMAL LUNG TISSUE

5. Draw a section of this slide in **Observation (1)** in the **Observation Section** on the next page. Label the cilia and columnar epithelium cells.

6. Now look for the *basal cells* and *basement membrane*. Label these cells on your drawing in **Observation (1).**

7. Remove the normal lung slide and place the smoker's lung slide on your microscope stage. Focus the slide under low-power. Repeat **Procedure 3** to focus the slide under high-power.

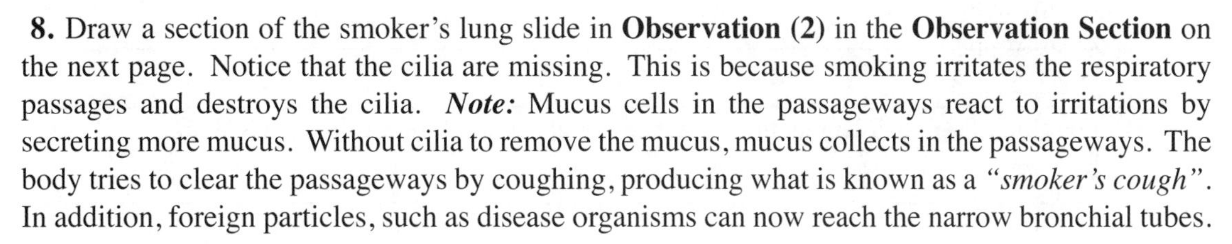

8. Draw a section of the smoker's lung slide in **Observation (2)** in the **Observation Section** on the next page. Notice that the cilia are missing. This is because smoking irritates the respiratory passages and destroys the cilia. ***Note:*** Mucus cells in the passageways react to irritations by secreting more mucus. Without cilia to remove the mucus, mucus collects in the passageways. The body tries to clear the passageways by coughing, producing what is known as a *"smoker's cough"*. In addition, foreign particles, such as disease organisms can now reach the narrow bronchial tubes.

This causes them to become irritated and constrict (become smaller). They then become clogged and less oxygen reaches the body cells.

9. Observe that the basal cell layer has thickened. This thickened layer contains abnormal precancerous cells that are very rare in non-smokers but are common in smokers. The abnormal cells increase as a smoker continues to smoke and decrease when smoking stops.

10. Label the abnormal cells on the drawing in **Observation (2).**

11. When you are finished with your laboratory activity, clean your lab area and return your lab materials and microscope to the supply table.

12. Answer the questions in the **Conclusion Section**.

Observations

(1) NORMAL LUNG TISSUE	(2) SMOKER'S LUNG TISSUE

Conclusions

1. State the functions of the following respiratory structures:

   Cilia: ____

   ____

   Mucus: ____

   ____

2. Describe the causes of a "smoker's cough". ______________________________

   ____

   ____

3. Do you think there is a connection between smoking and lung disease? Explain.

   ____

   ____

Name________________________ Class____________________ Date__________

REVIEW ACTIVITIES

Important Terms

DIRECTIONS: Define the following terms in the spaces provided.

alveoli ____

____

asthma ____

____

breathing ____

____

bronchi ____

____

bronchioles ____

____

bronchitis ____

____

cellular respiration ____

____

diaphragm ____

____

emphysema ____

____

epiglottis ____

____

exhalation ____

____

external respiration ____

____

glottis ____

____

Name______________________ **Class**__________________ **Date**__________

inhalation ____

____

internal respiration ____

____

larynx ____

____

lung cancer ____

____

lungs ____

____

nostrils ____

____

pharynx ____

____

pleural membrane ____

____

pneumonia ____

____

respiration ____

____

respiratory system ____

____

trachea ____

____

Name________________________________ Class______________________ Date______________

Skill Practice

Part A. Label the parts of the respiratory system by placing the correct term on the line next to each part.

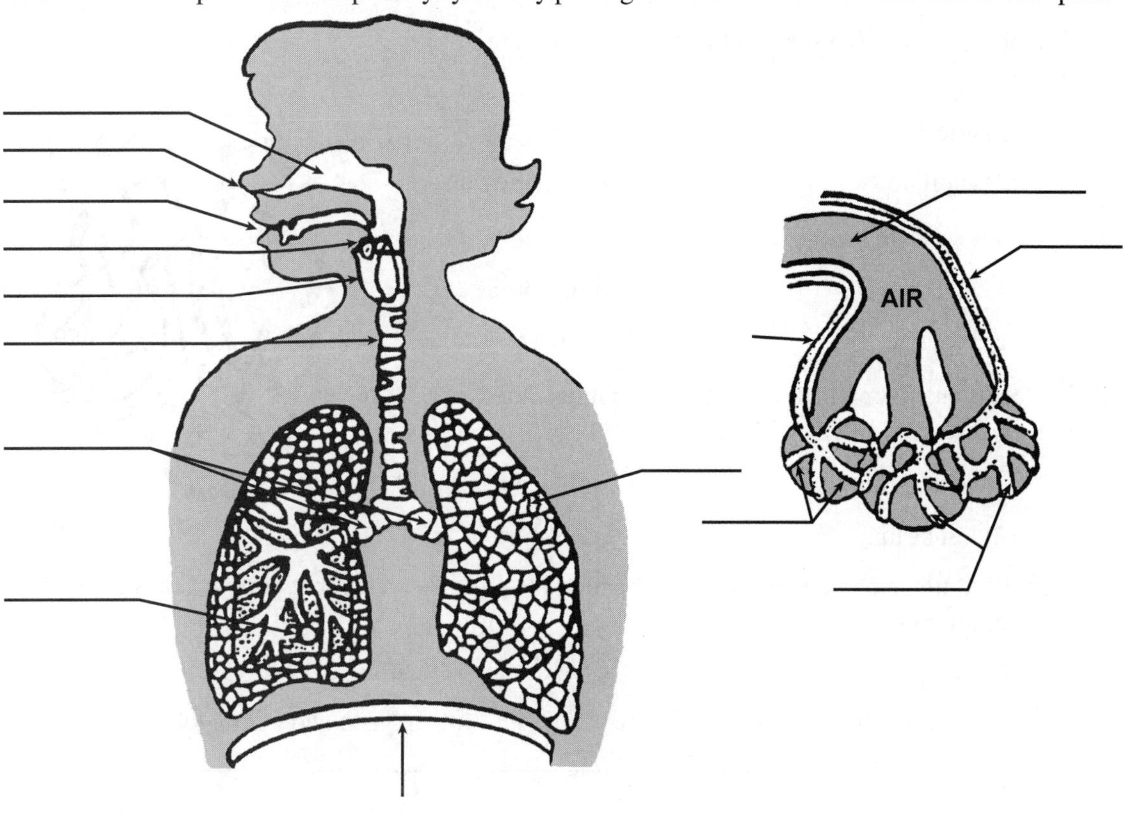

Part B. In the space at the left of each item in Column A, place the letter of the term or phrase in Column B that is most closely related to that item.

Column A

_________ **1.** This closes the windpipe during swallowing.

_________ **2.** The vocal cords are found here.

_________ **3.** An incurable disease involving the air sacs.

_________ **4.** Main organs of breathing.

_________ **5.** Location of lungs.

_________ **6.** Intake of air.

_________ **7.** Inflammation of the bronchial tubes.

_________ **8.** Warms, moistens, and cleans air.

_________ **9.** Dome-shaped muscle.

_________ **10.** Air sacs in the lungs.

Column B

a. bronchitis
b. lungs
c. inhalation
d. nasal cavity
e. larynx
f. diaphragm
g. chest cavity
h. epiglottis
i. pharynx
j. emphysema
k. exhalation
l. stomach
m. alveoli

Name________________________ Class ____________________ Date __________

Part C. Base your answers to questions 1 through 4 on the diagram at the right that represents part of the human respiratory system.

1. The blood vessels (B) surrounding these air sacs are known as

(1) arteries (3) veins

(2) capillaries (4) lymphatic ducts

2. These air sacs are known as

(1) alveoli (3) bronchioles

(2) bronchi (4) tracheae

3. The heart chamber which most directly pumps blood to the vessel network at A is the

(1) right atrium (3) right ventricle

(2) left atrium (4) left ventricle

4. Compared to the blood entering at A, the blood leaving the vessel network at C has a lower concentration of

(1) oxygen (3) carbon dioxide

(2) hemoglobin and carbon dioxide (4) oxygen and hemoglobin

Part D. Base your answers to questions 1 through 3 on the diagrams to the right that represent models of the human respiratory system and on your knowledge of biology.

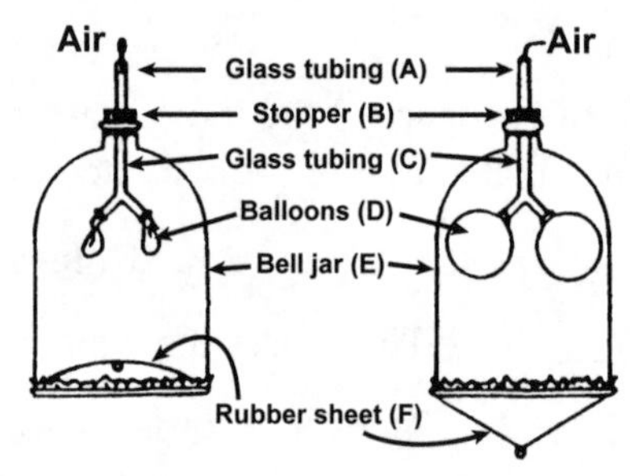

1. The rubber sheet in this model most likely represents the human

(1) ribs (3) lungs

(2) chest (4) diaphragm

2. Bronchitis, an inflammation or irritation of the bronchi of humans may be expected to occur within a human structure represented in the diagram by

(1) F (3) C

(2) B (4) E

3. The rib cage is represented by structure

(1) E (3) C

(2) F (4) D

Name________________________ Class__________________ Date__________

CHAPTER 10: QUIZ

A. FILL-IN QUESTIONS

DIRECTIONS: Complete each of the following statements by writing the correct word or phrase in the space provided.

1. Cellular respiration releases ______________________ from food.

2. The ______________________ is the dome-shaped muscle that aids in breathing.

3. The scientific name for the windpipe is the ______________________.

4. Air is filtered by hair-like structures called ______________________.

5. The exchange of gases between the blood and the body cells is ______________________ respiration.

6. The trachea divides into two tubes called ______________________.

7. The voice box is located in the ______________________.

8. The large, spongy organs responsible for gas exchange in humans are the ______________.

9. Air enters and leaves the lungs because of ________________ changes in the chest cavity.

10. During exhalation the diaphragm moves __________ and the ribs move __________.

11. The inflammation of the lining of the bronchial tubes is ______________________.

12. Humans have ________________ lungs.

13. ______________________ is the uncontrollable growth of tumor cells in the lungs.

14. Air enters the respiratory system through the ______________________.

15. The pharynx is commonly called the ______________________________.

16. The ______________________ membrane covers the lungs.

17. The life process responsible for releasing energy from nutrients is __________________.

18. Exercise ____________________ the breathing rate.

19. Gas exchange takes place at the ______________________ of the lungs.

20. An infection of the lungs caused by a bacteria or virus is ______________________.

B. MULTIPLE-CHOICE QUESTIONS

DIRECTIONS: Circle the number of the expression that best completes each of the following statements.

1. In humans, oxygen enters the bloodstream from the

(1) diaphragm (3) trachea
(2) air sacs (4) nasal cavity

2. A process that releases energy from food molecules is

(1) reproduction (3) respiration
(2) excretion (4) transport

Name________________________ Class __________________ Date __________

3. The alveoli are part of the

(1) stomach (3) small intestine

(2) lung (4) kidney

4. Which substances are the waste products of respiration?

(1) sugar and salt (3) water and carbon dioxide

(2) carbon dioxide and sugar (4) sugar and starch

5. The structure that is lined with cilia is the

(1) mouth (3) capillary

(2) alveolus (4) trachea

6. Air is inhaled as a result of muscular contractions of the

(1) rib muscles and diaphragm (3) diaphragm and heart

(2) rib muscles and stomach (4) diaphragm and esophagus

7. Which activity is represented by the word equation shown below?

glucose + oxygen $\xrightarrow{\textbf{enzymes}}$ **carbon dioxide + water + energy**

(1) inhalation (3) cellular respiration

(2) exhalation (4) cellular digestion

8. The voice box is called the

(1) larynx (3) trachea

(2) bronchial tubes (4) air sacs

9. Which human system contains air sacs known as alveoli.

(1) respiratory (3) reproductive

(2) circulatory (4) digestive

10. Which respiratory system disorder is a severe form of an allergy?

(1) lung cancer (3) emphysema

(2) bronchitis (4) asthma

C. ESSAY QUESTION

DIRECTIONS: Use complete sentences to answer the question in this part.

1. State two harmful effects of cigarette smoking on the human body.

____

____

____

____

____

Name________________________________ Class________________________ Date______________

Chapter 11: Excretion

A. EXCRETION. Cellular activities, such as respiration, produce wastes. Some of these wastes are harmful to the body and must be removed. An upset in the balance of body chemicals can lead to serious health problems or death. **Excretion** is the removal of the wastes of cell activities from the body. Do not confuse excretion with egestion. The wastes of excretion are liquids and gases. Solid wastes are removed during egestion.

REVIEW QUESTIONS

1. What is excretion? ____

____

2. The wastes of excretion are in the form of ____________________ and ____________________.

B. METABOLIC WASTES. Wastes produced by life activities (metabolism) are called **metabolic wastes.** Carbon dioxide, water, urea, and mineral salts are metabolic wastes. Carbon dioxide is a gaseous waste formed during aerobic respiration. Water is produced by aerobic respiration and other cellular activities. **Urea** is a nitrogen waste resulting from the breakdown of the amino acids produced during protein digestion. The breakdown of various compounds in the cell form mineral salts.

REVIEW QUESTIONS

1. Metabolic wastes are produced by ______________________________ activities.

2. Complete the following chart.

METABOLIC WASTE	HOW PRODUCED

C. THE ROLE OF BLOOD IN EXCRETION. The wastes of excretion leave body cells and are secreted into intercellular fluid. Wastes pass from intercellular fluid into the blood plasma by the process of diffusion. Blood plasma transports these excretions to excretory organs that remove them from the body.

Name ______________________ Class ________________ Date __________

REVIEW QUESTIONS

1. Describe the role of blood in excretion. ______________________________

____

D. THE EXCRETORY SYSTEM. The **excretory system** removes cellular wastes from the body. By getting rid of wastes the excretory system helps maintain a proper balance of body chemicals. The organs of the excretory system are the skin, lungs, urinary system and liver.

REVIEW QUESTIONS

1. What is the purpose of the excretory system?

____

____

2. Name the organs of the excretory system. ______________________________

____

E. SKIN. The **skin** is made up of an outer layer called the **epidermis** and an inner layer called the **dermis** (Figure 11-1). The skin contains **sweat glands** that excrete perspiration through skin pores. **Perspiration** is made up of nitrogenous wastes (urea), salts, and water. The skin is also involved in controlling body temperature. When perspiration evaporates from the skin heat is absorbed from skin cells. This absorption of heat lowers body temperature. This results in cooling the body. You might have experienced this yourself when, on a hot summer day, you fanned yourself to get cool.

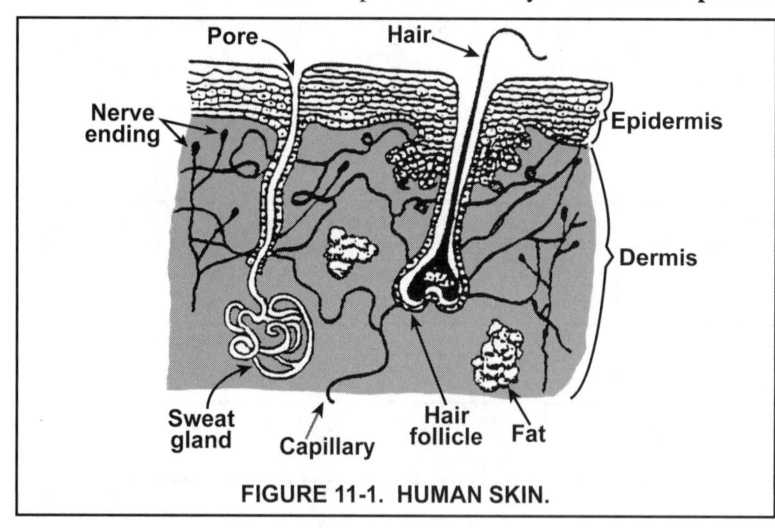

FIGURE 11-1. HUMAN SKIN.

REVIEW QUESTIONS

1. The outer layer of the skin is called the ____________________ and the inner layer is the ____________________.

Name_______________________________ Class ____________________ Date __________

2. How does the skin control body temperature? ______________________________

____

____

F. LUNGS. The function of the lungs in respiration was discussed in Chapter 10. The lungs also play a role in excretion. Lungs excrete carbon dioxide and water vapor by diffusion and exhalation.

REVIEW QUESTIONS

1. The lungs excrete ______________________ and ____________________

by the processes of ____________________ and ____________________.

G. HUMAN URINARY SYSTEM. Some of the body's excretions leave by way of the urinary system. The **urinary system** consists of the kidneys, ureters, urinary bladder, and the urethra (Figure 11-2). The **kidneys** are bean-shaped organs that lie along the back wall of the abdomen. Each kidney is made up of masses of microscopic subunits called **nephrons.** The kidneys act as filters in the removal of urea and excess water and salts from the blood. Useful substances also diffuse out of the blood into the kidneys. The useful substances are returned to the blood before the blood leaves the kidneys. Each kidney sends excretions, called **urine,** into a tube called the **ureter**. Urine, made up of urea and water, flows through ureters to the sac-like **urinary bladder.** The bladder stores urine temporarily. The urinary bladder opens into a single tube, the **urethra,** through which the urine leaves the body.

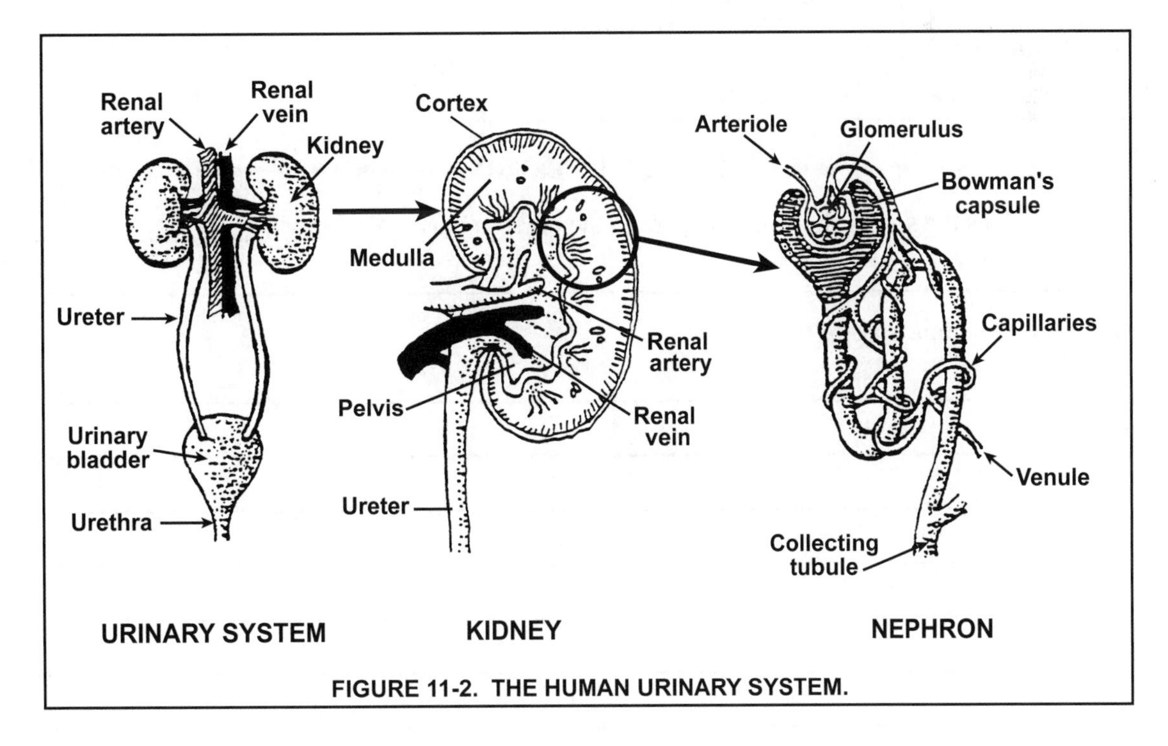

FIGURE 11-2. THE HUMAN URINARY SYSTEM.

Name ______________________ Class ____________________ Date ___________

REVIEW QUESTIONS

1. Name the organs of the human urinary system and state one function of each organ.

____

____

____

____

____

____

____

H. LIVER. The **liver** is the largest internal organ in the body (Figure 11-3). It produces **urea**, a nitrogenous waste, by breaking down excess amino acids. Other functions of the liver include the removal of poisons, such as alcohol, from the blood and the storage of extra sugar in the form of animal starch (glycogen). The liver changes glycogen into glucose and secretes it back into the bloodstream when the body needs energy.

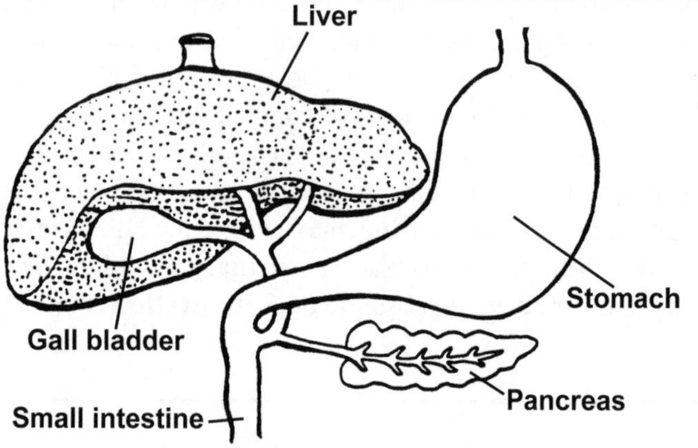

FIGURE 11-3. THE LIVER.

REVIEW QUESTIONS

1. How does the size of the liver compare to the other organs in the body? ______________

____

2. State three functions of the liver.

____

____

____

____

____

____

____

Name________________ Class________________ Date__________

I. EXCRETORY SYSTEM DISORDERS. Disorders of the excretory system can involve the kidneys, skin, liver, as well as other parts of the body.

Excretory System Disorders

♦ **Kidney Stones. Kidney stones** are collections of solid material that may block the kidneys, ureters, or bladder.

♦ **Gout. Gout** is a disease associated with the production and deposition of uric acid crystals in joints. It is a very painful condition that produces symptoms similar to arthritis.

♦ **Uremia.** During **uremia** urea and other wastes are not filtered out of the blood. The body cells become poisoned and there is urine in the blood.

♦ **Skin Problems.** One cause of skin problems, such as **blackheads** and **acne**, is the clogging of skin pores.

♦ **Cirrhosis of the Liver. Cirrhosis of the liver** is a disease of the liver caused by damage to its cells. This leads to a type of high blood pressure that can cause serious complications. The most common cause is drinking large amounts of alcoholic beverages. Hepatitis, an inflammation of the liver, can also lead to this disease. There may be no symptoms in the early stages of the disease. It is usually discovered during routine medical examinations or blood tests. Later symptoms are mild jaundice (yellow skin), edema (fluid collection in tissues), mental confusion and vomiting of blood. In men, enlargement of breasts and loss of body hair can occur. The treatment is to slow down the disease. This is done by eliminating alcoholic beverages. Liver transplants are the only chance of long-term cure.

REVIEW QUESTIONS

1. Describe three diseases of the excretory system. ________________

Name ____________ Class ____________ Date ____________

CAREER OPPORTUNITIES

NURSING: Nurses are important members of the health care profession. Their job involves taking care of people's physical and emotional health problems. Nurses monitor the condition of sick and injured patients providing treatment to restore their health. A nurse must have a thorough understanding of all the systems of the human body. They must know how to use scientific reasoning along with their training and education to help treat and comfort people who are sick or injured.

There are many types of nursing practices, some are very specialized and require much education, other types are not as highly skilled, and demand less education. Nurses work in a variety of environments. Teaching nurses work in schools and nursing schools. Many nurses are employed by hospitals, nursing homes, doctor's offices, factories, and medical clinics. There are even visiting public health nurses who go into people's homes to help them with their medical problems.

In most states nurses must be licensed to practice their profession. They must also graduate from an accredited nursing school. Nursing programs are offered by both two-year community colleges, and four-year colleges or universities. Some states require registered nurses to have a Bachelor of Science degree or a Bachelor of Science in Nursing degree. Nursing teachers, researchers, and specialists usually have a master's degree or a doctorate. Practical nurses only have to finish an accredited program. In some cases this can be accomplished in one year. In all cases a high school background that is strong in science is highly recommended for those interested in a nursing career.

*****

REVIEW QUESTIONS

1. Name and describe one career where a knowledge of the human body is important.

Name________________________________ Class ________________________ Date ____________

LAB INVESTIGATION: EXCRETORY STRUCTURES

OBJECTIVE

Upon completion of this activity you should be able to identify several kidney structures and state their functions.

LABORATORY PROCEDURE

Materials: Mammal kidney (preserved or fresh), dissecting pan, dissecting pins, dissecting scissors, scalpel, safety goggles, disposable rubber gloves, forceps, lab apron, and paper towels.

1. Collect your laboratory materials from the supply table and take them to your lab area. Work in pairs or alone as your teacher directs. ***Important: Wear safety goggles, rubber gloves, and laboratory apron while doing this activity.***

2. Cover your dissecting pan with a paper towel. Place the kidney in the dissecting pan.

3. Observe the external (outer) structure of the kidney. *Kidneys* are bean-shaped organs that lie along the back wall of the abdomen. They filter urea and excess water and salts from the blood. Find the blood vessels that enter and leave the kidney. Refer to the diagram on this page and locate the *renal artery, renal vein,* and *ureter.* The renal arteries bring unfiltered (impure) blood to the kidneys and the renal veins carry filtered (purified) blood away from the kidneys. The ureter carries urine, a combination of urea (a nitrogen waste), excess salts, and water, to the *urinary bladder*. The bladder stores urine temporarily.

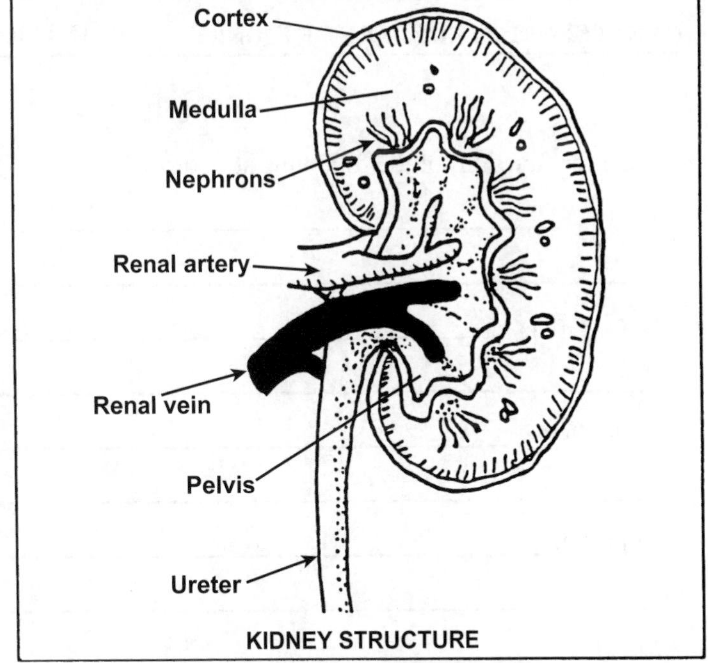

KIDNEY STRUCTURE

4. Draw the external structure of the kidney in **Observation (1)** in the **Observation Section** on the next page. Label the renal artery, renal vein, ureter, and kidney.

5. Use your scalpel to cut the kidney in half lengthwise. Pin down the kidney halves with the dissecting pins so that the cut surfaces are showing. Refer to the diagram on this page and locate the *cortex, medulla,* and the *pelvis*. The *nephrons* are located in the medulla and pelvis but are too small to see. The nephrons are the filtering units of the kidney.

Name__________ Class__________ Date__________

6. Draw the internal (inside) structure of the kidney in **Observation (2)** in the **Observation Section** below. Label the cortex, medulla, pelvis, and nephrons.

7. When you are finished with your laboratory activity, wrap the kidney in the paper towel and throw it away. Clean your materials and lab area and return your materials to the supply table.

8. Answer the question in the **Conclusion Section**.

OBSERVATIONS

(1) EXTERNAL STRUCTURE OF KIDNEY	(2) INTERNAL STRUCTURE OF KIDNEY

CONCLUSIONS

1. State the functions of the following structures:

Kidney. __________

____

Renal Artery. __________

____

Renal Vein. __________

____

Nephron. __________

____

Medulla. __________

____

Urinary Bladder. __________

____

Cortex. __________

____

Name __________ Class __________ Date __________

REVIEW ACTIVITIES

Important Terms

DIRECTIONS: Define the following terms in the spaces provided.

cirrhosis __________

dermis __________

epidermis __________

excretion __________

excretory system __________

gout __________

kidney stones __________

kidneys __________

liver __________

metabolic wastes __________

nephron __________

perspiration __________

skin __________

Name________________________ Class __________________ Date ___________

sweat glands ____

____

urea ____

____

ureter ____

____

urethra ____

____

urinary bladder ____

____

urinary system ____

____

urine ____

____

Name__________ Class__________ Date__________

Skill Practice

Part A. Label the following diagrams of the excretory system.

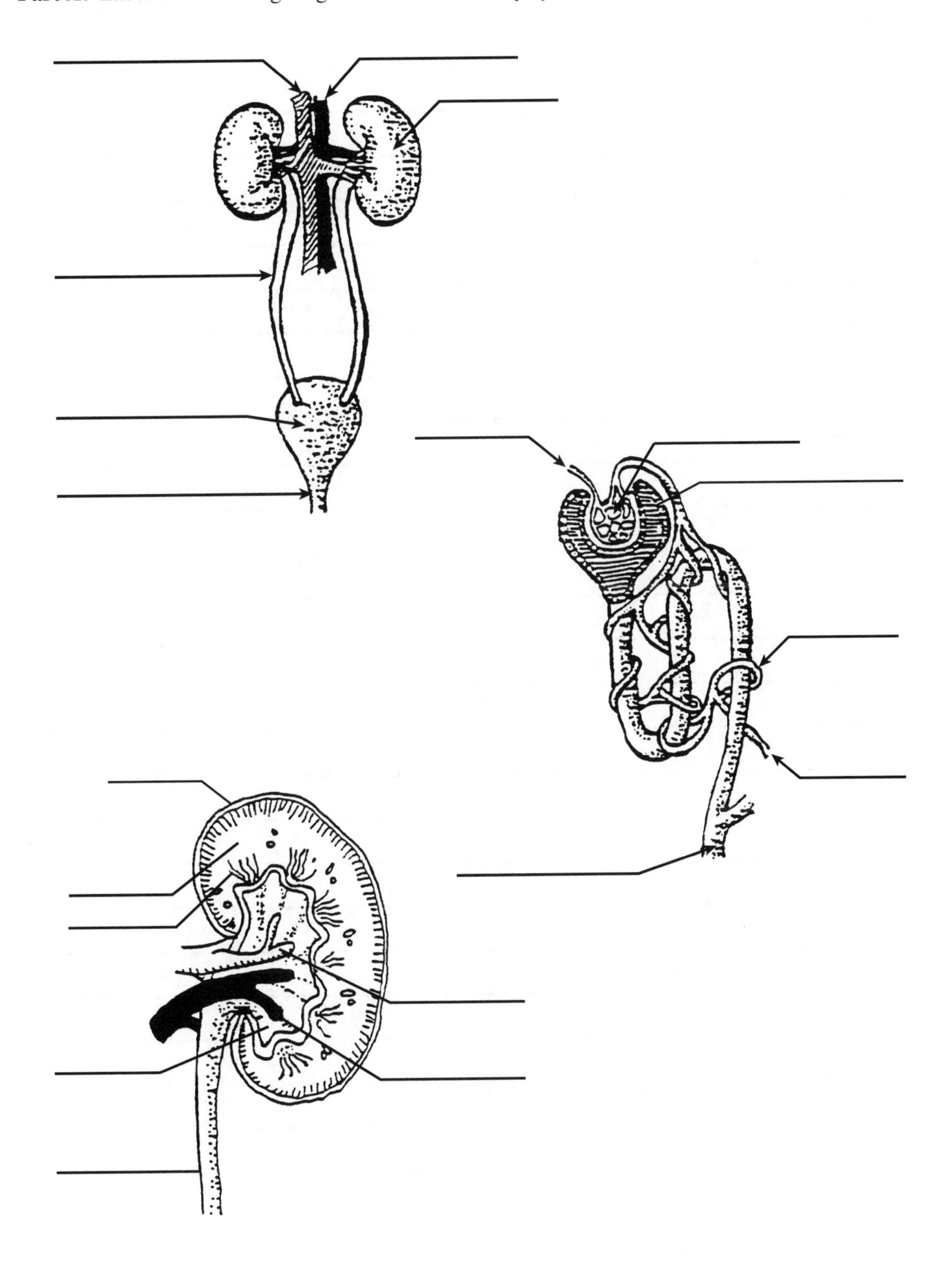

Name____________________ Class________________ Date__________

Part B. Write a paragraph about the excretory system using the following terms: **urea, kidney, urine, excretion, skin, lungs, urinary system, perspiration, ureters, urethra, urinary bladder, liver.**

Name______________________ Class______________________ Date__________

CHAPTER 11: QUIZ

A. FILL-IN QUESTIONS

DIRECTIONS: Complete each of the following statements by writing the correct word or phrase in the space provided.

1. Urea, salts, and water excreted through the skin is called ______________________.
2. The outer layer of the skin is the ______________________.
3. Wastes pass from intercellular fluid into ______________________ by diffusion.
4. The bean-shaped organs that lie along the back wall of the abdomen are the ____________.
5. The removal of the wastes of cell activities from the body is called ______________.
6. When perspiration evaporates from the skin, the skin feels ______________________.
7. ______________ is a nitrogen waste resulting from the breakdown of amino acids.
8. The ______________________ excrete carbon dioxide and water vapor.
9. The watery excretion of the kidneys is called ______________________.
10. The ______________________ is the inner layer of the skin.
11. The excretory system removes ______________________ wastes from the body.
12. The ______________________ connects the urinary bladder with the kidney.
13. The ______________________ filter urea and excess water from the blood.
14. Kidneys, ureters, urinary bladder, and urethra make up the ______________ system.
15. The urethra carries urine away from the ______________________.
16. The largest internal organ in the body is the ______________________.
17. Accumulations of solid material that block the kidneys are ______________________.
18. The liver changes glycogen into ______________________.
19. ______________________ is a disease with symptoms similar to arthritis.
20. Clogging of skin pores causes ______________________.

B. MULTIPLE-CHOICE QUESTIONS

DIRECTIONS: Circle the number of the expression that best completes each of the following statements.

1. The cell gets rid of wastes by the process known as
   (1) synthesis (3) growth
   (2) excretion (4) digestion
2. Which organ removes urea from the bloodstream?
   (1) large intestine (3) kidney
   (2) lung (4) stomach
3. Which is a cellular waste product excreted by the lungs?
   (1) water (3) ammonia
   (2) calcium (4) iodine

Name_________________________ Class____________________ Date___________

4. The carbon dioxide produced in an animal cell is usually
   (1) stored (3) ingested
   (2) digested (4) excreted

5. Which of the following are human metabolic wastes?
   (1) urea and carbon dioxide (3) mineral salts and enzymes
   (2) oxygen and nitrogen (4) water and alcohol

6. The blood assists in the elimination of waste products by
   (1) producing antibodies
   (2) transporting excretions to the kidneys
   (3) engulfing pathogenic bacteria
   (4) transporting oxygen

7. In the diagram of skin shown below, which structure has an excretory function?

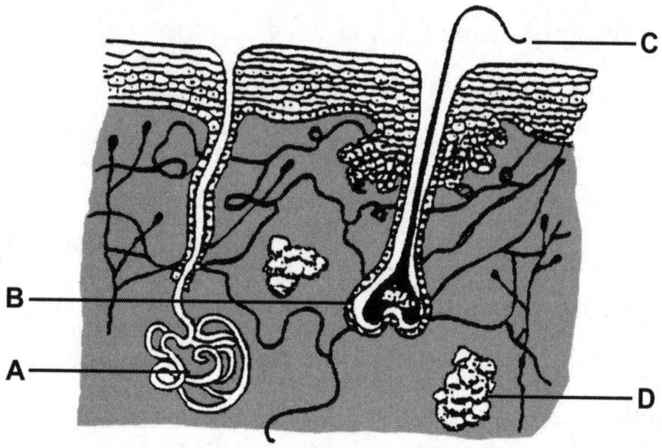

   (1) A (3) C
   (2) B (4) D

8. Urea and excess water are filtered from the blood by the
   (1) kidneys (3) muscles
   (2) gallbladder (4) skin

9. Which is an excretion of the human body?
   (1) oxygen gas (3) carbon dioxide
   (2) nitrogen gas (4) carbon monoxide

10. The skin helps to lower body temperature when
   (1) water evaporates from the skin surface
   (2) hormones are produced on the skin surface
   (3) fat is deposited in the lower skin layer
   (4) carbon dioxide leaves the sweat glands

C. ESSAY QUESTION

DIRECTIONS: Use complete sentences to answer the question in this part.

1. Name one career where a knowledge of the human body is important.

____

____

____

____

Name______________________________ Class______________________ Date____________

Chapter 12: Regulation

A. REGULATION. Our environment, both inside and outside our body, is constantly changing. **Regulation** is the life process by which cells and organisms respond to changes within and around them. The structures and actions of the nervous and endocrine systems control and regulate the body. These two systems allow us to adjust to internal as well as external environmental changes.

Review Questions

1. What is regulation? ____

____

2. The ____________________________ system and the ____________________________ system control and regulate the body.

B. NERVE REGULATION. If you were to put your hand on a hot stove you would quickly, without thinking, remove your hand. This is an example of nerve regulation. There are three parts to nerve regulation: the stimulus, the response, and the impulse. A **stimulus** is a specific change in the environment that affects the nervous system. The heat in the previous example is the stimulus. A **response** is a reaction to this stimulus. Quickly removing your hand so that you will not be burned was a response.

Many organs and glands of the body receive stimuli that are translated into impulses. An **impulse** is an electrical or chemical message that is carried by nerve cells. The impulses are then transferred to the central nervous system. The central nervous system then sorts out and interprets incoming impulses. The impulses are then sent to organs or glands. These organs and glands provide certain responses to these impulses.

Review Questions

1. What is the difference between a stimulus and a response? ____________________________

____

____

2. An electrical or chemical message carried by nerve fibers is called a/an ________________.

3. When you hear a sudden loud sound, you jump. Name the stimulus and the response.

____

____

Name ______________________ Class ____________________ Date ___________

C. HUMAN NERVOUS SYSTEM. The human nervous system is divided into the central nervous system and the peripheral nervous system (Figure 12-1). The **central nervous system** includes the brain and spinal cord. The **peripheral nervous system** is made up of nerves that lie outside the central nervous system. The peripheral nervous system carries impulses to and from the central nervous system.

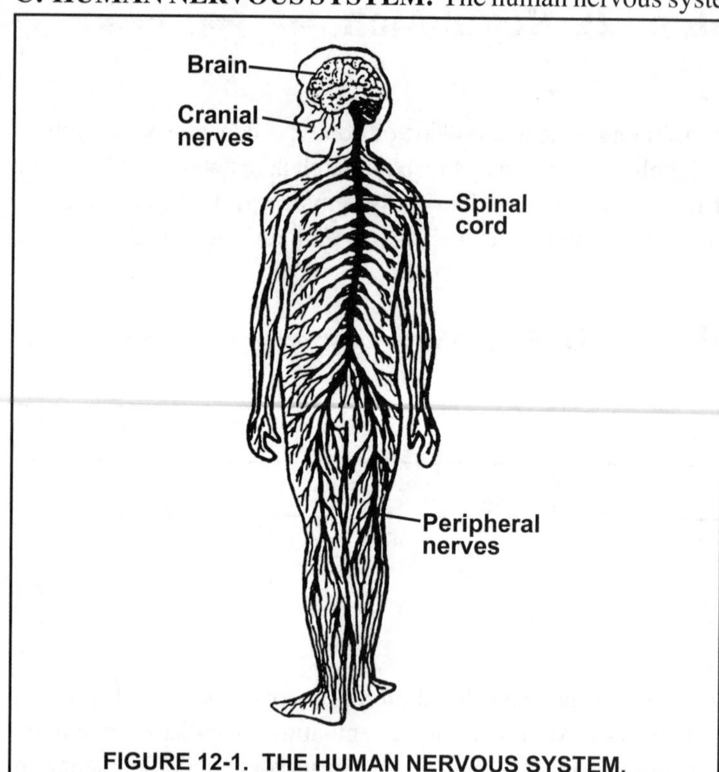

FIGURE 12-1. THE HUMAN NERVOUS SYSTEM.

REVIEW QUESTIONS

1. Name the two parts of the nervous system. ______________________________

____

2. The brain and the spinal cord make up the ____________________ nervous system.

3. The nerves that lie outside the central nervous system make up the ____________________ nervous system.

D. NERVE CELLS. The basic unit of the nervous system is the **nerve cell**. Nerve cells are also called **neurons** (Figure 12-2). Nerve cells receive impulses and send them to various body parts. They make up the structure of the nerves, brain, spinal cord, and receptors. A nerve cell is made up of a cell body, dendrites, and an axon. The **cell body**, or **cyton**, contains the nucleus and cytoplasm. Cell bodies often are present in groups called **ganglia.** The ganglia coordinate incoming and outgoing impulses. Dendrites and axons extend from the cell body. **Dendrites** are branched parts of a neuron that receive impulses from other neurons or sense organs. The impulses are then sent to the cell body. The **axon** is a single long fiber that carries impulses away from the cell body. A neuron has many dendrites but only one axon. Between the dendrites of one neuron and the axon of another is a space called a **synapse.** Impulses cross the synapse by means of chemical neurotransmitters.

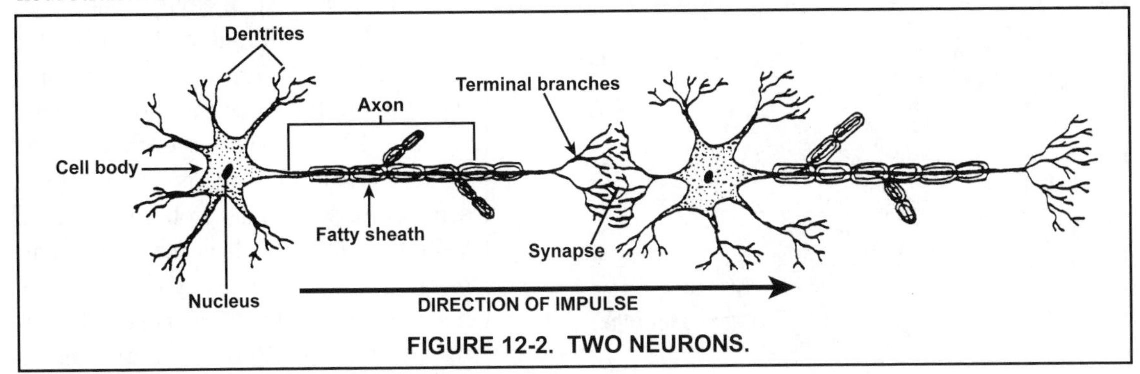

FIGURE 12-2. TWO NEURONS.

REVIEW QUESTIONS

1. Another name for a nerve cell is ____________________.
2. The basic unit of the nervous system is the ____________________.
3. State the function of each of the following structures:

   cyton: ____

   ____

   axon: ____

   ____

   dendrite: ____

   ____

   synapse: ____

   ____

   ganglia: ____

   ____

E. NERVES. A **nerve** is a bundle of neurons or parts of neurons. They are held together by a tough protective membrane. Nerves are classified as sensory, motor, or mixed. **Sensory neurons** carry impulses to the central nervous system. **Motor neurons** carry impulses from the central nervous system to various body parts such as muscles or glands. **Mixed nerves** contain both sensory and motor fibers. A nerve is like a telephone cable line carrying messages to and from your home.

REVIEW QUESTIONS

1. What is a nerve? ____
2. The ____________________ neurons carry impulses to the central nervous system.

   The ____________________ neurons carry impulses from the central nervous system to various body parts. ____________________ contain both sensory and motor fibers.

Name________________________ Class____________________ Date__________

F. THE BRAIN. The **brain** is the major control center of the body. It is located in the head in an area called the cranial cavity. The bones of the skull surround and protect the brain. The cerebrum, cerebellum, and medulla are the three parts of the brain (Figure 12-3). The **cerebrum** is the center of thinking, memory, emotions, sensory impulse interpretation, and all voluntary activity. It is the largest part of the brain. You use your cerebrum when you take a test. The **cerebellum** is responsible for coordination of muscles and is the center of balance. When you bounce a basketball you use your cerebellum. Alcohol reduces the ability of the cerebellum to coordinate muscle activity. This results in slurred speech and unbalanced walking.

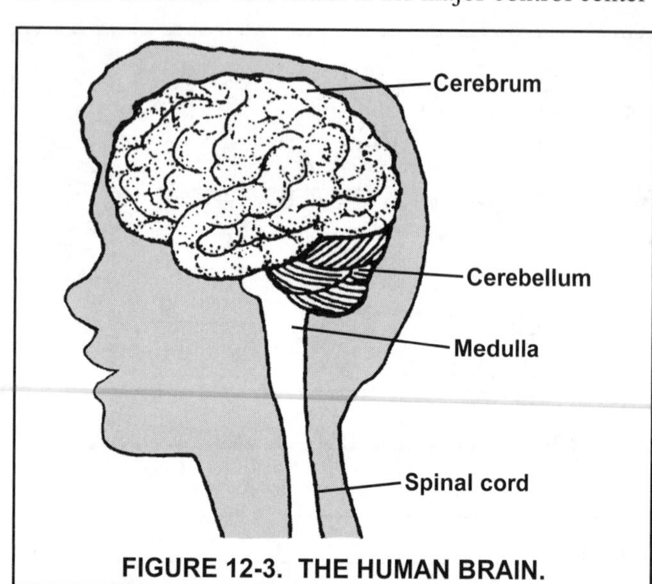

FIGURE 12-3. THE HUMAN BRAIN.

The **medulla** or brain stem is the center of respiration, heartbeat, and other involuntary activities. Your medulla controls all the activities of your body that you cannot control. Breathing and peristalsisare examples of activities controlled by the medulla.

REVIEW QUESTIONS

1. The major control center of the body is the ________________________.

2. Complete the following chart.

PART OF BRAIN	FUNCTION
cerebrum	
cerebellum	
medulla	

G. THE SPINAL CORD. The **spinal cord** is the tubular mass of nerve cells that extends from the brain stem downward through the center of the spinal column. It is surrounded and protected by the vertebrae of the spinal column (backbone). The spinal cord relays impulses to and from the brain and is the center of some reflex actions.

Name__________________________ Class__________________ Date__________

Injury to the spinal cord can result in paralysis and sometimes death. **Paralysis** is caused by severe damage to the spinal cord. It results in loss of feeling and muscle function in the lower parts of the body. Paralysis occurs when impulses to and from the lower body muscles cannot be transmitted to the brain.

REVIEW QUESTIONS

1. Describe the spinal cord. ____

____

____

2. What is the function of the spinal cord? ____

____

3. What causes paralysis? ____

____

H. RECEPTORS. Receptors are special structures that are sensitive to stimuli. Receptors *receive* messages. External receptors, called **sense organs**, include the eyes, ears, nose, tongue, and skin. Stimuli for these receptors are light, sound, chemicals, and temperature and pressure changes. Internal receptors are located in the internal organs. They allow the brain to detect hunger, thirst, muscle position, and carbon dioxide levels in the blood.

REVIEW QUESTIONS

1. Receptors ____________________ messages.

2. Name five sense organs. ____

I. INVOLUNTARY BEHAVIOR. The total response of an organism to stimuli is known as **behavior**. The responses may be inborn or acquired (learned), voluntary or involuntary. **Involuntary behavior** occurs automatically without conscious control. Some involuntary actions are inborn while others are learned. Examples of involuntary actions that are inborn include contraction of heart and diaphragm muscles, secretion of glands, and simple reflexes such as knee jerks and iris movements. Examples of involuntary actions that are acquired by the individual through repetition include writing one's name, riding a bicycle, and playing a musical instrument.

REVIEW QUESTIONS

1. The total response of an organism to stimuli is known as ____________________.

2. Involuntary behavior occurs ______________ without ______________ control.

Name ____________________ Class ____________________ Date __________

3. State one example of inborn involuntary behavior.

____

____

4. Name one type of acquired involuntary action. ____________________

____

J. THE REFLEX ARC. The **reflex** is an example of involuntary behavior. It is an inborn involuntary response to a particular stimulus. In a reflex response nerve impulses travel in a set pathway called a **reflex arc** (Figure 12-4). The path an impulse follows in a reflex arc is as follows:

Receptor ⟶ Sensory Neuron ⟶ Interneuron ⟶ Motor Neuron ⟶ Effector

The receptors in a knee jerk reflex are the nerve endings in the knee. The **receptors** receive the message. The sensory neuron passes along the message to the spinal cord. The **interneuron** connects the sensory neuron with the motor neuron. The motor neuron sends the message to the muscle in the leg called the **effector**. An effector *does something*. In this case it jerks the knee. A reflex arc is a short cut for nerve impulses. The message does not have to take the *long* route to the brain where thinking occurs. A reflex action is an automatic action and does not require thought. Blinking is another example of a reflex.

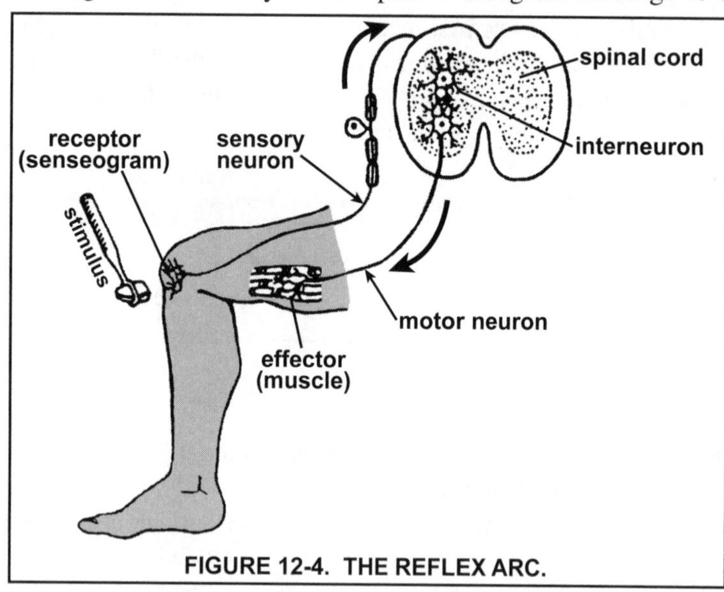

FIGURE 12-4. THE REFLEX ARC.

REVIEW QUESTIONS

1. Describe the path of a reflex arc.

____

____

Name______________________ Class______________________ Date__________

K. VOLUNTARY BEHAVIOR. Voluntary behavior requires thinking. The impulses start in the brain and are carried by nerve cells to muscles or glands. The muscles or glands respond in a certain way. Examples of voluntary actions include measuring with a meter stick, picking up a book, and building a model airplane.

Review Questions

1. What is meant by voluntary behavior? ______________________________________

____

2. State two examples of voluntary behavior. ______________________________________

____

L. NERVOUS SYSTEM DISORDERS. Some disorders of the nervous systems are cerebral palsy, meningitis, and polio.

Nervous System Disorders

♦ **Meningitis. Meningitis** is an inflammation of the membranes that surround the brain and spinal cord. This disease is caused by bacteria. Symptoms include severe headache and stiffness of the neck. Meningitis can be fatal. Antibiotics are used to treat meningitis.

♦ **Cerebral Palsy. Cerebral palsy** is a group of birth disorders characterized by disturbances of the motor functions. It is a crippling disorder and treatment is still experimental.

♦ **Polio. Polio** is a viral disease of the central nervous system that can cause paralysis. It can be prevented by immunization.

Review Questions

1. Complete the following chart concerning diseases of the nervous system.

DISEASE	SYMPTOMS	TREATMENT

Name____________________________ Class____________________ Date____________

M. EFFECTS OF DRUGS ON THE NERVOUS SYSTEM. Drugs can be harmful or helpful depending on how they are used. The incorrect use of a drug is called **drug abuse.** A **drug** is defined as a medicine, such as aspirin and penicillin, used to treat or cure disease or pain in the body. A drug can also be a substance that has a strong effect on the mind or body and that can become habit forming. Heroin and cocaine are habit forming drugs.

Drugs affect the central nervous system (CNS) in many different ways. Some drugs create a feeling of **euphoria** (well being). Other drugs cause a decrease in **inhibitions**—an inability to stop doing something that a person would not normally do. Using some drugs results in **tolerance** when they are taken continually for a few weeks. This means that increasingly larger amounts are needed to get the desired effect. There are some drugs that cause **stimulation** (excitement) and feelings of high energy. **Physical dependence,** or **addiction,** can result from using drugs. When the drug is withheld the addict suffers physical illness and withdrawal symptoms. The effects of some common drugs on the nervous system are described in Table 12-1.

DRUG	EFFECT ON MOOD	ACTION ON BODY	DANGERS OF ABUSE
Alcohol	Euphoria, relaxation, release of inhibitions.	Depresses CNS, affects eyes, coordination, judgment, reaction time.	Physical dependence, damage to pancreas, liver cirrhosis, possible brain damage.
Cocaine	Euphoria, excitation followed by depression.	CNS stimulation followed by depression, dilates pupils, local anesthesia.	Mental slowness, convulsions, hallucinations, unconsciousness, death from overdose.
Amphetamines (uppers/pep pills)	Euphoria, stimulation, hyperactivity.	Stimulates CNS to increase heart rate, raises blood pressure, dilates pupils.	Tolerance, possible physical dependence, hallucinations, death from overdose.
Morphine, Heroin	Euphoria, reduction of pain.	Depresses CNS, depresses reflexes, pupils get smaller, slows coordination.	Tolerance, physical dependence, convulsions, death from overdose.
Caffeine	Increases mental alertness, decreases fatigue, and drowsiness.	Acts on cerebrum, relaxes smooth muscle, stimulates cardiac and skeletal muscle.	Very large doses stimulate centers in the medulla (may slow the heart, toxic doses may cause convulsions.
Nicotine	Psychologically lessens tension.	Stimulates nervous system.	Tolerance, physical dependence.
LSD	Overexcitation, sensory distortions, hallucinations.	Alters levels of transmitters in brain, strong CNS stimulator, dilates pupils, sometimes unequally, increases heart rate, raises blood pressure.	Irrational behavior.
Marijuana	Euphoria.	Slows coordination, impairs depth perception, alters sense of timing, inflames eyes.	In large doses, sensory distortions, hallucinations. Evidence of lowered sperm counts and testosterone (male hormone) levels.

TABLE 12-1. EFFECTS OF DRUGS ON NERVOUS SYSTEM.

Name________________________ Class____________________ Date__________

Review Questions

1. What is meant by the term "drug abuse"? ____

____

2. Euphoria is a sense of ______________________.

3. What happens when a person's inhibitions are decreased? ________________________

____

4. List four drugs. State the effects of each drug, its action on the body and the dangers of its abuse.

____

____

____

____

____

____

____

____

____

____

____

____

____

____

Name_________________________ Class ____________________ Date __________

N. CHEMICAL REGULATION. The endocrine system is responsible for chemical regulation. Stimuli may cause certain glands to secrete chemical messengers known as **hormones**. These hormones cause other parts of the body to respond.

REVIEW QUESTIONS

1. The endocrine system is responsible for ________________________.

2. What is a hormone? ________________________________.

O. HUMAN ENDOCRINE SYSTEM. The **endocrine system** includes the endocrine glands and their hormones (Figure 12-5). The glands of the endocrine system are called **ductless glands**. Ductless glands release hormones directly into the bloodstream. The bloodstream transports hormones throughout the body. Each hormone acts on a certain kind of tissue called its **target tissue**.

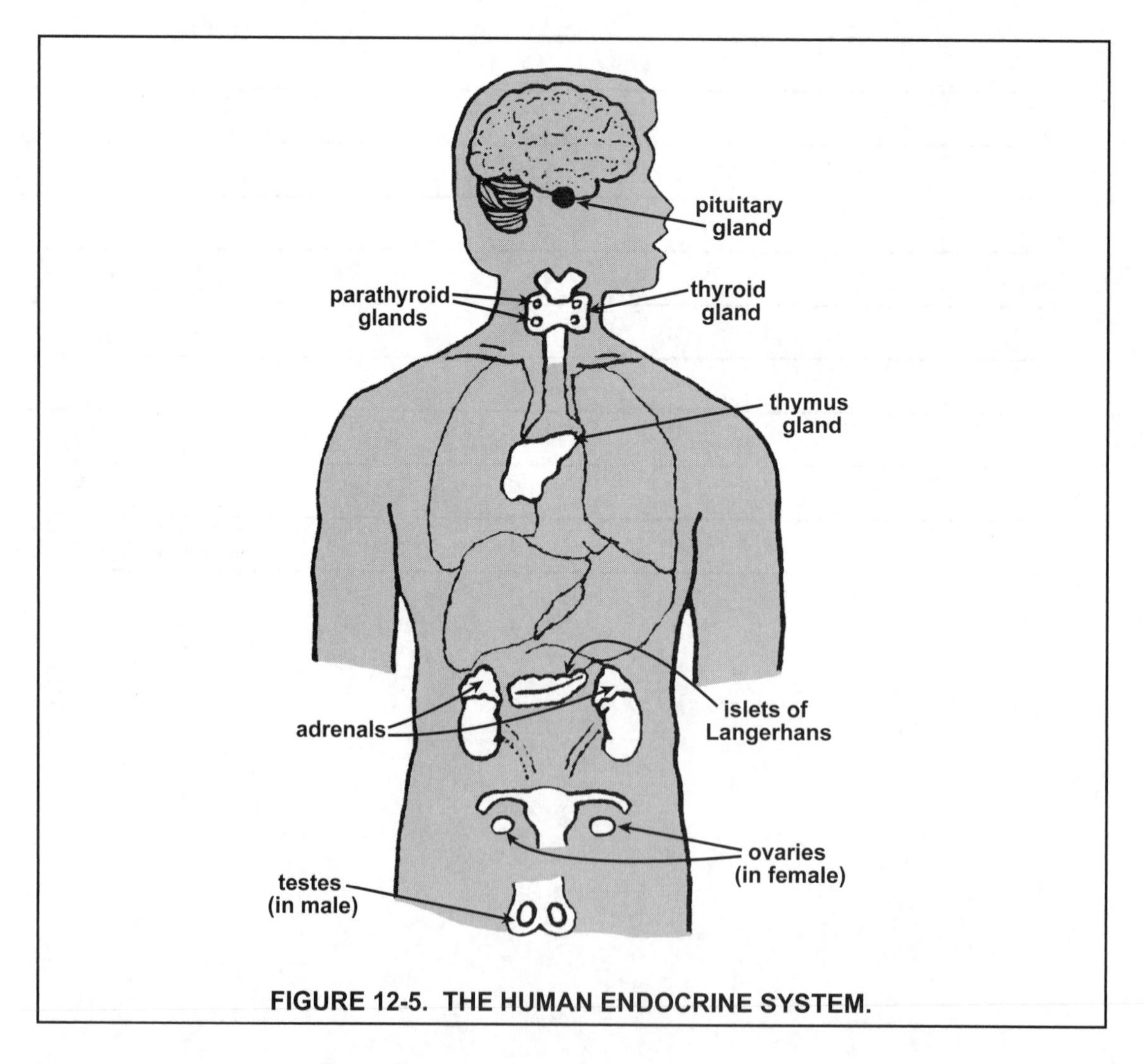

FIGURE 12-5. THE HUMAN ENDOCRINE SYSTEM.

Name______________________ Class______________________ Date____________

P. HUMAN ENDOCRINE GLANDS. The endocrine glands, the hormones they secrete, and their functions, are shown in Table 12-2. (Sex hormones are covered in Unit 5.)

GLAND AND LOCATION	HORMONE	FUNCTION	OVERSECRETION OR UNDERSECRETION
Pituitary *Location*: base of brain	Growth hormone	Stimulates the elongation of the long bones of the body. Also affects various metabolic activities, including the metabolism of glucose.	*Oversecretion*–in childhood, ***giantism***. In adults, ***acromegaly*** (bones of face, hands, and feet enlarge). *Undersecretion*–in childhood, ***dwarfism***.
Thyroid *Location:* in the neck	Thyroxin	Regulates rate of metabolism in body. Essential for normal physical and mental development.	*Oversercretion*–(of thyroxin) nervousness, weight loss. *Undersecretion*–(of thyroxin) in childhood, ***cretinism*** (mental retardation, small size). *Iodine Deficiency*–results in ***goiter,*** an enlargement of thyroid gland.
Parathyroid *Location:* embedded in back of thyroid gland	Parathormone	Controls the metabolism of calcium, necessary for normal nerve and muscle function, blood clotting, healthy bones and teeth.	*Undersecretion*–Nerve disorders, brittle bones, clotting problems.
Adrenal *Location:* on top of each kidney	Cortisone	Regulates carbohydrate, protein, and fat metabolism. Promotes conversion (change) of fats and proteins to glucose.	*Oversecretion*–***Cushing's disease*** (high blood glucose levels, excess fat). *Undersecretion*–***Addison's disease*** (low blood glucose level, weight loss).
	Adrenaline	Raises blood sugar level and increases heartbeat and breathing rates.	*Undersecretion*–Inability to deal with stress.
Islets of Langerhans *Location:* Pancreas	Insulin	Stimulates glucose uptake by cells.	*Oversecretion*–low blood sugar. *Undersecretion*–***Diabetes*** (high blood sugar).
	Glucagon	Promotes conversion (change) of glycogen to glucose.	*Oversecretion*–High blood sugar.

TABLE 12-2. HORMONES OF THE ENDOCRINE SYSTEM.

REVIEW QUESTIONS

1. State the cause of each of the following endocrine system disorders.

Goiter: ____

Diabetes: ____

Giantism: ____

Name ______________________ Class ________________ Date __________

Addison's disease: ______________________________

Acromegaly: ______________________________

2. Complete the following chart.

GLAND	LOCATION	HORMONE SECRETED
Parathyroid		
Adrenal		
Thyroid		
Pituitary		
Islets of Langerhans		

3. State the function of each of the following glands.

Pituitary: ______________________________

____

____

Adrenal: ______________________________

____

____

Thyroid: ______________________________

____

____

Islets of Langerhans: ______________________________

____

____

Parathyroid: ______________________________

____

____

Name______________________ Class____________________ Date __________

LAB INVESTIGATION: TESTING TASTE BUDS

OBJECTIVE

Upon completion of this activity you should be able to name the four primary taste sensations and state where on the tongue the receptors (taste buds) for each taste sensation is located.

LABORATORY PROCEDURE

Materials: Cotton swabs, small paper cups each marked either *bitter, salty, sweet,* or *sour*, containing diluted lemon juice (sour), sugar water (sweet), salt water (salty), or quinine water (bitter), water for rinsing if room has no sinks, and boxes of paper tissues. (*Note:* Dilute quinine sulfate solution or bitters may be substituted for quinine water.)

1. Go to the supply table and get four cotton swabs, four pieces of paper tissue and four paper cups containing bitter, salty, sweet, and sour solutions. Take your materials to your lab area.

2. Different parts of your tongue have different taste receptors called *taste buds*. *Receptors* are the parts of neurons that receive impulses. Taste buds are located at the ***tip, behind the tip, sides,*** and ***back of the tongue***. You are going to perform taste tests to determine which part of your tongue tastes each of the following sensations: bitterness, saltiness, sweetness, and sourness. The four taste areas are shown on the diagram on this page.

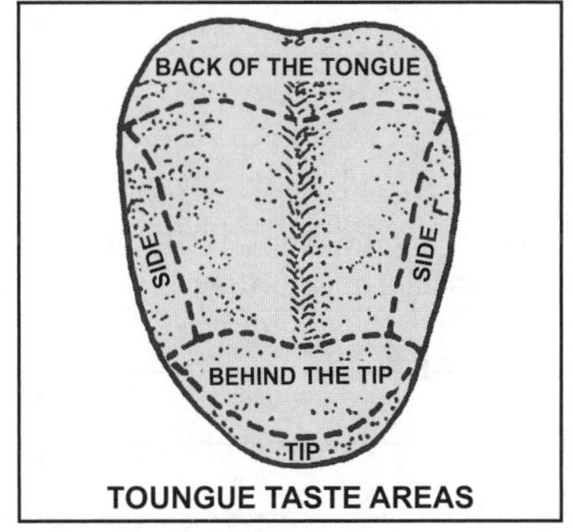

TOUNGUE TASTE AREAS

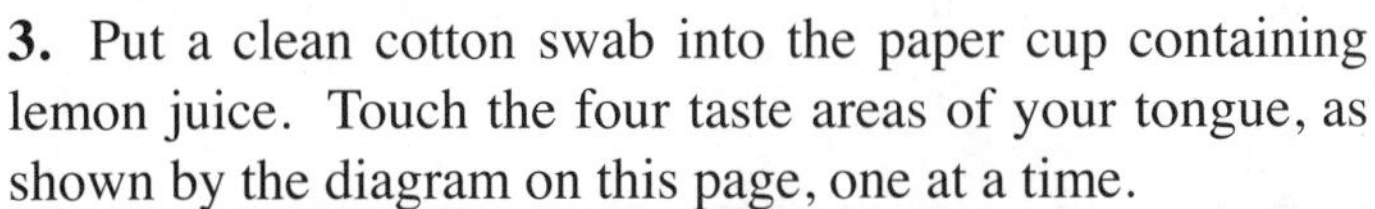

3. Put a clean cotton swab into the paper cup containing lemon juice. Touch the four taste areas of your tongue, as shown by the diagram on this page, one at a time.

4. On which area of your tongue did you taste sourness? Was it at the tip of your tongue, behind the tip of your tongue, at the sides of your tongue, or at the back of your tongue? Place a check (√) in the appropriate box in the **Observation Section** on the next page.

5. Rinse out your mouth with water and dry your tongue. ***Important: Be sure to go to a lab sink and rinse out your mouth after each taste test. Then wipe your tongue with a piece of paper tissue and throw away the paper tissue and used cotton swab.***

6. Repeat **Procedure 3** using the salt solution. On which area of your tongue did you taste saltiness? Place a check (√) in the appropriate box in the **Observation Section** on the next page.

7. Rinse out your mouth with water and dry your tongue. Repeat **Procedure 3** using the bitter solution. On which area of your tongue did you taste bitterness? Place a check (√) in the appropriate box in the **Observation Section** on the next page.

8. Rinse out your mouth with water and dry your tongue. Repeat **Procedure 3** using the sweet solution. On which area of your tongue did you taste sweetness? Place a check (√) in the appropriate box in the **Observation Section** on the next page.

Name ______________________ Class __________________ Date __________

9. When you are finished with your laboratory activity, clean your lab area and return any unused materials to the supply table.

10. Answer the questions in the **Conclusion Section**.

OBSERVATIONS

TASTE AREA	SWEETNESS	SALTINESS	BITTERNESS	SOURNESS
Tip of tongue				
Behind the tip				
Sides of tongue				
Back of tongue				

CONCLUSIONS

1. Name the four primary taste sensations and state where on the tongue the taste buds for each taste sensation is located.

   ____

   ____

   ____

   ____

   ____

2. Compare your taste test results with those of your classmates. Were their results the same as your results? ____

   ____

   ____

   ____

   ____

   ____

3. A taste bud is called a ______________________ because it receives messages.

Name________________________ Class____________________ Date__________

REVIEW ACTIVITIES

Important Terms

DIRECTIONS: Define the following terms in the spaces provided.

adrenaline ____

____

brain ____

____

cerebellum ____

____

cerebrum ____

____

cretinism ____

____

cyton ____

____

dendrites ____

____

diabetes ____

____

ductless glands ____

____

effector ____

____

ganglia ____

____

glucagon ____

____

goiter ____

____

hormones ____

____

Name ____________________ Class ________________ Date __________

impulse ____

____

insulin ____

____

interneuron ____

____

Islets of Langerhans ____

____

medulla ____

____

motor neuron ____

____

nerve ____

____

neuron ____

____

parathormone ____

____

receptors ____

____

reflex ____

____

regulation ____

____

response ____

____

sensory neuron ____

____

stimulus ____

____

synapse ____

____

thyroxin ____

____

Name________________ Class________________ Date__________

Skill Practice

Part A. Label the parts of the endocrine system on the diagram below by placing the correct term on the line provided.

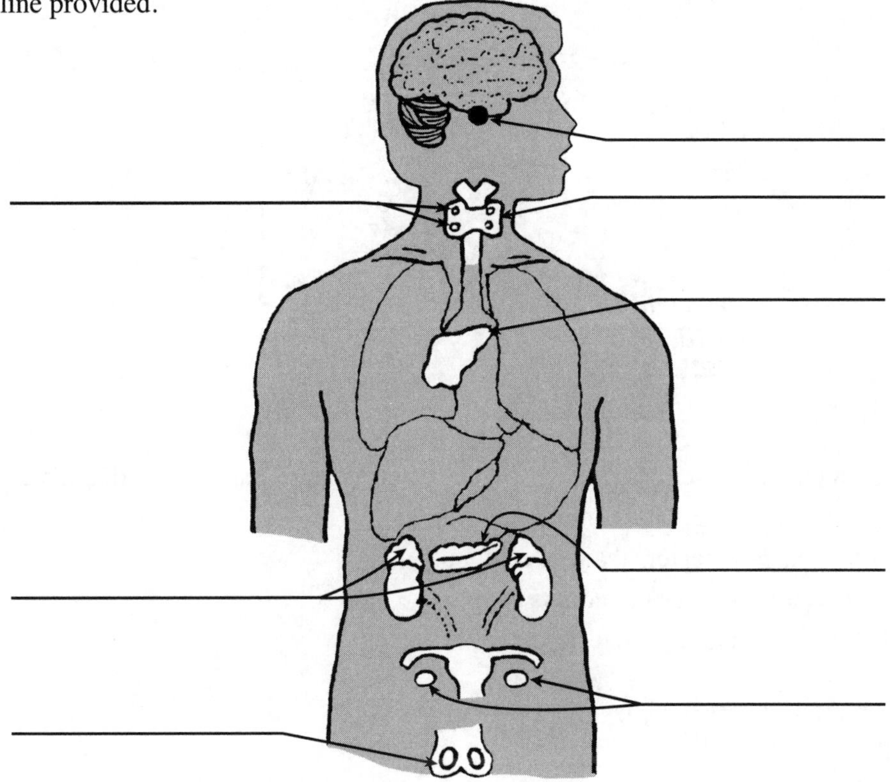

Part B. Label the parts of the following diagram. Draw an arrow showing the direction that an impulse travels.

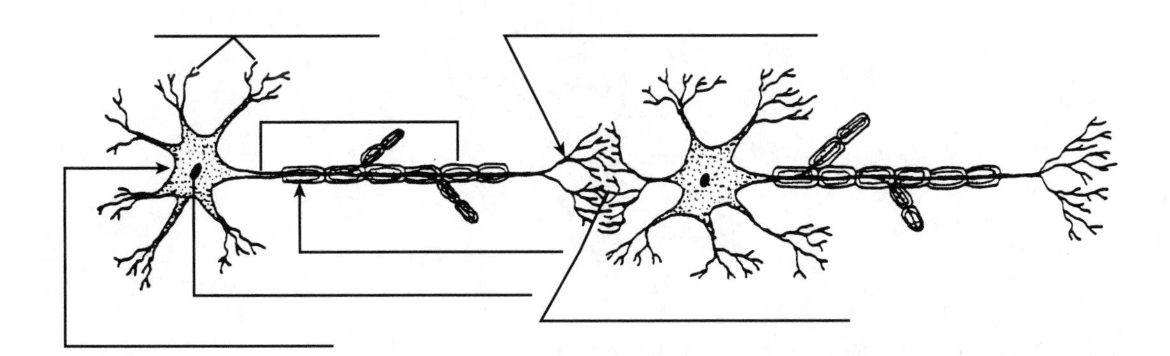

Name______________________ Class__________________ Date__________

Part C. Base your answers to questions 1 and 2 on the diagram below which represents a simple nerve pathway in the human body and on your knowledge of biology.

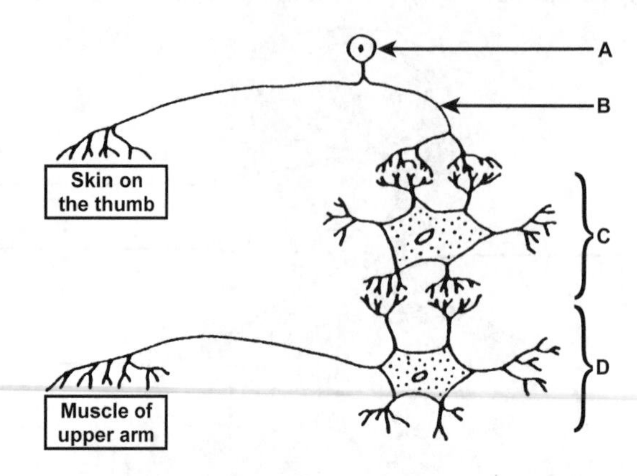

1. Which statement best describes the skin on the thumb as represented in the diagram?

(1) It contains receptors that interpret stimuli.

(2) It contains receptors that detect stimuli.

(3) It is an effector that interprets stimuli.

(4) It is an effector that detects stimuli.

2. An interneuron is represented by

(1) A (3) C

(2) B (4) D

Part D. Base your answers to questions 1 through 4 on the diagram below.

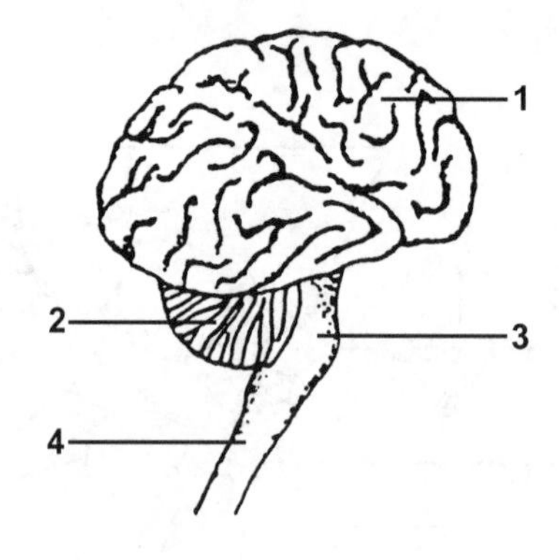

1. Which number represents the spinal cord? ____________________

2. Which number represents the medulla? ____________________

3. Which number represents the cerebrum? ____________________

4. Which number represents the cerebellum? ____________________

Name________________________________ Class_________________________ Date______________

CHAPTER 12: QUIZ

A. FILL-IN QUESTIONS

DIRECTIONS: Complete each of the following statements by writing the correct word or phrase in the space provided.

1. The space between the dendrites of one nerve cell and the axon of another is the ______________________________.
2. A ______________________________ is a bundle of neurons or parts of neurons.
3. The basic unit of the nervous system is the ______________________________.
4. The part of the brain used for thinking is the ______________________________.
5. The cell body is called the ______________________________.
6. A reaction to a stimulus is called a ______________________________.
7. ______________________________ receive messages.
8. The part of the brain responsible for coordination is the ______________________________.
9. An example of involuntary behavior is the ______________________________.
10. The ______________________________ nervous system includes the brain and spinal cord.
11. An inflammation of the membranes that surround the brain and spinal cord is ____________.
12. ______________________________ are chemical messengers.
13. The ______________________________ gland is located at the base of the brain.
14. The life process by which organisms respond to changes in the environment is ____________.
15. The endocrine system has ______________________________ glands.
16. A ______________________________ is a specific change in the environment.
17. Calcium metabolism is controlled by the ______________________________ gland.
18. The Islets of Langerhans are located in the ______________________________.
19. The thyroid gland is located in the ______________________________.
20. A deficiency of iodine results in ______________________________.

B. MULTIPLE-CHOICE QUESTIONS

DIRECTIONS: Circle the number of the expression that best completes each of the following statements.

1. The terms ***stimulus*** and ***impulse*** are most closely related to which body system?
   (1) nervous
   (2) circulatory
   (3) respiratory
   (4) excretory

2. The secretion of ductless gland is called
   (1) an enzyme
   (2) a vaccine
   (3) a hormone
   (4) a vitamin

Name______________________Class__________________Date__________

3. Which system functions with the brain in coordinating body activities?
   (1) digestive (3) endocrine
   (2) excretory (4) respiratory

4. Which part of the nervous system regulates heartbeat and the rate of respiration?
   (1) spinal cord (3) cerebellum
   (2) cerebrum (4) medulla

Directions 5-7: Base your answers to questions 5 and 7 on the diagram below and on your knowledge of biology.

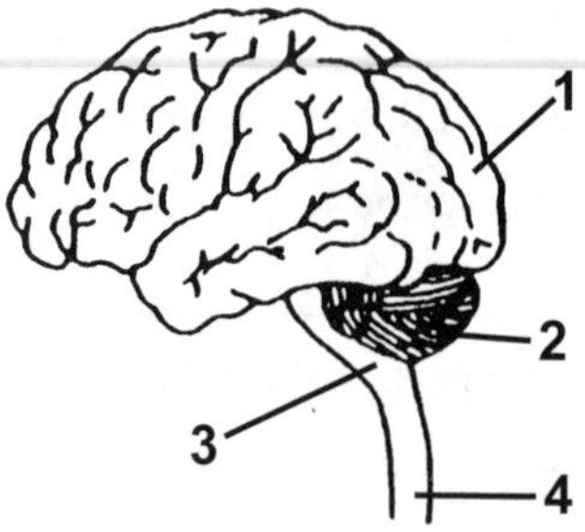

5. The vision center of the brain is located in area
   (1) 1 (3) 3
   (2) 2 (4) 4

6. Which part of the brain controls balance and coordination?
   (1) 1 (3) 3
   (2) 2 (4) 4

7. Which area controls thinking and memory?
   (1) 1 (3) 3
   (2) 2 (4) 4

8. A change in the environment that causes a living thing to respond is known as
   (1) a stimulus (3) a habit
   (2) an impulse (4) a reflex

9. Which is an involuntary action?
   (1) picking up a book (3) building a model
   (2) secreting saliva (4) measuring something

10. To which system do ductless glands belong?
   (1) transport (3) endocrine
   (2) respiratory (4) urinary

C. ESSAY QUESTION

DIRECTIONS: Use complete sentences to answer the question in this part.

1. Name one endocrine hormone and state one effect of oversecretion or undersecretion.

____

____

____

____

____

____

Name______________________________Class__________________________Date______________

Chapter 13: Locomotion

A. LOCOMOTION. The interaction of muscles with the skeleton that results in body movements is known as **locomotion**. Locomotion increases the chances for survival of an organism by allowing the organism to gather food, seek shelter, and escape dangerous situations. Locomotion also increases the chances for survival of a species by enabling members of the species to find suitable mates. Human locomotion involves the interaction of joints and tissues such as bone, cartilage, muscles, tendons and ligaments.

REVIEW QUESTIONS

1. What is locomotion? ____

____

2. State two advantages of locomotion. ________________________________

____

B. BONES. Bone is a type of connective tissue. It is composed of relatively few cells surrounded by large amounts of a hard intracellular material. The intracellular material is composed mainly of calcium compounds. The hardness of bone is due to the presence of calcium and phosphorus minerals. Bones make up the major part of the framework of the human endoskeleton and come in many shapes and sizes. Bones support and protect body organs. They also provide a place for muscle attachment.

The bones of your legs and arms are called long bones (Figure 13-1). The ends are covered with cartilage and are capable of growth. The outer covering is a tough membrane called the **periosteum**. Long bones contain living blood, fat, and bone cells. Red and white blood cells are produced in the inner tissue, called **marrow**, of some bones.

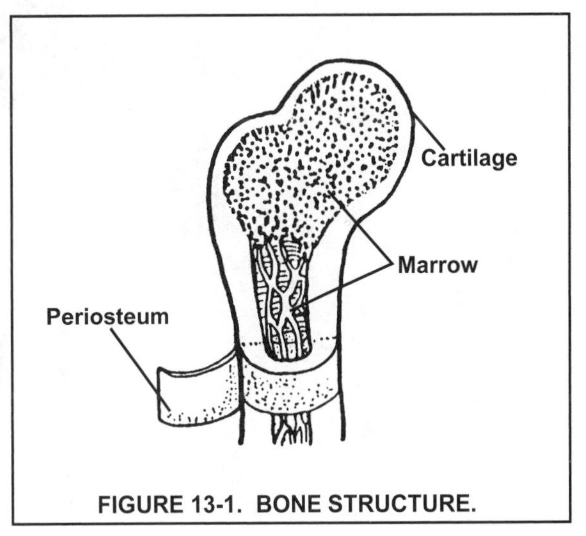

FIGURE 13-1. BONE STRUCTURE.

REVIEW QUESTIONS

1. The bones of the skeleton ________________ and ________________ body organs.

2. The ________________________ is the tough outer covering of bones.

3. What cells are produced by bone marrow? ________________________________

Name________________________ Class____________________ Date__________

C. HUMAN ENDOSKELETON. An **endoskeleton** is an inner skeleton. It acts as a framework for supporting other organs of the body. It also protects internal organs and allows body movement. The human endoskeleton has 206 bones (Figure 13-2). It is composed of a skull, vertebral column (spinal column), breastbone and ribs, and limbs (arms and legs).

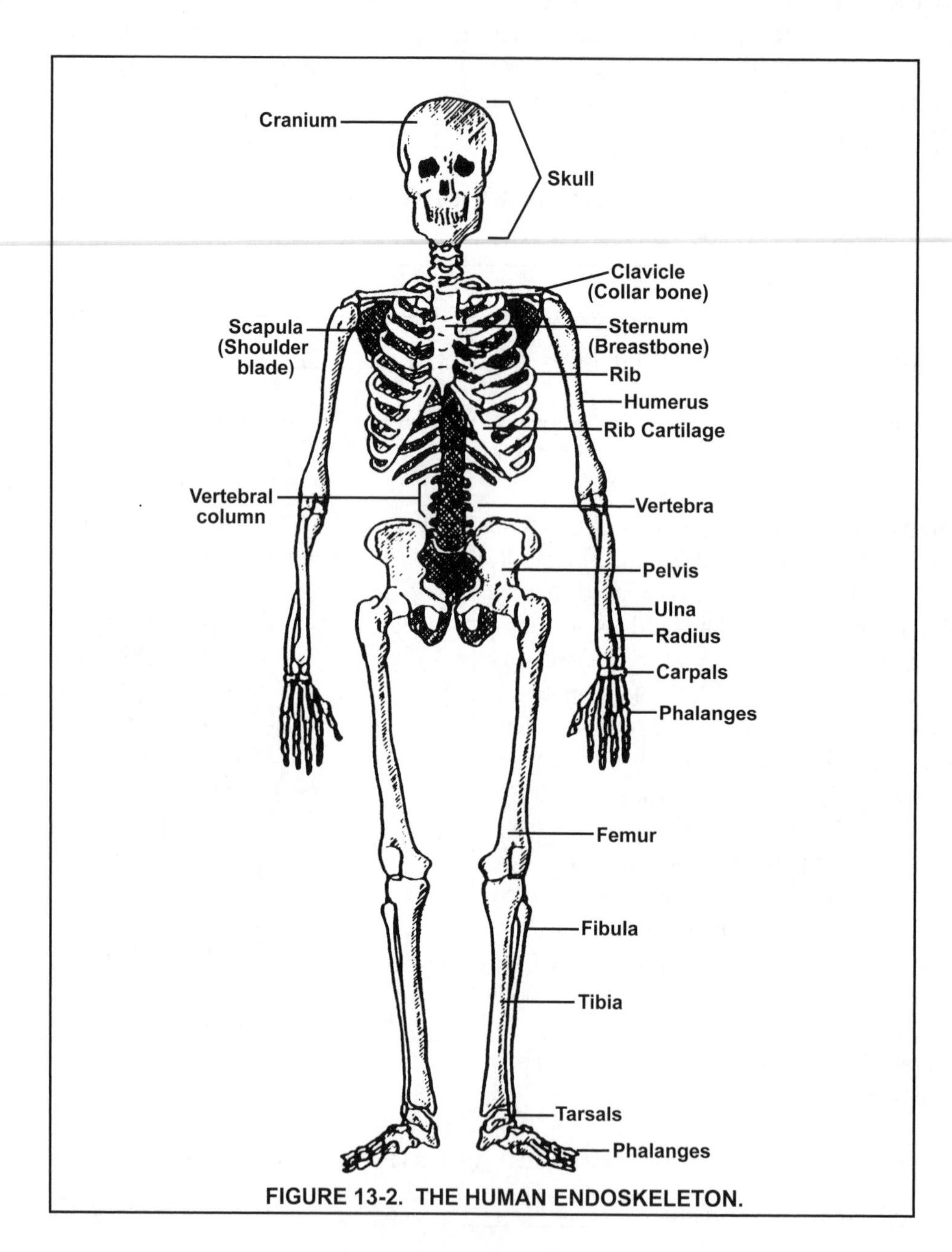

FIGURE 13-2. THE HUMAN ENDOSKELETON.

REVIEW QUESTIONS

1. How many bones are in the human skeleton? ________________.

2. An endoskeleton is an ____________________ skeleton.

3. Name two functions of the human skeletal system. ______________________________

____

____

D. CARTILAGE. The fibrous, flexible, elastic connective tissue found in the human skeleton is called **cartilage.** In the human embryo the skeleton is made up mostly of cartilage. By adulthood most of the cartilage has been replaced by bone. In the adult cartilage is found in the nose, ears, and trachea, at the ends of ribs and other bones, and between the vertebrae. At the ends of bones cartilage provides flexibility. Between bones cartilage provides cushioning. In the ears, nose, and trachea, cartilage provides flexible rather than rigid support.

REVIEW QUESTIONS

1. What is cartilage? ______________________________

____

2. Name three places in the human where cartilage is found. ______________________________

____

3. How does cartilage change from the embryo stage to adulthood. ______________________________

____

E. JOINTS. Bones are connected at places called **joints** (Figure 13-3). Most joints allow bone movement. **Ball and socket joints** are located at the hip and shoulder. They permit circular movement. **Hinge joints** are located at the elbows and knees. They allow a back and forth movement. Hinge joints do not permit as much movement as ball and socket joints. **Pivot joints** are found where the skull joins the vertebral column. Pivot joints permit a rotating movement. The wrist and ankle have **gliding joints** that allow a sliding action. **Fused joints** are not movable and are located in the skull. Fluids in joints help keep joints cushioned and lubricated.

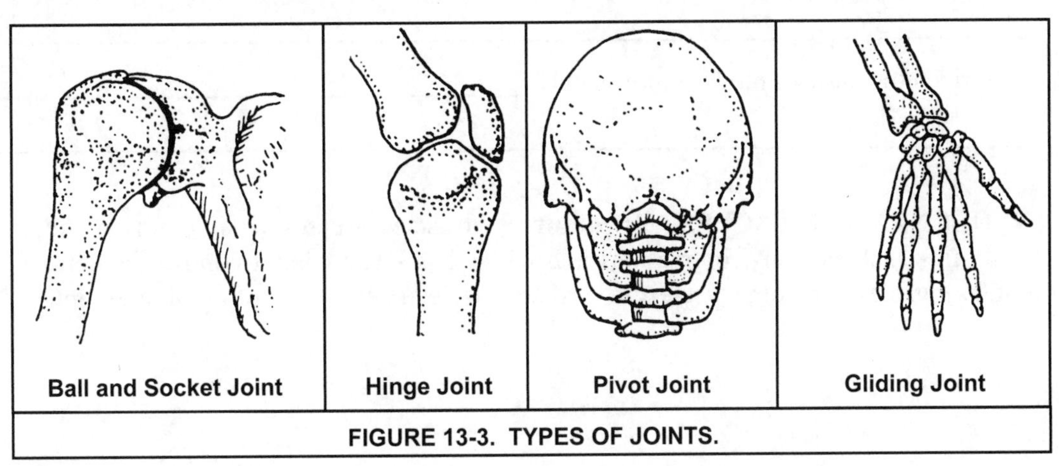

FIGURE 13-3. TYPES OF JOINTS.

Name________________________ Class____________________ Date__________

REVIEW QUESTIONS

1. Joints are located where ________________________ connect.

2. Complete the following chart.

NAME OF JOINT	LOCATION	FUNCTION

F. MUSCLES. The human body contains three kinds of muscle tissue: skeletal muscle, smooth muscle, and cardiac muscle (Figure 13-4). **Muscles** produce body movement by pulling on bones when they contract. Muscles also produce body heat when they contract. Muscles can be voluntary or involuntary.

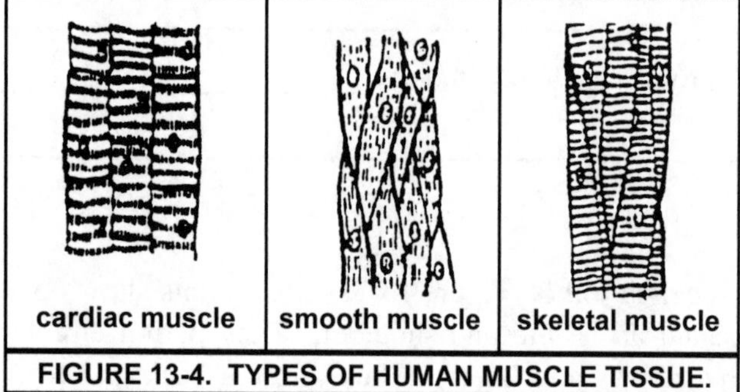

FIGURE 13-4. TYPES OF HUMAN MUSCLE TISSUE.

REVIEW QUESTIONS

1. Name the three types of human muscle tissue. ________________________

____

2. Describe how muscles produce movement. ________________________

____

G. INVOLUNTARY MUSCLES. **Involuntary muscles** are responsible for involuntary body activities such as heart contractions and peristalsis. You cannot control the actions of involuntary muscles. Smooth muscle and cardiac muscle are examples of involuntary muscles.

Name________________________ Class________________________ Date__________

Smooth muscle is found in the walls of arteries and organs of the body. Contraction of smooth muscle is controlled by the nervous system. **Cardiac muscle,** found in the walls of the heart, causes the heart to beat.

REVIEW QUESTIONS

1. Muscles that you cannot control are called ____________________ muscles.
2. Smooth muscle and cardiac muscles are examples of ____________________ muscles.
3. Cardiac muscle is found in the ____________________ and smooth muscle is found in ____.

H. VOLUNTARY MUSCLES. **Voluntary muscles** attach to the skeleton and can be controlled for locomotion. **Skeletal (striated) muscle** is a type of voluntary muscle. Striated muscles are attached to the bones of the skeleton. The bones and body parts are moved by the contraction of these muscles. Skeletal muscles usually function in opposite pairs. One muscle of the pair is an **extensor** that extends (straightens) the limb. The other muscle is a **flexor** that bends the limb. The biceps and triceps of the upper arm are an example of a pair of muscles that function in this way (Figure 13-5). The bicep, a flexor, is located on the front of the upper arm. When the **bicep** contracts the forearm is pulled toward the front of the shoulder causing the arm to bend. The **tricep**, an extensor, is located on the back of the upper arm. When the tricep contracts the arm straightens out.

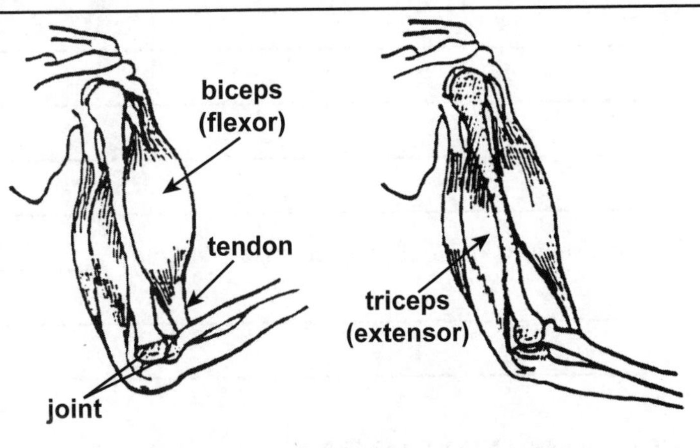

FIGURE 13-5. A PAIR OF SKELETAL MUSCLES.

REVIEW QUESTIONS

1. ____________________ muscles attach to the skeleton and can be controlled for locomotion.
2. Name one type of voluntary muscle. ____________________
3. State the difference between a flexor and an extensor. ____
4. What is the difference between a bicep and a tricep. ____

Name________________________ Class____________________ Date__________

I. MUSCLE ACTION Nerves direct impulses to muscles causing them to contract. The energy needed for the muscle to contract comes from energy stored in chemicals such as glycogen. Muscle cells will continue to operate even if they do not receive sufficient oxygen. If the muscle does not receive enough oxygen to carry on aerobic respiration, the muscle cells change to anaerobic respiration. During anaerobic respiration they produce lactic acid. Lactic acid causes muscles to hurt. This condition is known as **muscle fatigue**. Rest after exercise supplies oxygen to fatigued muscle cells. During this rest-recovery period, the lactic acid is removed and energy-storing compounds are rebuilt. If a person does not rest after muscle fatigue, permanent injury to the muscle can occur.

REVIEW QUESTIONS

1. What causes muscle fatigue? ______________________________

____

____

____

____

2. What should you do if you get muscle fatigue? ______________________________

____

____

J. TENDONS AND LIGAMENTS. Tendons and ligaments are both composed of connective tissue (Figure 13-6). **Tendons** are bands of dense tissue that connect muscles to bones. **Ligaments** are tough bands of tissue that hold bones together at joints.

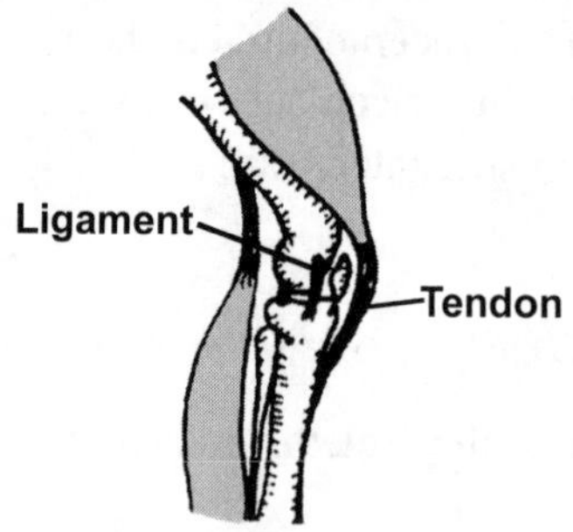

FIGURE 13-6. LIGAMENTS AND TENDONS.

REVIEW QUESTIONS

1. What is the difference between a tendon and a ligament? ______________________________

____

____

Name________________________ Class____________________ Date__________

K. MUSCLE-BONE DISORDERS. Some disorders of the musculoskeletal system are fractures, hernias, sprains, arthritis, and tendonitis.

Muscle-Bone Disorders

♦ **Fractures. Fractures** are broken bones. The bone is usually broken directly across its width but can also be broken lengthwise or spirally. Fractures can be closed (simple) or open (compound). In a closed fracture the broken bone ends stay under the skin and little or no surrounding skin and tissues are damaged. In an open fracture one or both bone ends stick out through the skin. Fractures are caused by a sudden injury that exerts more force on the bone than it can support. The common symptom of a fracture is swelling and tenderness at the place of the fracture. In some cases the bone ends are deformed or stick out. Pain is often severe and is usually made worse by any movement of the area. Anyone suffering a suspected or known fracture should be taken to a hospital. Do not try to force the bone back into place.

♦ **Sprains.** A tearing or stretching of the ligaments that hold together the bone end in a joint is called a **sprain**. Sprains are caused by a sudden pull or twist. The main symptoms of a sprain are pain and tenderness in the affected area and rapid swelling. Sometimes there is discoloration of the skin and an inability to use the joint. Because a sprain and a fracture have similar symptoms the sprain should be x-rayed to be sure that it is not a fracture. Treat a sprain by applying an ice pack to reduce swelling then wrap the joint with a compression bandage and rest it in a raised position until the pain and swelling begin to drop. Take aspirin or other pain killers to relieve pain.

♦ **Hernias.** In a **hernia** an organ or tissue sticks out through a weak area in the muscle or other tissue that usually contains it such as the abdominal wall. The cause is usually a weakness in the wall. The first symptom is a bulge in the wall. Treat by wearing a supportive garment or truss. In severe cases surgery is performed.

♦ **Arthritis.** An inflammation of the joints is called **arthritis.** Arthritis causes stiffness, swelling, soreness, or pain. **Osteoarthritis** is a type of arthritis that results from wear and tear on the cartilage at the joints. **Rheumatoid arthritis** causes swelling and pain and can occur at any age. Sometimes the joints stiffen in a deformed position. Cortisone and other medications are used in the treatment of arthritis.

♦ **Tendonitis. Tendonitis** is an inflammation of a tendon. Tendonitis usually occurs at bone junctions. Usually pain is felt in the wrist or ankle after extensive use such as running or using a computer. This condition is common in athletes and typists.

REVIEW QUESTIONS

1. Name one disorder of the musculoskeletal system. State its symptoms and treatment.

____

____

Name ______________________ Class __________________ Date __________

CAREER OPPORTUNITIES

ATHLETIC TRAINER: A person specially trained to give first aid to athletes who are injured in sports activities is called an **athletic trainer**. All sports use trainers who are on hand to give first aid on the field or on the court, and treatment before or after a game. When necessary physicians examine injuries after trainers have given first aid. To qualify for this job a person should first obtain a license in some kind of health profession, such as physical therapy, physical assistantship, or nursing. A knowledge of anatomy, physiology, chemistry, and physics is needed. Certification is optional but desirable.

*****

PHYSICAL THERAPIST: **Physical Therapists** help people with injuries and diseases of the nerves, bones, or muscles, get back the use of these injured parts. They work along with doctors by giving and interpreting tests and helping patients with exercises and other treatments. Specialized training, certification, and a bachelor's degree are required.

*****

REVIEW QUESTIONS

1. Describe one job that requires a knowledge of the musculoskeletal system.

____

____

____

____

____

____

____

____

____

____

____

____

____

Name________________________ Class____________________ Date___________

LAB INVESTIGATION: LOCOMOTION STRUCTURES

OBJECTIVE

Upon completion of this activity you should be able to identify and state the functions of bones, muscles, joints, ligaments, and tendons.

LABORATORY PROCEDURE

Materials: Uncooked chicken wing, dissecting pan, dissecting pins, dissecting scissors, scalpel, safety goggles, dissecting needle, forceps, lab apron, and paper towels.

1. Collect your laboratory materials from the supply table and take them to your lab area. Work in pairs or alone as your teacher directs. ***Important: Wear safety goggles and a laboratory apron while doing this activity.***

2. Cover your dissecting pan with a paper towel. Place the chicken wing in the dissecting pan with the cut end facing you.

3. Carefully remove all the skin from the chicken wing by using forceps to lift the skin at the cut end of the wing and to cut the skin lengthwise with the dissecting scissors. Then pull the skin away from the wing.

4. Draw a diagram of your chicken wing in **Observation (1)** in the **Observation Section** on the next page.

5. Observe the pink fleshy material surrounding the bones. The pink fleshy structures are *muscles*. Muscles move bones. Label the muscles on your observation drawing.

6. Follow a muscle with your probe to the point where it attaches to a bone. The white cords that attach to muscles to the bones are the *tendons*. Label the tendons **Observation (1).**

7. Use the dissecting needle to pull the muscles away from the sides of the bones. Cut the muscles away from the bones with your dissecting scissors. *Bones* protect and support the body. They are the framework for *endoskeletons* (inner skeletons). Draw a diagram of your chicken wing bones in **Observation (2)** in the **Observation Section** on the next page. Label the bones on your observation drawing.

8. Observe the area where the bones are joined. Bend your chicken wing. The flexible areas where bones are connected are called *joints*. Label the joints **Observation (2)**.

Name________________________ Class ____________________ Date __________

9. Pull the bones away from each other at the joints. The tough, white cords that connect the bones are the *ligaments*. Use your scalpel to separate the bones by cutting through the ligaments. Notice how strong the ligaments are. Label the ligaments in **Observation (2).**

10. When you are finished with your laboratory activity, wrap the chicken wing in the paper towel and throw it away. Clean your materials and lab area and return your materials to the supply table.

11. Answer the question in the **Conclusion Section**.

OBSERVATIONS

(1) MUSCLES AND TENDONS	(2) BONES, JOINTS, AND LIGAMENTS

CONCLUSIONS

1. State the functions of the following structures:

   Bones. ____

   ____

   Muscles. ____

   ____

   Joints. ____

   ____

   Ligaments. ____

   ____

   Tendons. ____

   ____

Name________________________ Class________________________ Date__________

REVIEW ACTIVITIES

Important Terms

DIRECTIONS: Define the following terms in the spaces provided.

ball and socket joints ____

____

biceps ____

____

bones ____

____

cardiac muscle ____

____

cartilage ____

____

extensor ____

____

flexor ____

____

fractures ____

____

fused joints ____

____

gliding joints ____

____

hernia ____

____

hinge joints ____

____

involuntary muscles ____

____

Name______________________ Class__________________ Date__________

joints ____

____

ligaments ____

____

locomotion ____

____

marrow ____

____

muscle fatigue ____

____

muscles ____

____

physical therapist ____

____

pivot joints ____

____

skeletal muscle ____

____

smooth muscle ____

____

sprain ____

____

striated muscle ____

____

tendons ____

____

triceps ____

____

voluntary muscles ____

____

Name________________________ Class____________________ Date____________

Skill Practice

Part A. Label the parts of the skeletal system by placing the correct term on the line provided.

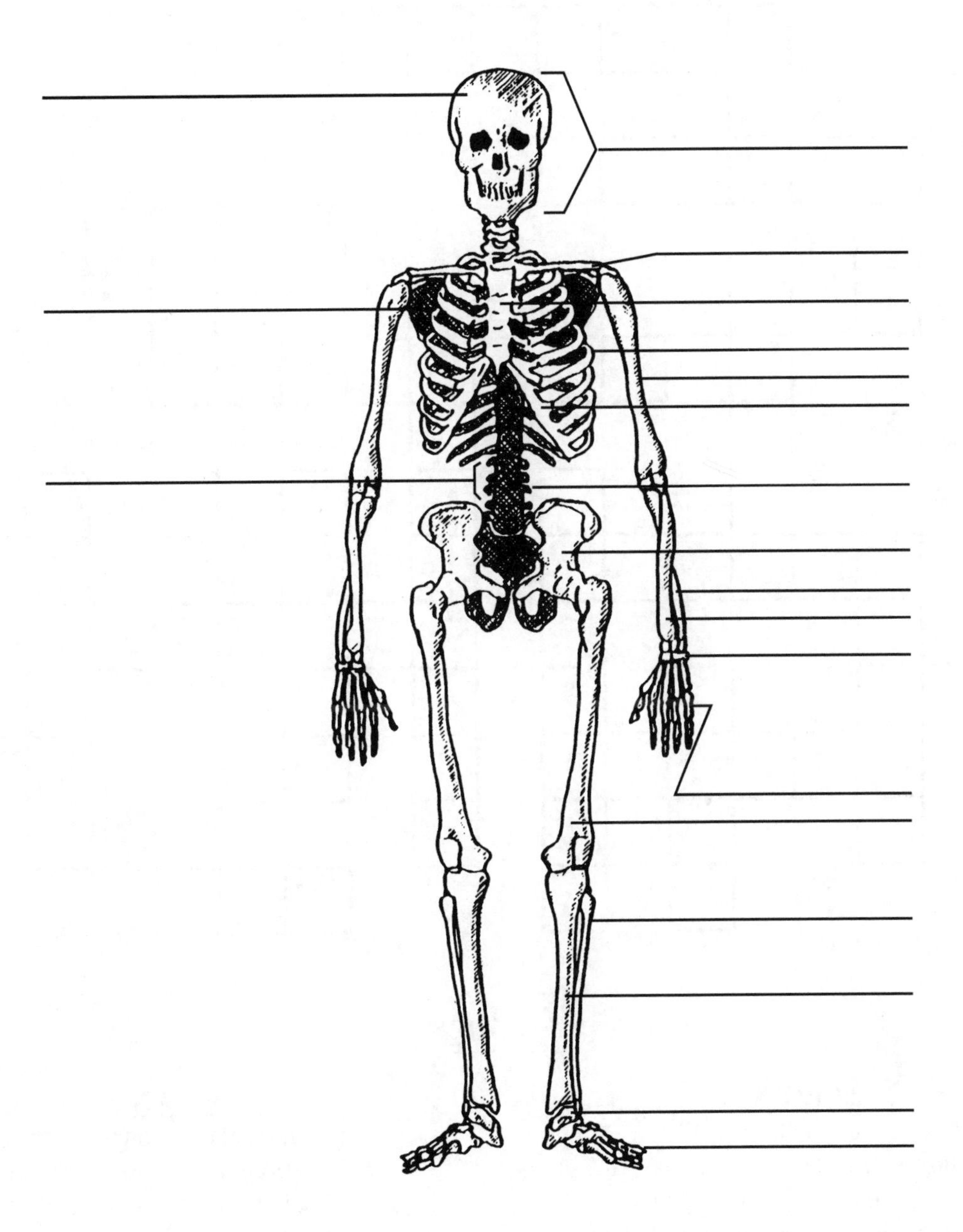

Name_________________________ Class___________________ Date__________

Part B. Complete the following crossword puzzle.

Crossword Puzzle

Clues

ACROSS

1. Muscle found in heart walls
2. Muscle disorder of abdominal wall
3. Has more cartilage than adult
6. Interaction of muscles with skeleton
10. Muscle that bends limbs
11. Connect muscles to bones
13. Locomotion allows animals to _____________ enemies
14. Some bones manufacture blood _____________

DOWN

1. Flexible, elastic connective tissue
2. Location of ball and socket joint
4. Make up framework of skeleton
5. Muscles you can control
7. Upper arm muscles
8. Type of joint located at elbow
9. Pull on bones when they contract
10. Joints that don't move
12. An artery _________ contains smooth muscle tissue

Name______________________________ Class______________________ Date____________

CHAPTER 13: QUIZ

A. FILL-IN QUESTIONS

DIRECTIONS: Complete each of the following statements by writing the correct word or phrase in the space provided.

1. A person specially trained to give first aid to injured athletes is called a/an ______________________________.
2. ______________________ produce body movement by pulling on bones.
3. Lactic acid causes muscle pain called ______________________________________.
4. The ____________________________ of the skeleton support and protect body organs.
5. A/an ____________________________ and a fracture have similar symptoms.
6. Anaerobic respiration occurs when muscles do not have enough ______________________.
7. ____________________________ is the interaction of muscles with the skeleton that causes body movement.
8. The bicep is an example of a type of muscle called a/an ____________________________.
9. Bands of tissue that connect bones to bones are ______________________________.
10. The type of joint located at the hip and shoulder is a/an ________________________ joint.
11. The __________________________ is an example of a flexor.
12. Red and white blood cells are produced in the ______________________________ of bones.
13. An example of a voluntary muscle is ____.
14. Bones are connected at ______________________________.
15. The walls of the heart are made up of ______________________________ muscle.
16. The muscles controlling heartbeat and peristalsis are called ____________________ muscles.
17. The fibrous, flexible, elastic connective tissue found in the human skeleton is ______________________________.
18. Bands of tissue that connect muscles to bones are ____________________________.
19. The stomach contains ________________________ muscle.
20. ____________________________ are broken bones.

B. MULTIPLE-CHOICE QUESTIONS

DIRECTIONS: Circle the number of the expression that best completes each of the following statements.

1. Muscle cells that continue to work when they do not have enough oxygen often produce
   (1) hydrochloric acid　　(3) lactic acid
   (2) hormones　　(4) alcohol
2. In humans, a ball and socket joint is located at the
   (1) knee　　(3) finger
   (2) elbow　　(4) shoulder

Name________________________ Class____________________ Date__________

3. A gliding joint is located in the

(1) hip (3) ankle
(2) knee (4) elbow

Directions (4-5): Base your answers to questions 3 and 4 on the diagram below and on your knowledge of biology.

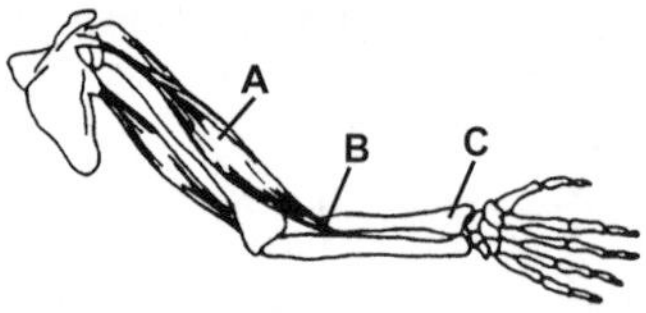

A
B
C

4. What stimulates structure A to contract?

(1) nerves (3) cartilage
(2) blood (4) oxygen

5. Structure B, which connects structure A to structure C, is known as

(1) an artery (3) a tendon
(2) a bone (4) a vein

6. Human muscle tissue becomes fatigued because of the production of

(1) oxygen (3) alcohol
(2) glucose (4) lactic acid

7. The human skeleton is composed of

(1) cartilage and tendons (3) bone and cartilage
(2) ligaments and tendons (4) bone and muscles

8. To be most efficient, muscles of the human body require a constant supply of

(1) oxygen and sugar (3) lactic acid and oxygen
(2) carbon dioxide and lactic acid (4) sugar and carbon dioxide

9. The function of ligaments in the human body is to

(1) join muscles to bones (3) coordinate body movements
(2) connect bones to bones at joints (4) protect internal organs

10. Examples of muscles that are voluntary are

(1) skeletal and cardiac (3) smooth only
(2) smooth and cardiac (4) skeletal only

C. ESSAY QUESTION

DIRECTIONS: Use complete sentences to answer the question in this part.

1. State one advantage provided by locomotion.

____

____

____

____

Name________________________________ Class___________________________ Date ______________

UNIT THREE TEST

Matching Questions

***DIRECTIONS:** In the space at the left of each item in Column A, place the letter of the term or phrase in Column B that is most closely related to that item.*

Column A	Column B
_______ **1.** Support and protect body organs.	**a.** Cartilage
_______ **2.** Rhythmic contractions.	**b.** Peristalsis
_______ **3.** Carry blood to heart.	**c.** Nutrients
_______ **4.** Change in environment.	**d.** Muscles
_______ **5.** Soft connective tissue.	**e.** Diaphragm
_______ **6.** Subunit of kidney.	**f.** Stimulus
_______ **7.** Carry blood away from heart.	**g.** Bones
_______ **8.** Dome-shaped muscle.	**h.** Nephron
_______ **9.** Produce body movement.	**i.** Veins
_______ **10.** Usable parts of food.	**j.** Larynx
	k. Arteries
	l. Ptyalin
	m. Feces

True–False Questions

***DIRECTIONS:** Write TRUE before each statement that is true and FALSE before each statement that is false.*

_______ **1.** The central nervous system includes the brain and spinal cord.

_______ **2.** Locomotion decreases the chances for survival of organisms.

_______ **3.** The lungs are a part of the excretory system.

_______ **4.** The pharynx is the voice box.

_______ **5.** Thin, one-celled, microscopic blood vessels are called veins.

_______ **6.** All people have the same blood type.

_______ **7.** Salivary glands are located in the chest cavity.

_______ **8.** Most digestion occurs in the large intestine.

_______ **9.** Beriberi is a vitamin deficiency disease.

_______ **10.** The largest percentage of body weight is water.

Name ______________________ Class ____________________ Date __________

Fill-In Questions

***DIRECTIONS:** Complete each of the following statements by writing the correct word or phrase in the space provided.*

1. ______________________ are nutrients that are used to build and repair body tissue.
2. A selection of foods that supply the body with enough energy and chemicals for good health is called a/an ______________________.
3. The physical breakdown of food is called ______________________ digestion.
4. The ______________________ is a tube that moves food from the mouth to the stomach.
5. ______________________ immunity is produced by injecting antibodies into the body.
6. The ______________________ is the largest internal organ in the body.
7. A message that is carried by nerve fibers is called a/an ______________________.
8. A cyton is a/an ______________________ cell.
9. Ductless glands are part of the ______________________ system.
10. Muscle fatigue is caused by ______________________ acid.

Multiple-Choice Questions

***DIRECTIONS:** Circle the number of the expression that best completes each of the following statements.*

1. Seeking shelter and escaping dangerous situations are advantages provided directly by the
   (1) ability of muscles to contract
   (2) digestive enzymes in the stomach
   (3) filtering action of the kidneys
   (4) white blood cells in the lymph system
2. Endocrine glands produce
   (1) white blood cells
   (2) hormones
   (3) bile
   (4) blood plasma
3. Kidney stones and cirrhosis of the liver are disorders of which body system?
   (1) digestive
   (2) circulatory
   (3) respiratory
   (4) excretory
4. Which organ acts as a filter in the removal of urea and excess water from the blood?
   (1) lung
   (2) kidney
   (3) urinary bladder
   (4) small intestine
5. Which is a disorder characterized by low oxygen levels in the blood?
   (1) diarrhea
   (2) acne
   (3) anemia
   (4) appendicitis
6. The blood-clotting process is started by
   (1) red blood cells
   (2) white blood cells
   (3) platelets
   (4) alveoli

Name________________ Class________________ Date__________

7. Blood proteins that protect against disease are known as

(1) antibodies
(2) toxins
(3) amino acids
(4) fatty acids

Directions (8-10): Base your answers to question 8 through 10 on the diagrams below of structures found in the human body and on your knowledge of biology.

(1) **(2)** **(3)** **(4)**

8. Which would transmit an impulse to a muscle or a gland?

(1) 1
(2) 2
(3) 3
(4) 4

9. Which circulates within the body?

(1) 1
(2) 2
(3) 3
(4) 4

10. Which is involved directly with the absorption into the blood of the end products of digestion?

(1) 1, only
(2) 1 and 2
(3) 3, only
(4) 2 and 4

Essay Question

DIRECTIONS: Use complete sentences to answer the question in this part.

1. State two ways that water can be excreted from the human body.

____

____

____

____

____

____

____

____

____

Class Notes

UNIT FOUR

DIVERSITY AMONG LIVING THINGS

LEARNING OUTCOMES: Upon completion of the study of this unit, you should be able to:

- Classify organisms according to the Linnaean system of classification.
- Identify and describe the basic functions necessary to maintain homeostasis.
- Identify and compare the adaptations of selected organisms for carrying out these life functions.
- Recognize that there is great biodiversity in the environment.
- Correlate biochemical reactions with psychological functions.
- Observe and recognize that structure and function complement each other and culminate in an organism's successful adaptation to its environment.

Chapter 14: Classification of Living Things

A. NEED FOR CLASSIFICATION. Living things have characteristics in common such as the functions or activities that are necessary to maintain life. However, the methods by which living things carry on these life functions differ tremendously. These differences indicate a great variety, called *biodiversity,* among living things. In order to study living things in an organized and efficient manner, biologists found it necessary to **classify** or group organisms in a logical way.

We use a system of classification when we look up a word in a dictionary. It would be very difficult to find a word if the pages of the dictionary were torn out and tossed in a pile on the floor. Instead, the words are arranged or *classified* for us in alphabetical order making it easier to locate individual words.

In the past many different systems of classification were used to classify organisms. One early system was based on an organism's color. Another system grouped living things according to habitats (places where organisms live). These methods were not successful because the groupings were too broad and made the study of organisms very difficult. Over time many other systems of classification were devised. Most of these systems were eventually discarded because of disagreement among scientists as to which system most accurately organized related organisms. **Taxonomy** is the science of naming and classifying organisms. Scientists who name and classify organisms are called **Taxonomists.**

Name______________________________ Class _______________________ Date _____________

REVIEW QUESTIONS

1. The science of naming and classifying organisms is called ______________________

2. ______________________________ are scientists who name and classify organisms.

B. BASIS FOR CLASSIFICATION. The most common basis for classifying organisms is similarities in structure. These structures may be whole external or outer structures (exoskeleton and appendages), internal or inner structures (organs or endoskeletons), or cellular structures (chloroplasts, nuclei). Biochemical and genetic similarities, similarities in patterns of embryological development, and fossil evidence are also used for classification.

REVIEW QUESTIONS

1. The most common basis for classifying organisms is ______________________

   ____

2. Also used for the classification of organisms are ______________________

   ____ and

   ____.

C. SYSTEMS OF CLASSIFICATION. One commonly used classification system assumes that present day forms of life developed from earlier forms. **Kingdom** is the largest classification group and contains the greatest number of different organisms. In this system biologists group organisms into a five-kingdom system: **Monera, Protista, Fungi, Plant,** and **Animal** (Table 14-1).

[***Note: Some scientists have adopted a six-kingdom system while others use a newer system called the three-domain system that contains six kingdoms. Domains are taxonomic groups of organisms that share similarities in basic cell biochemistry.***]

We will study the five-kingdom system that is based on the following standards: **(1)** The presence or absence of a nuclear membrane within the cell. **(2)** Whether the organism is unicellular (one-celled) or multicellular (many-celled). **(3)** Type of nutrition.

In the five-kingdom system of classification, monerans are considered to be the most primitive (oldest) organisms and animals are thought to be the most recent organisms. Monerans differ from other living things because they lack a distinct membrane-bounded nucleus and other cell organelles. Cells that lack a distinct membrane-bounded nucleus are called **prokaryotic.** Cells with a definite membrane-bounded nucleus are **eukaryotic**. Protists, fungi, plants, and animals are all eukaryotic.

Protists are mainly unicellular (one-celled) plant-like or animal-like organisms. Fungi differ from all other organisms in their basic cellular structure. Fungi are nonphotosynthetic (lack chlorophyll) and have cell walls. Plants are organisms that are multicellular, mainly photosynthetic, with at least one tissue level of organization. Animals are multicellular, nonphotosynthetic organisms with at least one tissue level of organization. Most animals have organs and organ systems.

Name________________________ Class________________________ Date____________

KINGDOM	CHARACTERISTICS	MEMBERS	EXAMPLES
Monera	Primitive cell structure; lacking a nuclear membrane and membranous organelles.	**Bacteria** **Blue-green algae**	decay bacteria, tuberculosis bacteria *nostoc*
Protista	Mainly unicellular organisms with plant-like and/or animal-like characteristics.	**Protozoa** (Nutrition is animal-like) **Algae** (Nutrition is plant-like)	paramecium, ameba (amoeba) spirogyra
Fungi	Cells are usually organized into branched, multinucleated filaments (except yeast) that absorb digested food from the environment. Contain no chlorophyll.	**True fungi**	mushroom, bread mold, yeast
Plantae (Plants)	Multicellular, photosynthetic (contain chlorophyll) organisms.	**Bryophytes** (Lack vascular tissue; no true roots, stems, leaves.) **Tracheophytes** (Have vascular tissue; true roots, stems, leaves.)	moss Geranium, fern, bean, pine tree, maple tree, corn
Animalia (Animals)	Multicellular organisms that ingest their food.	**Coelenterates** (Hollow-body, 2 cell layers.) **Annelids** (Segmented body walls.) **Mollusks** (1 or 2 part shell.) **Arthropods.** (Jointed appendages, exoskeleton) **Chordates** (Dorsal nerve cord.)	hydra, jellyfish earthworm, sandworm clam, snail grasshopper, lobster, spider shark, frog, human

TABLE 14-1. FIVE-KINGDOM SYSTEM.

Review Questions

1. The five-kingdom classification system assumes that present day forms of life developed from

____.

Name_________________________ Class_____________________ Date___________

2. ____________________ is the largest classification group.

3. Name the five kingdoms that make up the five-kingdom classification system.

____

____

4. Some scientists have adopted a six-kingdom system while others use a newer system called

____

5. Define the term domain. ____

____

D. SUBDIVISIONS OF KINGDOMS. The members of each kingdom share some major characteristics but they are a highly dissimilar group of organisms. Thus, for the purposes of classification, each kingdom is subdivided into smaller and smaller groups ending with the smallest group, which includes all organisms of the same kind. Each kingdom is divided into *phyla* (singular, *phylum*). Each **phylum** is divided into smaller groups called **classes**. Classes are divided into **orders**, orders into **families**, families into **genera** (singular, **genus**), and genera into **species**. A species includes all organisms of the same kind. These organisms are very similar to one another and can mate and produce fertile offspring. Table 14-2 compares the classification of some common organisms.

GROUP	HUMAN	HOUSE CAT	CORN	LADY BEETLE
Kingdom	Animalia	Animalia	Plantae	Animalia
Phylum	Chordata	Chordata	Tracheophyta	Arthropoda
Class	Mammalia	Mammalia	Spermatophyta	Insecta
Order	Primates	Carnivora	Angiospermae	Coleoptera
Family	Hominidae	Felidae	Commelinales	Coccinellidae
Genus	Homo	Felis	Zea	Hippodamia
Species	sapiens	domestica	mays	convergens

TABLE 14-2. CLASSIFICATION OF COMMON ORGANISMS.

REVIEW QUESTIONS

1. List, in correct order, the main classification groups. Start with the largest group and end with the smallest group. ____

____

2. The ____________________ group includes all organisms of the same kind. These organisms are ____________________ to one another and can ________________ and produce ________________.

3. Complete the following table by comparing classification groups.

CLASSIFICATION GROUP	HOUSE CAT	HUMAN
Kingdom		
Phylum		
Class		
Order		
Family		
Genus		
Species		

E. SCIENTIFIC NAMES. Before scientists agreed upon a method of naming organisms using scientific names living things were referred to by common names**.** Common names are local names given to an organism in a certain geographic region. These names can be confusing because there may be more than one common name for the same organism. Woodchuck, ground hog, and gopher are common names for the same organism. Common names also may be misleading since they often contain a word that does not correctly describe the organism. For example, neither the starfish nor the silverfish is a fish.

In the 18th century a Swedish naturalist **Carolus Linnaeus** devised a widely used classification system. This system separates organisms into smaller and smaller subgroups based on similar characteristics. To avoid confusion, organisms are given Latin scientific names that are accepted worldwide. Latin is used for scientific naming because it is the universal language of science. Scientific names consist of a genus and species name for each organism. These names are written in italics. The genus name is *capitalized* and the species name is *not capitalized*. For example, the scientific name for humans is ***Homo sapiens***. Because each different organism is identified by two names, this system is called the **binomial nomenclature system** (two–name naming system). Examples of scientific names for some common organisms are shown in Table 14-3.

SCIENTIFIC NAME	COMMON NAME
Homo sapiens	man
Canis familiaris	dog
Canis latrans	coyote
Felis tigris	tiger
Felis leo	lion
Felis domestica	house
Zea mays	corn
Acer saccharum	sugar maple

TABLE 14-3. COMPARING SCIENTIFIC AND COMMON NAMES.

Name ______________________ Class ____________________ Date __________

Review Questions

1. Who is responsible for our present system of classification?

____

2. Why are scientific names used to name organisms? ______________________

____

3. The language that is used to name organisms is ______________________.

4. What does the term *binomial nomenclature* mean? ______________________

____

5. The scientific name of an organism consists of a ____________ and a ____________ name. These names are written in ________________. The ________________ name is capitalized and the ______________ name is not.

6. The scientific name for the sugar maple is ______________________.

CAREER OPPORTUNITIES

TAXONOMIST: A **taxonomist** is a scientist who identifies and classifies organisms. For example, **plant taxonomists** identify and classify plants. **Animal taxonomists** identify and classify animals. In order to be a taxonomist you must have at least a four year college degree in one of the natural sciences-usually botany or zoology. Most taxonomists have a master's degree and some have a doctoral degree.

*****

MUSEUM CURATOR: **Museum curators** are in charge of museums or museum departments. They are responsible for planning exhibits, acquiring materials, development, care, and classification of collections. They also do lab research and field studies including museum sponsored expeditions. Characteristics you need have to be a curator are patience, a logical mind, a creative imagination, physical stamina, administrative ability, ability to work with people, and good communication skills. The educational requirements for museum curators are: a college preparatory high school course including one or more languages, a bachelor's degree in natural sciences, a master's degree, and sometimes a Ph. D. Some colleges offer courses in museum studies.

*****

Review Questions

1. Name and describe one career opportunity for someone interested in taxonomy.

____

____

____

Name_______________________________ Class____________________ Date___________

LAB INVESTIGATION: CLASSIFICATION

OBJECTIVE

Upon completion of this activity you should be able use a classification key to classify organisms.

LABORATORY PROCEDURE

Materials: Paper and pencil.

1. Below is a mosquito classification key. Classification keys are used by biologists to classify unknown organisms according to structural characteristics. This key shows various characteristics used to identify the differences between ***Anopheles***, ***Deinocerites***, ***Culex***, ***Psorophora***, and ***Aedes*** mosquitoes. The characteristics used are shape and length of antennae, length of palps, shape of abdomen tip, and presence of long scales on hind legs.

2. Study the key. Notice that each characteristic has two choices, for example, **1a** or **1b**. To do **procedure 3**, you will need to refer back to this key. At each step in **procedure 3**, you will have to make a choice. Most choices eliminate organisms until you reach the correct one. It is very important that you follow the directions in the key. Now go to **procedure 3** that is located on the next page.

MOSQUITO GENERAL CLASSIFICATION KEY

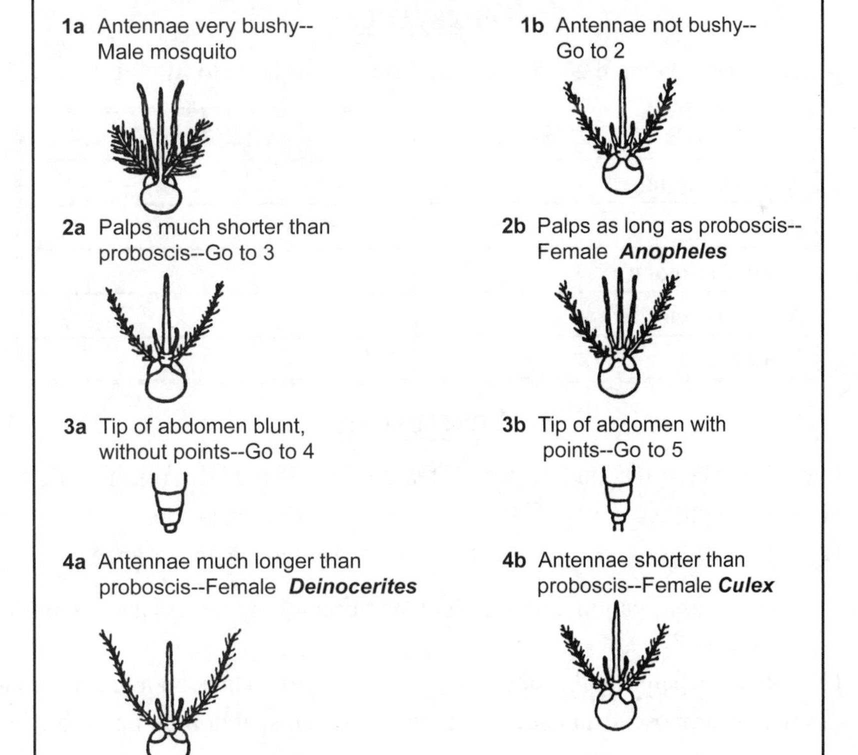

Name_______________________________ Class_______________________ Date___________

3. Below is a diagram of the mosquito you are to identify. It is labeled **UNKNOWN FEMALE MOSQUITO.** Follow the directions on the classification key in **procedure 2** until you have isolated one group. This should be the genus (***Anopheles***, ***Deinocerites***, ***Culex***, ***Psorophora***, or ***Aedes***) of the organism you are trying to identify. As you observe each characteristic write your choice in the table. For example, look at the antennae of the **UNKNOWN FEMALE MOSQUITO**. If the antennae are very bushy **write 1a** in the observation table. If the antennae are not bushy **write 1b** in the table. If you wrote **1b**, go to the next step in the classification key. Continue down the list of characteristics until you have identified the mosquito. **STOP** when you have identified the genus of the mosquito. You **DO NOT** have to fill out the entire table.

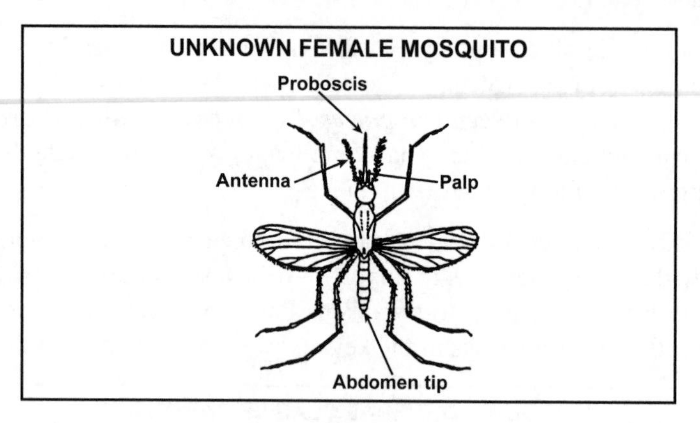

Observations

1. Write your observations in the table below. You **do not** have to fill out the entire table.

CHARACTERISTIC	CHOICE
Antennae type	
Palps	
Tip of Abdomen	
Antennae length	
Hind Legs	

Conclusions

1. According to the classification key, which feature identifies male from female mosquitoes?
   (1) palp length
   (2) leg scales
   (3) abdomen points
   (4) antennae appearance

2. According to the classification key, which characteristics are necessary to identify a **female *Anopheles*** mosquito?
   (1) antennae, palps, and proboscis
   (2) wings, proboscis, and scales on legs
   (3) eyes, scales on legs, and abdomen tip
   (4) palps, abdomen tip, and wings

3. According to the classification key, the unknown female mosquito shown above belongs to the genus known as
   (1) *Deinocerites*
   (2) *Culex*
   (3) *Psorophora*
   (4) *Aedes*

Name________________________ Class______________________ Date__________

REVIEW ACTIVITIES

Important Terms

DIRECTIONS: Define the following terms in the spaces provided.

Animalia ____

____

binomial nomenclature ____

____

Carolus Linnaeus ____

____

classify ____

____

eukaryotic ____

____

Fungi ____

____

Homo sapiens ____

____

kingdom ____

____

Monera ____

____

Plantae ____

____

prokaryotic ____

____

Protista ____

____

taxonomist ____

____

taxonomy ____

____

Name______________________ Class __________________ Date __________

Skill Practice

Part A. Complete the following chart.

KINDOM	CHARACTERISTICS	MEMBERS	EXAMPLES
Animalia			
Plantae			
Fungi			
Protista			
Monera			

Part B: Match the letter of the term in Column 1 with its description in Column 2. Write your answers on the lines next to the numbers in Column 2.

COLUMN 1	COLUMN 2
a. Fungi	_______ **1.** Largest division of a Kingdom
b. Genus	_______ **2.** Multicellular, ingest their food
c. Kingdom	_______ **3.** Group of closely related species
d. Phylum	_______ **4.** Includes the greatest number of organisms
e. Species	_______ **5.** Multicellular, photosynthetic organisms
f. Animalia	_______ **6.** Kingdom of bacteria and blue-green algae
g. Plantae	_______ **7.** One-celled plants and animals
h. Monera	_______ **8.** Largest division of a phylum
i. Class	_______ **9.** Many-celled, nonphotosynthetic, cell walls
j. Protista	_______ **10.** Smallest classification group

Name______________________ Class______________________ Date__________

CHAPTER 14: QUIZ

A. FILL-IN QUESTIONS

***DIRECTIONS:** Complete each of the following statements by writing the correct word or phrase in the space provided.*

1. The most common basis for grouping organisms is ______________________.
2. The ______________________ is the largest classification group and contains the greatest number of different organisms.
3. ______________________ is the science of naming and classifying organisms.
4. Our present classification system is based on a system invented by ______________________.
5. The scientific name for humans is ______________________.
6. Most biologists group organisms into a ______________________ kingdom system.
7. Binomial nomenclature is a ______________________name naming system.
8. The language used in classification is ______________________.
9. Each phylum is divided into smaller groups called ______________________.
10. Classes are subdivided into groups called ______________________.
11. The kingdom that includes humans is the ______________________ kingdom.
12. Many taxonomists divide living things into five kingdoms: monerans, protists, fungi, animals, and ______________________.
13. Organisms with cells that lack a nuclear membrane are classified in the kingdom ______________________.
14. The smallest grouping of organisms is the ______________________ group.
15. Multicellular organisms that contain chlorophyll are classified as ______________________.
16. *Homo sapiens* is the scientific name for ______________________.
17. An example of an organism that is classified as Monera is ______________________.
18. Organisms classified as Protists have ______________________ cell(s).
19. An example of a Fungi is the ______________________.
20. Latin is used in scientific naming in order to avoid ______________________.

B. MULTIPLE-CHOICE QUESTIONS

***DIRECTIONS:** Circle the number of the expression that best completes each of the following statements.*

21. Which two organisms belong to the same genus but are different species?
    (1) *Rana pipiens* and *Culix pipiens*
    (2) *Chrysemys picta* and *Clemmys insculpta*
    (3) *Clemmys guttata* and *Clemmys insculpta*
    (4) *Rosa rugosa* and *Carex rosea*

Name________________________ Class __________________ Date __________

22. Most biological classification systems are based on the idea that
(1) all life began in dry, desert-like areas of Africa
(2) present-day forms of life developed from earlier forms
(3) all advanced forms of life developed from the ameba
(4) animals living in the same habitat will have the same body structures

23. The scientific name of an organism is made up of the organism's
(1) kingdom and phylum (3) phylum and species
(2) class and phylum (4) genus and species

24. Scientific classification is based primarily on similarities in
(1) age (3) body structures
(2) habitat (4) eating habits

25. The two cats *Felis leo* and *Felis tigris* are classified into different
(1) kingdoms (3) phyla
(2) classes (4) species

26. *Salmonella typhosa* is an organism which causes food poisoning. The word *"Salmonella"* represents this organism's
(1) phylum (3) species
(2) genus (4) order

27. Simple organisms such as yeasts, algae, and protozoans are all classified as
(1) arthropoda (3) plants
(2) animals (4) protists

28. In the present system of classification, the smallest grouping of related organisms is the
(1) phylum (3) genus
(2) kingdom (4) family

29. According to modern classification, the euglena, which has no cell wall and yet produces its own food by photosynthesis, is classified as
(1) a plant (3) an animal
(2) a protist (4) a fungus

30. Within which group do the organisms show the least variation in characteristics?
(1) phylum (3) family
(2) class (4) species

C. ESSAY QUESTION

DIRECTIONS: Use complete sentences to answer the question in this part.

1. State one reason why scientists believe it is necessary to classify organisms.

____

____

____

____

____

Name________________________ Class____________________ Date__________

Chapter 15: Simple Organisms

A. INTRODUCTION. Living things are either simple or complex in structure and function. Those organisms that are less complex in structure and function are referred to as simple organisms. Viruses, bacteria, fungi, algae, and protozoa are classified as simple organisms.

REVIEW QUESTIONS

1. Name five simple organisms. ____

____

B. VIRUSES. A **virus** is not a cell. It is made up of genetic material inside a protein coat (Figure 15-1). Viruses are smaller than most cellular organisms and can only be seen with an electron microscope. There is disagreement as to whether viruses should be called organisms or even whether a virus is "alive". Most taxonomists do not place them anywhere in the classification system. Viruses do not carry on most metabolic activities. They can only reproduce inside a living cell called the **host** cell. Outside the host cell a virus is "lifeless" and often exists as a crystal. A virus has no means of locomotion.

Viruses influence our lives in both positive and negative ways. They cause infections in both plants and animals. Some viruses cause tumors and warts. They also destroy cells and are responsible for human diseases such as polio, measles, mumps, influenza, hepatitis, colds, and AIDS. Recent research has linked certain cancers to the activity of some viruses. Certain viruses are used in the control of insect pests. Others are used in genetic research. Scientists have been able to use viruses to biologically control caterpillars of the European pine sawfly and the gypsy moth.

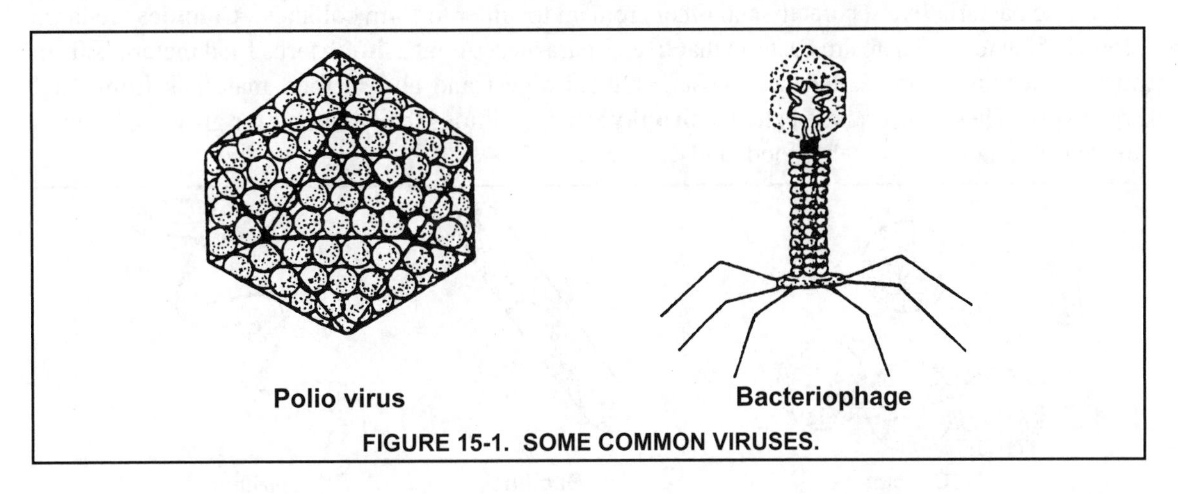

FIGURE 15-1. SOME COMMON VIRUSES.

REVIEW QUESTIONS

1. List two characteristics of viruses. ______________________________________

____

____

Name ______________________ Class ____________________ Date __________

2. State two ways that viruses help us. ______________________________

____

3. Name two ways that viruses are harmful. ______________________________

____

____

____

____

C. BACTERIA. Bacteria are microscopic unicellular (one-celled) organisms that lack a nuclear membrane. They are classified in the kingdom Monera. Bacteria may have been among the earliest forms of life to appear on earth and are so well adapted that they are found everywhere. Bacteria can live successfully on land, in water, and in the air. They also live in and on both living and dead plants and animals. Most bacteria are heterotrophs. **Heterotrophs** are organisms that cannot make their own food.

Although thousands of different species of bacteria have been identified there are three main types or shapes (Figure 15-2). These types are called **coccus** (round-shaped), **bacillus** (rod-shaped), and **spirillum** (spiral-shaped). A bacterium is made up of a thick cell wall that encloses and protects cellular material. Some bacteria are able to form spores. A **spore** is a cell with a protective coat. The protective coat makes it possible for the bacteria to survive during harsh conditions. Some of these conditions are extreme drying, heat, or cold. Bacteria have been found to survive for long periods of time because of their protective coats. When conditions become favorable spores begin to grow and reproduce normally.

Some bacteria live separately and others remain together to form colonies. **Colonies** are large groups of bacteria. There are bacteria that live as parasites. A **parasite** absorbs food materials from other living organisms called their hosts. Others digest and absorb food materials from dead organisms. These bacteria are called **saprophytes.** Conditions that are good for growing bacteria are warmth, moisture, suitable food, and darkness.

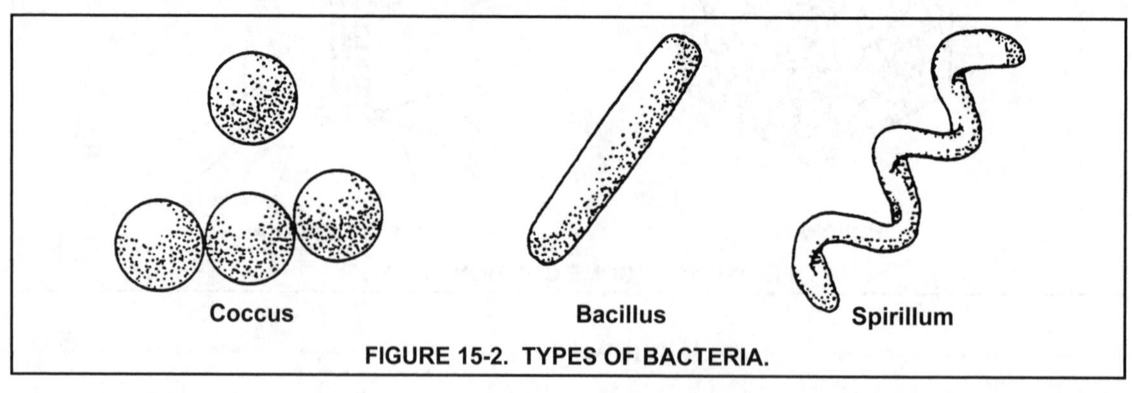

FIGURE 15-2. TYPES OF BACTERIA.

REVIEW QUESTIONS

1. List three characteristics of bacteria. ______________________________

____

2. Heterotrophs are organisms that ______________________ make their own food.

3. Name and draw three types of bacteria.

BACTERIA TYPE	DRAWING

4. Conditions that are favorable for bacterial growth are ____________ , ____________ ,

____________________ and ____________.

D. BENEFICIAL AND HARMFUL BACTERIA. Most bacteria are free-living and beneficial (helpful) to humans. Bacteria are decomposers that cause decay. **Decomposers** are organisms that break down dead organisms and return the nutrients to the soil. This is very important because decay is necessary for natural recycling processes. During decay complex substances are broken down into simple compounds that can be used again by other organisms. Bacteria are used in sewage disposal plants and home septic systems to break down solid wastes into simpler substances that can be disposed of more easily.

Many bacteria are used to produce food and life saving drugs. For example, bacteria are used to make cheese, pickles, yogurt, vinegar, and sauerkraut. By using methods of gene transplanting bacteria have been encouraged to produce substances, such as insulin, are is valuable to humans. The human intestinal tract contains millions of bacteria. Many of these bacteria help the digestive process and others produce vitamins. Bacteria are also used in tanning leather, curing tobacco, and producing silage (food) for feeding cows.

Some bacteria are not beneficial to man. Bacteria spoil food by secreting enzymes into the food causing it to rot. Along with enzymes other substances produced by bacteria are released into the food. Some of these substances are toxic making the food poisonous to humans and other organisms. Bacteria in large numbers can pollute (dirty) lakes, streams, and drinking water. Substances produced by bacteria in these water supplies can cause the death of other organisms. During respiration bacteria reduce the dissolved oxygen content in these water supplies.

Many bacteria are pathogenic. A **pathogen** is an organism that causes disease and/or infection. Some bacterial diseases of humans are tuberculosis, tetanus, and strep throat. Antiseptics, disinfectants, and antibiotics are used to control pathogenic bacteria. An **antibiotic** is a chemical that can stop the growth of some bacteria. Bacteria are able to produce types that are resistant to certain antibiotics. When this happens new antibiotics must be developed. Bacteria can also be killed in foods by pasteurization, canning, chemical preservatives, radiation, steam/pressure, salt curing, and dehydration (drying). Some bacteria can live anaerobically (without oxygen) and cause **botulism**, a dangerous type of food poisoning, in foods that have not been properly canned. Two other anaerobic bacteria cause the venereal diseases **gonorrhea** and **syphilis**. A **venereal disease**

Name____________________ Class____________________ Date__________

is a contagious disease that a person gets through sexual contact. Gonorrhea causes sterility. Syphilis can result in death. Both diseases can be treated successfully by antibiotics if detected early enough.

Review Questions

1. Decomposers are organisms that ____

____

2. Discuss why decay is an important process. ____________________________________

____

____

3. Name three food products produced by bacteria. __________________________________

____

4. State three harmful effects of bacteria. ____

____

5. ____________________, ____________________, and ____________________ are chemicals that can stop the growth of some harmful bacteria.

6. What is a pathogen? ____

____

7. Name two diseases caused by bacteria. ____

____

8. Define the term *venereal disease* and state two examples. ________________________

____

____

E. FUNGI. Fungi are simple organisms that lack roots, stems, and leaves. They are **nonmotile** (cannot move around) and exist in a variety of forms. Fungi lack chlorophyll and cannot make their own food. Like bacteria most fungi live as saprophytes or parasites. Because fungi are neither true plants nor animals they are classified in a separate kingdom called Fungi. Some types of fungi are yeasts, mushrooms, mold, puffballs, and mildews (Figure 15-3).

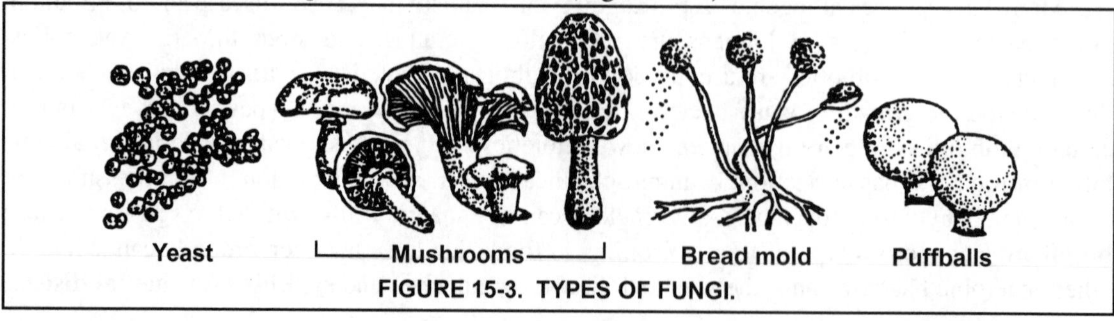

FIGURE 15-3. TYPES OF FUNGI.

Name________________________ Class________________________ Date____________

Fungi (Figure 15-3) live on or in their food supply. The body of a fungus, such as bread mold, consists of a mass of hairlike filaments. The root-like filaments called **rhizoids** penetrate the food source and secrete digestive enzymes. This is called extracellular digestion. The end products of digestion are then absorbed into the rhizoids and distributed to the cells of the organism..

Like bacteria fungi can be either beneficial or harmful to humans. Some fungi are decomposers causing the decay of dead plant and animal tissues. These decay products help keep soil fertile. Fungi, such as molds and yeasts, grow in and on foods causing them to spoil. **Athlete's foot,** and **ringworm,** which are human skin disorders, are caused by fungi. Other fungi cause destructive plant diseases, such as corn smut and wheat rust. **Corn smut** is a disease that results in large deformed growth on ears of corn. **Wheat rust** is a disease that infects young wheat plants and causes severe damage to wheat crops. Both diseases cause heavy losses to our food supply. **Mushrooms** are examples of helpful fungi that are used directly for food. Fungi are also used to make cheese. The carbon dioxide and ethyl alcohol released as waste products by yeast fermentation are used in the baking and alcoholic beverage industries. Fungi are used to produce the antibiotics penicillin and streptomycin. **Penicillin** is produced from the *Penicillium* mold and streptomycin comes from the soil fungus *Streptomyces*.

REVIEW QUESTIONS

1. List three characteristics of fungi. ____
____

2. Some examples of fungi are ____________________, ____________________, ____________________ and ____________________.

3. Fungi are heterotrophic organisms that live ______________ or ______________ their food.

4. Digestive enzymes in fungi are secreted by the ____________________________.

5. Digestion in fungi is ____________________________ digestion.

6. Describe two ways that fungi are beneficial. ________________________________
____
____

7. Describe two ways that fungi are harmful. __________________________________
____
____

F. ALGAE. Algae are plant-like unicellular or simple multicellular organisms classified in the kingdom Protista. They lack true roots, stems, and leaves and are found as single cells, sheets of cells, balls of cells, or as chain-like filaments. Algae vary in size from microscopic to more than 50 meters in length. They contain chlorophyll and carry on photosynthesis, therefore, are called autotrophs. **Autotrophic** organisms can make their own food. Algae live mainly in the water. Others live in damp soil and even under desert rocks. Some algae have locomotion structures, while others cannot move around. Algae are classified according to color. Two examples of algae are **spirogyra** and **protococcus** (Figure 15-4).

Name ______________________ Class ____________________ Date __________

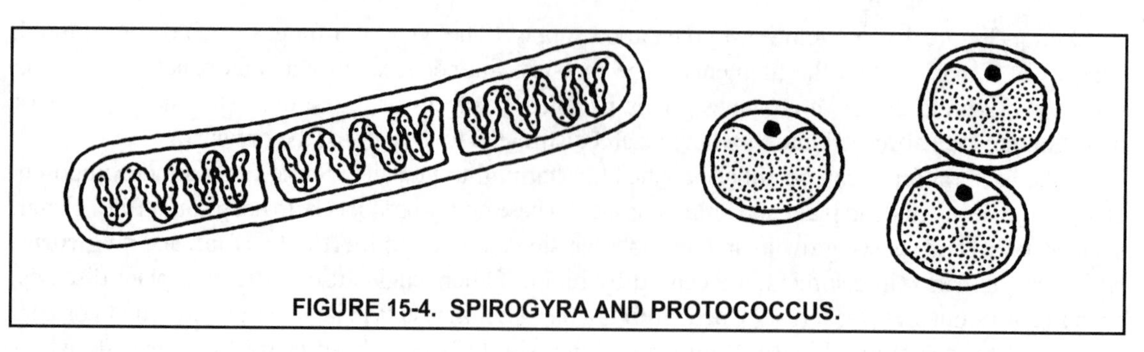
FIGURE 15-4. SPIROGYRA AND PROTOCOCCUS.

REVIEW QUESTIONS

1. Algae are classified in the kingdom ______________________.
2. ______________________ organisms can make their own food.
3. Two examples of algae are ______________________ and ______________________.

G. ECONOMIC IMPORTANCE OF ALGAE. Algae are the principal food producers in **aquatic** (water) environments. They are the basic source of food and oxygen for most organisms that live in water. Because they are so numerous they provide a major portion of our world's food supply. Algae also are used by industry. Seaweed, an alga, is used as a soil fertilizer. Some soups, flour, and ice creams contain products of algae. Laboratories use **agar,** a red alga, for growing bacteria and other organisms. Large numbers of certain types of algae in water supplies often contaminate the water making it unfit for drinking.

REVIEW QUESTIONS

1. Algae are the principal food producers in ______________________ environments.
2. State two ways that algae are used in industry. ______________________

   ____
3. State one way that algae is harmful to man. ______________________

   ____

H. PROTOZOA. Protozoa are microscopic unicellular animals. The prefix *proto* means first and the suffix *zoa* means animal. Protozoa are thought to be one of the first animals to inhabit the earth and can be either simple or complex.

Two commonly studied protozoa are the amoeba (ameba) and the paramecium (Figure 15-5). The **amoeba (ameba)** is a simple microscopic freshwater protozoan. It has no definite shape and looks like a "blob" of protoplasm. The **paramecium,** classified as a complex protozoan, has a definite slipper-like shape. This shape is due to a tough outer covering called the **pellicle**. This organism contains two nuclei: a small nucleus, called the **micronucleus**, and a large nucleus called the **macronucleus**.

Name________________________________ Class________________________________ Date____________

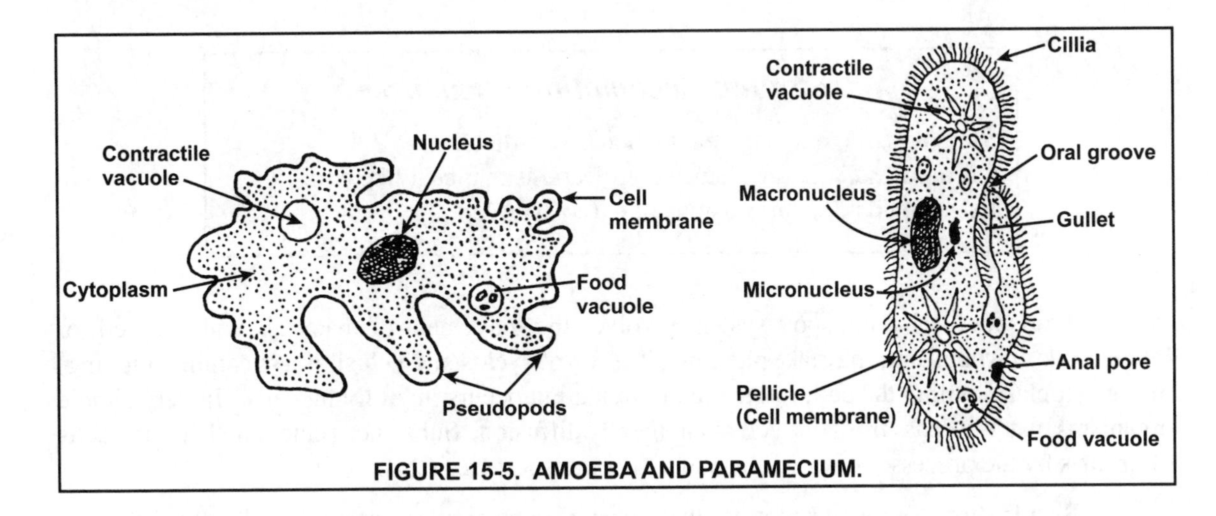

FIGURE 15-5. AMOEBA AND PARAMECIUM.

REVIEW QUESTIONS

1. Protozoa are thought to be the first ______________________________ to inhabit the earth.
2. Two commonly studied protozoa are the __________________ and the __________________.
3. ______________________________ are microscopic unicellular animals.

I. LIFE FUNCTIONS IN PROTOZOA. Protozoa have special cell *organelles* (little organs inside the cell) that perform their life functions. The majority are free-living but some are parasitic.

♦ **Nutrition.** Protozoa are heterotrophic (cannot make their own food) and exist in many different forms. In simple protozoa, such as the amoeba, food is ingested by **phagocytosis**–a process in which extensions of the cell **(pseudopods)** surround and engulf the food. In more complex protozoa, such as the paramecia, food is brought into the cell by the beating of **cilia,** which direct food particles into the oral groove. Digestion is intracellular (inside the cell) where food is enclosed in a **food vacuole.** The end products of digestion then pass into the cell cytoplasm by diffusion. Undigested wastes are egested when the food vacuole merges with the cell membrane and are expelled or undigested materials are egested through a fixed opening called the **anal pore.**

♦ **Locomotion.** Most protozoa are motile and are classified into groups according to their method of locomotion. Locomotion is the ability to move from place to place. Organisms that are able to move from place to place are said to be **motile.** Organisms that are not capable of locomotion and that tend to remain in the same place attached to a surface are called **sessile.** Many small aquatic organisms cannot move around on their own. These organisms are carried around by water currents or blown around in the air. Protozoa move around in a variety of different ways. Some algae and protozoans move by means of a **flagellum**, a long hair-like organelle, which waves back and forth and propels the organism through the water. Others move by a flowing of their cytoplasm, forming projections called pseudopods, or by the beating of many short hair-like structures known as cilia. The coordinated beating of the cilia act like "little oars" that propel the organism rapidly through the water.

Name_________________________ Class___________________ Date__________

Protozoan Locomotion Structures

Flagella .... long, single, hair-like structures.
Cilia .... tiny, hairlike projections that beat like oars.
Pseudopods .... protrusions of cytoplasm.

♦ **Transport.** The transport system involves the movement of materials within a cell, or **intracellular circulation,** may take place by diffusion or cyclosis. **Cyclosis** is a streaming (moving) of the cytoplasm within the cell. Intracellular circulation occurs in all living cells. In very simple organisms materials pass from one cell to another by diffusion. Substances enter and leave the cells of protists by the processes of diffusion and active transport (see Chapter 5).

♦ **Respiration.** During respiration, the exchange of respiratory gases takes place by diffusion. The thin moist membrane, through which the exchange occurs, is the outer membrane of the organism and is in direct contact with the water or air of the environment.

♦ **Excretion.** In many one-celled organisms there are no special excretory structures. Excretion takes place by diffusion through the cell membrane and by active transport through contractile vacuoles. In fresh water protozoa, such as the ameba and paramecium, wastes diffuse out of the cell through the cell membrane into the surrounding water. Fresh water organisms have a problem with water balance because water tends to enter the cell by osmosis. They contain **contractile vacuoles** that collect excess water and excrete it from the cell into the environment by a process called active transport (as studied in Chapter 5). Water enters the cells of fresh water organisms by osmosis because the salt concentration inside the cell is higher than that of the surrounding water, making the water concentration inside the cell lower than that of the surrounding water. Energy is needed to remove excess water because the excess water must be excreted against the concentration gradient. This movement maintains equilibrium between the water concentration inside the cell and the water concentration outside the cell. Salt water organisms have the opposite problem. Because the salt concentration of the water is higher than that inside the cell, water tends to leave the cells by osmosis into the surrounding water. Because of this, salt water organisms possess adaptations that keep water from leaving their cells (Figure 15-6).

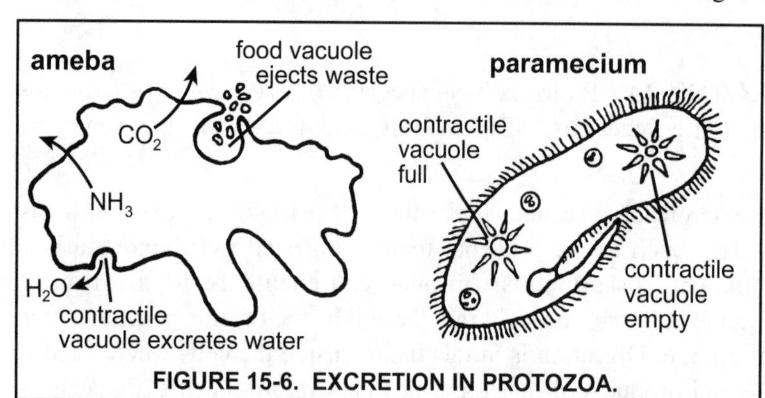

FIGURE 15-6. EXCRETION IN PROTOZOA.

♦ **Regulation.** Protozoa do not have true nervous systems. They do, however, respond to stimuli such as heat, light, food, and chemicals. Simple protozoa move toward warmth and food but away from irritating chemicals and intense light. More complex protozoa have a simple interconnected neurofibril system that reacts to certain stimuli such as movement toward food and movement away from acids. They can also reverse their direction of movement to avoid bumping into objects.

Name____________________ Class __________________ Date __________

◆ **Reproduction.** Reproduction in protozoa is both asexual and sexual. In simple protozoa, such as the amoeba, reproduction is a simple type of asexual reproduction called **binary fission.** The paramecium has both asexual and sexual methods of reproduction. Asexual reproduction is by binary fission and sexual reproduction is by a simple process called **conjugation**. (Reproduction will be covered in more detail in a later unit.)

REVIEW QUESTIONS

1. Reproduction in protozoa is both ________________ and ________________.
2. Organisms that are able to move around are called ____________________.
3. Name and describe three types of locomotion used by protozoa. ____________________
____
____
4. In simple organisms, the exchange of respiratory gases takes place by ________________.
5. The gas exchange surface in simple organisms is the ________________ membrane.
This membrane is in ____________________ with the environment.
6. Explain why water enters the cells of freshwater protozoa. ____________________
____
____
7. Protozoa respond to stimuli such as ________________________________.
8. Complete the following chart.

Protozoan Locomotion Structures

________________	long, single, hair-like structures
________________	tiny, hairlike projections that beat like oars
________________	protrusions of cytoplasm

J. PROTOZOA AND THE ENVIRONMENT. Protozoa can benefit or harm the environment. They benefit the environment by feeding on small organisms and in turn are fed on by larger organisms. In this way they occupy an important link in aquatic food chains. Some protozoa help digest food in the digestive tracts of animals such as cattle and termites. This type of relationship is called **symbiosis.** In a symbiotic relationship there is a close association between two different species of organisms. For example, termites eat cellulose fibers in wood but do not have the enzyme to digest the tough fibers. The protozoa produce an enzyme that breaks down the fibers into a form that can be used by both the protozoan and the termite. The termites benefit because they can digest their food. The protozoan benefit because they are protected from the outside environment and have a regular food supply. The shells of certain protozoa also have economic value because they produce limestone and chalk. [You will study more about symbiosis in Chapter 29].

Name______________________ Class__________________ Date__________

Protozoa harm the environment by causing human diseases such as malaria, African sleeping sickness, and amoebic dysentery. The organism that causes the disease **malaria** is a parasitic protozoan called *Plasmodium***.** This organism has a complex life cycle that involves more than one host. Part of the life cycle is spent inside the salivary glands of the female *Anopheles* mosquito. When an infected mosquito, called a vector, bites a human it injects some of the parasites into the blood causing the person to get malaria. The infected mosquito is called a **vector** because it carries disease organisms.

REVIEW QUESTIONS

1. In the life cycle of malaria, the host is the vector is the______________________.

2. Describe one way that protozoa benefit man. ______________________

____

CAREER OPPORTUNITIES

WATER TREATMENT SPECIALIST: Water treatment specialists treat water so that it is safe to drink. Operators control processes and equipment to remove solid materials, chemicals, and microorganisms from the water. They are required to operate and maintain pumps, pipes, valves, and processing equipment. This job also involves reading and interpreting meters and gauges, operating chemical feeding devices, taking samples of water and performing chemical and biological laboratory analyses. In addition, some jobs involve making minor repairs to valves, pumps, and other equipment. Workers work both indoors and outdoors.

They start their training as attendants or operators-in-training and learn skills on the job under the direction of an experienced operator. Larger plants combine on-the-job training with formal classroom or self-paced study programs. A high school diploma is usually required and courses in chemistry and biology should be taken. There are two year associate degree programs offered by some colleges. One year certificate programs are also available as well as correspondence courses. Most states require that you pass of a certifying examination. There are different types of certificates and educational requirements according to the level of job responsibility.

*****

REVIEW QUESTIONS

1. Name and describe one career opportunity for people interested in working with protists.

____

____

____

____

____

____

Name________________________ Class________________________ Date__________

LAB INVESTIGATION: PROTISTS

OBJECTIVE

Upon completion of this activity you should be able to identify some structural and functional characteristics of two representative protists.

LABORATORY PROCEDURE

Materials: Paramecia culture, Amoeba culture, medicine droppers, slides, cover slips, *Protoslo*, compound microscope.

1. Collect your laboratory materials from the supply table and take them to your lab area.

2. Place the name of each protist that you are to observe in column 1 of the **Observation Table** at the bottom of this page. As you observe each protist, place your observations in the table.

3. Obtain a culture of amoeba from your teacher. Put a cover slip on the culture. Observe the amoeba under the microscope under low power and then observe it under high power. Try to focus on one individual organism.

4. Observe the organism for several minutes. What does it look like? Draw a sketch of the organism and describe its characteristics in the **Observation Table** on the next page.

5. Now look for the locomotion and food-getting methods, if present. If the organism moves, describe the type of movement. If the organism is feeding, describe the feeding method. Write your observations in the **Observation Table** on the next page.

6. Next place a drop of paramecium culture on a clean slide. Put a cover slip on the culture. Observe the organism under the microscope under low power and then under high power. Try to focus on one individual organism. If the organism is moving too fast, put a drop of *Protoslo* under the cover slip.

7. Observe the organism for several minutes. What does it look like? Draw a sketch of the organism and describe its characteristics in the **Observation Table** on the next page.

8. Now look for the locomotion and food-getting methods, if present. If the organism moves, describe the type of movement. If the organism is feeding, describe the feeding method. Write your observations in the **Observation Table** on the next page.

9. When you are finished with your laboratory activity, clean your lab area and return your laboratory materials to the supply table.

10. Now answer the questions in the **Conclusion Section** on the next page.

Name________________________ Class____________________ Date____________

Observations

NAME OF PROTIST	DRAWING	CHARACTERISTICS (SIZE/SHAPE/COLOR)	TYPE OF LOCOMOTION AND FOOD-GETTING

Conclusions

1. What characteristic(s) did both protists have in common? ____________________

2. How were the protists different? ____________________

3. Describe the feeding method of one protist. ____________________

Name________________________ Class________________________ Date____________

REVIEW ACTIVITIES

Important Terms

DIRECTIONS: Define the following terms in the spaces provided.

algae ____

____

antibiotic ____

____

autotroph ____

____

bacillus ____

____

bacteria ____

____

binary fission ____

____

botulism ____

____

cilia ____

____

coccus ____

____

conjugation ____

____

contractile vacuole ____

____

decomposer ____

____

flagella ____

____

food vacuole ____

____

Name______________________ **Class**__________________ **Date**__________

gullet ____

heterotroph ____

motile ____

mushroom ____

nonmotile ____

pathogen ____

protozoa ____

pseudopods ____

rhizoids ____

saprophytes ____

spirillum ____

spore ____

syphilis ____

venereal disease ____

virus ____

Name________________________ Class____________________ Date__________

Skill Practice

Part A. Base your answers to questions 1 through 5 on the reading passage below and on your knowledge of biology. Underline the correct answer.

Lyme Disease

Thousands of people have been bitten by deer ticks and infected with the bacterial spirochete *Borrelia burgdorferi*, the cause of Lyme disease. About half of these people will not realize that they have been infected. After the initial infection, their immune systems will begin to control the bacterium, but not eliminate it altogether. Up to several years after the tick bite, the victims may develop complications such as crippling arthritis, neurological damage, and cardiac malfunctions. Now, researchers think they have determined one way *B. burgdorferi* manages to elude an activated immune system.

Five white-footed mice were infected with *B. burgdorferi*. The blood of the mice was sampled shortly thereafter, and it was confirmed that the mice were producing large quantities of antibodies that attacked the invading bacteria.

Four months later, *B. burgdorferi* were extracted from the infected mice and mixed with the same type of mouse antibodies. This time the bacteria initiated only a weak response, indicating that the antibodies were less able to recognize the bacteria. Since antibodies recognize a bacterium by binding to specific protein molecules on the bacterial surface, these surface molecules may somehow have changed over time. In this way, the bacteria are better able to escape early recognition by antibodies produced by the human immune system.

---

1. Shortly after the initial infection, the mice apparently

a.) got rid of the bacteria

b.) had no reaction to the infection

c.) produced antibodies against the disease

d.) suffered permanent neurological damage.

2. The organisms that cause Lyme disease are able to

a.) cause problems in plants as well as several species of animals

b.) change their proteins, thus making recognition by the mouse's immune system more difficult

c.) destroy mouse antibodies by chemically breaking them down into harmless end products

d.) be transmitted directly from one more to another

3. According to the passage, which symptom of lyme disease in humans might appear several years after the intial tick bite?

a.) a severe rash c.) kidney failure

b.) a high fever d.) joint inflammation

4. Which kingdom includes the organism that causes Lyme disease?

a.) Monera c.) Fungi

b.) Protista d.) Animal

5. The genus name of the organism that causes Lyme disease is

a.) *spirochete* c.) *burgdorferi*

b.) *Bacterium* d.) *Borrelia*

Name________________________ Class____________________ Date__________

Part B. Complete the following crossword puzzle.

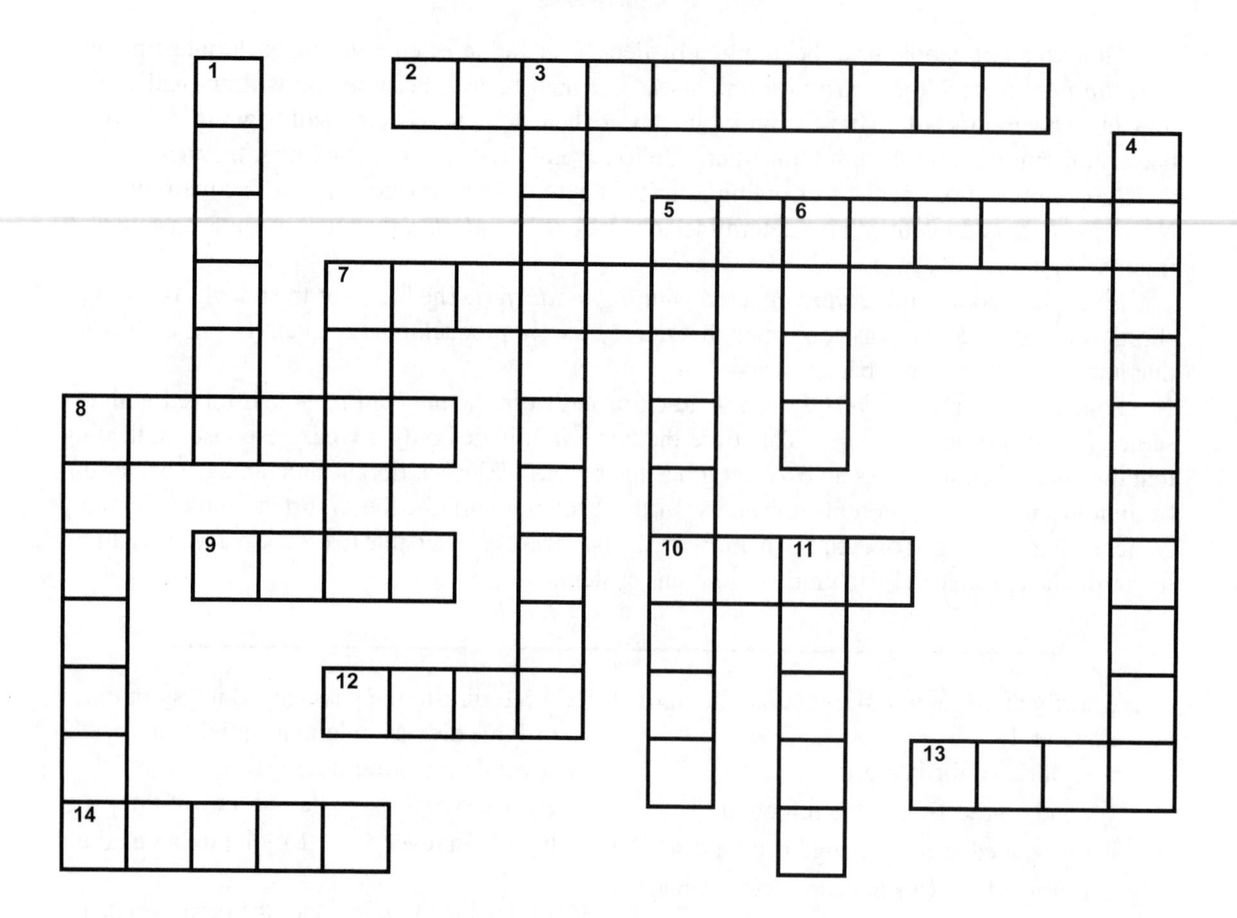

Clues

ACROSS

2. Stops growth of some bacteria
5. Tough outer covering of paramecium
7. Round-shaped bacteria
8. Able to move around
9. ______ pore for egestion
10. Groove for ingestion in paramecium
12. Name of cell where virus lives
13. Material used for growing bacteria
14. One-celled plants

DOWN

1. Passageway for food in paramecia
3. Tiny poisonous hair
4. Breaks down dead organisms
5. "False foot"
6. Spirogyra forms ______ chains
7. Locomotion in paramecium
8. Disease caused by protozoa
11. One-celled protozoan

Name____________________________ Class____________________________ Date__________

CHAPTER 15: QUIZ

A. FILL-IN QUESTIONS

DIRECTIONS: Complete each of the following statements by writing the correct word or phrase in the space provided.

1. Motile organisms have the ability to ______________________________.
2. The *Anopheles* mosquito carries the disease______________________________.
3. A close association between two different species or organisms is called ______________.
4. A simple organism made up of genetic material inside a protein coat is a ______________.
5. Conjugation is a simple type of ______________________ reproduction.
6. The principal food producers in water environments are ______________________.
7. A virus reproduces inside a cell called the ______________________________ cell.
8. ______________________________ are examples of protozoans.
9. Coccus is ______________________________ shaped bacteria.
10. Botulism is a dangerous type of ______________________________.
11. The paramecium uses ______________________________ for locomotion.
12. Athlete's foot and ringworm are human skin disorders caused by ______________.
13. ______________________ are organisms that break down dead organisms and return the nutrients to the soil.
14. ______________________ are organisms that digest and absorb food materials from dead organisms.
15. The first animals to inhabit the earth are thought to be ______________________.
16. ______________________ are examples of fungi that are used for food.
17. A pathogen is an organism that causes ______________________.
18. Yeasts and mushrooms are classified in the group ______________________.
19. A______________________ disease is a contagious disease that a person gets through sexual contact.
20. Protozoans digest food in structures called ______________________________.

B. MULTIPLE-CHOICE QUESTIONS

DIRECTIONS: Circle the number of the expression that best completes each of the following statements.

1. Which organisms are decomposers?
   (1) bacteria
   (2) algae
   (3) horses
   (4) frogs
2. Which disease would most likely result in the permanent inability to have a child?
   (1) gonorrhea
   (2) bronchitis
   (3) ulcers
   (4) pneumonia

Name________________________ Class__________________ Date__________

3. Which is a characteristic of viruses?
   (1) They are producers.
   (2) They are not composed of cells.
   (3) They have no economic uses.
   (4) They function as decomposers.

4. Which group of organisms is represented in the diagrams?

   (1) algae
   (2) protozoa
   (3) fungi
   (4) bacteria

5. Bacteria are best described as
   (1) microscopic and multicellular
   (2) microscopic and unicellular
   (3) large and multicellular
   (4) large and unicellular

6. The paramecium is an example of
   (1) an alga
   (2) an animal
   (3) a protozoan
   (4) a plant

7. Which diseases are caused by protozoans?
   (1) malaria and African sleeping sickness
   (2) colds and flu
   (3) athlete's foot and ringworm
   (4) cancer and hemophilia

8. Organisms that cause disease are known as
   (1) pathogens
   (2) protozoans
   (3) antibodies
   (4) scavengers

9. Mushrooms are classified as
   (1) plants
   (2) fungi
   (3) bacteria
   (4) viruses

10. Which tends to slow down the growth of bacteria?
   (1) agar
   (2) moisture
   (3) warmth
   (4) light

C. ESSAY QUESTION

DIRECTIONS: Use complete sentences to answer the question in this part.

1. State two reasons why early treatment of a sexually transmitted disease is important.

____

____

____

____

____

____

Name________________________ Class____________________ Date____________

Chapter 16: Multicellular Plants

A. GENERAL CHARACTERISTICS. Multicellular plants are complex plants and are classified in the kingdom *Plantae*. Most are multicellular photosynthetic organisms with chloroplasts, cell walls, and true roots, stems, and leaves. Photosynthetic plants need light, oxygen, water, carbon dioxide, and minerals and are known as producers. A **producer** (or **autotroph**) is an organism that makes its own food from inorganic materials in the environment. Complex green plants, along with algae (simple plants), are the major producers in nature. Through photosynthesis they provide food for organisms that cannot make their own food such as animals, nongreen plants, fungi, and bacteria. There are a few complex plants that do not have chloroplasts, therefore they cannot carry on photosynthesis. Two examples of nonphotosynthetic plants are dodder and indian pipe.

REVIEW QUESTIONS

1. List four characteristics of complex plants. ______________________________

____

____

2. Name two nonphotosynthetic complex plants. ______________________________

____

3. A producer is an organism that makes its own ______________ from ______________ materials in the ______________________.

4. A producer is also known as a/an ______________________________.

5. Name three organisms that depend on plants for their survival. ______________________

____

B. VASCULAR AND NONVASCULAR PLANTS. Complex plants exist in many different forms and are classified as either nonvascular or vascular. **Vascular plants** have **vascular tissue**. Vascular tissue transports (carries) materials throughout the plant. **Nonvascular plants** do not have specialized tissues for conduction (movement of materials) and support. They transport water and nutrients by osmosis and diffusion. Plants that do not have vascular tissue are very small without vascular tissue there is no way to carry water long distances. Nonvascular plants are classified in the phylum *Bryophyta*. Examples are mosses and liverworts (Figure 16-1). **Mosses** are common plants and seem to be everywhere—in sidewalk cracks, on the sides of trees, and on rotting logs. They look like a green carpet. Each clump of moss is really a group of tiny individual plants. **Liverworts** are not as common as mosses. Their name comes from the flat liverlike shape of the main body of the plant. They are found in moist places such as streams. Neither mosses nor liverworts have true roots, leaves, or stems.

Name______________________________ Class ______________________ Date __________

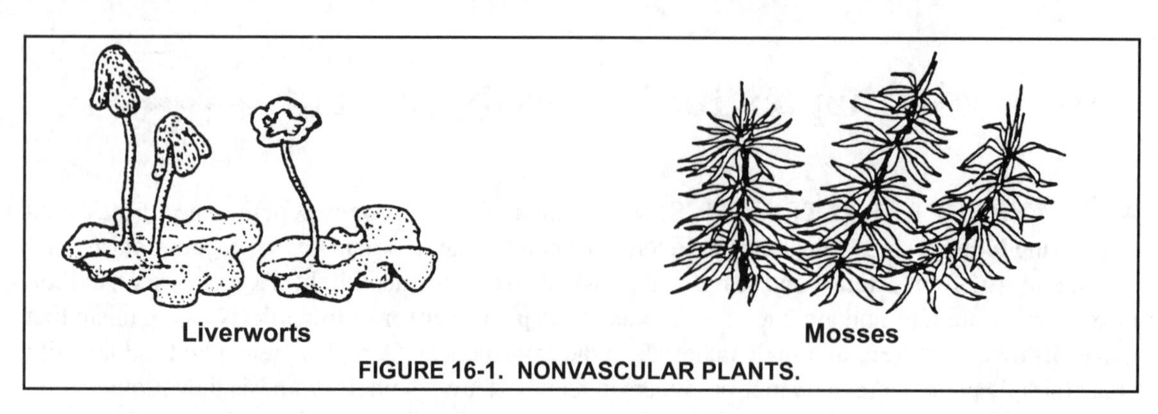

FIGURE 16-1. NONVASCULAR PLANTS.

Vascular plants are classified in the *Tracheophyta* phylum. They have true roots, stems, and leaves. Grasses, trees, shrubs, flowers, and ferns, are examples of vascular plants (Figure 16-2). Vascular plants are plants that have specialized tissues for conduction and support called vascular tissue. The two main types of vascular tissue are called xylem and phloem tissue. **Xylem** tissue is a system of tubes that conduct water and minerals from the soil *up* to the leaves. **Phloem** tissue is composed of tubes that transport materials *throughout* the plant. Vascular tissue is located in leaves, stems, roots, and flowers. Because they have vascular tissue vascular plants, unlike nonvascular plants, can grow to be very high.

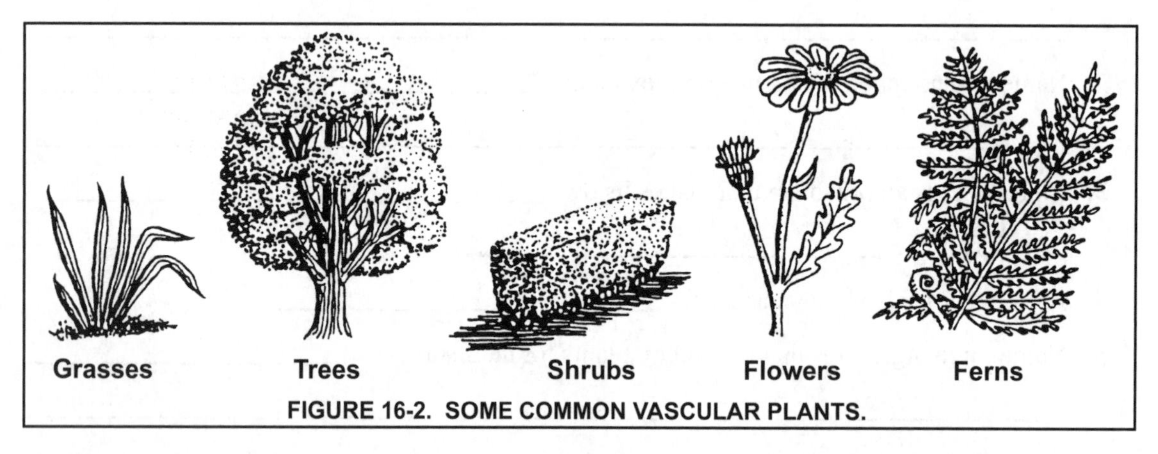

FIGURE 16-2. SOME COMMON VASCULAR PLANTS.

Seedless plants and seed plants are two types of vascular plants. **Seedless plants** do not have seeds and reproduce by means of swimming sperm. Because their sperm need water to swim seedless plants must live in wet areas. Ferns are the largest and most familiar group of seedless vascular plants. Ferns are commonly found in damp woodland environments. **Seed plants** reproduce by forming seeds. The two groups of seed plants are gymnosperms and angiosperms. **Gymnosperms** produce their uncovered seeds in cones and usually keep their leaves throughout the year. Evergreens are examples of gymnosperms. **Angiosperms** are flowering plants. Their seeds are enclosed in a seed coat. Common angiosperms are maples, oaks, vegetables, grasses and flowers.

Review Questions

1. What is meant by the term "vascular tissue"? ______________________________

____

2. Nonvascular plants are plants that do not have ______________________________

____

3. Name two nonvascular plants. ______________________________

4. A vascular plant is a plant that has ______________________ tissue.

5. Name three vascular plants. ______________________________

____

6. Water and dissolved minerals are conducted up to the leaves through __________ tissue.

7. ______________________ tissue transports materials throughout the plant.

8. An example of a seedless plant is the ______________________.

9. What is the difference between a gymnosperm and an angiosperm? ______________

____

____

____

C. INSECTIVOROUS PLANTS. There are some less common vascular plants, such as venus flytrap, that are fun to know about because of their unusual characteristics. **Venus flytrap** is an insectivorous plant. An **insectivorous plant** eats insects. It is able to make its own food by photosynthesis but it also can trap and eat insects. This makes it both heterotrophic and autotrophic. The **pitcher plant** is another example of an insect-eating plant (Figure 16-3).

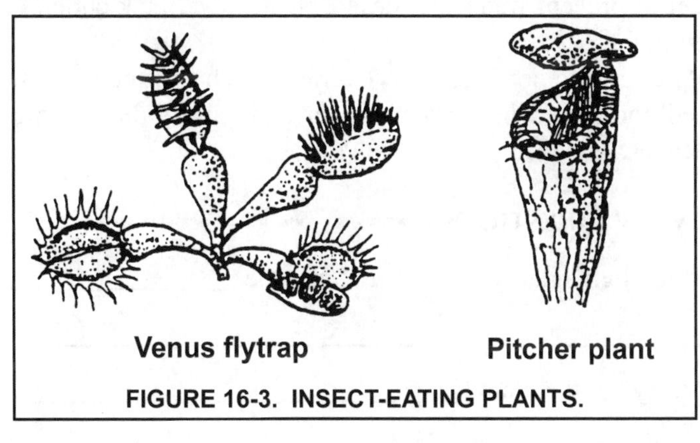

FIGURE 16-3. INSECT-EATING PLANTS.

REVIEW QUESTIONS

1. Name two insect-eating plants. ______________________________

D. PHOTOSYNTHETIC PLANTS. Most multicellular plants are autotrophs because they make their own food by the process of photosynthesis. During **photosynthesis** light energy is converted into the chemical energy of organic molecules. It is an important process because nearly all of the chemical energy available to living organisms in food and fuel comes directly or indirectly from photosynthesis. Almost all of the oxygen in the air comes from photosynthesis.

Name________________________ Class____________________ Date____________

The **leaf** (Figure 16-4) is called the "food factory" of photosynthetic plants because most photosynthesis (food-making) takes place in the leaf. The specialized structure of the leaf makes it well adapted for the process of photosynthesis. The structures and/or modifications that enable each kind of organism to carry out its life functions are known as **adaptations.** The leaves are arranged on stems so that they can receive the most amount of light. The leaf has a large flat surface for maximum light absorption and has **stomates** and **air spaces** for gas exchange. There are many **chloroplasts** located in the **palisade** and **spongy layers** for photosynthesis. Bean-shaped **guard cells** in the **epidermis** (outer covering) also contain chloroplasts. When light is present guard cells carry on photosynthesis causing the guard cells to swell and become larger in size. During darkness the guard cells contract and become smaller. This process regulates the opening and closing of stomates.

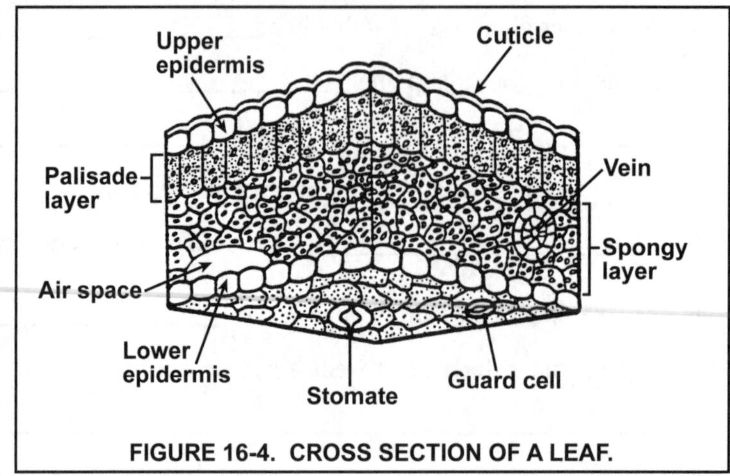

FIGURE 16-4. CROSS SECTION OF A LEAF.

Veins contain xylem and phloem cells for the transportation of materials. The upper part of the leaf contains a waxy covering that prevents water loss. This waxy covering is called the **cuticle.** The thickness of the cuticle varies according to the plant's environment. Plants that live in moist environments have thin cuticles. In order to prevent water loss desert plants have thick cuticles. Cactus is an example of a common desert plant.

In addition to photosynthesis the leaf performs other functions. Nutrients such as proteins, fats, vitamins, oils, and starches are produced and stored in the leaf. Water and carbon dioxide are returned to the atmosphere through the leaves.

REVIEW QUESTIONS

1. Photosynthesis is the process by which light energy is converted into the ________________

____

2. Why is the leaf called the "food factory" of the plant? ______________________________

____

3. What is the relationship between the thickness of a plant's cuticle and its environment?

____

____

____

4. Name two functions other than photosynthesis that take place in the leaf.

____

____

5. Complete the chart by stating the function of each leaf structure.

STRUCTURE	FUNCTION
Stomate	
Air Spaces	
Chloroplasts	
Palisade Layer	
Spongy Layer	
Guard Cells	
Cuticle	
Veins	

E. CHEMISTRY OF PHOTOSYNTHESIS. In the photosynthesis reactions shown below energy from light is trapped by chlorophyll and used to make simple sugars (glucose) from carbon dioxide and water. Light energy, chlorophyll, and enzymes must be present for photosynthesis to occur. Oxygen and water are released as by-products of the reactions. [Water is present on both sides of the chemical equation because it is both a raw material of the reaction and a product of the reaction.]

[Word Equation] CARBON DIOXIDE + WATER $\xrightarrow[\text{Chlorophyll and Enzymes}]{\text{Light Energy}}$ GLUCOSE + WATER + OXYGEN

[Chemical Equation] $6CO_2 + 12H_2O \xrightarrow[\text{Chlorophyll and Enzymes}]{\text{Light Energy}} C_6H_{12}O_6 + 6H_2O + 6O_2$

During photosynthesis two major sets of reactions occur: the light or photochemical reactions and the dark or carbon fixation reactions. Photosynthesis begins with the **light reactions,** which require the presence of light. These reactions take place in stacks of membranes inside the chloroplasts called grana (Figure 5-8). The grana contain the chlorophyll and enzymes necessary for the light reactions. The **dark reactions**, which do not require light, take place in the stroma of the chloroplasts. In the course of the dark reactions, carbon dioxide from the air and hydrogen atoms from the light reactions are converted to glucose. This process is called **carbon fixation.**

Although light is the source of energy for photosynthesis only certain wavelengths of light can be used by plants. White light, such as sunlight, is made up of many different wavelengths of light. You know these wavelengths as the colors of the rainbow. The wavelengths of light that are most efficient for photosynthesis are red and blue wavelengths because they are absorbed by chlorophyll to a greater degree than other wavelengths. Wavelengths of green light are less effective because they tend to be reflected by chlorophyll instead of absorbed. Plants appear green because of the green wavelengths reflected by chlorophyll.

The speed at which photosynthesis takes place is affected by a number of different factors. Some of these factors are temperature, light intensity, carbon dioxide level, and the concentrations of certain minerals such as nitrogen, magnesium, iron, copper, manganese, and zinc.

REVIEW QUESTIONS

1. During photosynthesis energy from ______________________________ is trapped by ______________________________ and used to make ______________________________ from carbon dioxide and ______________________________. ______________________________ is a by-product of the reactions.

2. Write both the word equation and the chemical equation for photosynthesis.

3. The wavelengths of light that are most efficient for photosynthesis are __________________ and __________________ lengths. Because green plants reflect __________________ light they cannot use it for photosynthesis.

4. List four conditions that affect the rate of photosynthesis. ______________________________

____

____

5. Name the two stages of photosynthesis. ______________________________

____

F. PLANT STEMS. **Stems** of plants are adapted for the support and display of leaves and flowers. Some stems are specialized for the storage of food. Some stems are green and carry on photosynthesis. The xylem and phloem of stems carry materials between the leaves and roots. Although the structure of stems differs from the structure of roots, the xylem and phloem are continuous throughout the plant. The structure and function of leaves in photosynthesis was discussed earlier in this chapter. The xylem and phloem of the leaves is continuous with that of the stems and roots. Plants contain specialized transport tissues called **xylem.** Xylem is vascular tissue that conducts water and dissolved minerals upward in the roots, stems, and leaves. The individual xylem cells are thick-walled, hollow, and connected. **Phloem** is vascular tissue that conducts dissolved organic food materials throughout the plant. The material in the phloem can move upward or downward as needed. Phloem cells are alive and mature xylem cells are not alive. In the leaves, the vascular tissue is in bundles called **veins.** Vascular plants whose stems increase in width each year are known as **woody plants** (Figure 16-5). The outer covering is called the **bark.** It is made

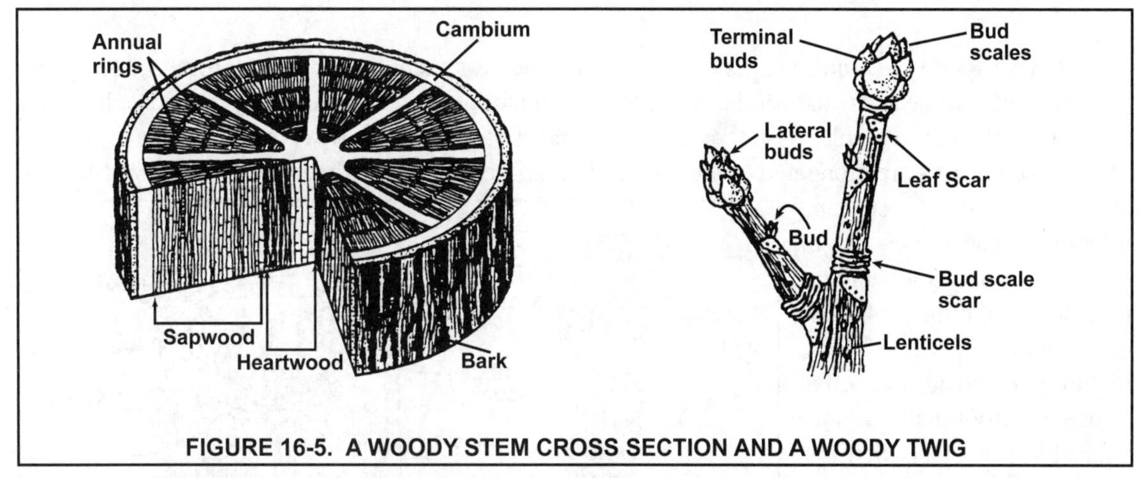

FIGURE 16-5. A WOODY STEM CROSS SECTION AND A WOODY TWIG

up of old dead phloem cells. Bark protects plants from injury and insects. Air passes through the bark into the internal stem tissues through tiny openings called **lenticels.** The growing region of the stem is the **cambium.** The cambium produces xylem cells toward the center of the stem and phloem toward the outside. Each year the cambium produces new layers of xylem and phloem. The xylem becomes the **annual rings** of the plant and the old phloem becomes the bark. You can determine the approximate age of a cut tree by counting its annual rings. The size of the rings results from the growing conditions at the time the cells were formed. Thin rings mean the growing season was dry and thick rings result from wet seasons. The functioning conducting xylem cells are called the **sapwood** and the inactive xylem cells are called the **heartwood**. Heartwood forms the mass of mature woody stems. Stems have adaptations that enable them to perform their life activities (Table 16-1).

STEM ADAPTATION	FUNCTION
Vascular tissue (xylem and phloem)	Transport.
Lenticels	Gas exchange
Chloroplasts in young stems	Photosynthesis.
Buds	Production of new tissues
Cambium	Lateral (sideways) growth
Stem tip	Vertical (length) growth

TABLE 16-1. STEM ADAPTATIONS.

REVIEW QUESTIONS

1. State three functions performed by the stem. ______________________________

____

____

____

2. Vascular plants whose width increases every year are called ________________ plants.

Name______________________ Class__________________ Date__________

3. ______________________ is a vascular tissue that conducts water and disolved minerals upward in the roots, stems, and leaves. ______________________ is a vascular tissue that conducts dissolved organic food material throughout the plant.

G. PLANT ROOTS. Roots are plant structures adapted for anchorage, nutrient storage, absorption of water and soluble salts, and for the conduction of materials to the stem. They have root hairs for absorption of water, vascular tissue for transport, and special areas (cortex) for food storage (Figure 16-6). **Root hairs** are elongated epidermal cells that increase the surface area of the root for the absorption of water and minerals. The movement of materials through the semipermeable membrane of root hairs involves both diffusion, including osmosis, and active transport. Root hairs absorb water by osmosis, which is a type of diffusion.

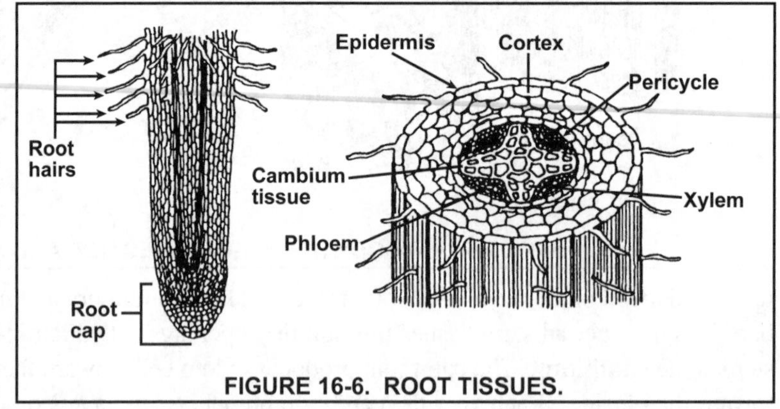

FIGURE 16-6. ROOT TISSUES.

During osmosis *water* moves from an area of high concentration into an area of low concentration. Dissolved materials pass into the root hairs by diffusion. Diffusion is the movement of materials from an area of high concentration to an area of low concentration.The root grows in the cambium and root tip. Roots are living growing parts of plants that require a supply of oxygen for aerobic respiration. They use oxygen that is mixed with soil. Before a seed or plant is planted soil must be loosened so air can mix with soil. This is done by humans by manually loosening the soil particles or by animals, such as the earthworm, as they move through the soil.

The cortex is inside the **epidermis,** which is the outer protective layer. The **cortex,** the biggest part of the root, stores food and moves water. Vascular tissue, called the **vascular cylinder,** is located in the center of the root. It is made up of xylem and phloem cells, cambium tissue, and a pericycle. Xylem cells conduct water and dissolved minerals.

The root xylem is joined to the stem and leaf xylem. It is one continuous tube of cells. If more water is lost during transpiration than is taken in though the roots the plant wilts or droops. Phloem cells carry food materials made by the plant. Cambium tissue produces xylem and phloem cells this results in an increase in root diameter. The **pericycle** forms the outer layer of the vascular cylinder. It produces the secondary roots. A **root cap** covers the end of the root to protect the growing tissue.

REVIEW QUESTIONS

1. Name three root adaptations. ____

____

____

2. The surface area of the root is increased for greater absorption by ____________________.

3. List three functions performed by the root. ______________________________________

____

____

4. What role do earthworms play in plant cultivation? ___________________________

____

H. TRANSPIRATION AND TRANSPIRATIONAL PULL. Transpiration is the loss of water vapor into the atmosphere through the stomates of leaves. During transpiration there is a continuous flow of water and minerals up xylem tissue from the root through the stem to the leaf. During photosynthesis the stomates of the leaves are open to exchange carbon dioxide and oxygen with the environment. When the stomates are open there is also a constant loss of water vapor by evaporation from the tissues of the leaf. To replace the water lost from the leaves there is an upward movement of water in the xylem. The water moves in a continuous column from the roots upward to the topmost parts of the plant. The water molecules in the column are held together by the forces of **cohesion** (the attractive force between like molecules) and **adhesion** (the attractive force between unlike molecules). The mechanism by which water moves upward in the xylem is best explained by the theory of **transpirational pull.** According to this theory the evaporation of water from the leaves exerts a pulling force on the column of water in the xylem. Other factors also affect the upward movement of water in the plant. **Root pressure,** the osmotic pressure that tends to force water into the cells of the root, also is involved in the upward movement of water in the xylem. Root pressure alone cannot explain how water rises to the top of tall trees.

REVIEW QUESTIONS

1. What is transpiration? ____

____

2. The osmotic pressure that tends to force water into root cells is ____________________.

3. The theory of transpirational pull attempts to explain ___________________________

____

I. RESPIRATION AND EXCRETION. In plants respiration takes place in the leaves, stems, and roots. Cellular respiration takes place all the time in both plant and animal cells. During respiration living things take in oxygen from the environment and release carbon dioxide. During photosynthesis, which takes place only when light energy is present, plants take in carbon dioxide from the environment and give off oxygen. Aerobic respiration and photosynthesis are opposite processes. During aerobic respiration sugar combines with oxygen to produce energy. Carbon dioxide and water are released into the atmosphere. During photosynthesis green plants use carbon dioxide and water to make sugar, oxygen, and water. The oxygen is released into the air and is used by organisms for aerobic respiration.

The outer covering of the leaf is not a good gas exchange surface because it is dry and impermeable. Gases and liquids cannot easily pass through it. Instead, respiratory gases enter through the leaf stomates and gas exchange takes place across the thin moist membranes of the internal cells. The stems of woody plants have small openings called **lenticels**. Environmental gases enter and leave the stem through the lenticels. In the roots the exchange of respiratory gases occurs across the moist cell membranes of the root hairs and other cells of the epidermis. Plants can recycle the waste gases of respiration and photosynthesis. Excess gases pass out of the plants through the stomates of the leaves, the lenticels of the stems, and the epidermal cells of the roots. Some waste products that might be toxic, such as organic acids, are stored in vacuoles. In this way they are separated from the other cell contents and cause no damage.

REVIEW QUESTIONS

1. In plants respiration takes place in the ______________________, ______________________, and ______________________.

2. When does respiration take place? ____

____

3. When does photosynthesis take place? ____

____

4. During respiration plants take in ______________________________ and give off ______________________________.

5. During photosynthesis plants take in ______________________________ and give off ______________________________.

6. Gases enter and leave the stem through the ______________________, the leaf through the ______________________, and the root through the ______________________.

7. Excess gases leave the plant through the ______________________________, ______________________________, and ______________________________.

J. CHEMICAL CONTROL IN PLANTS. In both plants and animals coordination of life activities involves chemical control in which chemicals are used to transmit messages from one part of the organism to another. These "chemical messengers" are called **hormones**. Plants have no nervous systems and their life activities are coordinated by hormones. Plant hormones regulate processes such as growth, tropisms, and reproduction. Developmental changes, including flowering, fruit formation, and seed development, are also controlled by hormones. There are no specialized organs for hormone production in plants. Hormones are produced mainly by cells in actively growing regions of the plant such as the cells in the tips of roots and stems and in buds and seeds. The effect of a plant hormone depends on the hormone, its concentration, and the tissue involved.

Auxins are an important kind of plant hormone that regulate plant growth. They influence the division, elongation, and differentiation of cells. External stimuli such as light, gravity, and the presence of water, cause an unequal distribution of auxins within the plant. The unequal distribution of these hormones causes unequal growth responses. Unequal growth responses in plants are called **tropisms**. Tropisms usually strengthen the chances of survival for the plant. An unequal auxin response takes place when one part or side of a plant grows more than the other side (Figure 16-7). This response to light stimuli is called **phototropism**. Phototropism occurs because there is a greater concentration of auxins present on the darker side of the stem. Auxins stimulate growth, therefore, an unequal concentration of auxins results in unequal cell growth. The darker side grows faster than the lighter side due to stimulation by more auxins. There are many different kinds of tropisms. The growth response of a plant to water is called **hydrotropism**, a response to gravity is **geotropism**, a response to chemicals is **chemotropism**, and a response to touch is known as **thigmotropism**.

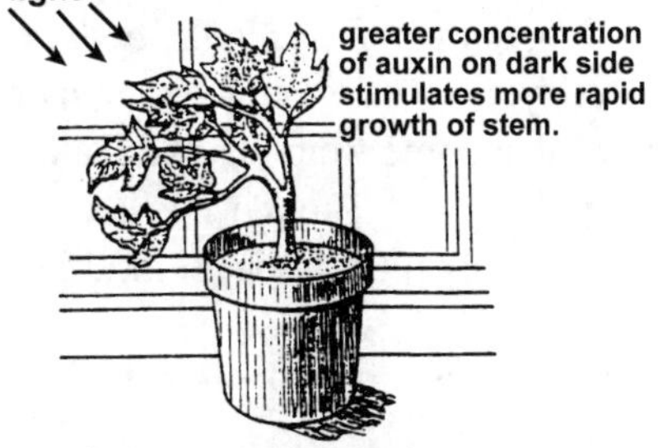

FIGURE 16-7. PHOTOTROPISM.

REVIEW QUESTIONS

1. What is meant by chemical control? ______________________________

____

2. Do plants have nervous systems? ______________________

3. A ______________________ is an unequal growth response in plants.

4. Complete the following chart.

TROPISM	STIMULUS
hydrotropism	
	gravity
chemotropism	
	light
thigmotropism	

5. Plant hormones are called ______________________.

K. ECONOMIC USES OF PLANTS AND PLANT PRODUCTS. Plants can be both beneficial and harmful to man. Some plant parts that are used directly for food are shown below.

Roots.............carrot, beet, radish, turnip	**Fruits**..................apples, tomatoes
Stems............white potato, asparagus	**Flowers**................cauliflower, broccoli
Leaves...........lettuce, spinach, cabbage	**Seeds**...................nuts, beans

Plants are also the source of many products used by humans such as rope, turpentine, fats, oils, drugs, dyes, fibers for clothing, flavorings, sugar, lumber, paper, and flour. The fibers attached to cotton seeds are used to make cotton fabric. Linen, a fiber used to make cloth, comes from the stems of flax plants. Digitalis is extracted from dried foxglove leaves and is used as medicine to treat heart disease. Morphine and codeine, strong pain killers, come from the poppy plant. Malaria is treated with the drug quinine found in the bark of the cinchona tree. Many plants are used as food seasonings. Basil, parsley, rosemary, oregano, cinnamon, ginger, vanilla, and horseradish are a few examples of seasonings that come from plants. Walnut oil and olive oil are used in cooking. Some plants or plant parts are poisonous. Though the stem of the rhubarb plant is safe to eat, the leaves are poisonous. Poison ivy, deadly nightshade, poinsettia, mistletoe, and philodendron plants are all poisonous.

REVIEW QUESTIONS

1. Name six plant parts that are used for food. ______________________

____

CAREER OPPORTUNITIES

HORTICULTURIST: Horticulture is the science and art of growing fruits, vegetables, flowers or ornamental plants. **Horticulturists** are involved with the study of growing, picking, and shipping plants. They study how to improve plants and how to find new and better ways to grow and create different plants. Horticulturists may own or manage greenhouses, plant nurseries, florist shops, or garden stores. Cooperative extension service workers, landscape architects, writers and editors of garden magazines and other publications, are other possible jobs for people who have studied horticulture. Education and training vary from job to job. A two-year degree in horticultural technology can qualify you for some jobs, while other jobs require a bachelor's degree with major in horticulture. Employment opportunities are good and working conditions vary. Some people work outdoors most of the time, while others work in greenhouses and offices. A great deal of physical labor is needed for some jobs, for example, working in a plant nursery.

*****

FORESTER: **Foresters** manage, protect, and develop forests. Forest rangers supervise the use of public lands. Smoke jumpers parachute into forest fires to help fight forest fires. Service foresters help farmers and other forest owners manage their land. They also work to help improve and modernize methods at lumber mills and wood processing plants. Working conditions vary depending on the kind of work. Rangers may live deep in the woods. They may be on call 24 hours a day and may be away from home for several days at time. Forest workers spend most of their time outdoors in all kinds of weather. A Forest Service job requires a bachelor's degree in forestry.

*****

REVIEW QUESTIONS

1. Name one career opportunity for someone interested in working with plants.

____

____

____

Name________________________ Class____________________ Date___________

LAB INVESTIGATION: PLANT PARTS AS FOOD

OBJECTIVE

Upon completion of this activity you should be able to identify some plant parts that humans use for food.

LABORATORY PROCEDURE

Materials: An assortment of vegetables and fruits such as, celery, beets, carrots, lettuce, cabbage, apples, tomatoes, cauliflower, broccoli, nuts, dry beans, and radishes. Reference books.

1. Your teacher has placed examples of common plant parts that humans use for food at various locations (stations) around the room. Each example is labeled according to its common name. You are to observe each food and decide which items are from **plant stems, plant roots, plant leaves** and **plant seeds**. (Some plants may have more than one part that is used for food.)

2. After you have made your decision record your answer by writing the plant name and the name of the part that is used for food in the **observation table** in the following section.

OBSERVATIONS

NAME OF PLANT	NAME OF PLANT PART USED FOR FOOD	NAME OF PLANT	NAME OF PLANT PART USED FOR FOOD

Name______________________ Class__________________ Date__________

Conclusions

1. List four plant parts that are used for food.

____

____

____

____

____

____

____

____

2. Name five plants (other than those you identified in the lab) that are used for food.

____

____

____

____

____

____

____

____

3. Make a list of plants that you have eaten in the last month.

____

____

____

____

____

____

____

____

Name________________ Class ________________ Date ________

REVIEW ACTIVITIES

Important Terms

***DIRECTIONS:* Define the following terms in the spaces provided.**

adaptation ________________________________

auxins ________________________________

angiosperms ________________________________

autotroph ________________________________

cambium ________________________________

chloroplasts ________________________________

cuticle ________________________________

dark reactions ________________________________

epidermis ________________________________

extracellular ________________________________

geotropism ________________________________

guard cells ________________________________

gymnosperms ________________________________

hormones ________________________________

hydrotropism ________________________________

Name____________________ **Class**________________ **Date**________

leaf

lenticels

palisade layer

phloem

photosynthesis

phototropism

producer

root

root hairs

spongy layer

stem

stomates

transpiration

tropism

vascular tissue

veins

xylem

Name______________________________ Class______________________ Date__________

Skill Practice

Part A. Base your answers to questions 1 through 5 on the passage below and on your knowledge of biology.

The Common Dandelion

The common dandelion, transported to the eastern shores of this country by early settlers from Europe, gradually spread westward. Today, the dandelion can be found from Maine to Oregon in backyards, along roadsides, on mountaintops, and in vacant lots.

The dandelion has been successful for a variety of reasons. Its taproot grows deep into the ground, making it difficult to uproot and enabling it to absorb water from great depths. The taproot also functions as a storehouse of food for the plant during the winter. Each flower produces nearly 200 seeds that are adapted to float on even the slightest breeze. Animals, cars, water, and other agents also aid in the dispersal of the seeds. The leaves of a dandelion grow in such a way that they spread in a circle around the stem. Since these leaves are long and broad, they often overshadow leaves of nearby grasses and herbs.

Although the dandelion is usually considered an undesirable weed, people have found uses for many of its parts. Its leaves are an excellent source of vitamins A and C, iron, and other essential minerals. These leaves, or greens, are used in salads or cooked like spinach. The flowers can be made into an amber-colored wine. The taproot can be roasted, ground up, and brewed into a delicious coffee substitute.

1. The leaves of the common dandelion are adapted for photosynthesis and
a) absorbing water from the atmosphere
b) shading out nearby competitors
c) producing many reproductive structures
d) converting raw materials to minerals

2. The highest concentration of starch in dandelion plants would most likely be found in the
a) leaves c) flowers
b) stems d) taproots

3. Although dandelion seeds are scattered in a variety of ways, they are best adapted for dispersal by
a) water currents c) air currents
b) humans d) insects

4. Dandelions most likely spread quickly throughout the United States because they
a) were a good food source for native grazing animals
b) produced many seeds and competed successfully with native plants
c) were cultivated in gardens by early European settlers
d) grew only in areas where native plants could not grow

5. Dandelions are cultivated by some people to
a) provide taproots for making salads
b) draw drinking water from great soil depths
c) produce a food source with essential vitamins and minerals
d) provide seeds for reforestation and covercropping

Name________________________ Class________________________ Date__________

Part B. Base your answers to questions 1 through 5 on the information and data table below and on your knowledge of biology.

For nine days two plants with the same genetic background and the same starting height were grown in an environment in which temperature was the single variable factor. The growth of the stems of the two plants was measured and recorded as indicated in the data table below.

(Time Days)	Length of Stem (mm)	
	Plant *A* (grown at 15°C)	Plant *B* (grown at 25°C)
1	15	21
3	30	50
5	44	78
7	53	96
9	54	99

***Directions* (Questions 1 through 4):** Using the information in the data table construct a line graph on the grid provided *at the bottom of this page* following the directions below.

1. Label the *axes,* including units, placing time on the horizontal axis and length on the vertical axis.
2. Mark an appropriate scale on each axis.
3. Plot the data for plant A, grown at 15°C, on the graph. Surround each point with a small circle. Connect the points. **Example:**
4. Plot the data for plant *B*, grown at 25°C, on the graph. Surround each point with a small triangle. Connect the points. **Example:**
5. Which conclusion can be made from the graph constructed and the information given in Questions 1 through 4?
   1. The growth rate of plant *A* was greater than the growth rate of plant *B*.
   2. The growth rate of plant B was greater than the growth rate of plant A.
   3. The growth rate of plant A was equal to the growth rate of plant B.
   4. Not enough information was obtained to make inferences about comparable growth rates.

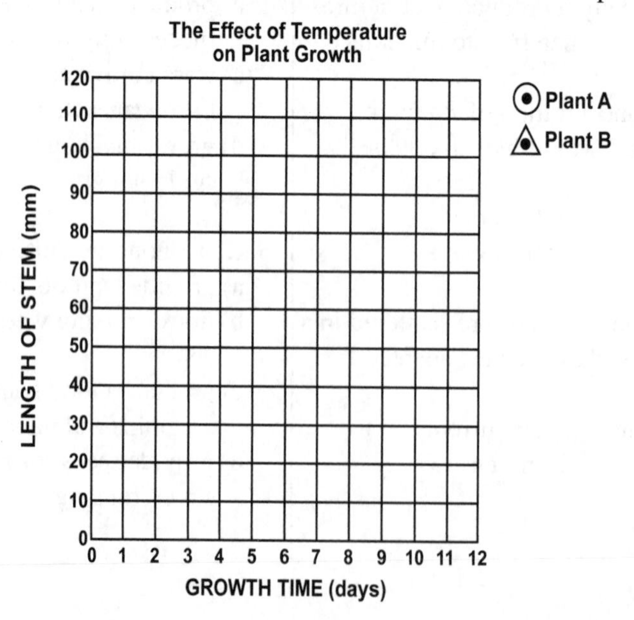

Name________________________ Class________________________ Date__________

CHAPTER 16: QUIZ

A. FILL-IN QUESTIONS

DIRECTIONS: Complete each of the following statements by writing the correct word or phrase in the space provided.

1. The waxy covering of a leaf is called the ________________________
2. Tissue that carries materials throughout the plant is called ________________________ tissue.
3. Food production occurs in the ________________________ and spongy layers of the leaf.
4. The loss of water vapor into the atmosphere through the leaves is called ________________________
5. ________________________ are tiny green plants that look like a green carpet.
6. Green plants make food by the process of ________________________.
7. A/An ________________________ is an organism that makes its own food from inorganic materials in the environment.
8. ________________________ is the pigment that gives leaves their green color.
9. Tiny openings in the stems of plants are known as ________________________.
10. The ________________________ is the food factory of vascular plants.
11. ________________________ tissue conducts water and minerals from the soil up to the leaves.
12. The functioning conducting xylem cells are called the ________________________ wood.
13. Bean-shaped structures in the epidermis of the leaf are the ________________________.
14. You can compute the age of a tree by counting its ________________________.
15. The venus flytrap is an example of a/an ________________________ plant.
16. Organisms have ________________________ that allow them to live successfully in particular environments.
17. The ________________________ anchors the plant in the ground.
18. Flowering plants are called ________________________.
19. ________________________ increase the water absorbing ability of roots.
20. The growing tissue of the root is protected by the ________________________.

B. MULTIPLE-CHOICE QUESTIONS

DIRECTIONS: Circle the number of the expression that best completes each of the following statements.

1. Which plant structure functions as an organ of anchorage and absorption?
   (1) root
   (2) leaf
   (3) bud
   (4) bark
2. Which plant part absorbs carbon dioxide through stomates?
   (1) leaf
   (2) stamen
   (3) stem
   (4) seed

Name________________________ Class____________________ Date__________

3. The green pigment found in plants is known as
   (1) phloem
   (2) chlorophyll
   (3) glucose
   (4) starch
4. Which organisms provide humans with the gas needed for aerobic respiration?
   (1) mushrooms
   (2) plants
   (3) horses
   (4) bacteria
5. A useful plant product is
   (1) wool
   (2) cotton
   (3) leather
   (4) plastic
6. Organisms that carry on photosynthesis are known as
   (1) consumers
   (2) producers
   (3) parasites
   (4) saprophytes
7. Which organisms are autotrophs?
   (1) bacteria
   (2) algae
   (3) horses
   (4) frogs
8. Gases move into and out of plant leaves mainly through openings known as
   (1) stomates
   (2) epidermis
   (3) guard cells
   (4) chloroplasts
9. Vascular tissue in stems consists of
   (1) bud scales and leaf scars
   (2) stomates and lenticels
   (3) spongy cells and palisade cells
   (4) xylem and phloem
10. Materials dissolved in water normally pass into a root hair by a process known as
   (1) respiration
   (2) excretion
   (3) diffusion
   (4) transpiration

C. ESSAY QUESTION

DIRECTIONS: Use complete sentences to answer the question in this part.

1. State two ways in which green plants are essential for the survival of living things.

____

____

____

____

____

____

____

____

____

____

____

____

Name______________________ Class______________________ Date__________

Chapter 17: Multicellular Animals

A. GENERAL CHARACTERISTICS. Multicellular animals are complex organisms that do not have cell walls and chloroplasts. Because they cannot make their own food animals depend on other organisms for their food supply and are known as **heterotrophs.** Heterotrophs must obtain preformed organic compounds (food) from other organisms. Most multicellular animals are **motile** but there are a few multicellular animals that are nonmotile (or **sessile**) during their adult form. There are more than a million known multicellular animal species on our planet. They are divided into two major groups—invertebrates and vertebrates.

Review Questions

1. List four general characteristics of multicellular animals. ______________________

____

____

____

2. Heterotrophs are unable to make ______________________ from ______________

______________________ materials.

3. Animals are divided into two groups called ______________________ or ______________________.

B. INVERTEBRATES. An **invertebrate** is a multicellular animal without a backbone (spine). Invertebrates are simpler in structure than vertebrates. Most animals are invertebrates. Only a small percentage of animals are classified as vertebrates. Both invertebrates and vertebrates have specialized organs that perform the life functions of nutrition, transport, respiration, excretion, regulation, locomotion, and reproduction. Some common examples of invertebrates are: sponges, hydra, starfish, worms, clams, and insects.

Review Questions

1. What is an invertebrate? ____

____

2. Name five invertebrates. ____

____

♦ **Sponges.** A **sponge** is an invertebrate animal that looks like a bag (Figure 17-1). Its body is full of openings or holes called **pores**. Because of this they are grouped in the phylum *Porifera*, which means "pore-bearing". Sponges have the simplest body structure of any complex animal. Their cells are not organized into tissues and organs. They live in either salt water or fresh water. In their adult stage they are sessile (stay in one place) usually attached to rocks, shells, or other objects.

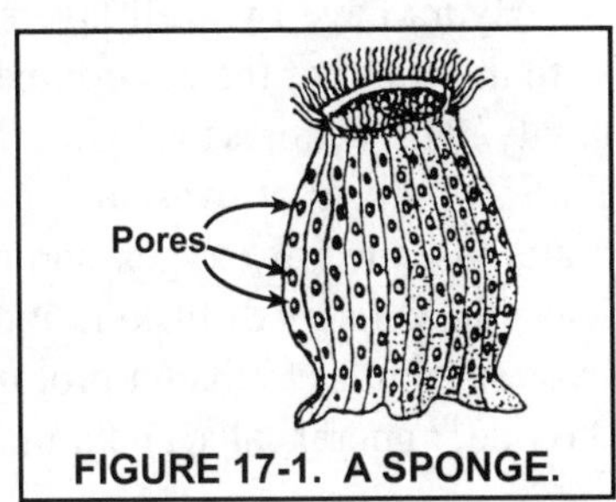

FIGURE 17-1. A SPONGE.

Name_____________________________ Class_______________________ Date____________

Sponges obtain food and oxygen from the water that flows through the pores of their bodies. Individual cells carry on respiration and excretion. They have a stiff internal skeleton that gives their body a definite shape. They can be found living alone or in groups (colonies).

REVIEW QUESTIONS

1. The sponge is an animal that looks like a ______________________.
2. The sponge's body is full of holes called ______________________.
3. Where do sponges live and describe how they obtain their food.

____

____

♦ **Hydra.** Jellyfish, hydra, sea anemones, and corals, are examples of animals classified in the phylum *Coelenterata*. The hydra is commonly studied as a representative example of these simple invertebrate animals. Although it is basically a sessile organism and tends to remain in the same place attached by one end it can move slowly by a type of somersaulting motion (Figure 17-2). The body can also contract and extend causing it to glide slowly across a surface.

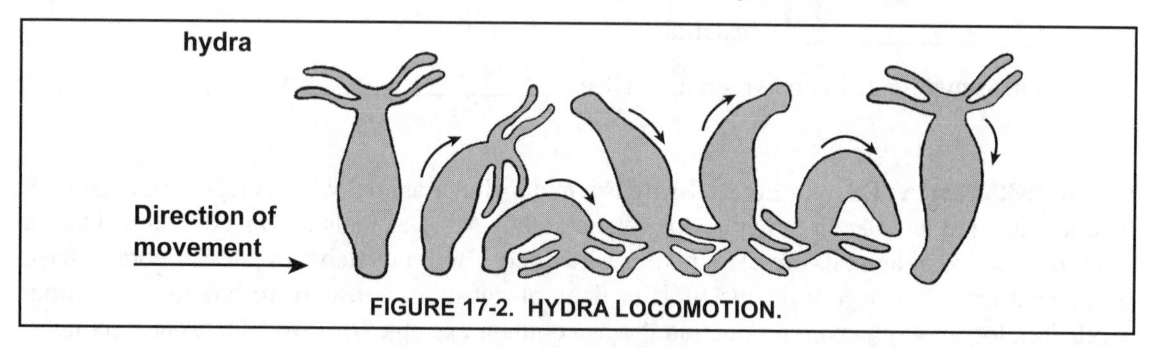

FIGURE 17-2. HYDRA LOCOMOTION.

The hydra is a small hollow-bodied animal with a saclike digestive cavity with one opening called the mouth. The mouth is surrounded by **tentacles** that move food into the mouth and digestive cavity. The tentacles contain **stinging cells** that shoot out poisonous threads that paralyze a food organism called the prey. The prey is then taken into the mouth of the hydra by its tentacles. Extracellular digestion takes place when cells in the lining of the digestive cavity secrete enzymes into the cavity. Other cells in the lining of the digestive cavity engulf the partly digested food by phagocytosis. Digestion is then completed by intracellular digestion within the cells of the organism. Undigested and indigestible material is egested from the digestive cavity through the mouth. This type of digestive tract is known as a two-way digestive system.

Hydra have two cell layers that are both in contact with water. The outer layer is in contact with the water of the environment and the inner layer is in contact with water in the gastrovascular cavity. This enables the hydra to survive without a special transport system. Flagellated cells in the lining of the gastrovascular cavity help to circulate materials throughout the cavity. Needed materials, such as oxygen and nutrients, can enter the hydra's cells by diffusion. Wastes can also leave the cells by diffusion. Intracellular circulation is by cyclosis and diffusion. Excretion in the hydra is similar to that in protozoans. All body cells are in contact with the environment. Carbon dioxide, mineral salts, and ammonia pass out of the cells by diffusion.

The hydra has no brain or central nervous system to control and coordinate the organism. It has modified neurons that form a **nerve net** between the two cell layers of its body wall. Nerve impulses can travel in all directions over the neurons of the nerve net. The hydra can coordinate its reaction to simple stimuli such as food by using its tentacles to catch and take in food.

REVIEW QUESTIONS

1. Food is taken into the mouth of the hydra by the _______________.

2. The hydra is basically a _______________ organism but sometimes can move slowly by a type of _______________.

3. Is digestion in the hydra intracellular or extracellular? _______________.

♦ **Starfish.** Spiny-skinned animals such as starfish, sea urchins, sand dollars, and sea cucumbers, are members of the phylum *Echinodermata* (*echino* = spine, *derm* = skin). They are **marine** (salt water) animals with an internal (inside) skeletons. The starfish looks like a disc with arms that radiate out from a main body (Figure 17-3). This star-like structure gives the starfish its name.

The common starfish has five rays or arms. The undersides of the arms have suction-like structures called **tube feet.** The tube feet are used for food-getting and locomotion. A mouth is located on the under surface of the animal. The starfish eats by attaching its tube feet to its food, usually clams or oysters, and prying them open. It then turns its stomach inside out and secretes digestive juices onto the food. The digested food is then taken into a mouth. Wastes are excreted by diffusion at the spiny surface.

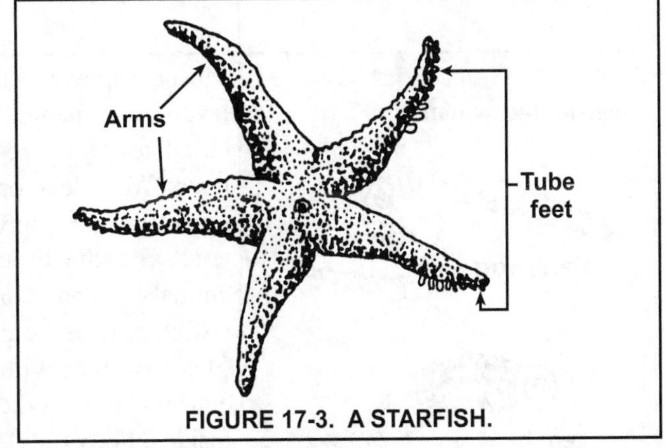

FIGURE 17-3. A STARFISH.

The simple nervous system of the starfish consists of a nerve ring that surrounds the mouth and a simple nerve cord extends down each arm. There is no brain but there are light-sensitive eyespots at the end of each arm. The starfish breathes through skin gills.

REVIEW QUESTIONS

1. A marine organism lives in _______________ water.

2. Describe the feeding process of the starfish. _______________

____

____

____

Name________________________ Class________________ Date__________

♦ **Worms.** There are many different kinds of worms. They are classified into three different phyla (Table 17-1).

WORM PHYLUM	CHARACTERISTICS	EXAMPLES
Platyhelminthes-(Flatworms) Tapeworm Planaria	Least complex worms. Flat-bodied, three cell layers. Have digestive, nervous, excretory, reproductive systems. Do not have circulatory and respiratory systems. Occur both free-living and parasitic.	Planaria(free-living) flukes, and tapeworms, (parasites).
Nematoda-(Roundworms) Ascaris Hookworm	Long, slender, smooth, tapered at both ends. Three cell layers, more complex than flatworms. Digestive systems with two openings, simple circulatory system and excretory, reproductive systems. Some free-living, most are parasites.	Ascaris (intestinal round-worm), hookworm, and trichina worm, (parasites).
Annelida-(Segmented worms) Earthworm Leech	Most complex worms. Three cell layers. Segmented body. Simple circulatory and respiratory systems. Well developed digestive, nervous, and reproductive systems. Breathe through skin. First animals to have a true **"tube-within-a-tube"** digestive system (digestive tube with mouth at one end and anus at other end, located inside a body tube).	Earthworm (free living) and leech (some parasitic).

TABLE 17-1. WORM CHARACTERISTICS.

The earthworm (Figure 17-4) is commonly studied in the classroom laboratory. The earthworm has a tubelike digestive system with openings at both ends. Food is ingested through the mouth and then passes through the **esophagus** to the **crop** where it is temporarily stored. From the crop food passes into the **gizzard** and it is broken down mechanically by grinding. The ground up food then goes into the **intestine** where chemical digestion occurs. The end products of digestion are absorbed into the blood and carried to all the cells of the body. Undigested material is egested through the **anus**—the opening at the end of the digestive tube. This type of digestive tract is called a *tube-within-a-tube one-way* digestive system.

Because many of the earthworm's cells are not in direct contact with the external environment it has an internal **closed circulatory system** with blood contained in vessels. The blood is pumped through the vessels by the contraction of **aortic arches** that serve as "hearts". The blood of the earthworm is red due to **hemoglobin** that is dissolved in the blood. Hemoglobin increases the blood's ability to carry oxygen. The blood carries respiratory gases between the external environment and the body cells and also carries wastes and other dissolved materials, including nutrients, which are the end products of digestion. Nutrients are absorbed from the digestive system and carried to the body cells. An infolding of the digestive tube (the **typhosole**) is an adaptation that increases the surface area for absorption of nutrients into the blood. The exchange of respiratory gases takes place through the earthworm's moist skin that is kept moist by the secretion of mucus. Oxygen from the environment diffuses through the skin and into the blood where it is picked up by hemoglobin and transported to the body cells.

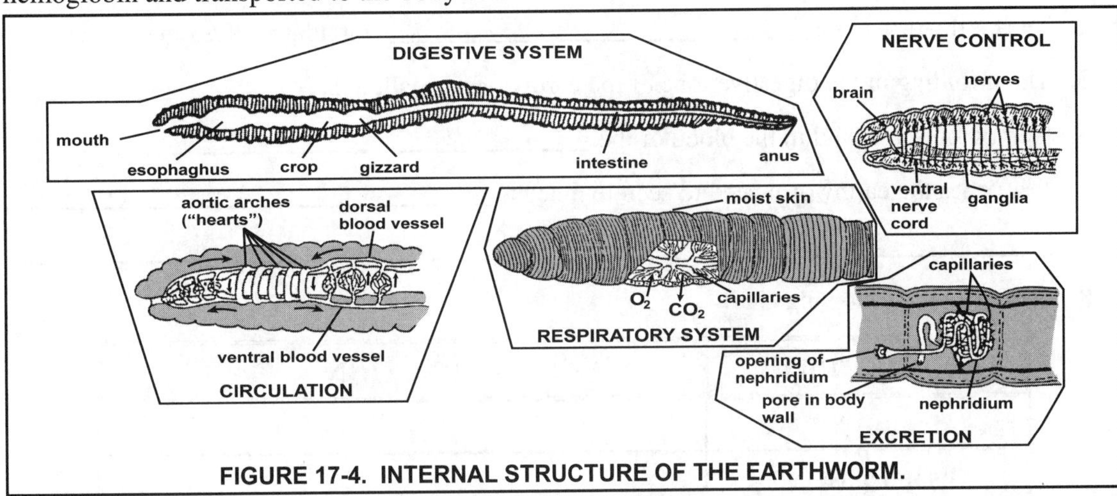

FIGURE 17-4. INTERNAL STRUCTURE OF THE EARTHWORM.

Carbon dioxide, a waste product produced by respiration in the body cells, diffuses into the blood and is carried to the skin. At the skin carbon dioxide diffuses out of the blood, through the skin, and into the environment. Carbon dioxide is excreted by diffusion through the moist skin. Other wastes are handled by the specialized excretory system. This system consists of pairs of excretory organs called **nephridia** found in most segments of the earthworm's body. Water, mineral salts, and urea are filtered out of the body fluids into the nephridia and then excreted into the environment.

The earthworm has a simple true nervous system. There is a primitive brain consisting of fused ganglia. **Ganglia** are tiny groups of simple nerve cell bodies. Extending from the brain is a ventral nerve cord with peripheral nerves attached. The presence of this central nervous system permits impulses to travel over definite pathways from receptors to effectors. Locomotion involves two sets of muscles (one circular, one longitudinal) and **setae,** which are bristles found on the ventral (underside) surface of the body segments. The setae anchor rear segments of the worm in the soil. The contraction of one set of muscles extends the earthworm body. Setae then anchor the front end of the worm in the soil. The contraction of one set of muscles extends the earthworm body. Setae then anchor the front end of the worm and contraction of the other set of muscles brings the back end of the worm forward. With this interaction of setae and muscles, the earthworm slowly moves through and on top of the soil.

REVIEW QUESTIONS

1. Name the three main groups of worms and state two examples of each.

____

____

____

____

Name_______________________________ Class_______________________ Date___________

2. What is the meaning of the term "tube-within-a-tube" digestive system?

____

____

3. Is digestion in the earthworm intracellular or extracellular? _______________

4. The earthworm has a _______________________ circulatory system.

5. The infolding of the digestive tube of the earthworm is called the _______________

6. Hemoglobin is found in the blood of the _______________________.

7. Why does the earthworm need to secrete mucus? _______________________

____

8. Complete the following chart.

STRUCTURE	FUNCTION
Mouth	
Esophagus	
Crop	
Gizzard	
Intestine	
Anus	

♦ **Insects.** Insects are considered the most successful invertebrates on Earth. This is because insects have the largest number of species (over 700,000) and can adapt to almost any environment. They are man's greatest competitor for food. Insects along with spiders, scorpions, ticks, mites, crayfish, centipedes, and millipedes, belong to the phylum *Arthropoda*. Arthropoda means "jointed legs". Butterflies, mosquitoes, fleas, bees, grasshoppers, ladybugs, and beetles are some common insects (Figure 17-5).

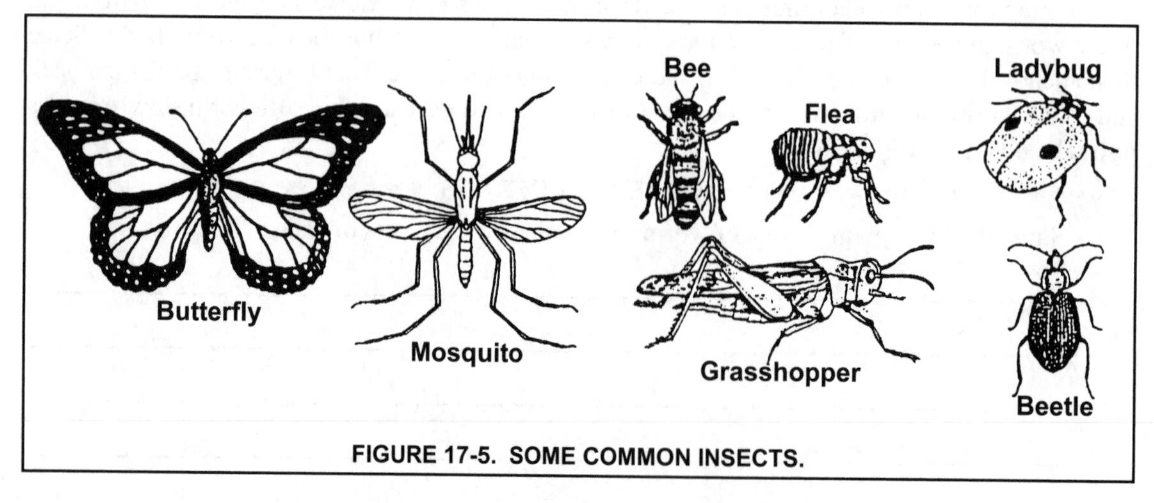

FIGURE 17-5. SOME COMMON INSECTS.

Name______________________________ Class________________________ Date____________

Insects have three body parts and three pairs of legs. The three body parts are a head, a thorax, and an abdomen. The **head** contains antennae, compound eyes, and mouth parts. Attached to the **thorax** are three pairs of legs and usually two pairs of wings. The heart, respiratory, and excretory organs are located in the segmented **abdomen**. Insects have well developed digestive, excretory, respiratory and circulatory systems (Figure 17-6).

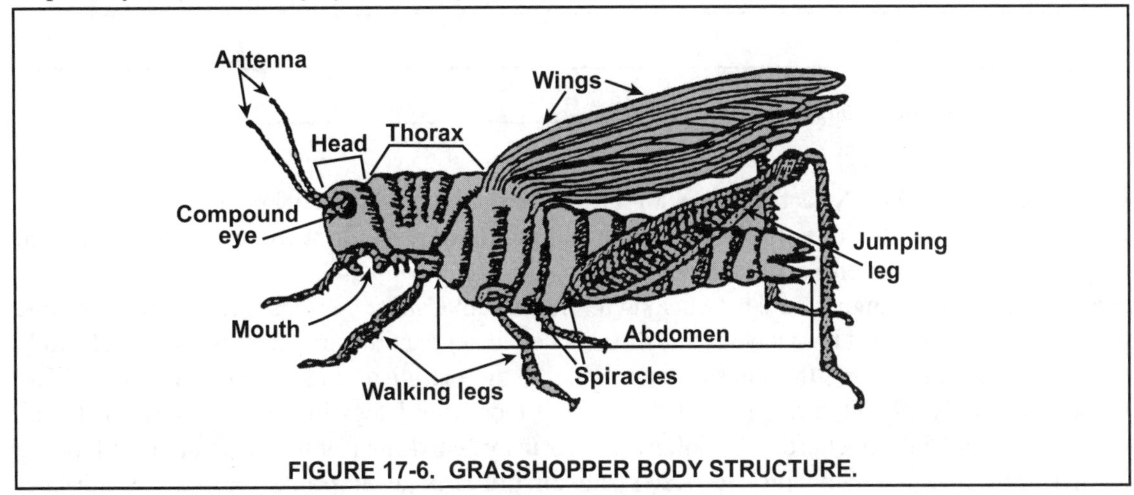

FIGURE 17-6. GRASSHOPPER BODY STRUCTURE.

All insects have an open circulatory system. The heart is a long dorsal tube with a strong muscle at the **anterior** (front) end that pumps blood through the aorta. The blood then flows into the body cavity toward the **posterior** (rear) end bringing food to all the organs. The blood also absorbs and carries away waste products and then returns to the heart.

Breathing takes place through openings called **spiracles** located along the sides of the abdomen. Air enters through the spiracles and is carried by a system of tubes called the **tracheae** to all body cells. Respiration occurs when oxygen diffuses into the tissue and carbon dioxide diffuses out through the tracheae. Insects do not have red blood cells to carry oxygen.

Insects have a **one-way digestive tube**. This means food enters the mouth and moves in one direction through a digestive tube. As food moves through the tube, digestive organs digest the food. Digestive wastes are egested through the anus. The important digestive and excretory organs of insects and their functions are:

Mouth...........................	Sucks in food.
Salivary glands............	Secrete juices into mouth to moisten food.
Esophagus.....................	Passes food to crop.
Crop..............................	Stores food.
Gizzard.........................	Grinds food into smaller pieces.
Stomach........................	Digests food.
Intestine........................	Collects undigested food.
Malpighian tubules.......	Collects cellular wastes and passes them into the blood.
Anus..............................	Passes digestive wastes out of body.

The nervous system of an insect is more complex than that of other invertebrates. Most insects have sense organs for hearing, touch, and smell. They also can see through two sets of eyes. The insect's body is protected by a tough outer covering called the **exoskeleton** (*exo* = outer, *skeleton* = framework). The exoskeleton is made of a hard material secreted by the insect called **chitin.**

Name ______________________ Class ______________ Date __________

REVIEW QUESTIONS

1. Name the three insect body parts. ______________________

2. Why are insects considered the most successful invertebrates? ______________________

____

____

3. Insects breathe through openings called ______________________.

C. VERTEBRATES. A **vertebrate** is a multicellular animal with a backbone. Vertebrates are more complex in structure than invertebrates. They account for only a small percentage (approximately five percent) of the animal kingdom. The main vertebrate groups are fish, amphibians, birds, reptiles, and mammals and they belong to the phylum *Chordata*. This means that some time during their development they have a notochord, a dorsal nerve cord, and gill slits. A **notochord** is a firm rod that runs along the **dorsal** (back) side of the organism and supports the body. The notochord is only present during the development of most chordates. In vertebrates the backbone develops around the notochord. The hollow tubular **nerve cord** runs along the dorsal length of the animal just above the notochord. In water animals **gill slits** develop into true gills but in land animals they change into structures that are more useful for life on land.

All vertebrates have a bony internal skeleton called an **endoskeleton** (*endo* = inner, *skeleton* = framework). The endoskeleton is made up of a **vertebral column** (backbone), a **skull**, and the bones of the **appendages** (arms, legs, fins, etc.). Vertebrates also have specialized organ systems that perform necessary life functions. The vertebrate organ systems are more complex than invertebrate organ systems. Table 17-2 is a summary of vertebrate organ systems.

SYSTEM	DESCRIPTION
Excretory	A pair of kidneys with tubes makes up the excretory system of some vertebrates—others use skin, lungs and sometimes gills.
Digestive	The vertebrate digestive system consists of a continuous tube from the mouth to the anus and digestive organs.
Endocrine	Glands, which secrete chemicals, make up the endocrine system.
Reproductive	Male or female reproductive organs are present in the reproductive system.
Nervous	Spinal cord, brain, nerves, and sense organs make up the nervous system.
Circulatory	They have a closed circulatory system, with two, three, or four heart chambers.
Muscular	The muscular system is made up of contracting tissue that is attached to bones or cartilage.
Skeletal	All vertebrates have a bony internal skeleton called an endoskeleton made up of a vertebral column, skull, and the bones of the appendages.
Respiratory	Respiration can take place through the moist skin, lungs, or gills.

TABLE 17-2. VERTEBRATE ORGAN SYSTEMS.

Name________________________ Class________________ Date________

Review Questions

1. Name three structures that chordates have in common. ______________________

____

2. List the five vertebrate groups. ______________________________

3. Name and describe three vertebrate systems. ____________________

____

____

♦ **Fish.** Fish are vertebrates that live in water. They have two-chambered hearts and most are covered with scales. They breathe through gills. **Gills** have tiny microscopic blood vessels that absorb dissolved oxygen from water. Fish swim with paired appendages called **fins**. They are **cold-blooded**, that is, their body temperature changes with the temperature of their environment. Some classification systems group all fish into the class *Pisces*. Other systems group fish into three classes: jawless fish (*Agnatha*), cartilaginous fish (*Chondrichthyes*), and bony fishes (*Osteichthyes*). Bony fish, such as goldfish and trout, make up the largest group and are the ones most familiar to you.

Jawless fish have jawless mouths and feed by sucking. They have smooth bodies with soft flexible skeletons made of cartilage. Some examples are lampreys and hagfishes. Cartilaginous fish have skeletons made of cartilage instead of bone. Their hinged jaws are lined with sharp pointed teeth. Sharks, skates, dogfish, and sting rays are cartilaginous fish. Bony fish have skeletons made of bone and are the largest group of fish. They live in saltwater and freshwater and have covered gills with a single opening on each side. Salmon, tuna, trout, goldfish, and eels are common bony fish. Examples of common fish groups are shown in Figure 17-7.

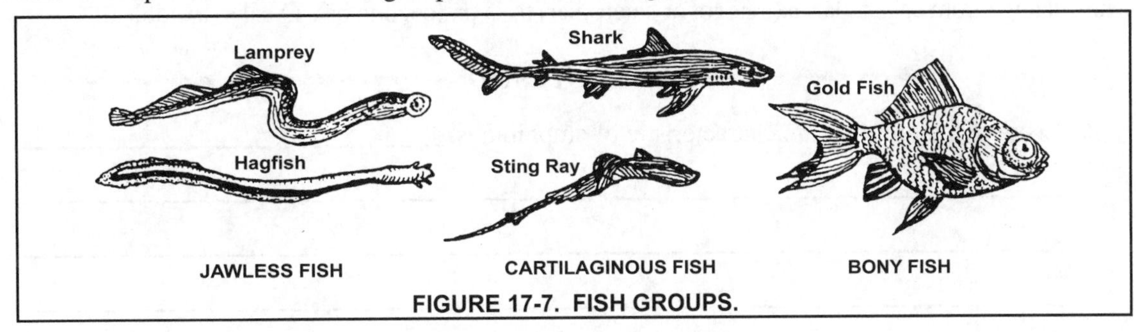

FIGURE 17-7. FISH GROUPS.

Review Questions

1. Name the three fish groups and give one example of each group. ____________

____

____

2. What is meant by the term "cold-blooded"? ______________________

____

3. What is the function of gills in fish? ___________________________

____

Name______________________________ Class______________________ Date____________

Amphibians. Amphibians lead a "double life". The word *amphibian* means "having two lives". Part of their life is spent in water and the other part is lived on land. Frogs, toads, salamanders, and newts are all amphibians (Figure 17-8). Amphibians generally have vertebrate characteristics. There are however, some special features that are characteristic to amphibians. They have smooth, thin, usually moist skin, with no scales. Their feet, when present, are webbed with no claws. Amphibians are cold-blooded and some eat plants (herbivores) in their larval stage. The **larval stage** is an immature stage in the development of an organism. The adult amphibian is a carnivore (flesh-eater). They have gills, lungs, and skin for respiration. As larvae their heart is two-chambered. In the adult there is a three-chambered heart with a well developed circulatory system. Their eggs are usually laid in water and fertilized externally (outside the body) as soon as they are laid.

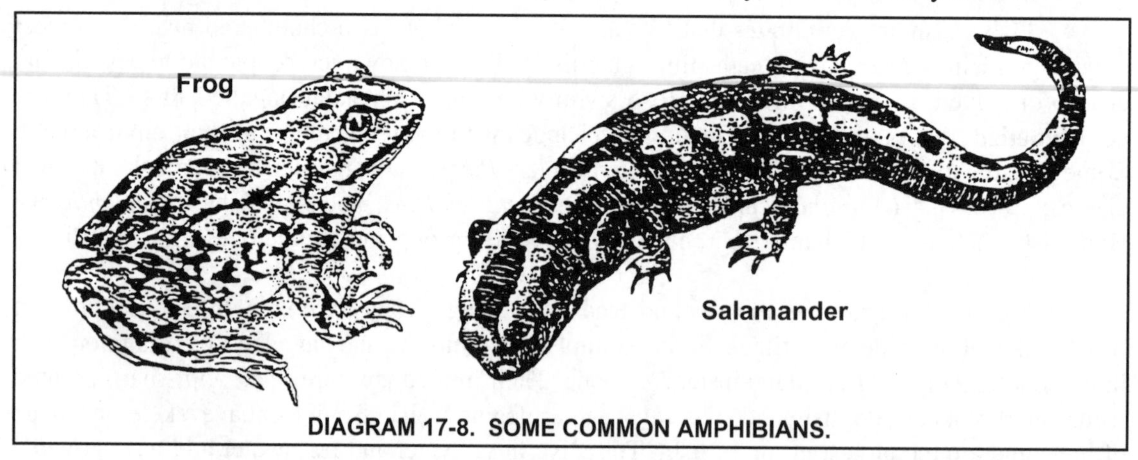

DIAGRAM 17-8. SOME COMMON AMPHIBIANS.

Amphibians undergo a series of changes called **metamorphosis** as they become adults. The stages of metamorphosis in the frog are the egg, larva (tadpole), and adult. [Insects also undergo metamorphosis. They change from eggs to larva (maggot or caterpillar) to pupa (cocoon or chrysalis) to adults.]

Review Questions

1. List five features that are characteristic of amphibians. ______________________

____

____

____

2. What is metamorphosis? ______________________

3. Where do amphibians live? ______________________

____

Reptiles. Unlike amphibians, reptiles are true land animals. They do not have to stay close to water to reproduce Reptiles have dry scaly skin that keeps them moist. They are cold-blooded and have lungs for breathing. Because they are cold-blooded, they are found more commonly in warm climates than in cool climates. Most reptiles have three-chambered hearts and their lungs are well developed. Reptiles have two pairs of limbs that allow them to creep along on land. Their feet have toes with claws that enable them to dig and climb. Most reptiles are carnivores

Name________________________ Class____________________ Date__________

and some are predators. A **predator** is an animal that kills and eats other animals. There are more than 5,000 species of reptiles. Some examples of reptiles are snakes, turtles, alligators, crocodiles, lizards, and Gila monsters (Figure 17-9).

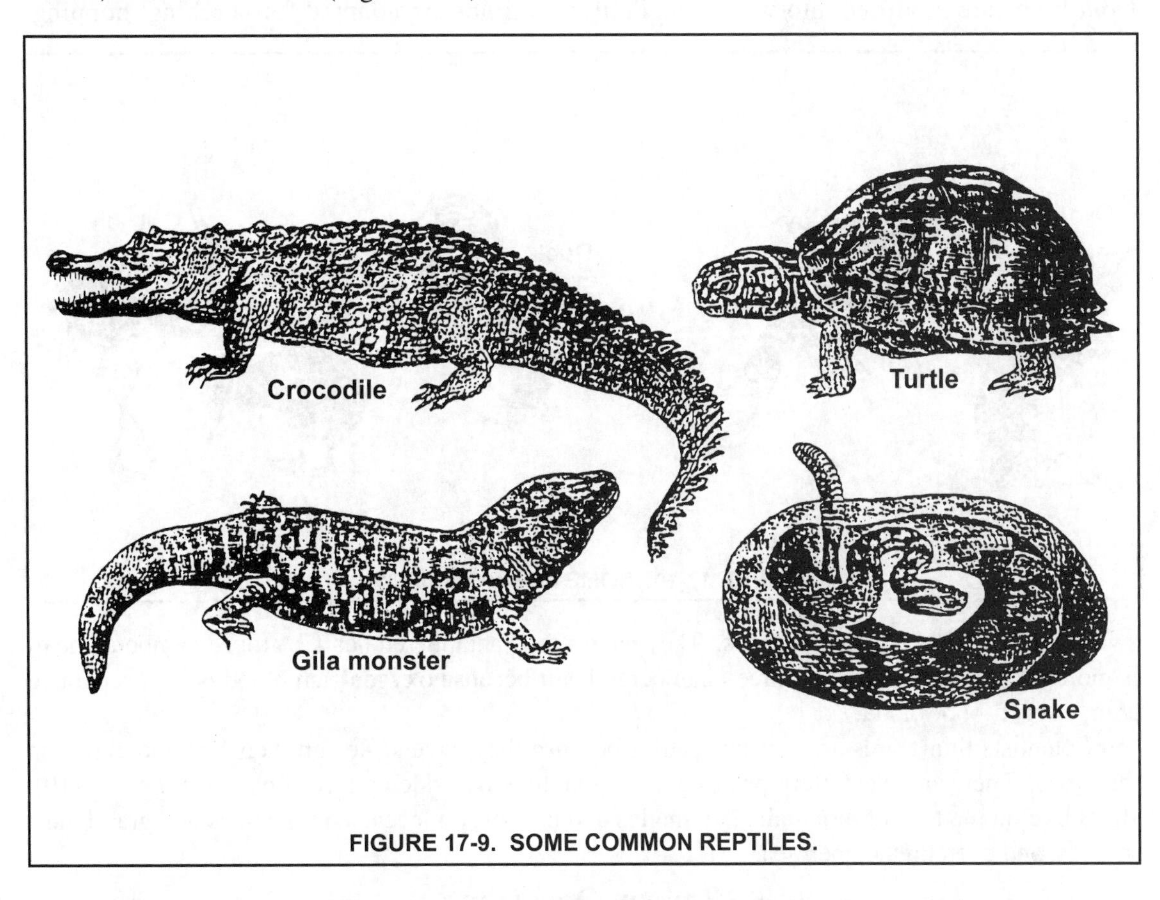

FIGURE 17-9. SOME COMMON REPTILES.

Review Questions

1. List five reptile characteristics. ____

____

____

____

____

2. Where do reptiles live? ____

3. Name three common reptiles. ____

____

♦ **Birds.** The characteristic that separates birds from other vertebrates is the possession of feathers. Feathers help keep their bodies warm. Feathers, wings, and air sacs in their bodies along with lightweight air-filled bones, enable them to fly. Birds, unlike fish, amphibians, and reptiles,

Name______________________________ Class ______________________ Date ____________

are warm-blooded. **Warm-blooded** animals maintain a constant body temperature even when the temperature around them changes. The bird's jaw is covered by a horny beak and they do not have teeth. Birds have different types of beaks that allow them to live in different environments. Their front limbs are modified into wings and their hind limbs are adapted for perching, hopping,

FIGURE 17-10. SOME COMMON BIRDS.

swimming, or other similar functions. They have a four-chambered heart. A four-chambered heart is more efficient than a two or three-chambered heart because oxygen-rich blood is kept separated from oxygen-poor blood.

Scientists think birds arose from reptiles because they have scales on their feet and claws on their toes. There are over 9,000 species of birds that live in a wide variety of places (Figure 17-10). Birds live on the tops of mountains, in jungles and deserts, on icecaps, in marshes and grasslands, in trees, and even on the open sea.

REVIEW QUESTIONS

1. Describe how birds are adapted for flying. ______________________________

____

2. What is meant by the term "warm-blooded"? ______________________________

____

3. What characteristic makes birds different from other vertebrates? ____________

____

♦ **Mammals.** Mammals are the animals most familiar to you. They are different from other vertebrates because they have fur or hair on their bodies and **mammary glands** that produce milk for feeding their young. Mammals give birth to living young after a period of development inside the mother. Other animals (some fish and snakes) bear living young, but only mammals develop attached inside the female. Mammals, like birds, have a four-chambered heart and are warm-blooded. They have a muscular diaphragm that moves air in and out of their lungs. Their nervous system, with its large brain, is more highly developed than any other animal group.

Name________________________ Class________________________ Date____________

Mammals are found almost everywhere on the Earth. They live in the air, in water, and on land. There are almost 5,000 species classified into three groups: **monotremes** (egg-laying mammals), **marsupials** (pouched mammals), and **placental mammals** (Table 17-3).

MAMMAL GROUP	CHARACTERISTICS	EXAMPLES
Monotremes – (Egg-Laying Mammals)	Females lay eggs that may be carried in a pouch on the abdomen or kept warm in a nest. After hatching the young are fed with milk from mammary glands. Feet have claws, reptile-like limbs, or webbed feet.	Duck-billed platypus and spiny anteater.
Marsupials – (Pouched Mammals)	Embryos develop in the mother's uterus (womb) for a few weeks; then are born and crawl undeveloped into a pouch where they complete their development. The young feed on mammary glands in mother's pouch. Their feet have claws	Kangaroo, koala, and opossum
Placental Mammals	Largest mammal group (over 90%). Young develop inside body of mother in an organ called a **uterus.** Materials between mother and developing embryo are exchanged through an organ called **placenta**. Young are born in a more mature stage than marsupials. Great variety — adapted to live in air, water, and on land. Most highly developed brain.	**Insect-Eating:** shrews, hedgehogs. **Flying:** bats. **Hoofed:** pigs, deer, horses. **Trunk-Nosed:** elephant. **Carnivorous:** tigers, lions, seals, walruses. **Aquatic:** whales, porpoises, dolphins. **Gnawing:** mice, rats, squirrels. **Rodentlike:** rabbits, hares. **Toothless:** anteaters, armadillos. **Primates:** Lemers, monkeys, apes, humans.

TABLE 17-3. MAMMAL GROUPS.

Name ______________________ Class ____________________ Date __________

REVIEW QUESTIONS

1. Mammals are different from other vertebrates because they have ____________________ and ____________________.

2. Name the three mammal groups and give two examples of each group.

____

____

____

3. List seven placental groups and give one example of each group.

____

____

____

____

____

4. Young develop inside body of mother in an organ called a __________. Material between mother and developing embryo are exchanged through an organ called ______________.

D. ECONOMIC USES OF ANIMALS AND ANIMAL PRODUCTS. Animals and animal products are of great economic importance. Animals and animal parts are used directly for food. We get meat, such as steak, from animal tissue. Seafood comes from animals, for example, clams, shrimp, cod, trout and salmon. Liver, a food rich in iron, comes from an organ of the cow. Animals are also the source of many products used by humans such as, leather, furs, antibodies (smallpox vaccine from cows), hormones (insulin from sheep), fertilizers (manure from animals), perfume, silk, hair, fats, and oils.

REVIEW QUESTIONS

1. Name five animal products that are of economic value to humans.

____

____

____

____

____

____

____

Name_______________________________ Class__________________________ Date____________

LAB INVESTIGATION: VERTEBRATES AND INVERTEBRATES

OBJECTIVE

Upon completion of this activity you should be able to name several characteristics of invertebrate and vertebrate animals.

LABORATORY PROCEDURE

Materials: A collection of at least 30 living and/or preserved vertebrate and invertebrate animals. Reference books.

1. Your teacher has placed examples of vertebrate and invertebrate animals at various locations (stations) around the room. Each example has a different number. You are to observe each animal and decide whether it is a vertebrate or an invertebrate.

2. After you have made your decision, record your answer by writing either *vertebrate* or *invertebrate* in the **Observation Table** below.

OBSERVATIONS

EXAMPLE	ANIMAL TYPE	EXAMPLE	ANIMAL TYPE
1		16	
2		17	
3		18	
4		19	
5		20	
6		21	
7		22	
8		23	
9		24	
10		25	
11		26	
12		27	
13		28	
14		29	
15		30	

Name____________________ Class____________________ Date__________

CONCLUSIONS

1. Define the term vertebrate. ____________________

____

____

2. List five vertebrate animals. ____________________

____

____

____

____

3. Define the term invertebrate. ____________________

____

____

4. List five invertebrate animals. ____________________

____

____

____

____

5. Which is the largest group of animals, vertebrates or invertebrates? ____________________

Name________________________ Class________________ Date__________

REVIEW ACTIVITIES

Important Terms

DIRECTIONS: Define the following terms in the spaces provided.

anterior ____

____

anus ____

____

aortic arches ____

____

chitin ____

____

closed circulatory system ____

____

cold-blooded ____

____

crop ____

____

dorsal ____

____

endoskeleton ____

____

exoskeleton ____

____

ganglia ____

____

gill slits ____

____

gizzard ____

____

hemoglobin ____

____

heterotrophs ____

____

invertebrate ____

____

Name____________________ **Class**________________ **Date**________

malpighian tubules ____

mammary glands ____

marine ____

marsupials ____

metamorphosis ____

monotremes ____

motile ____

nephridia ____

notochord ____

sessile ____

spiracles ____

stinging cells ____

tentacles ____

tracheae ____

vertebrates ____

warm-blooded ____

Name________________ Class________________ Date____________

Skill Practice

Part A. Base your answers to questions 1 through 5 on the reading passage below and on your knowledge of biology.

The Sea Lamprey

Prior to the construction of the Welland Canal over 60 years ago, sea lampreys could travel no farther west than Lake Ontario. When the canal opened, it allowed ships moving up the St. Lawrence River to pass around Niagara Falls, but it also allowed the lampreys to enter Lake Erie, Lake Huron, and eventually all of the Great Lakes.

The lamprey has a thin body similar to that of an eel, a slimy brownish skin, and a tail and two single dorsal fins for swimming. The adult can be 60 centimeters long and weigh about 500 grams. The lamprey's head has a small undeveloped eye on each side and a nasal opening on top leading to a sac containing nerve endings that aid in smell. There are seven oval gill slits on each side of the head that open into pouches containing many feathery gills.

Rather than a jaw, the lamprey has a funnel-like mouth lined with many sharp teeth. The tongue, located in the middle of the mouth, has tooth-like projections. This mouth allows the lamprey to attach to a host fish. Then using it many teeth it tears a hole through the body of the fish and sucks out its blood and body fluids. When the host fish dies or weakens the lamprey moves on. Lampreys feed mainly on lake trout but will attack whitefish, pike, and others. They have greatly reduced the number of desirable fish species in the Great Lakes.

1. The sea lamprey can best be described as
a) a parasite
b) a marsupial
c) an herbivore
d) an autotroph

2. The movement of the sea lamprey into the Great Lakes as a result of the construction of the Welland Canal is an example of
a) overhunting
b) technological oversight
c) exploitation
d) poor land-use management

3. Based on the description in the passage, which diagram best represents what a student's laboratory drawing of a sea lamprey should look like?

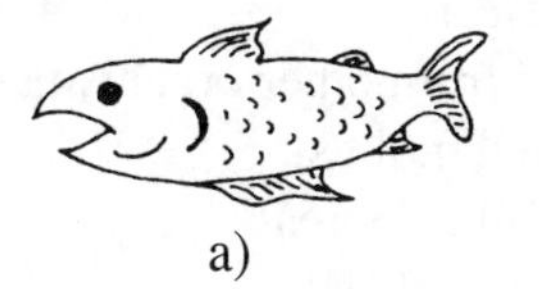
a)

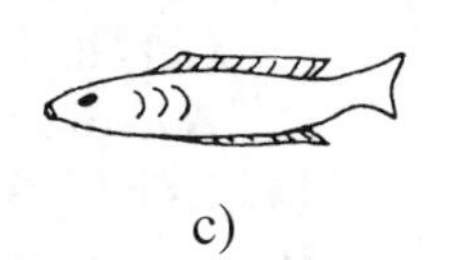
c)

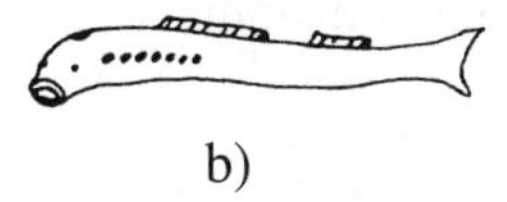
b)

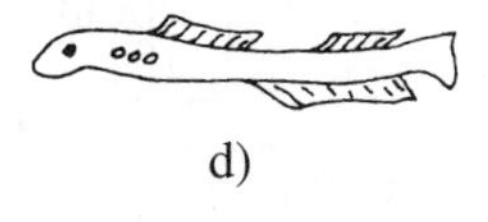
d)

4. Since the lamprey uses the blood and body fluids of host fish for nourishment, it digestive tract is probably
a) very complex in order to hydrolyze the large food molecules the lamprey obtains from the environment
b) nonexistent since as an adult the lamprey reproduces, but does not eat
c) simple since much of the lamprey's food is already in a soluble form
d) simple because the lamprey's many teeth are used to chew food into small pieces

5. The lamprey is able to attach to a host fish by means of its
a) gill slits
b) dorsal fins
c) nasal opening
d) funnel-like mouth

Name_______________________ Class___________________ Date__________

Part B. Complete the following crossword puzzle.

Crossword Puzzle

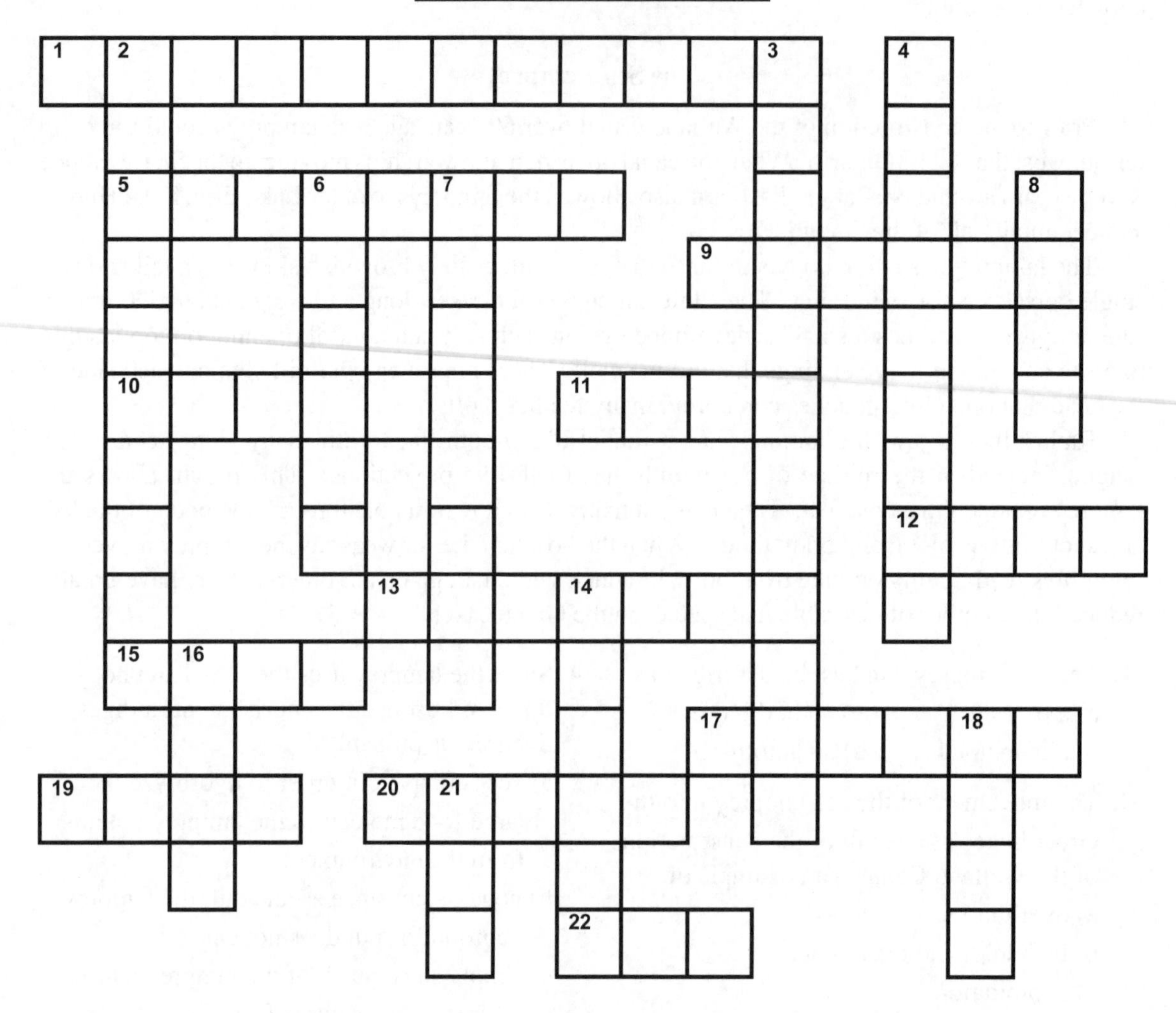

Clues

ACROSS

1. Any animal without a backbone
5. Long string-like appendages
9. Upper or back side of an organism
10. Member of phylum *Coelenterata*
11. Member of phylum *Arthropoda*
12. Common insects
13. Organisms that don't move around
15. ________ fish have tube feet
17. Organisms that can move around
19. Used by fish for swimming
20. Another word for backbone
22. Monotremes are ________ laying mammals

DOWN

2. Firm rods develop into a backbones
3. An inner skeleton
4. Pouched mammal
6. Part of an insect
7. Gets its food from other organisms
8. A hard shelled mollusk
14. Its body is full of pores
16. A common bony fish
18. An example of a carnivore
21. A common hoofed mammal

Name________________________ Class____________________ Date__________

CHAPTER 17: QUIZ

A. FILL-IN QUESTIONS

DIRECTIONS: Complete each of the following statements by writing the correct word or phrase in the space provided.

1. The ________________ is an organism that cannot make its own food.
2. Animals without backbones are classified as ________________.
3. Marine animals live in ________________.
4. Insects have ________________ for grinding food.
5. Vertebrates with mammary glands are classified as ________________.
6. A ________________ is a firm rod that runs along the dorsal side of vertebrates.
7. Structures in water animals that develop into true gills are called ________________.
8. The jellyfish has long, string-like appendages called ________________.
9. ________________ animals have body temperatures that change with the environment.
10. ________________ are multicellular organisms that do not have cell walls and chloroplasts.
11. ________________ is a series of changes that occurs in the life cycle of amphibians.
12. Animals that look like bags and have pores are called ________________.
13. An endoskeleton is a/an ________________.
14. An example of a mollusk that is a bivalve is the ________________.
15. ________________ are animals with three body parts and three pairs of legs.
16. Animals with backbones are classified as ________________.
17. An organism with dry scaly skin is a/an ________________.
18. An example of a spiny-skinned animal is the ________________.
19. Monotremes are described as ________________mammals.
20. An example of a segmented worm is the ________________.

B. MULTIPLE-CHOICE QUESTIONS

DIRECTIONS: Circle the number of the expression that best completes each of the following statements.

1. Which life form is classified as an invertebrate?
   (1) snake (3) frog
   (2) dog (4) grasshopper
2. Which product is manufactured from animal tissue?
   (1) leather (3) sugar
   (2) turpentine (4) paper
3. Animals cannot use the energy of the Sun to produce food because they *lack*
   (1) cytoplasm (3) chromosomes
   (2) chlorophyll (4) fats

Name________________________ Class____________________ Date__________

4. A placenta may be formed in female
(1) amphibians (3) birds
(2) reptiles (4) mammals

5. Which of the following animals is a predator?
(1) coyote (3) sheep
(2) rabbit (4) sponge

6. Perch, toads, snakes, and turtles are classified as
(1) protists (3) arthropods
(2) protozoans (4) vertebrates

7. A useful animal product is
(1) wool (3) grain
(2) cotton (4) plastic

8. Which of the following is a vertebrate?
(1) earthworm (3) mosquito
(2) frog (4) starfish

9. Frogs feed on living insects. This diet would place frogs in which group?
(1) carnivore (3) decomposer
(2) herbivore (4) producer

10. Which of the diagrams shown below represents an annelid?

(1)

(3)

(2)

(4)

C. ESSAY QUESTION

DIRECTIONS: Use complete sentences to answer the question in this part.

1. State the difference between a vertebrate and an invertebrate.

____

____

____

____

Name________________________ Class____________________ Date__________

UNIT FOUR TEST

Matching Questions

DIRECTIONS: In the space at the left of each item in Column A, place the letter of the term or phrase in Column B that is most closely related to that item.

	Column A	Column B
_________	**1.** Multicellular organisms that can't make their own food.	**a.** Transpiration
_________	**2.** Animals without a backbone.	**b.** Phloem
_________	**3.** Pouched mammals.	**c.** Animals
_________	**4.** Conducts water from roots to leaves.	**d.** Marsupials
_________	**5.** Loss of water vapor from plant.	**e.** Vertebrates
_________	**6.** Makes food for plants.	**f.** Plants
_________	**7.** One-celled organism.	**g.** Sponge
_________	**8.** Animals with backbones.	**h.** Amoeba
_________	**9.** Conducts materials throughout plant.	**i.** Leaf
_________	**10.** Pore-bearing animal.	**j.** Invertebrates
		k. Perspiration
		l. Binary fission
		m. Xylem

True–False Questions

DIRECTIONS: Write TRUE before each statement that is true and FALSE before each statement that is false.

_________ **1.** Decomposers are organisms that break down dead organisms.

_________ **2.** The paramecium moves with pseudopods.

_________ **3.** A virus is not a cell.

_________ **4.** The kingdom is the smallest classification group.

_________ **5.** Scientific names and common names are the same thing.

_________ **6.** Bacteria and fungi are complex organisms.

_________ **7.** A spore is a cell with a protective coat.

_________ **8.** Nonvascular plants have specialized tissues for conduction of materials.

_________ **9.** The waxy covering on the leaf is called the palisade layer.

_________ **10.** Sessile animals cannot move around.

Name________________________ Class____________________ Date__________

Fill-In Questions

DIRECTIONS: Complete each of the following statements by writing the correct word or phrase in the space provided.

1. The ________________________ has tentacles and stinging cells.
2. Animals that maintain a constant body temperature are called ________________________.
3. Vascular tissue is ________________________ tissue.
4. ________________________ are common nonvascular plants that look like a green carpet.
5. The leaf has ________________________ and air spaces for gas exchange.
6. Stems grow in length at their ________________________.
7. Coccus, spirillum, and bacillus are all shapes of ________________________.
8. Mushrooms are examples of ________________________ that are used for food.
9. Taxonomy is the science of ________________________.
10. African sleeping sickness and malaria are caused by organisms called ________________________.

Multiple-Choice Questions

DIRECTIONS: Circle the number of the expression that best completes each of the following statements.

1. The scientific name of dog, *Canis familiaris*, is made up of the dog's
   (1) genus and species (3) kingdom and phylum
   (2) phylum and species (4) class and phylum
2. Which organisms are noncellular?
   (1) protozoans (3) trees
   (2) algae (4) viruses
3. Which organisms can **not** produce their own food?
   (1) fungi (3) algae
   (2) ferns (4) roses
4. Decomposers are important for
   (1) producing oxygen (3) chlorophyll production
   (2) natural recycling (4) making sugar
5. The present system of classification is based on the idea that
   (1) There are very few different organisms
   (2) there is no similarity among organisms
   (3) there can be no common ancestry
   (4) present-day life developed from earlier forms

Name_______________ Class_______________ Date_______________

6. Vascular tissue in stems is composed mostly of

(1) cambium and xylem
(2) lenticels and phloem
(3) xylem and phloem
(4) stomates and lenticels

7. The loss of water vapor from a leaf is known as

(1) fermentation
(2) transpiration
(3) photosynthesis
(4) nutrition

8. The opening in a leaf through which gases move in and out is known as the

(1) epidermis
(2) chloroplast
(3) waxy cuticle
(4) stomate

9. Roots and root hairs are plant structures that are specialized for

(1) photosynthesis and absorption
(2) anchorage and photosynthesis
(3) anchorage and absorption
(4) photosynthesis and respiration

10. Which products are obtained from plants?

(1) antibodies and fur
(2) plastic and leather
(3) glass and cotton
(4) paper and sugar

Essay Question

DIRECTIONS: Use complete sentences to answer the question in this part.

1. State two ways that bacteria are useful to humans.

Class Notes

Name________________________ Class__________________ Date__________

UNIT FIVE

REPRODUCTION AND DEVELOPMENT

LEARNING OUTCOMES: Upon completion of the study of this unit, you should be able to:

- Define reproduction and relate the process of reproduction and development to species survival.
- Differentiate between sexual and asexual patterns of reproduction.
- Identify the major structure and processes involved in animal and plant sexual reproduction.
- Identify the major types of asexual reproduction in animals, plants, and simple organisms.
- Describe the stages of cell division.
- Distinguish between the two major forms of cell division.
- Relate the importance of chromosomes in the maintenance of characteristics of organisms.

Chapter 18: Cell Reproduction

A. NEED FOR REPRODUCTION. Reproduction is the life process during which living things produce other living things of the same species. Reproduction is not necessary for the life of one individual organism. However it is necessary for the continued survival of a particular group of organisms. A species (group) must reproduce regularly in order for the species to survive from generation to generation. If a certain species stopped reproducing for even one generation the species would vanish. For example, *one* individual dog can live a normal life span without ever reproducing but the entire dog species (*Canis familiaris)* would disappear if *all* dogs stopped reproducing.

REVIEW QUESTIONS

1. The life process by which living things produce new living things of the same species is called ______________________________.
2. What would happen to a species if it stopped reproducing? ______________________________

____

____

Name______________________ Class______________________ Date__________

B. CELL DIVISION. All cells arise from other cells by cell division. When cells grow to a certain size they must either divide or die. This happens because cell growth causes a cell's volume to increase at a faster rate than its surface area. If a cell continued to grow without dividing the surface area would become too small to hold the cell's contents. Imagine a balloon into which you have blown too much air. Soon the balloon surface would be unable to contain the air and the balloon would burst. The same thing would happen to a cell if it did not divide.

Cell division is a complex series of changes in the nucleus of a cell that leads to the production of two new cells. The new cells are called **daughter cells**. The nuclei of the daughter cells are usually identical to each other and to that of the parent cell. The daughter cells grow and increase in size until they divide and produce two more daughter cells. The continuation of this process results in organism growth and reproduction.

REVIEW QUESTIONS

1. Explain why cells must divide. ____

____

____

____

2. The complex series of changes in the nucleus of a cell that leads to the production of two new cells is called ______________________.

3. The new cells produced by cell division are called ______________________.

C. MITOSIS. All cells in the body (except sex cells) are produced by the process of mitotic cell division. Mitotic cell division is also called mitosis. **Mitosis** involves a complex series of changes in the nuclei of body cells that produce identical (same) daughter cells—that is they have exactly the *same number* and *type* of chromosomes as the parent cells. In Chapter 5 you learned that chromosomes are long threadlike structures located in the nucleus of the cell. They contain hereditary information organized as genes. Genes control cell activities and genes can be passed on to the next generation.

Along with its function in producing offspring during asexual reproduction mitotic cell division also results in growth and repair of body tissues in multicellular organisms. Sometimes cell division gets out of control. This can happen when cells are exposed to certain chemicals or radiation that cause increased mutation rates. One result of this exposure is an increased chance of cancer. **Cancer** is a group of diseases that are often characterized by the uncontrolled division of certain abnormal cells.

REVIEW QUESTIONS

1. What is mitosis? ____

____

____

2. The group of diseases caused by uncontrolled cell division is ______________________.

3. Chromosomes are made up of structures called ______________________.

Name________________ Class________________ Date________________

D. STAGES OF MITOSIS. Although the events of mitosis are an ongoing process they are generally described in terms of separate phases or **stages** (Figure 18-1). Separating mitosis into stages makes the process easier to study. The stages of mitosis are: interphase, prophase, metaphase, anaphase, and telophase.

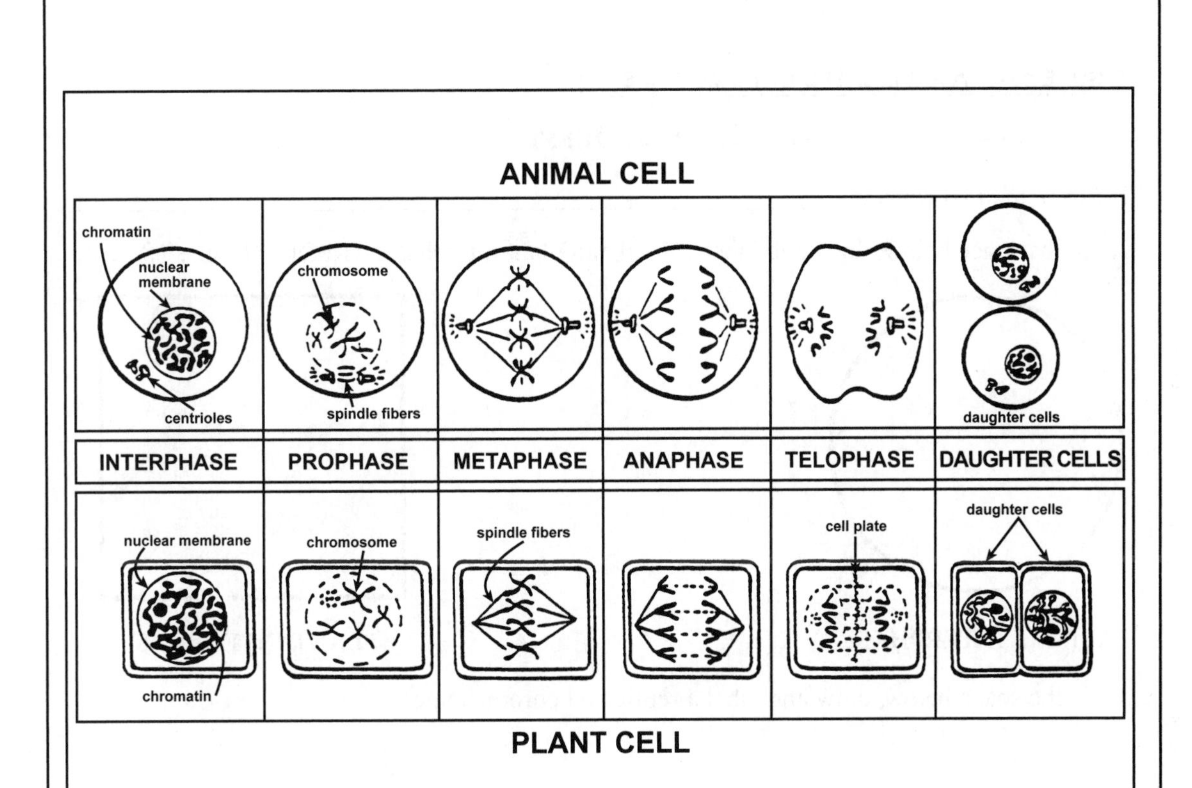

FIGURE 18-1. STAGES OF MITOSIS IN PLANT AND ANIMAL CELLS.

REVIEW QUESTIONS

1. Name the stages of mitosis. ____

____

2. Explain why mitosis is separated into stages. ____

____

Name________________________ Class________________________ Date____________

E. INTERPHASE. Interphase is the period between cell divisions. During interphase the single stranded chromosomes replicate. The term *replicate* means to make an exact copy. This results in double stranded chromosomes (Figure 18-2). Each strand of a double stranded chromosome is called a **chromatid.** The two chromatids are joined by a structure called the **centromere**. The chromosomes can not be seen during interphase.

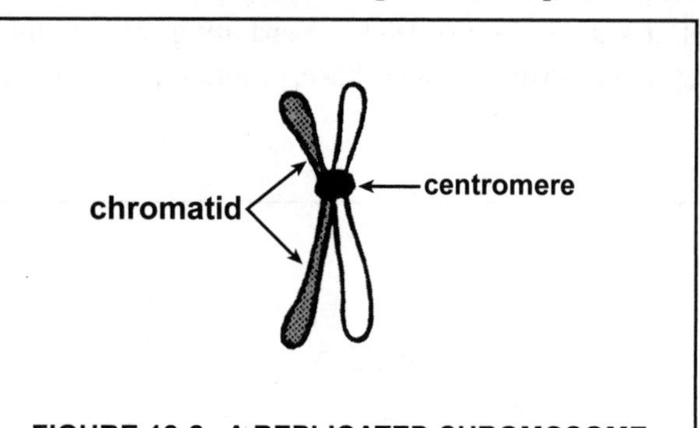

FIGURE 18-2. A REPLICATED CHROMOSOME.

REVIEW QUESTIONS

1. To *replicate* means to ____.

2. In the space below, draw and label animal and plant interphase. (Refer to Figure 18-1.)

ANIMAL INTERPHASE **PLANT INTERPHASE**

3. In the space below, draw and label a replicated chromosome.

F. PROPHASE. In **prophase** the double stranded chromosomes become visible (able to be seen) and the nuclear membrane surrounding them disappears. A **spindle apparatus**, consisting of fibers, forms between opposite poles of the cell.

REVIEW QUESTIONS

1. Describe prophase. ____

____

____

2. Draw and label animal and plant prophase. (Refer to Figure 18-1.)

ANIMAL PROPHASE

PLANT PROPHASE

G. METAPHASE. During **metaphase** the centromeres of the double stranded chromosomes become attached to the spindle fibers. The chromosomes move toward the middle of the cell and line up at the **cell equator** (midline).

REVIEW QUESTIONS

1. Draw and label animal and plant metaphase. (Refer to Figure 18-1.)

ANIMAL METAPHASE

PLANT METAPHASE

2. At metaphase the chromosomes line up at the ______________________.

H. ANAPHASE. During **anaphase** the centromeres replicate and move apart. The two chromatids of each double stranded chromosome move to opposite poles of the cell. Each chromatid is now a single stranded chromosome and there is a complete set of chromosomes at each pole (opposite ends) of the cell.

REVIEW QUESTIONS

1. Describe anaphase. ____

____

____

____

Name________________________ Class ____________________ Date __________

2. Draw and label animal and plant anaphase. (Refer to Figure 18-1.)

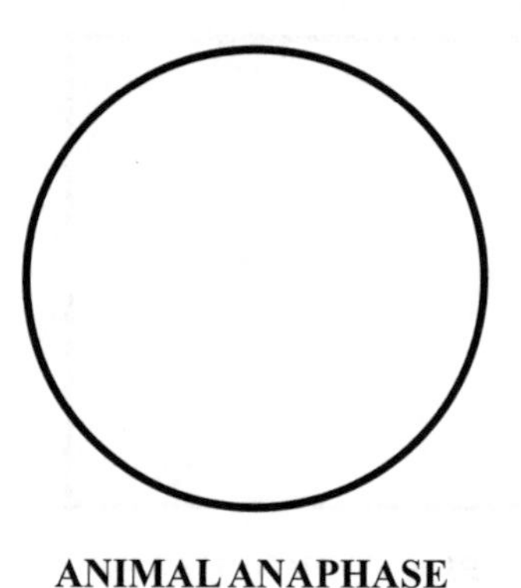

ANIMAL ANAPHASE

PLANT ANAPHASE

I. TELOPHASE AND CYTOPLASMIC DIVISION. The last stage of mitosis is telophase. In **telophase** a nuclear membrane forms around each set of chromosomes forming two identical nuclei. At the end of mitosis the cytoplasm generally divides forming two new identical daughter cells.

REVIEW QUESTIONS

1. Draw and label animal and plant telophase. (Refer to Figure 18-1.)

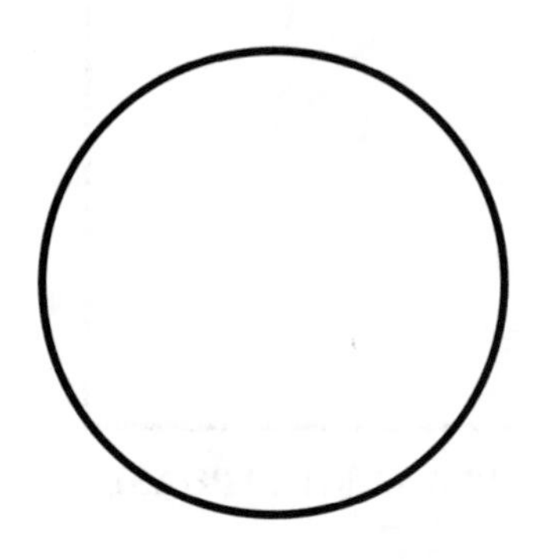

ANIMAL TELOPHASE

PLANT TELOPHASE

J. COMPARISON OF MITOSIS IN PLANT AND ANIMAL CELLS. The process of mitosis is similar in plant and animal cells but there are a few differences (Table 18-1).

ANIMAL CELLS	PLANT CELLS
Have **centrioles** that are involved in the formation of the spindle apparatus.	Do not have centrioles.
Cytoplasmic division involves a "pinching in" of the cell membrane.	Cytoplasm divides by formation of **cell plate** that becomes part of the cell wall.

TABLE 18-1. COMPARISON OF MITOSIS IN PLANT AND ANIMAL CELLS.

Name________________________ Class________________________ Date____________

REVIEW QUESTIONS

1. Compare plant mitosis and animal mitosis. ________________________________

____

____

____

K. MEIOSIS. The process of **meiosis** involves two cell divisions and produces cells that are different from the parent cell. Meiosis produces cells that have *one half the number* of chromosomes as the parent cells (Figure 18-3). Meiosis takes place during sexual reproduction when **sex cells**, called the egg and sperm, are produced in sex organs. A complex series of changes in the cell nuclei form sex cell nuclei that have one half the number of chromosomes found in a species normal body cell. One half the normal number of chromosomes is called the **monoploid** (or **n**) number. In humans the monoploid number (n) is 23.

When the egg and sperm unite during fertilization the species normal chromosome number, called the **diploid** or (**2n**) number, is restored (brought back). The diploid chromosome number in humans is 46. Fertilization restores the species normal chromosome number that was halved during meiosis **(n+n=2n)**. If meiosis did not take place the fertilized egg would have double the chromosome number **(2n+2n=4n)**. If this process continued each generation of offspring would have double the chromosome number of its parents.

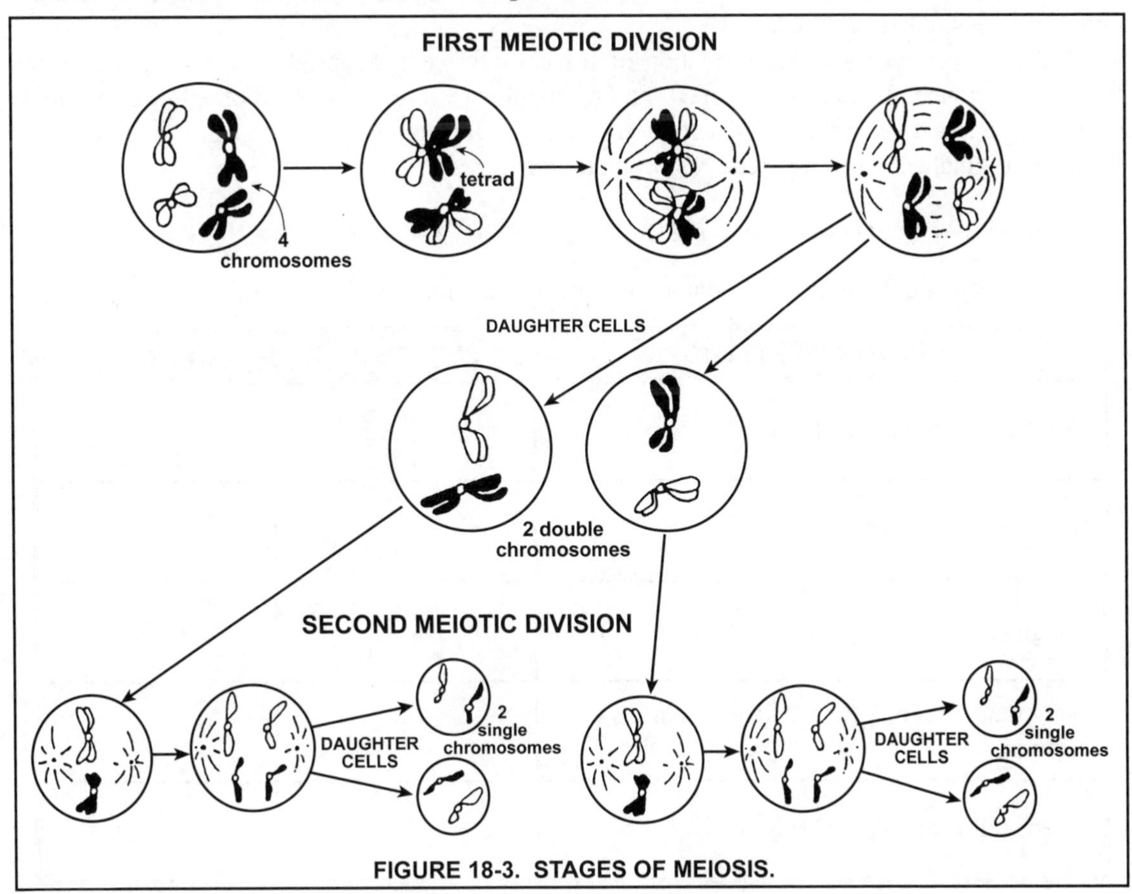

FIGURE 18-3. STAGES OF MEIOSIS.

Name________________________ Class________________________ Date____________

REVIEW QUESTIONS

1. The process of meiosis involves ________________________ cell divisions.
2. Sex cells are called ________________ and ________________
3. Does meiosis produce cells that are the same as or different from the parent cell?

   ____

4. What is the difference between a monoploid number and a diploid number?

   ____

   ____

5. What would happen to the chromosome number of each generation if meiosis did not take place? ____

   ____

L. COMPARISON OF MITOSIS AND MEIOSIS. Mitosis is the form of cell division that accounts for growth and replacement of cells in multicellular organisms. In one celled and other simple organisms mitotic cell division is a form of asexual reproduction. Mitosis results in the formation of two diploid daughter cells that are identical to the parent cell and to each other. During mitosis there is only one division.

Meiosis occurs only in the formation of sex cells for sexual reproduction. It results in the formation of four cells. Each cell contains half the number of chromosomes (monoploid or **haploid**) of the original cell. The cells produced by meiotic cell division are different from each other and from the original cell. Meiosis requires two cell divisions.

REVIEW QUESTIONS

1. Complete the following chart comparing mitosis and meiosis.

CHARACTERISTIC	MITOSIS	MEIOSIS
Number of daughter cells.		
Number of cell divisions.		
Daughter cells are diploid or haploid.		
Daughter cells and parent cell are identical or different.		
Parent cell is diploid or haploid.		

Name________________________ Class____________________ Date__________

LAB INVESTIGATION: OBSERVING ANIMAL MITOSIS

OBJECTIVE

Upon completion of this activity you should be able to identify several stages of mitosis in animal cells.

LABORATORY PROCEDURE

Materials: Prepared slide of whitefish egg mitosis, lens paper, a compound microscope, and reference books or animal mitosis models.

1. Collect your laboratory materials from the supply table and take them to your lab area. Clean your microscope lenses and prepared slide with the lens paper.

2. In this lab you will observe animal cell mitosis. *Mitosis* is a complex series of changes in the nuclei of cells that results in cells that are genetically identical to the dividing cell. Mitosis takes place in *stages* or *phases*. The dividing cell is called the *parent cell* and the two new cells are called *daughter cells.*

3. Place the prepared slide of whitefish mitosis on the microscope stage. Focus the slide using the low power objective. Refer to the diagram on this page to be sure you have located the dividing cells. They are stained a purple pink. The two stages that are shown on the diagram on this page are late *anaphase* (located on the left) and *interphase* (on the right).

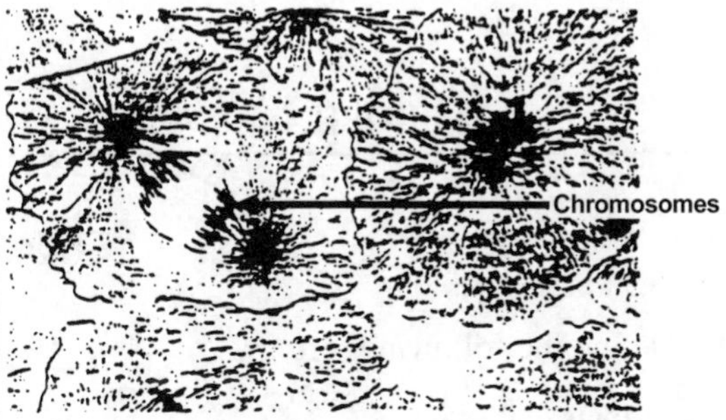

4. Scan your slide under low power to locate the *chromosomes.* They are stained dark purple pink on your prepared slide. The chromosomes are labeled on the diagram on this page. Chromosomes are composed of genetic material and *replicate* (duplicate) during mitosis.

Chromosomes

CELLS OF A WHITEFISH EMBRYO

5. Now look for a cell that is in *prophase.* Refer to your reference materials to be sure you have located prophase cells. Once you have located a prophase cell carefully center your cell and switch your microscope to high power. If your cells are not clearly focused under high power refocus them by ***using only the fine adjustment knob to focus upwards.***

6. Draw one prophase cell in the **Observation (1)** in the **Observation Section** on the next page. Label the chromosomes, nuclear membrane, and spindle fibers. Use your textbook or reference materials to help you identify the cell structures.

7. Change your microscope back to low power and find a cell that is in *metaphase.* Refer to your reference materials to be sure you have located metaphase cells. Repeat **Procedure 5** to focus the slide under high power.

Name________________________ Class________________________ Date__________

8. Draw one metaphase cell in the **Observation (2)** in the **Observation Section** on this page. Label the chromosomes, nuclear membrane, and spindle fibers. Use your textbook or reference materials to help you identify the cell structures.

9. When you are finished with your laboratory activity clean your lab area and return your lab materials and microscope to the supply table.

10. Answer the questions in the **Conclusion Section**.

OBSERVATIONS

(1) PROPHASE.	(2) METAPHASE.

CONCLUSIONS

1. Define the following terms:

   Mitosis. ____

   ____

   Parent Cell. ____

   ____

   Daughter Cells. ____

   ____

2. How many daughter cells are formed as a result of mitosis? ____________

3. Are the daughter cells formed as a result of mitosis identical to the parent cell? ____________

Name____________________ Class____________________ Date__________

REVIEW ACTIVITIES

Important Terms

DIRECTIONS: Define the following terms in the spaces provided.

anaphase ____

____

cancer ____

____

cell division ____

____

cell equator ____

____

cell plate ____

____

centrioles ____

____

centromere ____

____

chromatid ____

____

daughter cells ____

____

diploid number ____

____

interphase ____

____

meiosis ____

____

metaphase ____

____

mitosis ____

____

Name________________ Class________________ Date________

monoploid number ____

____

prophase ____

____

reproduction ____

____

sex cells ____

____

spindle apparatus ____

____

telophase ____

____

Name________________________ Class________________________ Date______________

SKILL PRACTICE

Part A. Which is the correct sequence (order) for the stages of mitotic cell division (mitosis) represented by the diagrams below?

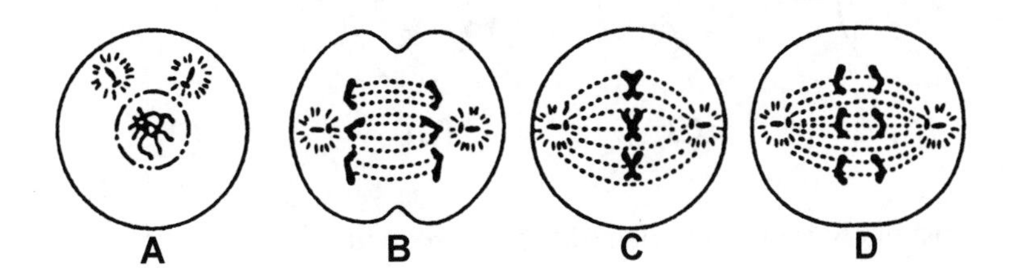

(1) A → B → C → D

(2) A → C → D → B

(3) B → A → D → C

(4) B → C → D → A

Part B. Which process is represented by the diagram below?

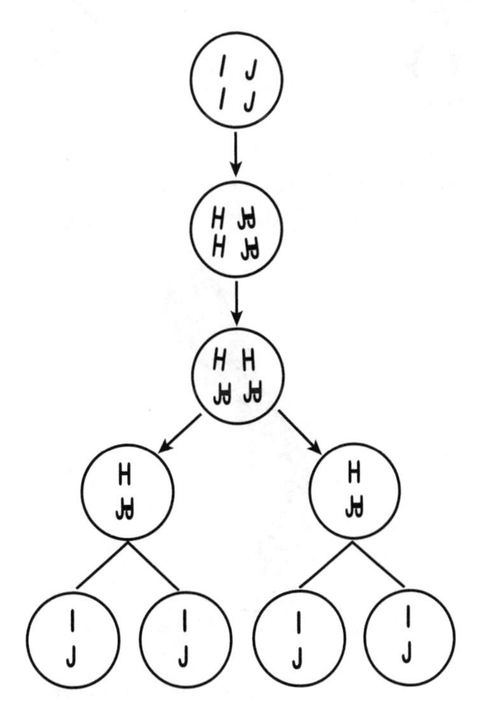

(1) germination

(2) mitotic cell division

(3) fertilization

(4) meiotic cell division

Name________________ Class________________ Date____________

Part C. The diagrams below represent the sequence (order) of events in a cell undergoing normal meiotic cell division (meiosis).

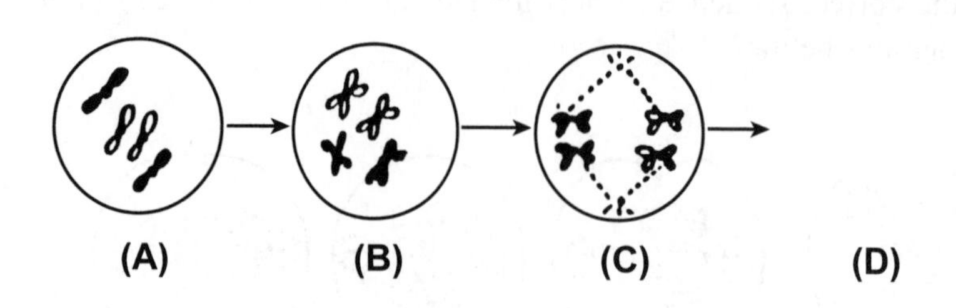

Which diagram most likely represents stage D of this sequence?

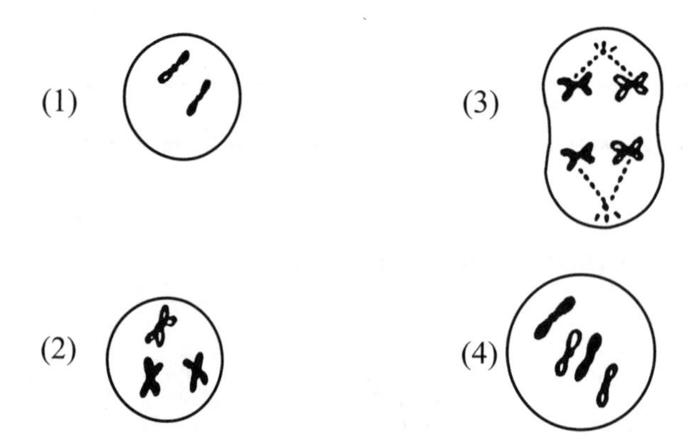

Part D. Base your answers to questions 1 and 2 on the diagram below that represents a microscopic structure observed during the process of cell division and on your knowledge of biology.

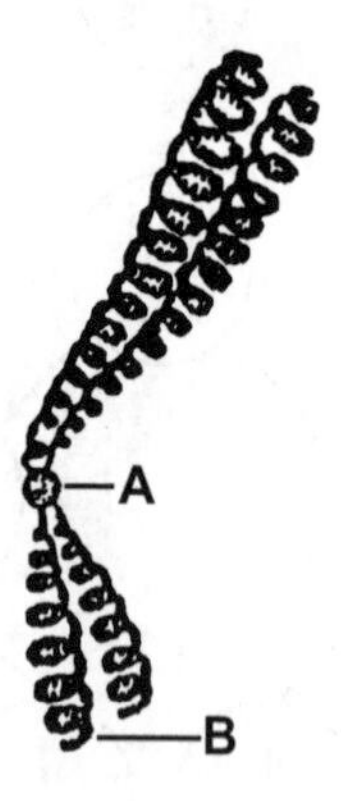

1. Letter A indicates a

(1) nucleolus
(2) ribosome
(3) centriole
(4) centromere

2. Letter B indicates a

(1) centrosome
(2) spindle fiber
(3) chromatid
(4) cell plate

Name________________________ Class________________________ Date____________

CHAPTER 18: QUIZ

A. FILL-IN QUESTIONS

DIRECTIONS: Complete each of the following statements by writing the correct word or phrase in the space provided.

1. The chromosomes are lined up on the cell equator during ____________________ stage of cell division.
2. A group of diseases characterized by uncontrolled cell division is called ________________.
3. ____________________ cells do not have centrioles.
4. A spindle apparatus forms during the ____________________ stage of cell division.
5. Each strand of a double stranded chromosome is called a/an ____________________.
6. A cell that is not dividing is said to be in the ____________________ stage of cell division.
7. If a species stopped reproducing it would ____________________.
8. The type of cell division that produces two identical cells is ____________________.
9. ____________________ is a type of cell division that requires two cell divisions.
10. The normal species chromosome number is called the ____________________ number.
11. During cell division the parent cell splits to form two ____________________ cells.
12. The egg and sperm unite during the process of ____________________.
13. One half the chromosome number is called the ____________________ number.
14. The centromere joins two ____________________.
15. During the ____________________ stage of cell division the centromeres replicate and move apart.
16. Plant cell cytoplasm divides by forming a/an ____________________ plate.
17. ______________ is a type of cell division that results in cells that are different from the parent.
18. The life function that is necessary for the survival of the species but not necessary for the survival of an individual organism is ____________________.
19. The last stage of mitosis is called ____________________.
20. In the animal cell cytoplasmic division involves a/an ______________ of the cell membrane.

B. MULTIPLE-CHOICE QUESTIONS

DIRECTIONS: Circle the number of the expression that best completes each of the following statements.

1. Which cell is produced as a result of meiosis?
   (1) red blood cell (3) sperm cell
   (2) nerve cell (4) kidney cell
2. Traits are passed on to the next generation by the
   (1) blood (3) genes
   (2) brain (4) liver

3. An example of a sex cell is a/an
   (1) spore (3) egg
   (2) zygote (4) centriole

4. A child has the same number of chromosomes as each parent because of the processes of fertilization and
   (1) transpiration (3) digestion
   (2) meiosis (4) repair

5. The process of mitosis results in
   (1) two cells with identical nuclei (3) four sperm cells
   (2) four cells with identical nuclei (4) one egg cell

6. The production of new organisms that are essentially the same as their parents is
   (1) digestion (3) excretion
   (2) reproduction (4) respiration

7. Which structures contain the genetic material of the cell?
   (1) chromosomes (3) cell membranes
   (2) cell walls (4) vacuoles

8. What is the diploid chromosome number in humans?
   (1) 23 (3) 69
   (2) 46 (4) 92

9. The process of cell division that produces two identical daughter cells is known as
   (1) meiosis (3) mitosis
   (3) zygote formation (4) fertilization

10. Growth in the size of multicellular organisms is the result of
   (1) cell excretion (3) egestion
   (2) cell division (4) peristalsis

C. ESSAY QUESTION

DIRECTIONS: Use complete sentences to answer the question in this part.

1. State one reason why reproduction is important to a species.

____

____

____

____

____

____

____

____

____

Name________________________ Class________________________ Date__________

Chapter 19: Asexual Reproduction

A. ASEXUAL REPRODUCTION. **Asexual reproduction** results from mitotic cell division (mitosis). During asexual reproduction one cell, called the parent cell, divides into two identical daughter cells. The new organisms, called offspring, are genetically identical to the parent cell. There is no fusing (joining) of cells in this type of reproduction.

Asexual reproduction is more common in invertebrate animals than in vertebrate animals. Unicellular and multicellular plants can reproduce both asexually and sexually. Types of asexual reproduction include binary fission, budding, sporulation, regeneration, vegetative propagation, and cloning.

REVIEW QUESTIONS

1. What is asexual reproduction? ____

____

____

2. Asexual reproduction is more common in ______________________ animals than in ______________________ animals.

3. Name three types of asexual reproduction. ________________________________

____

B. BINARY FISSION. Binary fission is the simplest type of asexual reproduction. During **binary fission** a one celled organism divides by mitosis to form two daughter cells of equal size. Both the nucleus and the cytoplasm divide equally. The chromosomes of the offspring are identical to that of the parent. Amebas, paramecia, and bacteria reproduce by binary fission (Figure 19-1).

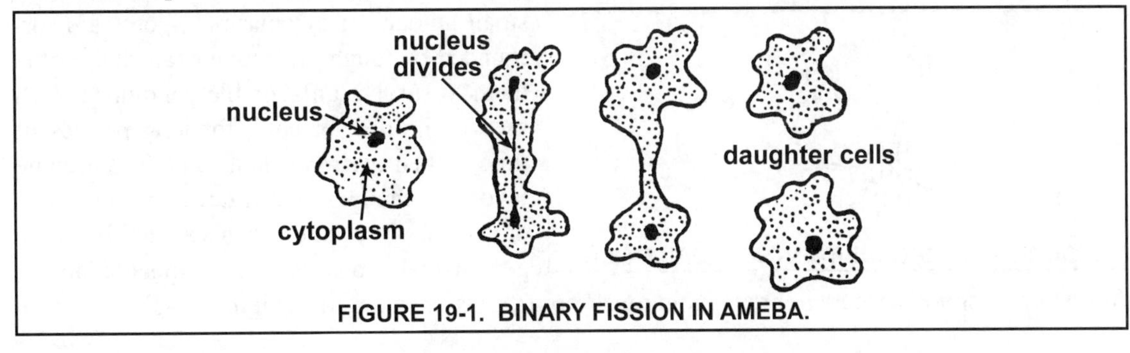

FIGURE 19-1. BINARY FISSION IN AMEBA.

REVIEW QUESTIONS

1. Describe binary fission. ____

____

____

____

Name______________________ Class______________________ Date__________

2. Name two organisms that divide by binary fission. ______________________________.

____

C. BUDDING. A type of asexual reproduction in which a new organism develops as an outgrowth of the parent is called **budding**. The new organism, called the **bud**, is a tiny duplicate of the parent organism. In budding the nucleus divides equally and the cytoplasm divides unequally. The bud and the parent may separate from each other or may remain together and form a colony. Budding (Figure 19-2) occurs in unicellular organisms (yeast) and in multicellular organisms (hydra).

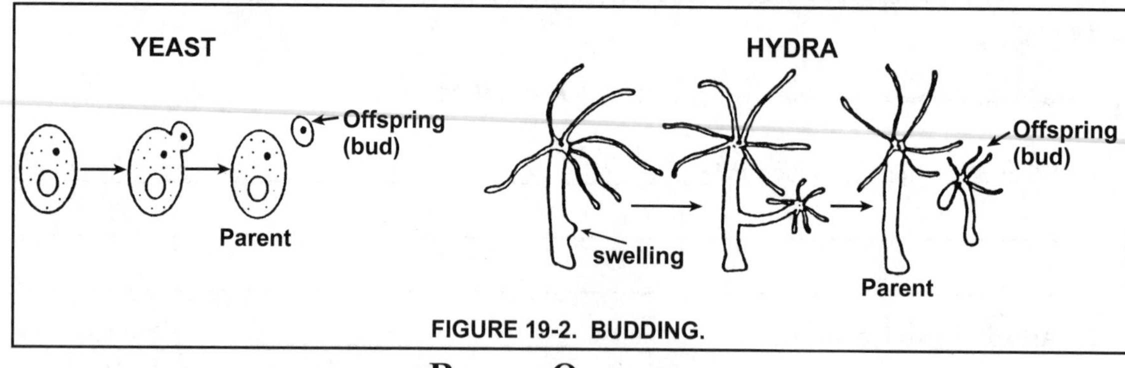

FIGURE 19-2. BUDDING.

REVIEW QUESTIONS

1. Budding results in equal division of the ____________________ and unequal division of the ____________________.
2. A one celled organism that reproduces by budding is ____________________.
3. ____________________ is a multicellular organism that reproduces by budding.

D. SPORULATION. **Spores** are specialized asexual reproductive cells that contain a nucleus and a small amount of cytoplasm. Spores are surrounded by tough protective coats that enable them to survive unfavorable conditions, such as extreme heat or cold, for long periods of time. When environmental conditions become favorable each spore can develop into a new organism. The new organism has the same genetic makeup as its parent. **Sporulation**, the formation of spores, occurs in bread mold,mushrooms, mosses, and ferns (Figure 19-3).

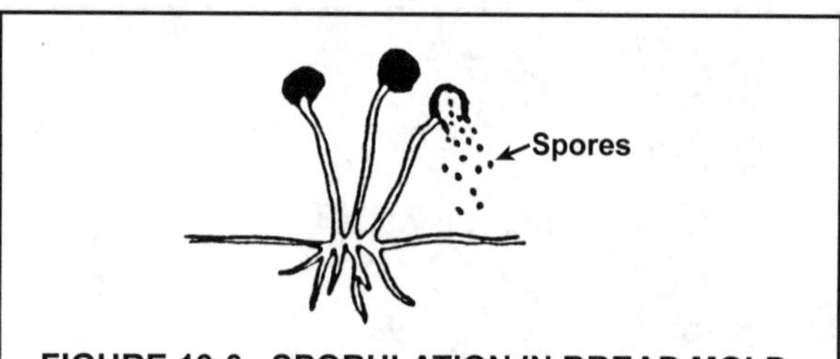

FIGURE 19-3. SPORULATION IN BREAD MOLD.

REVIEW QUESTIONS

1. What is a spore? ____

____

2. State one advantage of spore formation. ______________________________

____

Name________________ Class________________ Date________

E. REGENERATION. Regeneration is the development of a new organism from a part of the parent organism. For example, in starfish a single arm can develop into a new starfish. Starfish eat oysters. Oyster fishermen once tried to kill starfish by cutting them into pieces. Instead of dying, each starfish piece grew into a new starfish.

Regeneration can also mean the replacement of lost body parts. For example, lobsters are able to grow a new claw to replace one that has been lost. Regeneration of lost body parts occurs mostly in invertebrates. Other animals that can regenerate are planaria and sponges (Figure 19-4).

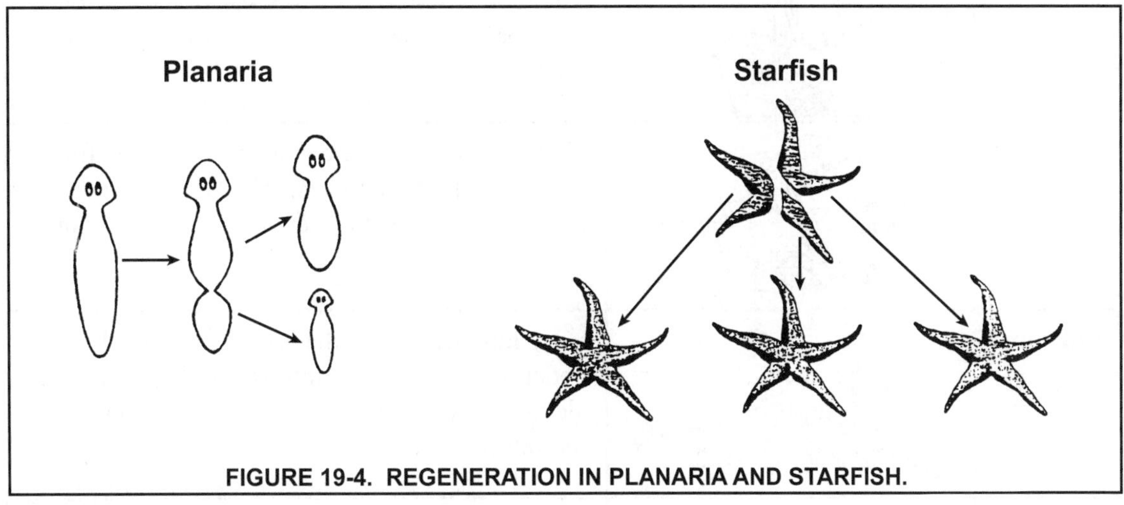

FIGURE 19-4. REGENERATION IN PLANARIA AND STARFISH.

REVIEW QUESTIONS

1. What is regeneration? ________________

____

2. Name two animals that reproduce by regeneration. ________________

____

F. VEGETATIVE PROPAGATION. Vegetative propagation is a form of asexual plant reproduction. In vegetative propagation a part of a plant, a root, a stem, or a leaf, grows into a new plant. The new plant is exactly the same as the parent plant. Commercial growers use vegetative propagation rather than seeds when they want to be sure that the offspring is identical to the parent. Seedless fruits and vegetables have to be reproduced by this method. Growers use this type of reproduction because it is fast, easy to use, and usually successful.

Vegetative propagation can occur naturally or artificially. **Natural vegetative propagation** occurs naturally without human interference. Types of natural vegetative propagation include **tubers, runners, rhizomes,** and **bulbs**. **Artificial vegetative propagation** occurs as a result of human activities. Two common methods of artificial vegetative propagation are **cuttings** and **grafting** (Table 19-1).

Name________________ Class________________ Date________

TYPE OF PROPAGATION	DESCRIPTION AND EXAMPLES
Runners	Stems that grow out over the surface of the soil from the existing stem. At points along the runner, new plants grow. Runners occur in strawberries and some grasses.
Bulbs	Underground stems specialized for food storage. The food is stored in the thick leaves of the bulb. Each bulb can develop into a new plant. Onions are bulbs.
Tubers	Underground stems are that contain stored food. White potatoes are tubers. The "eyes" of the potato are buds that can develop into new plants
Rhizomes	Long modified stems that grow horizontally under the soil. New plants are produced at nodes along the stem. Lawn grasses, ferns, and irises reproduce by rhizomes.
Cuttings	Pieces of roots, stems, or leaves, develop into new plants under proper conditions. Roses, sugar cane, and bananas are propagated this way.
Grafting	A cutting from one plant, called the **scion**, is attached to the main body of a rooted plant called the **stock**. The scion keeps its own identity. Seedless oranges and grapes are propagated by grafting.

TABLE 19-1. KINDS OF VEGETATIVE PROPAGATION.

REVIEW QUESTIONS

1. What is vegetative propagation? ________________________________

____

____

2. Name three plants that reproduce by vegetative propagation. ________________

____

Name________________________ Class____________________ Date__________

LAB INVESTIGATION: BREAD MOLD REPRODUCTION

OBJECTIVE

Upon completion of this activity you should be able to name the reproductive cells of bread mold.

LABORATORY PROCEDURE

Materials: Petri dish containing a piece of moldy bread, hand lens, microscope slide, cover slip, forceps, water, medicine dropper, and compound microscope.

1. Collect your laboratory materials from the supply table and take them to your lab area. Clean your microscope lenses and slide with the lens paper.

2. Examine your moldy bread with a hand lens. Refer to the diagram on this page to help you locate the mold. Draw your observations of the bread mold in the **Observation (1)** in the **Observation Section** on the next page.

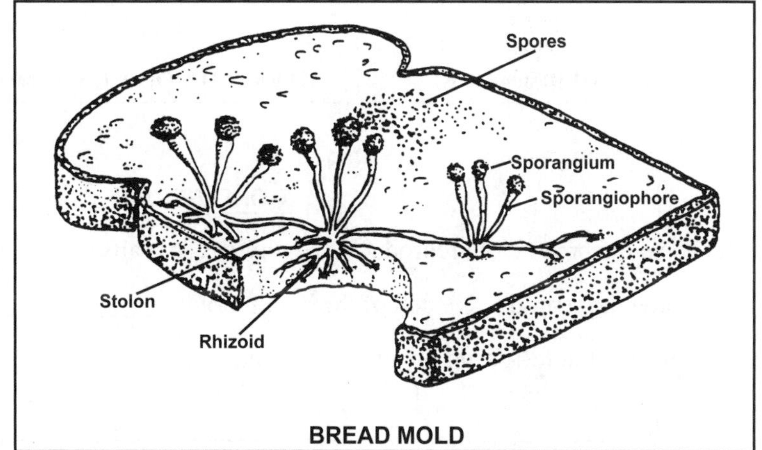

BREAD MOLD

3. Find the white thread-like structures that spread across the bread. These are the *stolons*. The stolons connect the *sporangiophores* and the root-like *rhizoids*. The sporangiophores stand upright sort of like little trees. The rhizoids grow down into the bread. Label the stolons, rhizoids, and sporangiophores on your bread mold drawing in **Observation (1).**

4. At the top of each sporangiphore is a black ball-shaped structure called *sporangium*. The sporangia produce the reproductive cells called *spores*. Label the sporangium and spores on your bread mold drawing in **Observation (1).**

5. Use your forceps to place some bread mold on a microscope slide. Add a drop of water and a cover slip. Place the slide on the stage of your compound microscope. Scan your slide under low power to locate the bread mold. Draw your observations of the bread mold in the **Observation (2)** in the **Observation Section** on the next page.

6. Once you have located the bread mold carefully center some spores and switch your microscope to high power. If your cells are not clearly focused under high power refocus them by ***using only the fine adjustment knob to focus upwards.*** Draw several bread mold spores in **Observation (3)** in the **Observation Section** on the next page.

Name________________ Class________________ Date________________

7. When you are finished with your laboratory activity throw away your bread mold. Clean your slides and lab area and return your lab materials and microscope to the supply table.

8. Answer the questions in the **Conclusion Section**.

LABORATORY PROCEDURE

(1) BREAD MOLD (hand lens)	**(2) BREAD MOLD (low power)**	**(3) SPORES**

CONCLUSIONS

1. Does the bread mold reproduce sexually or asexually? ________________
2. Name the reproductive cell of the bread mold. ________________
3. Describe the following bread mold structures:

Stolon. ________________

____

Rhizoid. ________________

____

Sporangium. ________________

____

Sporangiophore. ________________

____

Spores. ________________

____

Name ____________ Class ____________ Date ____________

REVIEW ACTIVITIES

Important Terms

DIRECTIONS: Define the following terms in the spaces provided.

asexual reproduction ____

____

binary fission ____

____

budding ____

____

bulbs ____

____

cuttings ____

____

grafting ____

____

regeneration ____

____

rhizomes ____

____

runners ____

____

scion ____

____

sporulation ____

____

stock ____

____

tubers ____

____

vegetative propagation ____

____

Name________________________ Class________________________ Date____________

Part A. On the line provided, identify the type of asexual reproduction represented in the diagrams below.

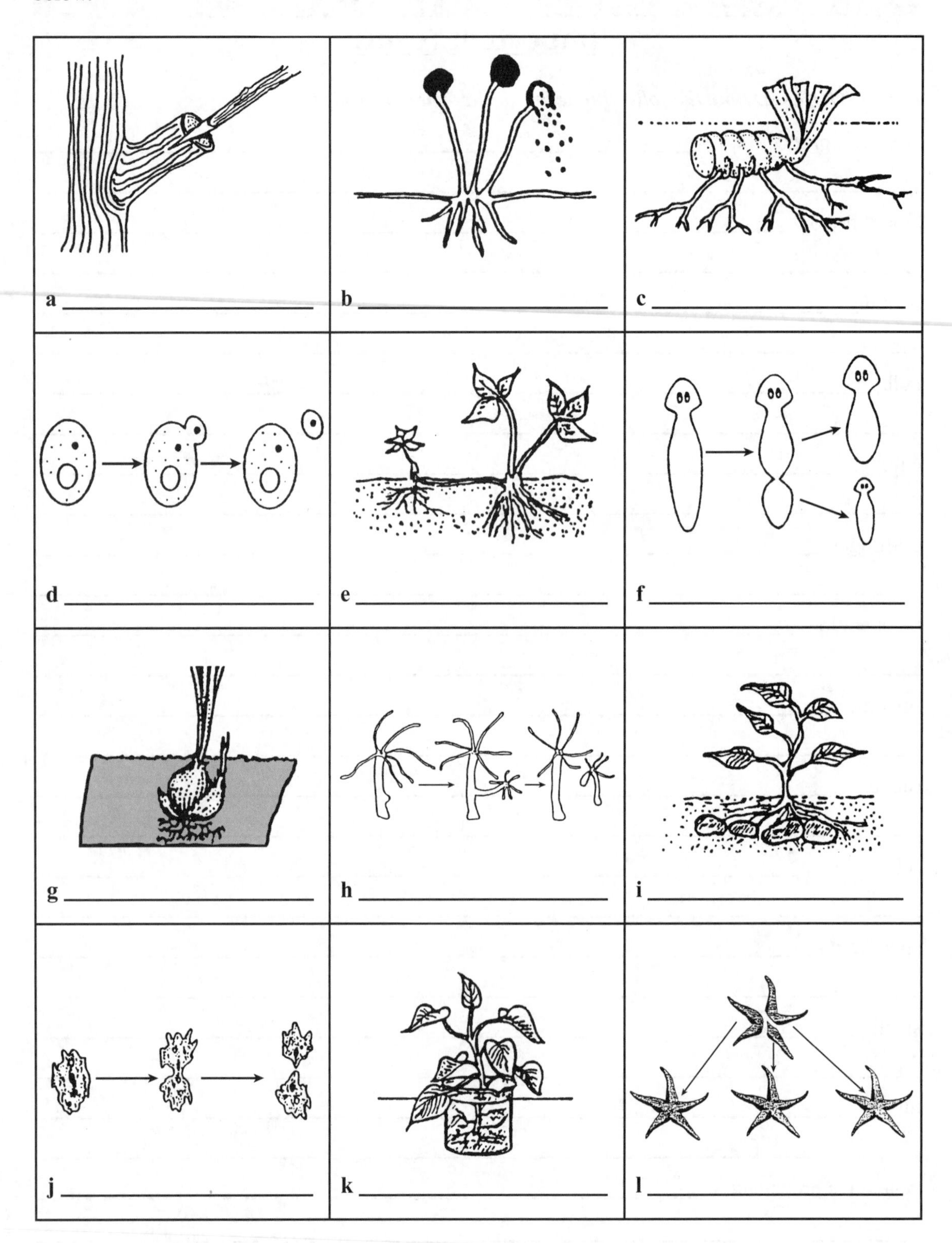

Name________________________ Class________________________ Date____________

CHAPTER 19: QUIZ

A. FILL-IN QUESTIONS

DIRECTIONS: Complete each of the following statements by writing the correct word or phrase in the space provided.

1. Reproduction involving one parent cell is called ________________________ reproduction.
2. The nucleus and cytoplasm divide equally during the type of asexual reproduction known as ________________________.
3. A type of asexual reproduction in which a new organism develops as an outgrowth of the parent is called ________________________.
4. Strawberries reproduce asexually by ________________________.
5. A ________________________ is a modified stem that grows horizontally under the soil.
6. Seedless fruits are propagated by ________________________.
7. The ability to replace a lost body part is called ________________________.
8. ________________________ are pieces of roots, stems, or leaves that develop into new plants.
9. Bread mold reproduces asexually by the process of ________________________.
10. Commercial growers use ________________________ rather than seeds when they want to be sure the offspring are identical to the parent.
11. An example of a bulb is the ________________________.
12. The ________________________ can reproduce by regeneration.
13. Stems that grow out over the surface of the soil from the existing stem are called ________________________.
14. ________________________ are specialized asexual reproductive cells that are surrounded by a tough protective coat.
15. The eyes on potatoes are actually ________________________.
16. The ________________________ is the rooted portion of the graft.
17. The ameba and paramecium reproduce asexually by ________________________.
18. Mushrooms reproduce asexually by means of ________________________.
19. Equal division of the nucleus along with unequal division of the cytoplasm occurs during the process of ________________________.
20. The production of a new plant by use of roots, stems, or leaves is ________________________.

B. MULTIPLE-CHOICE QUESTIONS

DIRECTIONS: Circle the number of the expression that best completes each of the following statements.

1. Which method of plant reproduction is illustrated by the diagram at the right?
   (1) bulbs (3) grafting
   (2) cuttings (4) runners

Name________________________ Class____________________ Date__________

2. A missing part of a starfish or a planarian can be regrown by the process known as
   (1) regulation (3) transport
   (2) regeneration (4) transpiration

3. Which process represents asexual reproduction of plants?
   (1) geraniums produced from cuttings (3) plant embryos produced by fertilization
   (2) maple trees produced from seeds (4) gametes produced in the ovary

4. Which diagram shown below represents reproduction by means of runners?

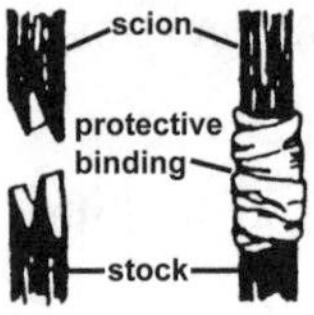

scion
protective binding
stock
(1)

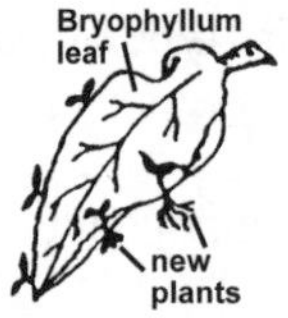

Bryophyllum leaf
new plants
(2)

(3)

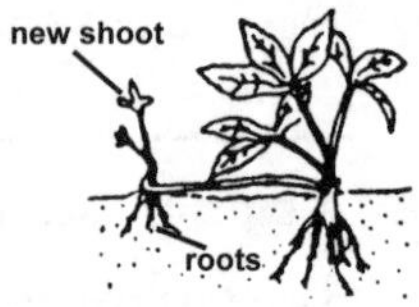

new shoot
roots
(4)

5. Vegetative propagation is a method of reproduction which
   (1) occurs in some multicellular plants
   (2) is commonly called sexual reproduction
   (3) results in genetically unlike offspring
   (4) is found in unicellular organisms

6. Special reproductive cells that can withstand unfavorable environmental conditions are called
   (1) buds (3) gametes
   (2) spores (4) grafts

7. Budding and fission are alike in that both
   (1) involve mitosis (3) do not form spindle fibers
   (2) involve cell plates (4) produce two daughter cells equal in size

8. By which process is the organism shown in the diagram at the right reproducing? 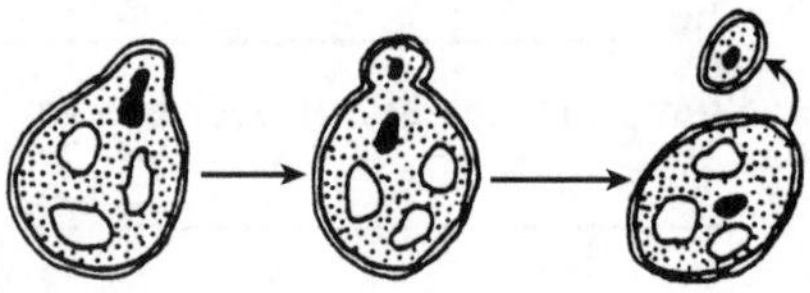
   (1) copulation (3) budding
   (2) regeneration (4) fertilization

9. Which of these forms of plant reproduction is likely to produce a new plant that is different from the parent plant?
   (1) cuttings (3) bulbs
   (2) seeds (4) runners

10. Red tulips are seldom grown from seed for commercial distribution because the
   (1) plants do not produce seeds
   (2) seeds may not be genetically like the parent plant
   (3) plants grow slower from bulbs
   (4) seeds take too long to germinate

C. ESSAY QUESTION

DIRECTIONS: Use complete sentences to answer the question in this part.

1. Name and describe one method of vegetative propagation. ______________________

____

____

____

Name______________________________ Class ____________________ Date __________

Chapter 20: Sexual Reproduction in Animals

A. SEXUAL REPRODUCTION. Sexual reproduction is a type of reproduction that involves two parents. The offspring are different from the parents. Sexual reproduction involves the fusion (joining) of two sex cell nuclei. Sex cells (egg and sperm) are formed from a type of cell division called meiosis. The sex cell nuclei fuse during the process of fertilization. The fertilized egg is called the **zygote**. The zygote divides by mitosis and develops into a new organism. The large variation (differences) in organisms is due in part to sexual reproduction.

Review Questions

1. Sexual reproduction is the type of reproduction that involves ________________ parents.
2. In sexual reproduction, are the offspring different from the parent? ________________.
3. Sexual reproduction involves the ____________________________ of two sex cells.
4. What is a zygote? ____

   ____
5. Sexual reproduction involves a type of cell division called ________________________.
6. What kind of reproduction causes variations in organisms?

   ____

   ____

B. GAMETOGENESIS. Gametogenesis is the development of mature sex cells called **gametes** (Figure 20-1). The formation of gametes involves meiosis of immature sex cells. Gametogenesis includes the processes of spermatogenesis and oogenesis. The process by which sperm develop in the testes of the male is called **spermatogenesis**. The process by which eggs develop in the ovaries of the female is called **oogenesis**. Gametogenesis takes place in reproductive organs called **gonads.** The male gonads are the **testes** and the female gonads are the **ovaries.** In some organisms, called **hermaphrodites**, both the male and female gonads are located on the same animal. The earthworm is an example of a hermaphrodite.

The male gamete is called the **sperm**. Sperm are monoploid and motile (able to move around). Many sperm are produced in comparison to few eggs. Each human gametogenesis produces four sperm to every one egg. The female gamete is called the **egg (ova).** The egg is larger than the sperm. It contains stored nutrients in the form of **yolk**. The egg is not capable of movement (nonmotile). One large egg and three smaller cells, called **polar bodies**, are formed during each oogenesis. The egg survives and if fertilized becomes the new organism. The polar bodies disappear.

Name____________________ Class ____________________ Date __________

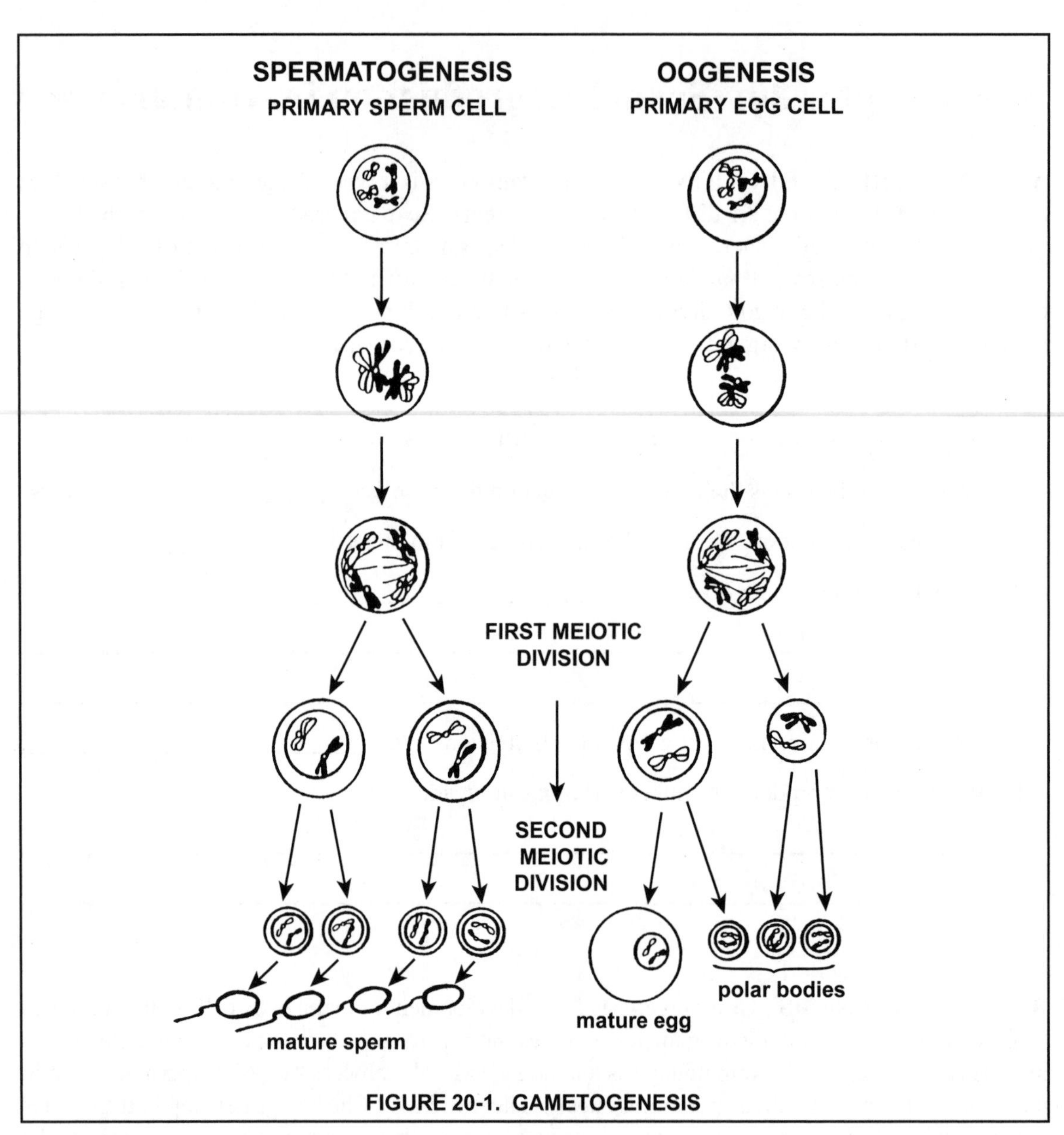

FIGURE 20-1. GAMETOGENESIS

Review Questions

1. What is gametogenesis? ____

   ____

2. Explain the difference between spermatogenesis and oogenesis.

   ____

   ____

3. The male gamete is called the ____________ and the female gamete is called the ____________.

4. The male gonads are the ____________ and the female gonads are the ____________.

Name________________________ Class________________________ Date____________

C. FERTILIZATION. **Fertilization** is the union (joining) of the egg and sperm nuclei. A monoploid or (n) sperm nucleus unites with a monoploid or (n) egg nucleus to form a diploid or (2n) zygote. Fertilization restores (brings back) the normal species chromosome number (2n) (Figure 20-2). Each organism has a different species chromosome number.

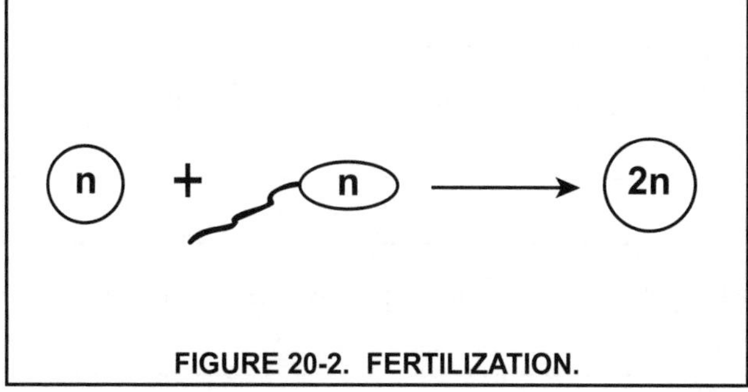

FIGURE 20-2. FERTILIZATION.

The new organism will not be identical to either parent because it contains genetic information from both the sperm cell and the egg cell. Half of the new organism's characteristics (traits) come from the female parent and the other half come from the male parent. (You will learn more about the inheritance of traits in Unit 6.)

Fertilization can be either external or internal. **External fertilization** takes place outside the body of the female. Sperm and eggs are released into the water and the sperm swim to the eggs. To be sure that at least some of the eggs are fertilized large numbers of sperm and eggs are deposited into the water at the same time. Many aquatic vertebrates, such as fish and amphibians, fertilize externally. **Internal fertilization** takes place inside the body of the female. The male deposits its sperm inside the reproductive tract of the female. The female reproductive tract has moist tissues to provide an environment for the sperm to swim toward the egg. Most terrestrial (land dwelling) vertebrates such as reptiles, birds, and mammals, fertilize internally.

REVIEW QUESTIONS

1. Fertilization is the union of an ____________________ and a ____________________.

2. During fertilization, a ________________ sperm cell unites with a ________________ egg cell to produce a ________________ zygote.

3. Draw and label a diagram showing the fertilization of an egg and a sperm.

4. ________________ fertilization takes place outside the body of the female.

5. Describe external fertilization. ____

____

____

6. Name two groups of animals that fertilize externally. ________________________

____

Name____________________ Class____________________ Date__________

7. Fertilization inside the body of the female is called ____________________.

8. Describe internal fertilization. ____________________

____

9. Why is the inside of the female's reproductive tract moist? ____________________

____

____

10. Name three animal groups that fertilize internally. ____________________

____

D. EMBRYONIC DEVELOPMENT. Embryology is the study of the development of an organism from fertilization until birth. Once fertilization has occurred the fertilized egg, or zygote, undergoes repeated mitotic cell divisions called **cleavage**. Cleavage results in a developing organism called the **embryo** (Figure 20-3).

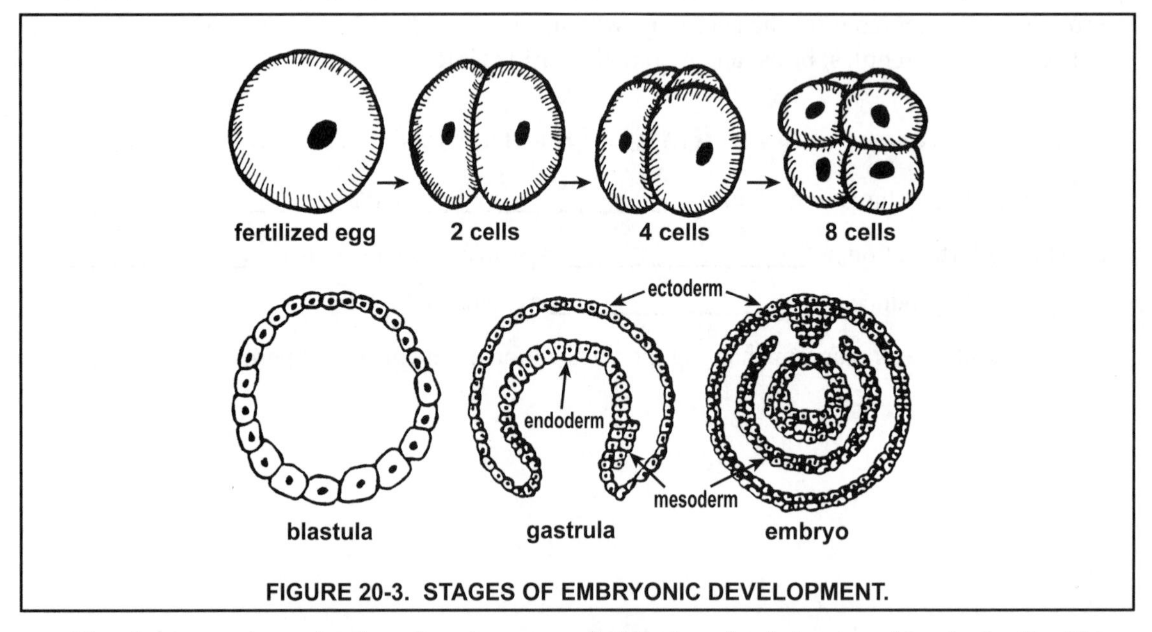

FIGURE 20-3. STAGES OF EMBRYONIC DEVELOPMENT.

The cleavage process begins when the zygote divides by mitosis into two identical cells. These two cells divide into four cells, which in turn divide into eight cells. This process continues and a solid ball of cells called the **morula**, is formed. As the cells continue to divide the center of the ball becomes hollow. The hollow ball stage is called the **blastula**. The blastula is made up of a single layer of cells.

The blastula stage is followed by the formation of the **gastrula.** During the formation of the gastrula one side of the blastula pushes inward. This results in the formation of a second inner layer of cells. The inner cell layer is called the **endoderm**. The outer cell layer is called the **ectoderm.** A third cell layer, the **mesoderm**, forms between the endoderm and ectoderm. The endoderm, ectoderm, and mesoderm layers continue dividing and forming all the tissues, organs, and organ

Name________________________________ Class____________________ Date____________

systems of the organism (Table 20-1). The three cell layers are called **primary germ layers.**

GERM LAYER	STRUCTURES FORMED
Ectoderm	Nervous system, skin, hair, nails
Mesoderm	Muscles, circulatory system, skeleton, excretory system, testes or ovaries
Endoderm	Lining of digestive and respiratory tracts, parts of the liver and the pancreas

TABLE 20-1. STRUCTURES FORMED FROM THE THREE GERM LAYERS.

REVIEW QUESTIONS

1. What is cleavage? ____

____

____

2. Cleavage results in a structure called the ______________________.

3. Name the three embryonic germ layers and the structures formed by each layer.

____

____

____

E. EXTERNAL DEVELOPMENT. After the formation of the three primary germ layers the embryo begins to grow and develop. **Growth** involves an increase in both the number and size of cells. The growth and development of the embryo can take place outside the body of the parent or inside the parent's body. **External development** involves the growth of the embryo outside the body of the parent. External development takes place in water or on land.

The eggs of many fish and amphibians are fertilized externally and develop externally in a water environment (Figure 20-4). The females lay their eggs in the water and the males deposit sperm over the eggs. Many eggs and sperm must be laid so that a few fertilized eggs reach adulthood. Most will be eaten by predators or lost through dryness and other factors. The developing embryo gets nourishment from yolk stored in the egg.

FIGURE 20-4. WATER DEVELOPMENT.

Name________________________ Class________________________ Date____________

The fertilized eggs of birds, many reptiles, and a few mammals (duckbill platypus and spiny anteater), develop externally on land. The embryos get nourishment from yolk stored in the egg. These organisms are adapted to external development on land because they have a protective shell and membranes that help to provide a favorable environment for embryonic development (Figure 20-5). The shells of bird and reptile eggs protect the soft inner parts and help prevent the loss of water from the eggs. The shells are porous and allow the exchange of respiratory gases. The embryonic membranes of a bird are as shown below:

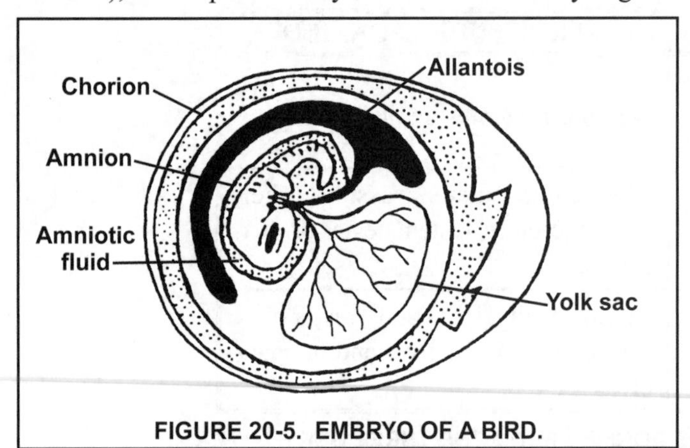

FIGURE 20-5. EMBRYO OF A BIRD.

Embryonic Membranes of a Bird

- **Chorion.** A membrane that lies directly under the shell and completely encloses the embryo and the other membranes.
- **Amnion (Amniotic Sac).** The membrane that lies just inside the chorion. It encloses the amniotic fluid.
- **Amniotic Fluid.** Cushions the embryo against shock. Together with the chorion keeps the embryo from drying out. Also prevents the embryonic tissues from sticking to the shell.
- **Yolk Sac.** Surrounds the yolk. Is a smaller membrane that grows from the digestive tract of the embryo. Blood vessels that penetrate the yolk sac and carry food (yolk) to the embryo.
- **Allantois.** Respiratory membrane and storage area for uric acid– a nitrogen-containing waste.

REVIEW QUESTIONS

1. Development of the embryo can take place ____________________ the body of the parent or ____________________ the parent's body.

2. External development takes place in ____________________ or on ____________________.

3. Name two groups of organisms that develop externally in water. ____________________

____

4. Why is it necessary for externally developing organisms to lay many eggs and sperm?

____

____

5. Name two groups of animals that develop externally on land. ____________________

____

Name________________________ Class__________________ Date__________

6. Name two mammals that develop externally on land. ____________________

7. State the function of:

allantois ____

____

chorion ____

____

amnion ____

____

amniotic fluid ____

____

yolk sac ____

____

8. Name two adaptations that help organisms develop on land. ____________________

____

____

F. INTERNAL DEVELOPMENT. During **internal development** the embryo grows inside the body of the female parent. Embryos that develop internally get greater protection from the environment than embryos that develop externally. Some fish and reptiles and most mammals develop internally.

Review Questions

1. Describe internal development. ____________________

____

G. PLACENTAL MAMMALS. Fertilization in mammals is internal. It takes place in the **oviducts** of the female. Most mammals develop internally in a specialized organ called the **uterus**. Mammal eggs contain little yolk, are very small, and do not provide food for the developing embryo. Developing mammals get food through a **placenta** inside the mother's uterus. The placenta is formed from both maternal and embryonic tissues (Figure 20-6). The exchange of nutrients, respiratory gases, and wastes between the mother and the embryo takes place through the placenta. There

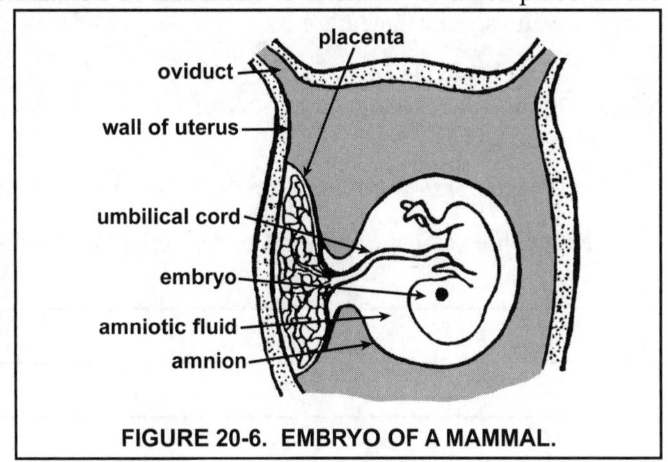

FIGURE 20-6. EMBRYO OF A MAMMAL.

is no direct connection between the circulatory systems of the mother and the embryo. The exchange of gases between mother and embryo occurs by diffusion and active transport. In placental mammals, the amnion, allantois, and yolk sac, become parts of the **umbilical cord** that connects the embryo to the placenta. Materials are carried between the embryo and the placenta by embryonic blood vessels located in the umbilical cord.

REVIEW QUESTIONS

1. Mammals develop internally in a specialized organ called the __________________.
2. Fertilization in mammals is internal in the __________________ of the female.
3. The __________________ provides food for the developing mammal.
4. The exchange of nutrients, respiratory gases, and wastes between the mother and the embryo takes place through the __________________.

CAREER OPPORTUNITIES

ZOO WORKERS: The operation of a zoo offers many different kinds career opportunities. Some of these jobs include zoo directors, curators (people in charge of different departments), veterinarians, keepers, and greenhouse workers. All of these jobs need people who love to work with animals. Directors oversee the entire operation of the zoo while curators are usually zoologists with special interests and education in certain animal areas such as reptiles, amphibians, or birds. Zookeepers feed the animals and clean their living areas. They have the closest contact with the animals and the animals' happiness and health depend on the keepers. Veterinarians take care of sick animals in the zoo hospital and greenhouse workers grow the special plants that are needed to reproduce the animals' original home environment.

The educational requirements for these jobs differ as does the salary that is received. Directors and curators need advanced degrees in zoology. Veterinarians have medical degrees from veterinary colleges. Greenhouse directors have received degrees in botany or agriculture and greenhouse workers must know how to grow and take care of plants. Zookeepers do not require any special education.

******

REVIEW QUESTIONS

1. Name three career opportunities for people who want to work in zoos.

____

____

____

____

Name________________________ Class____________________ Date____________

LAB INVESTIGATION: EMBRYOLOGY

OBJECTIVE

Upon completion of this activity you should be able to identify several stages of cleavage in the embryonic development of vertebrates.

LABORATORY PROCEDURE

Materials: Prepared slides of frog embryology: early cleavage, late cleavage, blastula, and neural fold stage. Cleavage models labeled and placed around the classroom and embryology charts and books for reference. Lens paper and compound microscope.

1. Collect your laboratory materials from the supply table, as your teacher directs, and take them to your lab area. Clean your microscope lenses and prepared slides with the lens paper.

2. In this lab you will observe several stages of frog embryology. *Embryology* is the study of the development of an organism from fertilization until birth. Once fertilization has occurred the fertilized egg, called the *zygote*, undergoes repeated cell divisions. These cell divisions are known as *cleavage.* The cleavage process begins when the zygote divides into two identical cells. These two cells divide into four cells which in turn divide into eight cells and so on until the embryo is formed.

3. Place the prepared slide of ***early cleavage*** on the microscope stage. Focus the slide using the low power objective. Refer to the cleavage models and reference materials to be sure you have located the dividing cells.

4. Once you have located and focused the cells under low power, carefully switch your microscope to high power. If your cells are not clearly focused under high power, refocus by ***using only the fine adjustment knob to focus upwards.***

5. Scan your slide to locate the *two-cell* and *four-cell cleavage stages.* Draw the two-cell and four-cell cleavage stages in **Observation (1)** in the **Observation Section** on the next page.

6. Place the prepared slide of ***late cleavage*** on the microscope stage. Focus the slide using the low power objective. Locate the *morula stage.* The morula looks like a solid ball of cells. Refer to the cleavage models and reference materials to be sure you have located the morula stage.

7. Repeat **Procedure 4** to focus under high power. Draw the morula cleavage stage in **Observation (2)** in the **Observation Section** on the next page.

8. Place the prepared slide of ***blastula*** on the microscope stage. Focus the slide using the low power objective. Locate the *blastula stage.* The blastula looks like a hollow ball of cells. Refer to the cleavage models and reference materials to be sure you have located the blastula stage.

9. Repeat **Procedure 4** to focus under high power. Draw the blastula in **Observation (3)** in the **Observation Section** on the next page.

10. Place the prepared slide of the ***neural fold stage*** on the microscope stage. Focus the slide using the low power objective. Locate the *ectoderm, endoderm* and *mesoderm* layers. These layers are known as the *primary germ layers*. They give rise to all the tissues, organs, and organ systems of the organism. The ectoderm is the outer cell layer, the endoderm is the inner layer of cells, and the mesoderm is the middle cell layer. Refer to the cleavage models and reference materials to be sure you have located the blastula stage.

11. Repeat **Procedure 4** to focus under high power. Draw the neural fold stage in **Observation (4)** in the **Observation Section** below. Label the ectoderm, endoderm and mesoderm.

12. When you are finished with your laboratory activity clean your lab area and return your lab materials and microscope to the supply table. Answer the questions in the **Conclusion Section**.

OBSERVATIONS

(1) EARLY CLEAVAGE.	**(2) LATE CLEAVAGE.**
(3) BLASTULA.	**(4) NEURAL FOLD STAGE.**

CONCLUSIONS

1. What is embryology? ____________________

____

2. The repeated cell divisions of the zygote are known as ____________________.

3. Name four cleavage stages. ____________________

____

4. Name the primary germ layers and state their functions. ____________________

____

____

Name________________ Class________________ Date________________

REVIEW ACTIVITIES

Important Terms

DIRECTIONS: Define the following terms in the spaces provided.

amnion ____

____

amniotic fluid ____

____

blastula ____

____

chorion ____

____

egg ____

____

embryo ____

____

embryology ____

____

fertilization ____

____

gametes ____

____

gametogenesis ____

____

gastrula ____

____

gonads ____

____

hermaphrodites ____

____

morula ____

____

Name______________________ Class______________________ Date__________

oogenesis ____

____

ova ____

____

ovaries ____

____

oviducts ____

____

placenta ____

____

sexual reproduction ____

____

sperm ____

____

spermatogenesis ____

____

testes ____

____

umbilical cord ____

____

uterus ____

____

zygote ____

____

Name______________________ Class______________________ Date__________

Skill Practice

Part A. Complete the following chart comparing sperms and eggs.

CHARACTERISTIC	SPERM	EGG (OVUM)
Structure (Draw and label a diagram.)		
Size (small or large)		
Locomotion (Motile or Nonmotile)		
Number (many or few)		
Food		
Where produced		

Part B. Base your answers to questions 1 through 5 on the diagram below and on your knowledge of biology. The letters indicate some stages in the reproduction and development of an animal.

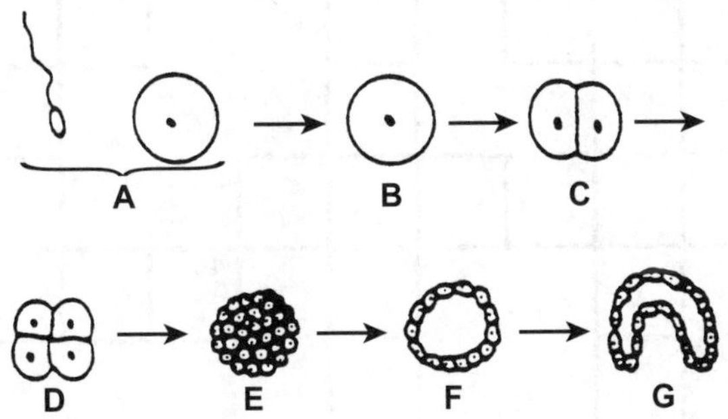

1. In which stage does each cell contain the monoploid number of chromosomes?
   (1) A
   (2) E
   (3) C
   (4) G

2. What process occurs in stages C through F?
   (1) fertilization
   (2) cleavage
   (3) gastrulation
   (4) differentiation

3. Which stage of development represents the gastrula?
   (1) A
   (2) B
   (3) F
   (4) G

4. Which stage of development represents the blastula?
   (1) A
   (2) B
   (3) F
   (4) G

5. Which process occurs in stage A?
   (1) fertilization
   (2) cleavage
   (3) gastrulation
   (4) differentiation

Name________________________ Class________________________ Date____________

Part C. Complete the following crossword puzzle.

Crossword Puzzle

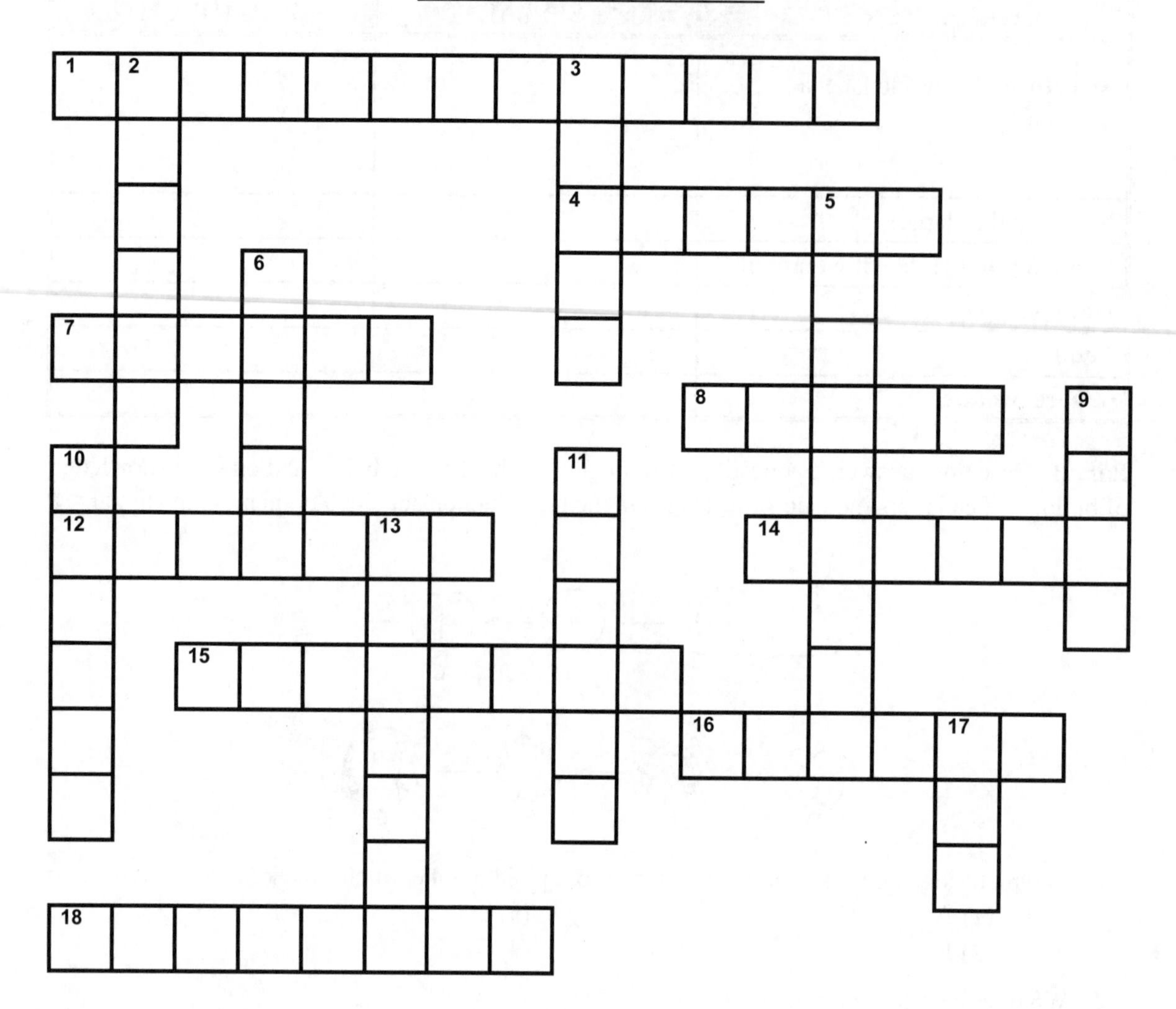

Clues

ACROSS

1. Has both male and female gonads
4. Membrane that holds amniotic fluid
7. Fertilized egg
8. Male gamete
12. Connects ovary with uterus
14. Reproduction requiring two parents
15. A primary germ layer
16. Male gonads
18. Source of food for developing mammal

DOWN

2. Developing organism
3. Female gonad
5. Production of eggs
6. Reproductive organ
9. Source of food in egg
10. Solid-ball stage in cleavage
11. Organ for internal development in mammals
13. Membrane directly under shell in birds
17. Female gamete

Name________________________ Class________________________ Date____________

CHAPTER 20: QUIZ

A. FILL-IN QUESTIONS

DIRECTIONS: Complete each of the following statements by writing the correct word or phrase in the space provided.

1. The female gonads are called the ________________________.
2. The hollow-ball stage of cleavage is the ________________________ stage.
3. The union of the egg and sperm nuclei is known as ________________________.
4. The fluid that cushions the embryo against shock is the ________________________ fluid.
5. The inner cell layer is the ________________________.
6. The fertilized egg is called the ________________________.
7. During ______________ development the embryo grows inside the body of the female parent.
8. The motile gametes are the ________________________.
9. Eggs contain stored food in the ________________________.
10. The male gonads are called the ________________________.
11. Oogenesis is the development of the ________________________.
12. The type of reproduction that involves two parents is ________________________.
13. Developing mammals get food through a/an ________________________ inside the mother's uterus.
14. ________________________ of bird and reptile eggs protect the developing embryo.
15. Spermatogenesis is the process by which ________________________ develop.
16. Ova is another name for the ________________________.
17. During fertilization the monoploid sperm nucleus unites with a/an ________________________ egg nucleus.
18. The ________________________ is the developing organism.
19. ________________________ is an increase in both the number and size of cells.
20. The male gamete is the ________________________.

B. MULTIPLE-CHOICE QUESTIONS

DIRECTIONS: Circle the number of the expression that best completes each of the following statements.

1. Oxygen is carried to the body of an embryo by the
   (1) amniotic sac
   (2) ovary
   (3) uterus
   (4) umbilical cord
2. An example of a sex cell is a
   (1) spore
   (2) zygote
   (3) gamete
   (4) gonad
3. The joining of a sperm cell with an egg cell is called
   (1) copulation
   (2) gestation
   (3) ejaculation
   (4) fertilization

Name________________________ Class________________________ Date____________

4. An egg is larger than a sperm cell because the egg
(1) swims to the sperm
(2) contains more chromosomes than the sperm
(3) moves more than the sperm
(4) contains stored food

5. In mammals fertilized eggs usually develop in the structure known as the
(1) placenta (3) ovary
(2) uterus (4) testes

Directions (6-10): Base your answers to questions 6 through 10 on the diagram below that represents an egg and on you knowledge of biology.

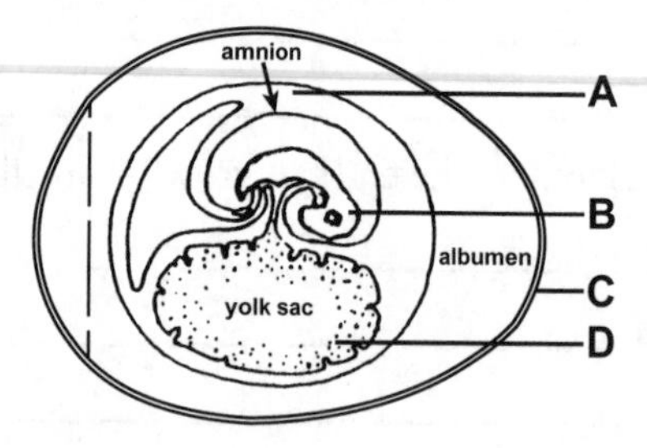

6. Structure B was produced as a result of the process of
(1) external fertilization (3) asexual reproduction
(2) internal fertilization (4) menstruation

7. Structure B represents the
(1) embryo (3) ovary
(2) uterus (4) placenta

8. Structure C is a special adaptation for
(1) developing externally on land (3) developing externally in water
(2) internal development (4) preventing the entrance and exit of gases

9. The structure containing nourishment for the period of development is
(1) A (3) C
(2) B (4) D

10. The structures represented in the diagram were produced by a
(1) frog (3) bird
(2) fish (4) protist

C. ESSAY QUESTION

DIRECTIONS: Use complete sentences to answer the question in this part.

1. State the difference between internal development and external development.

____

____

____

____

____

Name________________________ Class________________ Date__________

Chapter 21: Human Reproduction

A. PUBERTY. Human reproduction is controlled by hormones secreted by the gonads (testes and ovaries). Your reproductive process begins with the production of eggs and sperm (gametes) when you reach the age of puberty. **Puberty** is the time when hormones produce physical changes in the human body that enable the body to produce gametes. These changes are called **secondary sex characteristics**. Males usually reach puberty at about age 12-14 and females reach puberty between the ages of 10-14. Some male and female secondary sex characteristics are as follows:

Female Secondary Sex Characteristics	*Male Secondary Sex Characteristics*
• Development of breasts (mammary glands) • Changes in body form • Growth of body hair	• Growth of beard and other body hair • Changes in body form • Lowered voice pitch

Other reproductive processes that are hormone controlled are the preparation of the female body for pregnancy, sexual intercourse, fertilization, pregnancy, and the production of milk for nourishment of the infant.

REVIEW QUESTIONS

1. Human reproduction is controlled by ______________________.
2. What is meant by the term "puberty"? ______________________

____
3. Name two male secondary sex characteristics. ______________________

____
4. Name two female secondary sex characteristics. ______________________

____
5. List four reproductive processes, other than puberty, that are controlled by hormones.

____

____

____

B. HUMAN MALE REPRODUCTIVE SYSTEM. The male reproductive system performs two major functions: the production of sperm and the deposition of sperm inside the female reproductive tract. The production of sperm takes place in a pair of male gonads called the **testes**

(Figure 21-1). The testes are held in a sac called the **scrotum**. The scrotum is an outpocketing of the abdominal wall. It keeps the temperature of the testes one or two degrees (centigrade) cooler than normal body temperature. This lower temperature is necessary for sperm production and storage.

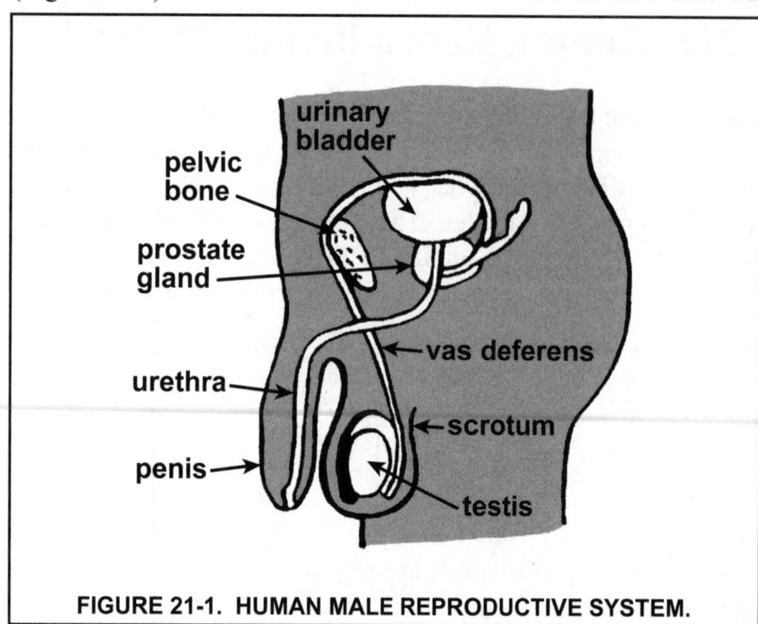

FIGURE 21-1. HUMAN MALE REPRODUCTIVE SYSTEM.

Sperm leave the testes and pass through tubes to the urethra. The **urethra** is a tube inside the penis. The **penis** is adapted for internal fertilization. As the sperm passes through tubes to the urethra, fluids are secreted into the tubes by glands. The fluids provide the sperm with the proper alkaline pH (basic environment) and supply glucose for energy. They also provide a liquid medium in which the sperm can swim. The ability to swim is an adaptation for life on land. The mixture of fluid and sperm is called **semen**. The process by which sperm pass out of the body is known as **ejaculation**.

REVIEW QUESTIONS

1. Name two functions performed by the male reproductive system. ____________________

____

____

2. The male gonads are called ____________________.

3. The sac-like structure, called the ____________________, holds the testes.

4. Explain why the temperature of the testes is lower than normal body temperature?

____

____

5. What is semen? ____________________

____

C. HUMAN FEMALE REPRODUCTIVE SYSTEM. The female reproductive system produces eggs (ova) and is the site (place) of fertilization and embryonic development (Figure 21-2). The production of eggs takes place in paired female gonads called **ovaries.** The ovaries are located inside the lower portion of the body cavity. The ovary produces eggs in structures called **follicles.** Follicles are tiny cavities surrounded by cells. The release of a mature egg from a follicle is called

Name________________________ Class________________________ Date____________

ovulation. After ovulation the egg passes through an **oviduct**. In humans, the oviduct is also called the **fallopian tube.** From the fallopian tube the egg moves to the uterus. The **uterus**, or womb, is shaped like a pear and has thick walls. The embryo develops in the uterus. The lower end of the uterus, the **cervix**, opens into a muscular tube called the vagina. The **vagina** is a muscular tube that leads from the uterus to the outside. The vagina receives semen during intercourse.

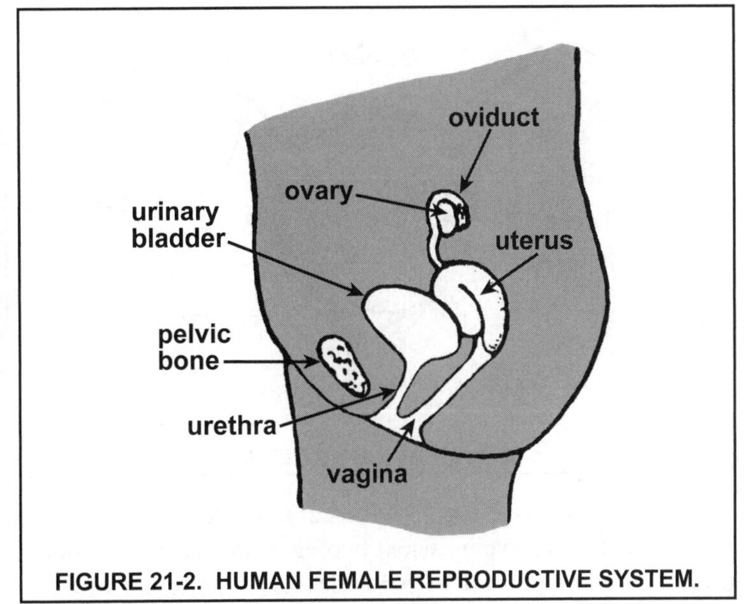

FIGURE 21-2. HUMAN FEMALE REPRODUCTIVE SYSTEM.

REVIEW QUESTIONS

1. State two functions of the female reproductive system. ____________________

____

2. Match the structure in Column A with its description in Column B. Place your answer on the line in Column B.

Column A		Column B
1. Ovaries	______	Receives semen during intercourse.
2. Follicles	______	The embryo develops here.
3. Ovulation	______	Produces the eggs.
4. Fallopian tube	______	Pair of female gonads.
5. Uterus	______	Opens into vagina.
6. Cervix	______	Another name for oviduct.
7. Vagina	______	Release of egg from follicle.
8. Oviduct	______	Connects follicle with uterus.

D. FERTILIZATION. During sexual intercourse (**copulation**) the penis becomes modified (erect) for the efficient transfer of sperm into the vagina. After sexual intercourse the sperm cells swim through the female reproductive tract and enter the oviducts. If they meet with an egg in the oviduct the egg and sperm cell may fuse (unite). The fusion of a sperm cell nucleus and an egg cell nucleus is called fertilization. A fertilized egg is a zygote. Fertilization generally occurs when the egg is in the upper portion of the oviduct. If the egg is not fertilized within about 24 hours after ovulation it breaks down and disappears. Cleavage of the fertilized egg begins while the egg is still in the oviduct. Six to ten days later the resulting embryo may become implanted (attached) in the lining of the uterus (Figure 21-3).

Name________________ Class________________ Date____________

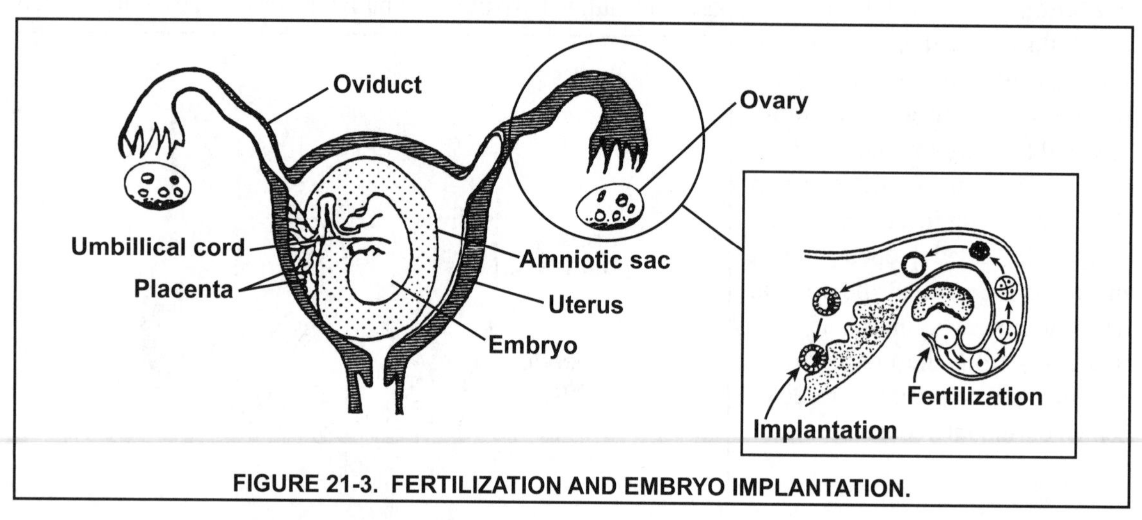

FIGURE 21-3. FERTILIZATION AND EMBRYO IMPLANTATION.

If more than one egg is released and fertilized at the same time multiple births may occur. **Fraternal twins** develop when two eggs are released at one time and each egg is fertilized by a different sperm. **Identical twins** develop from one zygote that separates into two cells early in cleavage.

It is now possible for fertilization to take place outside the human body (***in vitro***). The fertilized egg is implanted in the uterus so that development can occur.

REVIEW QUESTIONS

1. Copulation is another name for ____________________.
2. Fertilization occurs when the ______________ and ______________ fuse.
3. What happens if the egg is not fertilized within about 24 hours? ____________________

   ____
4. Where does fertilization occur? ____________________.
5. How long after fertilization does the embryo become attached to the lining of the uterus?

   ____
6. What is the difference between fraternal twins and identical twins? ____________

   ____

   ____

E. PRENATAL DEVELOPMENT AND BIRTH. When the fertilized egg arrives in the uterus it implants itself in the thickened, spongy uterine wall. The gastrula forms, differentiation and growth occur. The developing embryonic membranes become part of the placenta and umbilical cord. After eight weeks of development the embryo is called the **fetus**. The period of time between the fertilization of the egg and the birth of offspring is called **gestation**. In humans the gestation period is nine months or approximately 266 days. During this time it is essential that the expectant mother provide good prenatal care by eating nutritious foods, avoiding alcohol, tobacco, and drugs, and by receiving proper medical attention regularly. Good prenatal care is important in the production of a healthy baby. Using tobacco, alcohol and drugs is thought to cause *Low Birth Weight Syndrome* and *Fetal Alcohol Syndrome* as well as other birth defects.

When gestation is completed the baby is forced from the uterus by muscular contractions controlled by a hormone from the pituitary. The period of time before birth is referred to as **prenatal** and the time after birth is called **postnatal**.

REVIEW QUESTIONS

1. At what time is the embryo called a fetus? ______________________________
2. The period of time before birth is referred to as ____________________ and the time after birth is called ____________________.
3. What can an expectant mother do to be sure she has a healthy baby? ____________________

   ____

   ____

   ____
4. Name two abnormal conditions that can result when an expectant mother uses alcohol, tobacco or drugs. ____

F. POSTNATAL DEVELOPMENT. Following birth the placenta is discarded from the mother's body and the mother begins producing milk from mammary glands located in the breasts. This milk is normally the best natural food for a newborn baby. The baby should receive regular medical attention and other postnatal care as it grows.

Following birth, growth and development of the individual continues at different rates. Although it is often assumed that development ends when the individual becomes a mature adult, it actually continues throughout life and ends only with death. **Aging** is the term that is applied to the developmental changes that occur in an organism from birth until death. The causes of aging are not fully understood. It appears that aging involves both hereditary and environmental factors.

REVIEW QUESTIONS

1. Describe the events that occur following birth. ______________________________

   ____

   ____

G. THE MENSTRUAL CYCLE. The menstrual cycle usually begins in females between the ages of 10 and 14. It is repeated approximately every 28 days. Hormones control the changes that occur in the ovaries and uterus. The **menstrual cycle** involves the release of a mature egg from a follicle and the preparation of the uterus for pregnancy. The duration of each cycle may vary considerably and may be interrupted by illness or other factors. The cycle stops during pregnancy. The menstrual cycle has four stages: the **follicle stage**, **ovulation**, the **corpus luteum stage**, and **menstruation** (Figure 21-4). The cycle starts at puberty and ends at **menopause**.

Name________________ Class________________ Date________

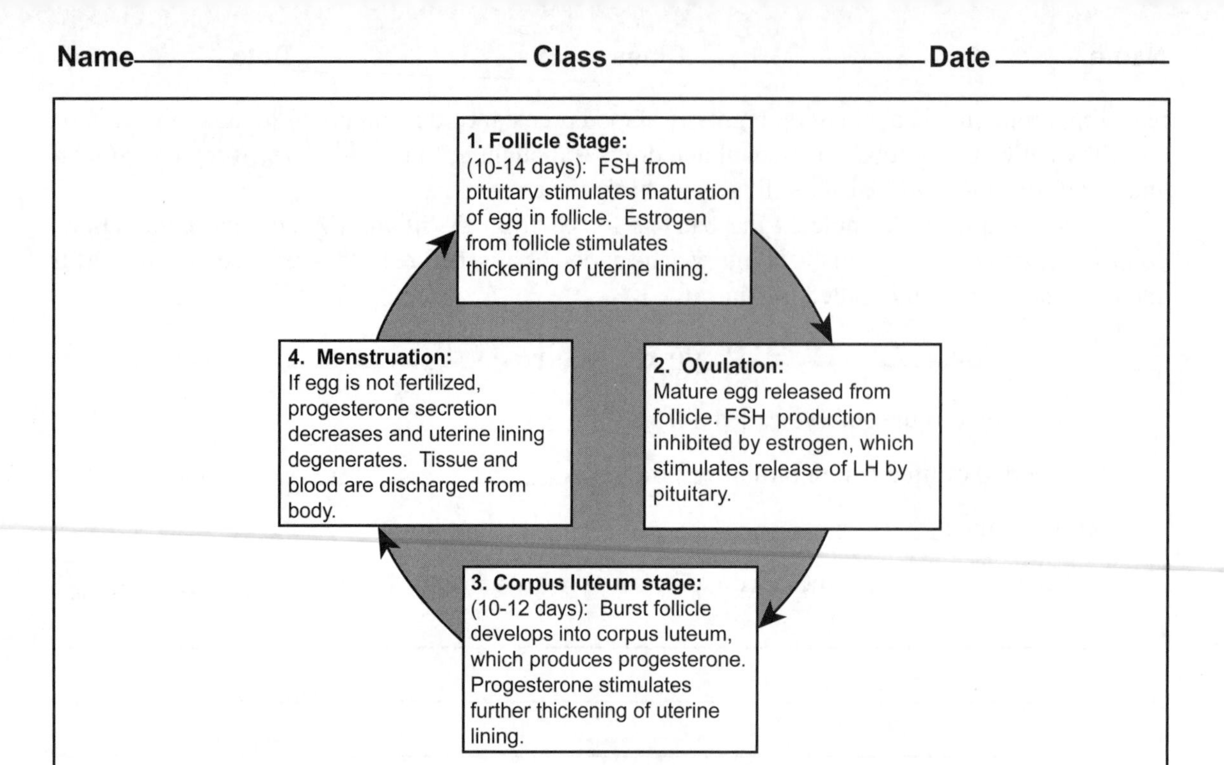

FIGURE 21-4. THE MENSTRUAL CYCLE.

REVIEW QUESTIONS

1. The menstrual cycle is controlled by ________________.

2. The menstrual cycle usually begins in females between the ages of ________________.

H. HUMAN REPRODUCTIVE DISORDERS. In some geographic areas sexually transmitted diseases have reached epidemic proportions in recent years. They may be transmitted by both males and females and may cause sterility or death if not treated by a competent physician. Early treatment usually leads to recovery. Some sexually transmitted diseases in humans are syphilis, gonorrhea, genital herpes, and AIDS.

It is very dangerous to diagnose and treat yourself if you suspect you have a sexually transmitted disease (STD). If you think you have a sexually transmitted disease go to a doctor and let her/him give you proper treatment.

Prostate enlargement and cancer are other disorders associated with the human reproductive tract. Prostate enlargement is most common in males over 40 years of age. Breast cancer is a major cause of death in women.

REVIEW QUESTIONS

1. Name two disorders of the human reproductive system. ________________

____

____

Name________________________________ Class ________________________ Date ______________

LAB INVESTIGATION: HUMAN REPRODUCTIVE CELLS

OBJECTIVE

Upon completion of this activity you should be able to recognize human egg and sperm cells.

LABORATORY PROCEDURE

Materials: Prepared slides of human ovary, CS showing follicles with ovum, and human sperm smear. Charts and books for reference. Lens paper and compound microscope.

1. Collect your laboratory materials from the supply table and take them to your lab area. Clean your microscope lenses and prepared slides with the lens paper.

2. In this lab you will observe human reproductive cells. Reproductive cells are called *gametes*. The male gamete is called the *sperm* and is composed of a head, a middle section, and a tail. The *head* contains the cell nucleus and the *middle section* is composed of mitochondria. The mitochondria supplies energy. The *tail* is a long flagella that is responsible for locomotion. Sperm are motile (able to move around). Many sperm are produced in comparison to few eggs. The production of sperm takes place in the male reproductive organs called the *testes*.

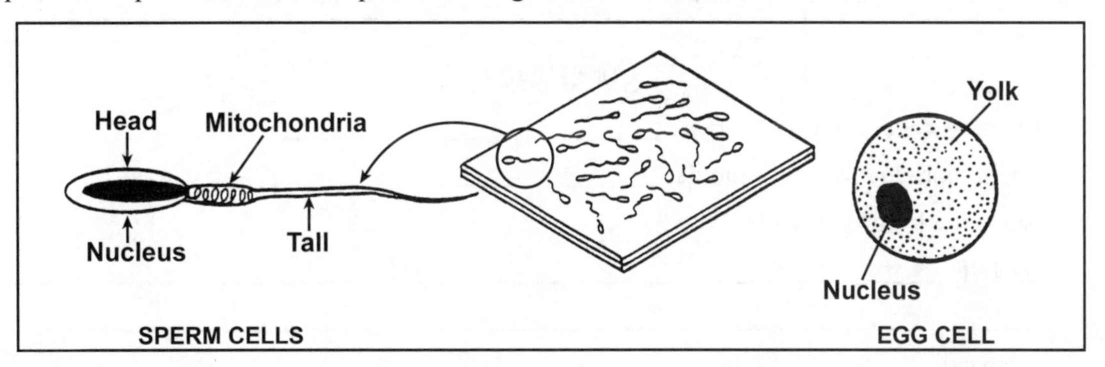

3. Place the prepared slide of ***human sperm cells*** on the microscope stage. Focus the slide using the low power objective. Refer to the diagram on this page to be sure you have located the sperm cells.

4. Once you have located and focused the cells under low power carefully switch your microscope to high power. If your cells are not clearly focused under high power refocus by ***using only the fine adjustment knob to focus upwards.***

5. Draw the sperm cells in **Observation (1)** in the **Observation Section** on the next page. Label the head, mitochondria, and tail.

6. The female gamete is called the *egg(ova).* The egg is larger than the sperm. It contains stored nutrients in the form of *yolk*. The egg is nonmotile. It is not capable of movement. The production of eggs takes place in the follicles of the female's reproductive organs called the *ovaries*. *Follicles* are tiny cavities surrounded by cells. They release mature eggs into the *oviducts* by a process called *ovulation*. Fertilization occurs in the oviducts.

Name________________________ Class________________________ Date____________

7. Place the prepared ***human ovary*** slide on the microscope stage. Focus the slide using the low power objective. Refer to the diagram on the preceding page to be sure you have located the egg cell. Repeat **Procedure 4** to focus under high power.

8. Draw the oviduct, ovary, and egg cell in **Observation (2)** in the **Observation Section** on this page. Label the egg cell, nucleus, yolk, follicle and oviduct.

9. When you are finished with your laboratory activity clean your lab area and return your lab materials and microscope to the supply table. Answer the questions in the **Conclusion Section**.

OBSERVATIONS

(1) SPERM CELLS.	(2) EGG CELL.

CONCLUSIONS

1. Which reproductive cell is larger? ____________________
2. Which reproductive cell is motile? ____________________
3. Define the following terms:

egg cell. ____

____

sperm cell. ____

____

follicle. ____

____

ovary. ____

____

testes. ____

____

oviduct. ____

____

egg yolk. ____

____

Name_______________ Class_______________ Date_______________

REVIEW ACTIVITIES

Important Terms

DIRECTIONS: Define the following terms in the spaces provided.

aging ____

____

cervix ____

____

copulation ____

____

ejaculation ____

____

fallopian tube ____

____

fetus ____

____

follicles ____

____

fraternal twins ____

____

gestation ____

____

identical twins ____

____

menopause ____

____

menstrual cycle ____

____

ovaries ____

____

ovulation ____

____

Name ______________________ Class ______________________ Date ______________

penis ____

____

postnatal ____

____

prenatal ____

____

puberty ____

____

scrotum ____

____

secondary sex characteristics ____

____

semen ____

____

testes ____

____

uterus ____

____

vagina ____

____

Name________________________ Class________________________ Date____________

Part A. Base your answers to questions 1 through 5 on the information and graph below and on your knowledge of biology.

The graph ***at the right*** was plotted after measuring the head-to-rump lengths of a developing prenatal (before birth) human at different times after fertilization.

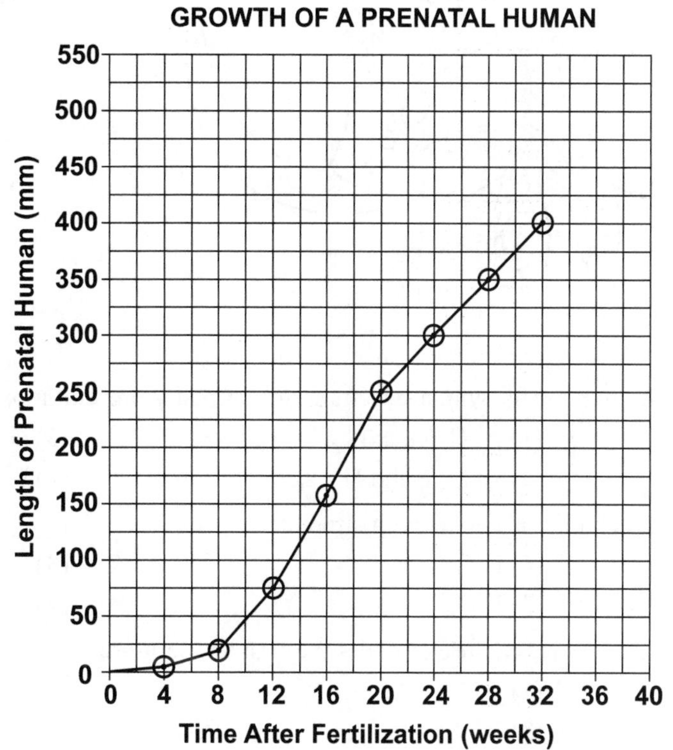

Part B.

1. Use the information presented in the graph to complete the data table below.

Growth of a Prenatal Human	
Time (weeks)	**Length (mm)**
	14
	75
	250
	400

2. What is the approximate length of the prenatal human at the end of week 30?
(1) 350 mm (3) 375 mm
(2) 360 mm (4) 410 mm

3. The greatest increase in the length of the prenatal human occurs between the
(1) 4th and 8th week
(2) 16th and 20th week
(3) 20th and 24th week
(4) 28th and 32nd week

4. A prenatal human is considered full term after 38 weeks. Based on the information provided in the graph, what would most likely be the approximate length of a 38-week-old prenatal human?
(1) 475 mm (3) 325 mm
(2) 400 mm (4) 9 mm

5. According to the graph, what is the approximate age of the prenatal human who is 60 millimeters long?
(1) 40 weeks (3) 3 weeks
(2) 22 weeks (4) 11 weeks

Name____________________ **Class**____________________ **Date**__________

Part C. Base your answers to questions 1 through 6 on the diagrams below and on your knowledge of biology.

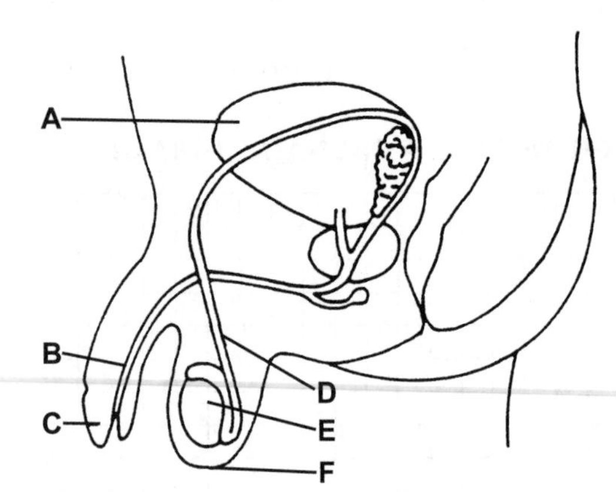

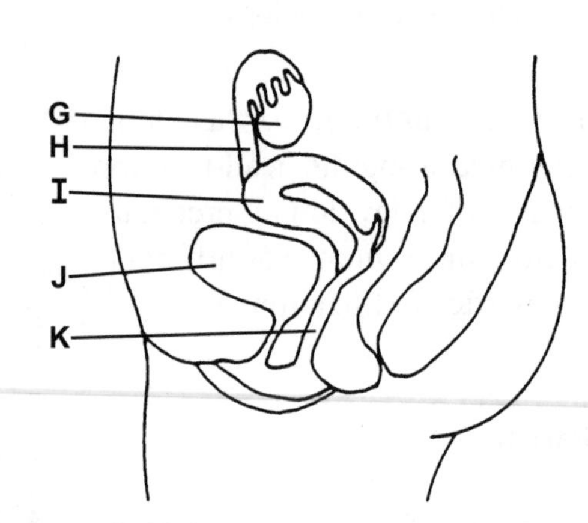

1. In humans, which structures are normally present in pairs?

(1) A, C, K, and I (3) D, E, G, and H
(2) B, D, J, and H (4) F, C, I, and G

2. Ovulation occurs with structure

(1) G (3) I
(2) H (4) J

3. Which structure provides the best temperature for sperm production?

(1) A (3) G
(2) F (4) D

4. Monoploid (n) cells are produced with structures

(1) A and J (3) B and I
(2) E and G (4) D and H

5. Hormones that regulate the development of secondary sex characteristics are produced within structures

(1) E and G (3) F and J
(2) C and K (4) A and H

6. In the space provided, place the names of the structures in the above diagram that correspond to each of the following letters

A ________________ **G** ________________
B ________________ **H** ________________
C ________________ **I** ________________
D ________________ **J** ________________
E ________________ **K** ________________
F ________________

Name________________________ Class________________________ Date____________

CHAPTER 21: QUIZ

A. FILL-IN QUESTIONS

DIRECTIONS: Complete each of the following statements by writing the correct word or phrase in the space provided.

1. The embryo develops in a structure called the ______________________.
2. The period of time between the fertilization of the egg and the birth of the offspring is called ______________________.
3. The testes are held in a sac called the ______________________.
4. Semen is a mixture of fluid and ______________________.
5. The female gonads are the ______________________.
6. ______________________the time when hormones produce physical changes in the human body.
7. Ovulation is the release of the ______________________.
8. ______________________ twins occur when two eggs are fertilized at the same time.
9. The ______________________ receives the sperm during intercourse.
10. The changes that occur at puberty are called ______________________.
11. Prenatal is the period of time ______________________ birth.
12. The ______________________ cycle involves the release of a mature egg from a follicle and the preparation of the uterus for pregnancy.
13. The male gonads are called ______________________
14. Syphilis is an example of a/an ______________________ disease.
15. ______________________ twins occur when a zygote separates early in cleavage.
16. The process by which sperm pass out of the body is ______________________.
17. Postnatal is the period of time ______________________ birth.
18. Human reproduction is controlled by ______________________.
19. Eggs and sperm are called ______________________.
20. The penis is adapted for ______________________ fertilization.

B. MULTIPLE-CHOICE QUESTIONS

DIRECTIONS: Circle the number of the expression that best completes each of the following statements.

1. Production of milk in human females occurs in the
   (1) pituitary gland
   (2) ovary
   (3) mammary glands
   (4) thyroid gland
2. Semen is a mixture of
   (1) sperm plus gland fluid
   (2) lymph plus gland fluid
   (3) hormones plus eggs
   (4) sperm plus plasma

Name________________________ Class________________________ Date____________

3. A reproductive system disorder associated **only** with males is
   (1) gonorrhea (3) liver cirrhosis
   (2) prostate enlargement (4) meningitis

Directions (4-6): Base your answers to questions 4 through 6 on the diagram of the reproductive system of a pregnant female shown at the right and on your knowledge of biology.

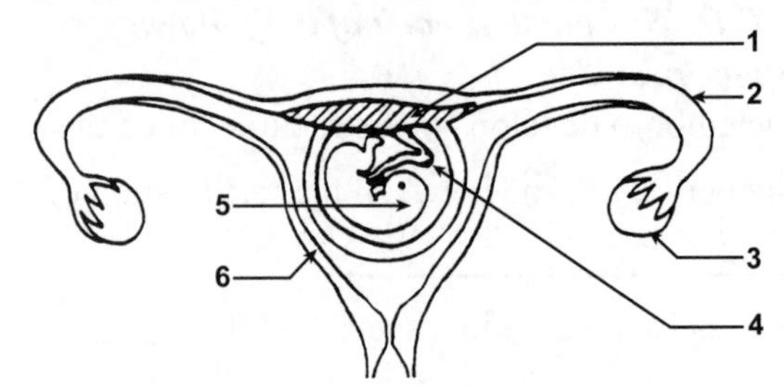

4. Within which structure does implantation and development of the embryo occur?
   (1) 5 (3) 6
   (2) 2 (4) 4
5. In which structure is the zygote usually formed?
   (1) 5 (3) 6
   (2) 2 (4) 4
6. Where is the egg produced?
   (1) 1 (3) 3
   (2) 2 (4) 4

Directions (7-10): For *each* phrase in questions 7-10 select the reproductive term, *chosen from the list below*, which is most closely related to that phrase. Then record its *number* in the space next to each question.

Reproductive Terms

(1) Amnion (4) Testis
(2) Fetus (5) Uterus
(3) Ovary

7. The organ which produces female sex hormones and egg cells. __________
8. A sac containing the embryo and a watery protective fluid. __________
9. Refers to a human embryo in the later states. __________
10. Serves as the site of prenatal development in humans. __________

C. ESSAY QUESTION

DIRECTIONS: Use complete sentences to answer the question in this part.

1. State one practice that should be used for good prenatal care.

____

____

____

____

Name________________________ Class____________________ Date__________

Chapter 22. Reproduction in Flowering Plants

A. FLOWERING PLANTS. To most people a flower is something attractive or something to eat. A flower is more than a pretty object or a source of food. The **flower** is the reproductive structure of flowering plants. The egg and sperm cells are produced by the flower and fertilization takes place inside the flower.

In many kinds of flowering plants each flower contains *both* male and female reproductive organs. This kind of flower is called a **perfect flower**. Tulips and apple blossoms are examples of perfect flowers. An **imperfect flower**, such as the flower of a corn or squash, has either male or female reproductive organs. This means that some flowers have only male reproductive organs while other flowers have only female organs. An imperfect flower cannot have both male and female reproductive organs on the same flower. A **complete flower** has petals, sepals, stamens, and pistils (Figure 22-1).

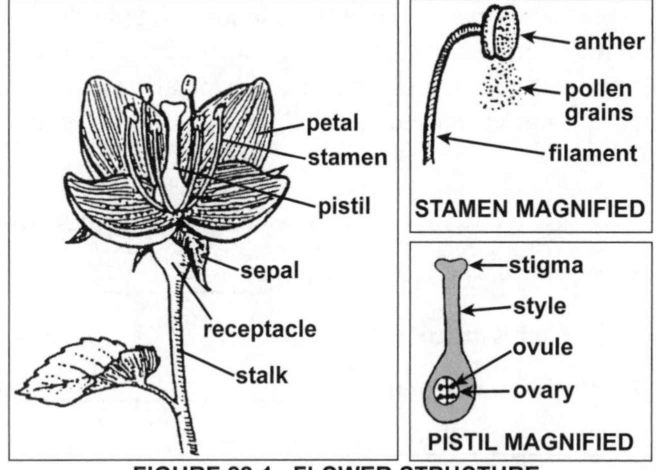

FIGURE 22-1. FLOWER STRUCTURE.

REVIEW QUESTIONS

1. The reproductive structure of flowering plants is the ______________________.

2. State the difference between perfect flowers and imperfect flowers.________________

____

____

3. Draw and label the parts of a flower.

B. FLOWER STRUCTURE. The base of a flower is called the **receptacle**. The leaflike structures at the base of the flower are the sepals. The **sepals** surround the flower and protect the flower during the bud stage The entire circle of sepals is called the **calyx**. Inside the calyx are the petals. **Petals** are brightly colored or white leaflike structures found inside the ring of sepals. The colors and/or odors produced by the petals attract some insects to carry out pollination. The circle of petals is called the **corolla**. **Stamens** are the male reproductive organs of flowers. A stamen consists of an anther and a filament. The knob like **anther** is located at the top and is supported by a slender stalk called the **filament**. Cells inside the anther undergo meiosis producing monoploid (n) nuclei. These cells become the male reproductive cells. They are enclosed in thick walled **pollen grains. Pistils** are the female reproductive organs of flowers. A pistil consists of a stigma, a style and an ovary. The **stigma** is located at the top of the pistil. It has a sticky surface so that pollen grains can stick to the stigma. The **style** connects the stigma with the ovary. At the base of the style is the **ovary**, which contains one or more **ovules**. Egg nuclei are produced by meiosis inside the ovules. The ovules contain the female reproductive cells. The sex cells of a flowering plant are the sperm nuclei and the egg nuclei. Sperm nuclei are in the pollen grains. Egg nuclei are in the ovules. Both kinds of nuclei contain genetic information important in determining the characteristics of offspring.

REVIEW QUESTIONS

1. The receptacle is located at the ______________________ of the flower along with leaflike structures called ______________________.

2. The calyx is a group of ______________________ and the corolla is a group of ______________________

3. Why are petals brightly colored? ____

4. The male reproductive organ of the flower is the ______________________. The female reproductive organ of the flower is the ______________________.

5. Why is the stigma sticky? ____

6. The ______________________ of the plant produces the male gamete and the ______________________ produces the female gamete.

7. Define the following terms.

ovule ____

____

pollen grain ____

____

style ____

____

filament ____

____

C. POLLINATION. The transfer of mature pollen grains from the anthers of stamens to the stigma of the pistils is called **pollination**. Pollination may be carried out by wind or by insects, birds, or other animals. Brightly colored petals and sweet odors are adaptations that attract insects or other animals for pollination. The animals feed on a sugary solution called **nectar.** The pollen from the anther sticks to the animal and is carried to the flower's stigma. Apples, roses, and cherries are pollinated by animals such as insects and hummingbirds. Plants that are wind pollinated do not usually have showy flowers. The wind blows the light pollen to the stigma of the flowers. Corn is an example of a wind pollinated plant. The thick walls of pollen grains prevent the contents from drying out and are an adaptation for reproduction in a dry land environment.

Self-pollination occurs when pollen is transferred from an anther to a stigma of the same flower or a stigma of another flower on the same plant. **Cross-pollination** occurs when pollen is transferred from an anther to a stigma of a flower on another plant (Figure 22-2).

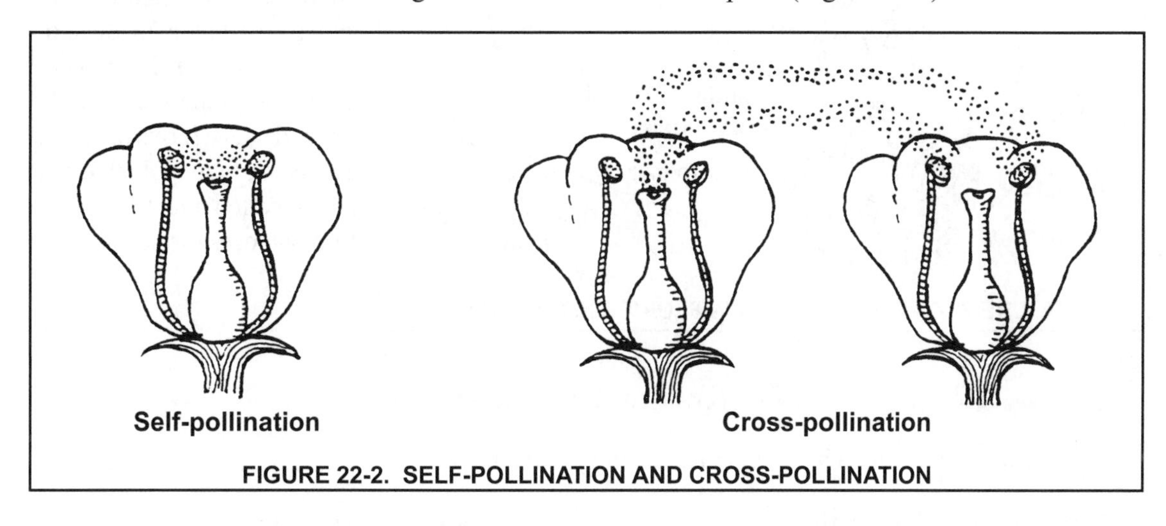

FIGURE 22-2. SELF-POLLINATION AND CROSS-POLLINATION

REVIEW QUESTIONS

1. Pollination is the transfer of ____________ from the ____________ of ____________ to the ____________ of ____________.

2. Name two organisms that aid in pollination. ____________

____

3. State the difference between cross-pollination and self-pollination. ____________

____

____

____

D. FERTILIZATION. After a pollen grain lands on a stigma it germinates and a **pollen tube** grows down through the style and into an ovule (Figure 22-3). The pollen tube is an adaptation for internal fertilization. One of the two monoploid nuclei of the pollen grain is called the **tube nucleus**. The tube nucleus regulates the growth of the pollen tube. The other nucleus replicates forming two **sperm nuclei**.

Name________________ Class________________ Date________

Fertilization takes place when the pollen tube reaches the ovule. The pollen tube enters the embryo sac that contains the monoploid **egg nucleus**. One sperm nucleus fuses with the egg nucleus to form the 2n zygote that becomes the embryo plant. The other sperm nucleus fuses with two other monoploid nuclei (the **polar nuclei**) in the embryo sac to form the triploid (3n) material that forms the **endosperm**. The endosperm provides food for the embryo plant.

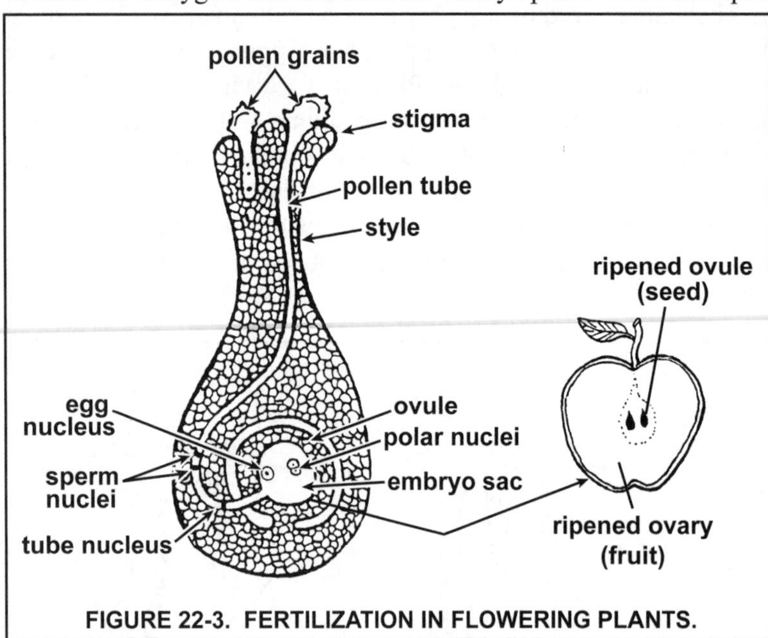

FIGURE 22-3. FERTILIZATION IN FLOWERING PLANTS.

The fertilized egg (zygote) develops into the plant embryo. After fertilization the ovule and ovary begin to develop and grow (ripen). The ripened ovule forms the **seed** and the ripened ovary forms the **fruit.** The part of an apple that you eat is called the fruit. The fruit encloses the seeds.

REVIEW QUESTIONS

1. Fertilization begins when the pollen grain germinates into a/an ________________ that grows down through the ________________ and into the ________________.

2. The pollen tube is an adaptation for ________________ fertilization.

3. The ________________ nucleus regulates the growth of the pollen tube.

4. One sperm nucleus fuses with the ________________ nucleus to form the zygote and the other sperm nucleus fuses with two ________________ to form the endoderm.

5. The endosperm is stored ________________ for the developing embryo plant.

6. The zygote develops into the ________________.

7. The ripened ovule forms the ________________ and the ripened ovary forms the ________________.

E. STRUCTURE OF SEED AND EMBRYO. The embryo plant is made up of the hypocotyl, epicotyl, and cotyledons (Figure 22-4). The **hypocotyl** develops into the roots, and in some species,it forms the lower portion of the stem. The **epicotyl** forms the upper part of the stem and the leaves. The **cotyledons** or **seed leaves**, contain nutrients for the developing plant embryo. Some seed plants, known as **monocots**, have one cotyledon. Corn and wheat are monocots. Other seed plants, known as **dicots**, have two cotyledons. Peas and beans are dicots.

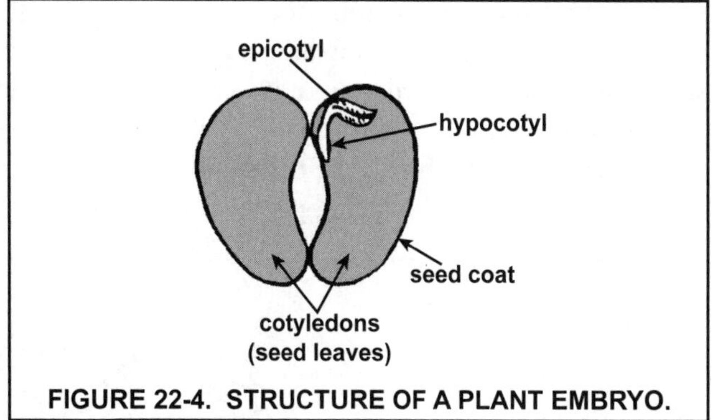

FIGURE 22-4. STRUCTURE OF A PLANT EMBRYO.

REVIEW QUESTIONS

1. State the function of the following:

epicotyl ______________________________

hypocotyl ______________________________

cotyledons ______________________________

F. SEED DISPERSAL. In order for seeds to survive they must be spread far away from the parent plant. If the new plant tries to grow near the parent plant the small plant will have to compete with the parent for conditions, such as water and oxygen, that are needed for survival.

In flowering plants seeds develop inside fruits–specialized structures that aid in seed dispersal. Fruits and seeds are dispersed (carried away from the parent plant) in a variety of ways. Some are carried by wind or water while others are picked up and carried on animals. Some fruits are eaten by animals and the seeds are later deposited with digestive wastes. Some examples of seed dispersal are listed below.

Method of Dispersal	*Examples*
Winds carrying seeds.......................................	dandelion, maple
Animals eating fruits.......................................	cherries, apples
Animals burying fruits.....................................	acorns
Barbs or spines attached to animals.................	cocklebur, burdocks
Carried by water..	coconut palm

REVIEW QUESTIONS

1. Name three methods of seed dispersal and state and example of each method.

____

____

____

Name________________ Class________________ Date__________

G. SEED GERMINATION AND GROWTH. When the seed reaches a place where conditions are favorable the seed **germinates** or begins to grow (Figure 22-5). The favorable conditions for germination are sufficient moisture, oxygen, and a proper temperature. The embryo plant uses food stored in the seed cotyledon until its leaves develop chlorophyll for photosynthesis.

Plant growth is accomplished by cell division in special growing regions of the plant. These regions are found at the tips of roots and stems and in the cambium of woody stems. Along with warmth, moisture, and oxygen, plant growth requires light, minerals, and carbon dioxide.

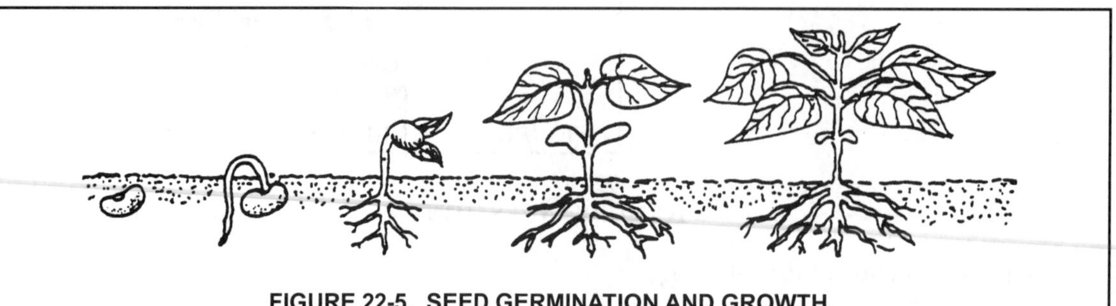

FIGURE 22-5. SEED GERMINATION AND GROWTH.

REVIEW QUESTIONS

1. To germinate means to ________________________________.
2. Name three conditions that are favorable for seed germination.

____

CAREER OPPORTUNITIES

PLANT BREEDERS: If you like working with plants you might want to be a plant breeder. **Plant breeders** are imaginative adventurous people who work to develop new and improved plants and flowers. Some plant breeders specialize in flower breeding. Their job is to create new and unusual flowers. Breeders must be very patient people because it usually takes from eight to ten years to develop a new plant variety. Once a new variety has been developed the plant can be produced commercially. The government allows breeders to patent new kinds of flowers. The breeders then collect royalties from other nurseries that raise their flowers.

To be a plant breeder you need to have a knowledge of plant reproduction, genetics, and basic farming techniques. Some breeders are graduates of two year and four year agricultural colleges. Other breeders have learned to breed plants by working in nurseries alongside professional breeders.

*****

REVIEW QUESTIONS

1. Name one career where a knowledge of plant reproduction would be useful.

____

____

Name________________________ Class ____________________ Date __________

LAB INVESTIGATION: FLOWER STRUCTURE

OBJECTIVE

Upon completion of this activity you should be able to identify the parts of a complete flower and state their functions.

LABORATORY PROCEDURE

Materials: A perfect flower (tulip, lily or gladiolus), hand lens, paper towels, scalpel or single-edged razor blade, water, medicine dropper, slide, cover slip and compound microscope.

1. Collect your laboratory materials from the supply table and take them to your lab area. Place your flower on the paper towel.

2. The *flower* is the reproductive structure of flowering plants. Look at the outside structure of your flower. The base of a flower is called the *receptacle*. The leaflike structures at the base of the flower are the sepals. The *sepals* surround the flower and protect the flower during the bud stage The entire circle of sepals is called the *calyx*. ***Note: Your flower may not have sepals or they may be hard to find. If this is so, ask your teacher for directions.*** Inside the calyx are the petals. *Petals* are brightly colored or white leaflike structures found inside the ring of sepals. The colors and/or odors produced by the petals may attract insects for pollination. The circle of petals is called the *corolla*. Use the diagram on this page to help you locate flower structures.

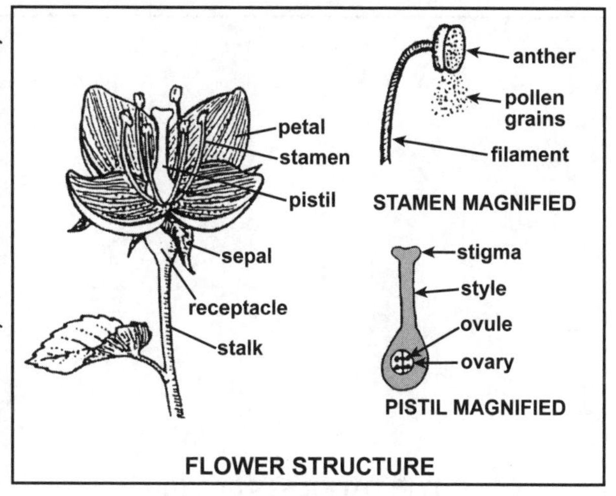

FLOWER STRUCTURE

3. Carefully remove some sepals and petals so the inner structures can be seen. Draw your flower observations in **Observation (1)** in the **Observation Section** on the next page. Label the stalk, receptacle, sepals, and petals.

4. Now find the pistil and stamens. *Stamens* are the male reproductive organs of flowers. *Pistils* are the female reproductive organs of flowers. Label the pistil and stamens on your flower drawing in **Observation (1)**.

5. Carefully remove the stamens from your flower. A stamen is made up of an anther and a filament. The knob like *anther* is located at the top and is supported by a slender stalk called the *filament*. Cells inside the anther undergo meiosis, producing monoploid (n) nuclei. These cells become the male reproductive cells. They are enclosed in thick-walled *pollen grains.* Label the anther and the filament on your flower drawing in **Observation (1)**.

6. Now remove the pistil from your flower. A pistil consists of a stigma, a style, and an ovary. The *stigma* is located at the top of the pistil. It has a sticky surface so that pollen grains can stick to the stigma. The *style* connects the stigma with the ovary. At the base of the style is the *ovary* that contains one or more *ovules*. Egg nuclei are produced inside the ovules. In the ovules are the female reproductive cells. Use your scalpel or razor blade to cut the flower in half lengthwise. Label the stigma, style, ovary, and ovules on your flower drawing in **Observation (1)**.

7. Place some pollen grains on a microscope slide by gently touching the anther with a wet slide. Add a drop of water and a cover slip. Place the slide on the stage of your compound microscope. Scan your slide under low power to locate the pollen grains. Once you have located and centered the pollen grains carefully switch your microscope to high power. If your grains are not clearly focused under high power refocus them by ***using only the fine adjustment knob to focus upwards.*** Draw some pollen grains in **Observation (2)** below.

8. When you are finished with your laboratory activity wrap your flower parts in the paper towel and throw it away. Clean your slides and lab area and return your lab materials and microscope to the supply table. Answer the questions in the **Conclusion Section**.

OBSERVATIONS

(1) FLOWER STRUCTURE	(2) POLLEN GRAINS (HIGH-POWER)

CONCLUSIONS

1. State the function of the following flower structures:

sepals. ____

____

petals. ____

____

pistil. ____

____

stamens. ____

____

pollen grains. ____

____

Name________________ Class________________ Date________________

REVIEW ACTIVITIES

Important Terms

DIRECTIONS: Define the following terms in the spaces provided.

anther ____

calyx ____

complete flower ____

corolla ____

cotyledon ____

cross-pollination ____

endosperm ____

epicotyl ____

filament ____

flower ____

fruit ____

germination ____

hypocotyl ____

imperfect flower ____

Name__________________ **Class**__________________ **Date**__________

nectar ____

ovary ____

ovule ____

perfect flower __________________________________

petal ____

pistil ____

pollen grain ___________________________________

pollen tube ____________________________________

pollination ____________________________________

seed ____

self-pollination _________________________________

sepal ____

stamens ______________________________________

stigma _______________________________________

style ____

Name________________________ Class________________________ Date____________

Skill Practice

Part A. Base your answers to questions 1 through 4 on the diagram of a flower at the right and on your knowledge of biology.

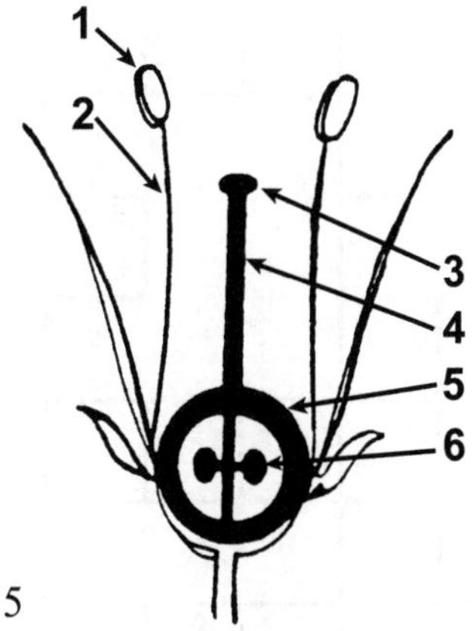

1. Which structure produces cells that form sperm nuclei?

(1) 1　　(3) 3

(2) 2　　(4) 4

2. In which structure do fertilization and development occur?

(1) 1　　(3) 3

(2) 6　　(4) 4

3. Which structures are collectively known as the pistil?

(1) 1, and 2　　(3) 1 and 6

(2) 2, 4, and 6　　(4) 3, 4, and 5

4. In the space provided, place the names of the structures in the above diagram that correspond to each of the following numbers.

1 ____________________　　**4** ____________________

2 ____________________　　**5** ____________________

3 ____________________　　**6** ____________________

Part B. Base your answers to questions 5 through 7 on the diagram of the internal view of a bean seed and on your knowledge of biology.

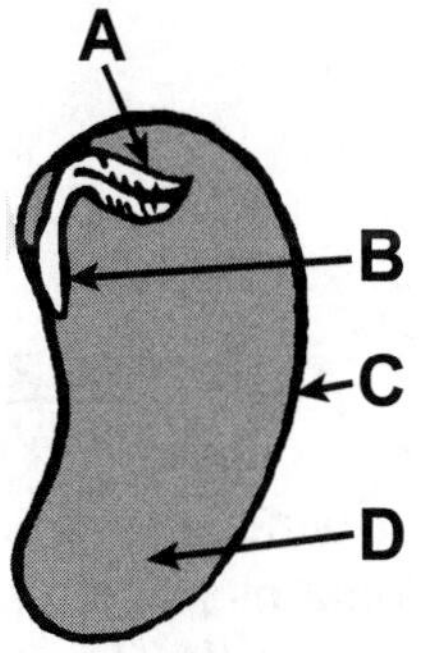

5. In which structure would most of the stored food for the embryo be found

(1) A　　(3) C

(2) B　　(4) D

6. The epicotyl and hypocotyl are represented by

(1) A and B　　(3) C and D

(2) B and D　　(4) A and C

7. In the space provided place the names of the structures in the above diagram that correspond to each of the following letters

A ____________________　　**C** ____________________

B ____________________　　**D** ____________________

Name________________ Class________________ Date__________

Part C. Complete the following crossword puzzle.

Crossword Puzzle

Clues

ACROSS

3. Forms upper part of stem
4. A ripened ovary
5. Contains nutrients for developing plant
6. Protects the flower bud
8. A ripened ovule
9. Attracts insects
11. Supports the anther
14. Develops into roots
16. Contains ovules
17. All of the sepals
18. Pollination on same flower

DOWN

1. All of the petals
2. Male reproductive structure
3. Food for embryo plant
4. Reproductive structure of plants
7. Flower with both male and female organs
10. Produces male reproductive cells
12. Sugary solution
13. Pollination involving two plants
15. Pollen_____ connects stigma to ovary

Name________________________ Class________________________ Date____________

CHAPTER 22: QUIZ

A. FILL-IN QUESTIONS

DIRECTIONS: Complete each of the following statements by writing the correct word or phrase in the space provided.

1. The ________________________ is the male reproductive organ of the flower.
2. A/an ________________________ flower contains both male and female reproductive organs.
3. Some plants manufacture nectar to attract ________________________ and birds.
4. During pollination a pollen grain is transferred to the ________________________ of the pistil.
5. Pollen is produced inside the ________________________.
6. The ________________________ is the whole circle of sepals.
7. The female reproductive organ of the flower is the ________________________.
8. Egg nuclei are produced by meiosis inside the ________________________.
9. Before green leaves are produced, the seedling is supplied with food by the ________________________.
10. The part of the seed that develops into the roots is the ________________________.
11. Monocots have ________________________ cotyledon.
12. The three parts of the pistil are the ________________________, style, and ovary.
13. The reproductive structure of flowering plants is the ________________________.
14. The cotyledons contain ________________________ for the developing plant embryo.
15. A fruit is a ripened ________________________.
16. The part of the seed that develops into the leaves is the ________________________.
17. An example of a plant that disperses its seeds by wind is the ________________________.
18. A seed is a ripened ________________________.
19. ________________________ is a term that means to begin to grow.
20. The corolla is all the ________________________ of the flower.

B. MULTIPLE-CHOICE QUESTIONS

DIRECTIONS: Circle the number of the expression that best completes each of the following statements.

1. Which of the following factors would *least* benefit plant growth rate?
   (1) warm temperature
   (2) high levels of sulfur dioxide
   (3) moderate moisture level
   (4) sufficient sunshine

2. A sweet smelling brightly colored flower would most likely be pollinated by
   (1) wind
   (2) water
   (3) insects
   (4) diffusion

3. Which function must happen before fertilization in flowering plants can occur?
   (1) ovulation
   (2) pollination
   (3) grafting
   (4) seed dispersal

Name________________________ Class________________________ Date____________

4. For what type of reproduction is the flower adapted?
   (1) sexual (3) asexual
   (2) budding (4) runners

5. On which structure shown in the diagram ***at the right***, must pollen land before fertilization can take place?
   (1) A (3) C
   (2) B (4) D

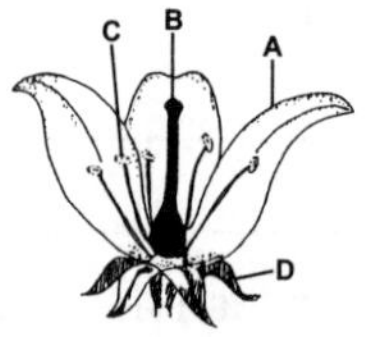

6. A fruit develops from the
   (1) leaf (3) root
   (2) flower (4) stem

Directions: (7-9): Base your answers to questions 7 through 9 on the diagram below that represents a flower and on your knowledge of biology.

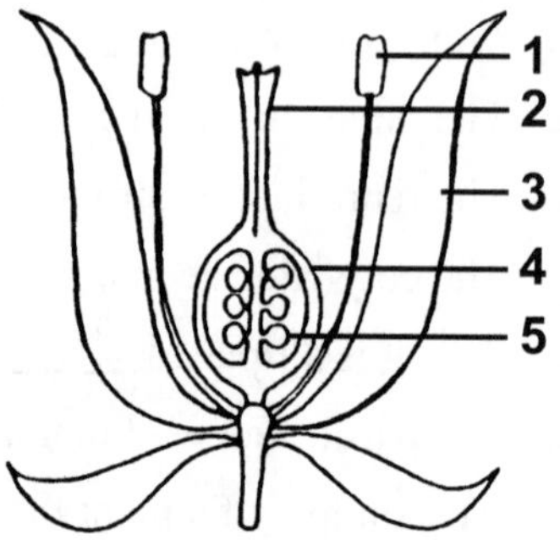

7. Which part of the flower will become the fruit?
   (1) 1 (3) 5
   (2) 2 (4) 4

8. The part of the flower which will become the seed is
   (1) 1 (3) 5
   (2) 2 (4) 4

9. The part of the flower which produces the pollen grains is
   (1) 1 (3) 3
   (2) 2 (4) 4

10. Which of the following is **not** needed to start the growth of a bean seed?
   (1) light (3) moisture
   (2) oxygen (4) proper temperature

C. ESSAY QUESTION

DIRECTIONS: Use complete sentences to answer the question in this part.

1. Name one occupation where a knowledge of plant reproduction would be useful.

____

____

____

____

____

____

Name________________________ Class________________________ Date__________

UNIT FIVE TEST

Matching Questions

***DIRECTIONS:** In the space at the left of each item in Column A, place the letter of the term or phrase in Column B that is most closely related to that item.*

Column A	Column B
_________ **1.** Cell division that produces identical cells.	**a.** Haploid
_________ **2.** A fertilized egg.	**b.** Ova
_________ **3.** Underground stems specialized for food storage.	**c.** Gonads
_________ **4.** One half the chromosome number.	**d.** Scion
_________ **5.** Reproductive organs.	**e.** Zygote
_________ **6.** Male reproductive cell.	**f.** Diploid
_________ **7.** The normal chromosome number.	**g.** Bulbs
_________ **8.** A part of a graft.	**h.** Sperm
_________ **9.** Cell division that produces different cells.	**i.** Mitosis
_________**10.** Another name for the egg.	**j.** Yolk
	k. Runners
	l. Meiosis

True–False Questions

***DIRECTIONS:** Write TRUE before each statement that is true and FALSE before each statement that is false.*

_________ **1.** Human females produce eggs in their ovaries.

_________ **2.** The morula is the solid-ball stage of cleavage.

_________ **3.** Change in body form at puberty is a secondary sex characteristic.

_________ **4.** The allantois cushions the embryo against shock.

_________ **5.** A perfect flower has both male and female sex organs.

_________ **6.** Asexual reproduction requires two parents.

_________ **7.** Fertilization takes place in the vagina.

_________ **8.** Development after birth is called prenatal development.

_________ **9.** Most mammals reproduce by external fertilization.

_________**10.** Binary fission produces daughter cells of *equal* size.

Name________________ Class________________ Date________________

Fill-In Questions

***DIRECTIONS:** Complete each of the following statements by writing the correct word or phrase in the space provided.*

1. Reproduction is the life process by which living things produce organisms of the same ________________.
2. The union of the egg and sperm nuclei is called ________________.
3. Two chromatids are joined by a structure called the ________________.
4. ________________ are the reproductive organs of flowering plants.
5. ________________ is a type of asexual reproduction that produces unequal daughter cells.
6. The human male gonads are called the ________________.
7. ________________ is a group of diseases that is often characterized by uncontrolled cell division.
8. Grafting is an example of ________________ propagation.
9. Cleavage results in a developing organism called the ________________.
10. Bread mold reproduces by ________________ formation.

Multiple-Choice Questions

***DIRECTIONS:** Circle the number of the expression that best completes each of the following statements.*

1. In the diagram below that represents an ameba name the activity that is taking place?

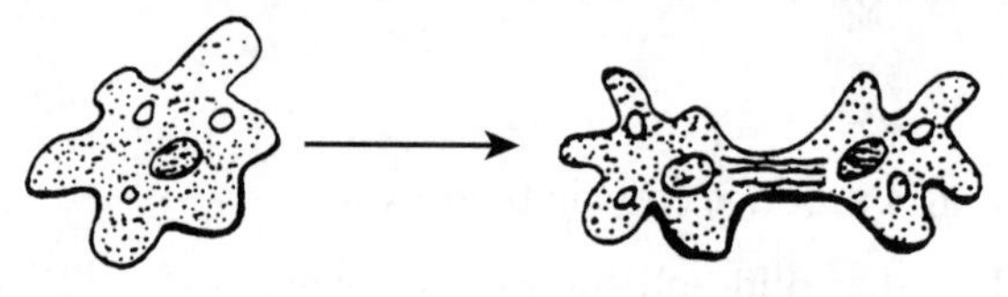

(1) photosynthesis (3) fertilization
(2) reproduction (4) meiosis

2. Which of these animals produces the greatest number of eggs in a year?
(1) sunfish (3) eagle
(2) human (4) rat

3. Secondary sex characteristics in the human male develop as a result of secretions from the
(1) testes (3) digestive system
(2) liver (4) nervous system

4. Egg cells with the smallest amount of yolk are produced by animals that reproduce by
(1) budding (3) fission
(2) external development (4) internal development

Name________________________ Class________________________ Date____________

5. When does ovulation usually occur in the human menstrual cycle?
   (1) during menstruation
   (2) during gestation
   (3) immediately after the menstruation period
   (4) about halfway between menstruation periods

6. A fruit is the product of the
   (1) leaf
   (2) stem
   (3) root
   (4) flower

7. Which statement is true of animal gametes such as those shown in the diagram below?
   (1) They are produced by females.
   (2) They contain yolk.
   (3) They can swim.
   (4) They are fertilized in an ovary.

8. Nutrients pass from a human mother to her embryo through the
   (1) amniotic fluid
   (2) uterus
   (3) urethra
   (4) placenta

9. In human females gametes are produced in the
   (1) oviducts
   (2) vagina
   (3) testes
   (4) ovaries

10. Which part of the plant is most directly involved in sexual reproduction?
   (1) roots
   (2) flower
   (3) stem
   (4) leaves

Essay Question

DIRECTIONS: Use complete sentences to answer the question in this part.

1. What are two steps that should be taken to help insure the health of a baby before it is born?

____

____

____

____

____

____

____

Class Notes

Name________________________ Class____________________ Date__________

UNIT SIX

GENETICS AND HEREDITY

LEARNING OUTCOMES: Upon completion of the study of this unit,you should be able to:

- Relate the importance of chromosomes in the maintenance of characteristics of organisms.
- Identify some of the major patterns of genetic inheritance.
- Predict the genotypes and phenotypes that may result from specific genetic crosses.
- Explain the relationship between DNA and the expression of genetic traits in the cell.

Chapter 23: Basic Genetics

A. WHAT IS GENETICS? You may have observed that sometimes brothers and sisters in the same family share similar **traits** (characteristics). They may all have the same hair color, eye color, and/or skin color. Examine your traits. Do you look like anyone in your family or do you have very different characteristics? You will learn how you got these traits when you study genetics. **Genetics** is the science of heredity. **Heredity** is the study of how traits are passed on from parent to offspring.

REVIEW QUESTIONS

1. A trait can also be called a/an ________________________.
2. The science of heredity is called ________________________.
3. Heredity is the study of how ________________ are passed on from parent to offspring.
4. List three human traits. ____.

B. VARIATION. The specific traits an organism inherits are determined during the life process of reproduction. Reproduction results in new organisms that closely resemble their parent(s). For example, dogs produce dogs, cats produce cats, and tulips produce tulips. A dog could not produce a cat or a tulip. Within each species there may be some slight **variations** (differences) among traits. However, these variations will fall within certain limits (Figure 23-1).

More trait variation is found in offspring produced by sexual reproduction than by asexual reproduction. This happens because during asexual reproduction traits are passed on through the genetic material found in the nucleus of ***only one parent organism***. In sexual reproduction traits are passed on through the combining of genetic material found in the nuclei of sperm and egg cells (male and female gametes). During sexual reproduction traits in the genetic material from *two parents* are brought together producing an organism with a new combination of traits. This new combination of traits results in variation. The offspring *resembles* its parents but is also *different* from them.

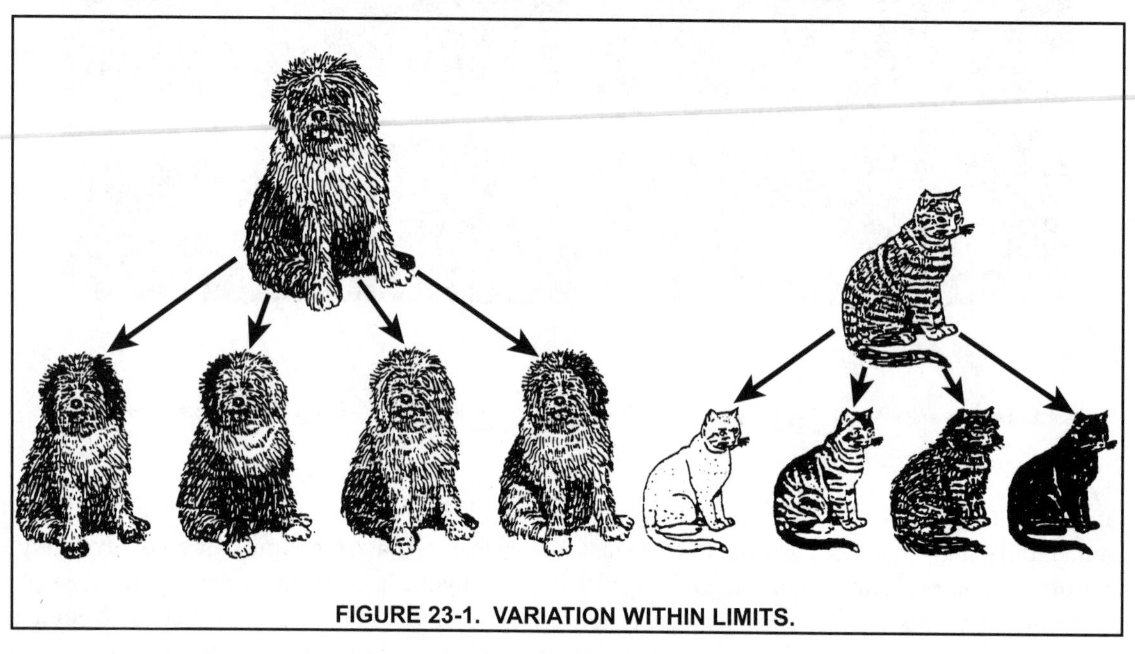

FIGURE 23-1. VARIATION WITHIN LIMITS.

REVIEW QUESTIONS

1. Differences in traits are known as ______________________.
2. More variation is found in organisms produced by ______________________ reproduction than by ______________________ reproduction.

C. SPECIES AND CHROMOSOME NUMBER. Each of the body cells of an organism normally contains the same number of chromosomes (genetic material) as each body cell in the parent organism(s). This chromosome number, known as the **species chromosome number**, is the same from generation to generation. The species chromosome number is the same as its diploid or 2n number. In asexual reproduction the chromosome number is maintained (kept the same) because of a type of nuclear division known as mitosis. In sexual reproduction the chromosome number is maintained by a type of nuclear division known as meiosis that is followed by fertilization.

Although the species chromosome number is normally the same for all members of a species it is different from the species chromosome number in other species. For example, humans have a species chromosome number of 46 (2n=46) and crayfish have more than 100 chromosomes in each body cell. Fruit flies have eight chromosomes, a certain species of roundworm has two, pea plants have 14, dogs have 48, and cats have 38 chromosomes. In most animals a change in chromosome number results in abnormalities and/or death of the organism. Some species and their species chromosome number are shown below.

Organism	*Chromosome Number*
human	46
crayfish	100
roundworm	2
pea	14
fruit fly	8
dog	48
cat	38

REVIEW QUESTIONS

1. The number of chromosomes in the body cell of an organism is called its

______________________________.

2. Is the species chromosome number of all organisms the same? ______________.

3. What happens to animals born with a change in species number? ______________

____

D. CHROMOSOME ARRANGEMENT. In an organism's body cells chromosomes are arranged in pairs. Figure 23-2 is a photograph, taken through a microscope, of human chromosome pairs. A photograph or chart of chromosomes arranged in pairs is called a **karyotype.**

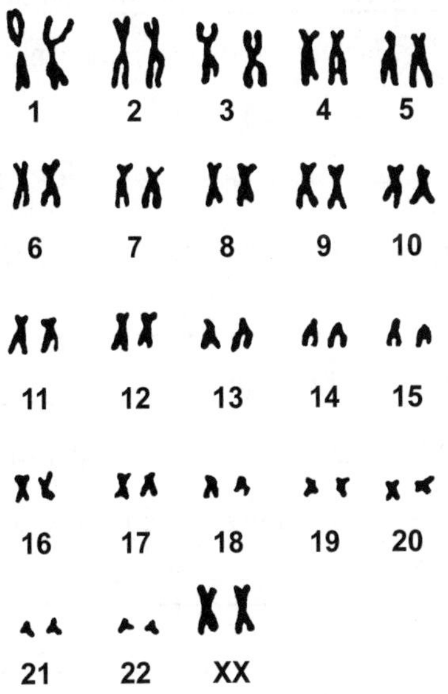

1 2 3 4 5

6 7 8 9 10

11 12 13 14 15

16 17 18 19 20

21 22 XX

FIGURE 23-2. A KARYOTYPE.

Name________________________ Class________________________ Date____________

1. What is a karyotype? ____

____

E. GENE-CHROMOSOME THEORY. Much research has been done in the field of genetics over the last 100 years. Before these studies were done people did not know very much about heredity. Many people thought that the inheritance of traits was somehow involved with the parents' blood. Today's knowledge about genetics is a result of genetic studies started by Gregor Mendel in the middle 1800's. Because his work was the first major study into the science of heredity Mendel is called the "father of genetics".

Mendel did not know about genes but thought that certain "**factors**" were responsible for traits passed from parents to offspring. When microscopes were developed, in the early 1900's, biologists were able to observe chromosome behavior in dividing cells. These investigations, along with breeding experiments with fruit flies (Drosophila), gave scientists important information about the relationship between genes and chromosomes. This information resulted in an important genetic theory known as the **gene-chromosome theory**. The gene-chromosome theory states that chromosomes (found in the nucleus of the cell) are made of small units called genes.

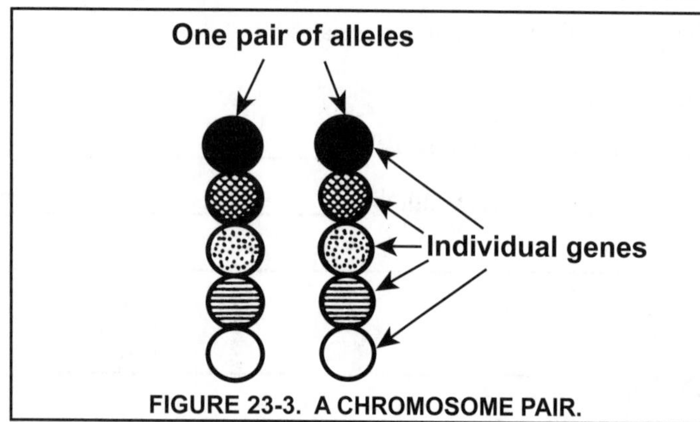

FIGURE 23-3. A CHROMOSOME PAIR.

Genes carry hereditary information and are found at specific locations along the chromosomes. **Alleles** are pairs of genes that carry the same traits and are located at the same place on pairs of chromosomes (Figure 23-3). Each chromosome may contain several hundred genes.

Review Questions

1. Today's knowledge about genetics is as result of genetic studies started by

   ________________________ in the middle 1800's.

2. Did Mendel know about genes? ________________________.

3. What term did Mendel use to identify genes? ________________________.

4. List the parts of the gene-chromosome theory. ________________________

   ____

   ____

Name________________________ Class________________________ Date____________

F. INHERITANCE OF TRAITS. During fertilization male and the female parents each contribute genetic information (traits) to the zygote (fertilized egg). Genetic traits are carried by chromosomes. For traits that are controlled by a single pair of genes one set of genes is contributed by the male parent and the other set comes from the female parent (Figure 23-4). As a result of this process an organism receives one half of its genetic information from its male parent and the other half from its female parent.

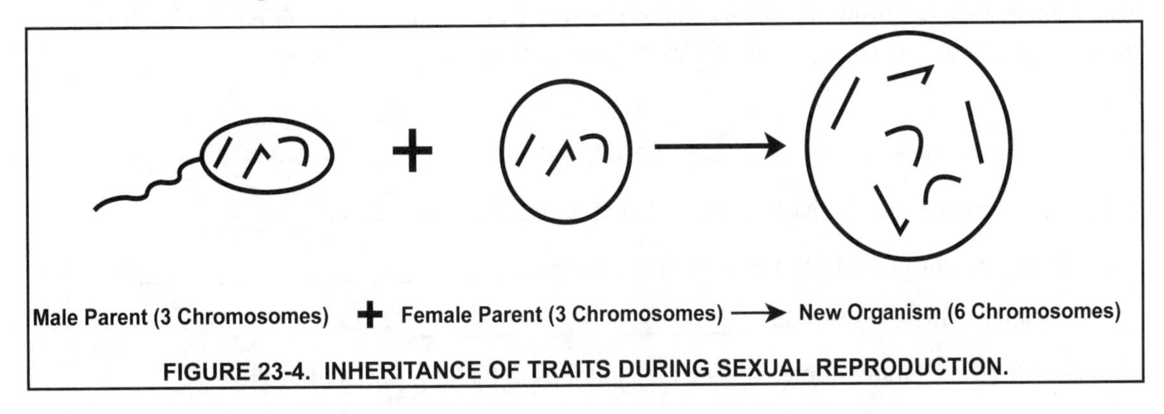

FIGURE 23-4. INHERITANCE OF TRAITS DURING SEXUAL REPRODUCTION.

REVIEW QUESTIONS

1. Explain how an organism receives its genetic information. ________________________

____

____

____

____

G. MENDEL'S EXPERIMENTS. Gregor Mendel conducted heredity experiments using common garden pea plants. Although he did not know about chromosomes and genes he made several hypotheses (scientific guesses) about the way in which traits are passed from generation to generation. To prove his hypothesis Mendel performed controlled experiments with pea plants. He used seven contrasting traits that were easy to identify. These traits are called **contrasting traits** because each trait has two very different forms. Contrasting traits are easy to observe and have no intermediate (in-between) forms. The seven contrasting traits studied by Mendel are listed below.

Trait	*Contrasting Forms*
stem length	tall or short
seed shape	round or wrinkled
seed color	yellow or green
seed coat color	grey or white
pod shape	inflated or constricted
pod color	green or yellow
flower position	axial or terminal

Name________________________ Class________________________ Date____________

Mendel used pea plants for his experiments because they had contrasting traits, they were easy to grow, and they produced large numbers of offspring in a short time. In addition, pea plants are pure-breeding plants. **Pure-breeding plants** are plants that produce seeds that grow into offspring with the same characteristics as the parent plants generation after generation. For example, pure-breeding tall plants always produce tall offspring and pure-breeding short plants always produce short plants. As a result of his experiments Mendel proposed that various characteristics of organisms are passed from one generation to the next by the transmission of pairs of factors. One factor is received from each parent. Today, Mendel's factors are called genes.

REVIEW QUESTIONS

1. The organism used by Mendel in his heredity experiments was the ____________________.

2. Two different forms of the same trait is known as ________________________.

3. An intermediate form is an ________________________ form.

4. List the seven traits studied by Mendel and the contrasting forms of each.

____

____

____

____

____

♦ **Dominance.** To find out how traits were passed from parents to offspring Mendel set up a series of experiments and carefully recorded his observations. In Mendel's first experiment he took pollen from pure-breeding tall plants and transferred it to the pistil of pure-breeding short plants (cross-pollination). The purebred plants were called the **parent (P) generation**. The offspring of a cross between two parent (P) generation plants were called the **first filial (F_1) generation.** Mendel observed that all the offspring in the F_1 generation were tall (Figure 23-5). He noticed that the trait for shortness did not appear.

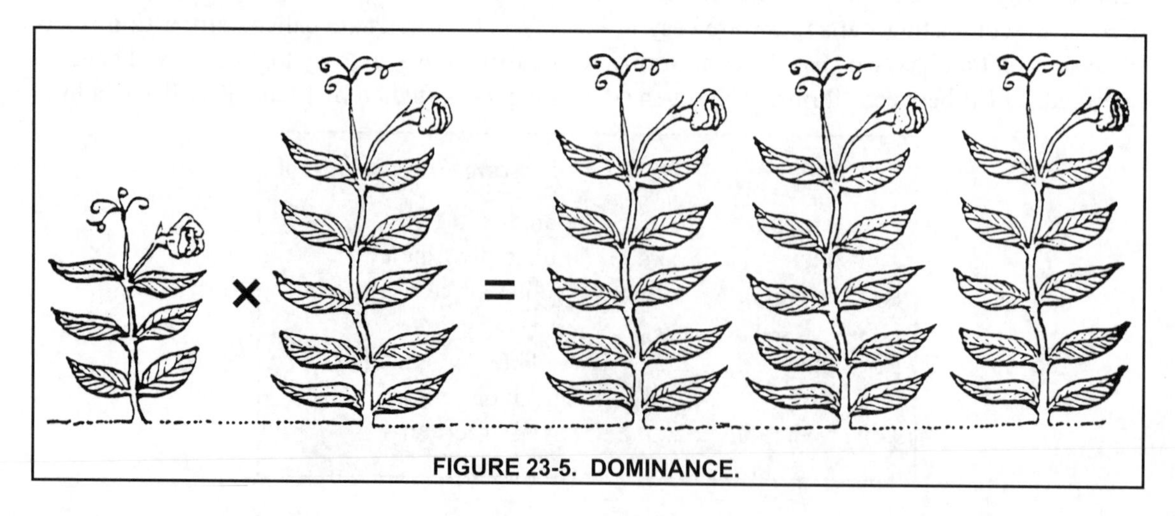

FIGURE 23-5. DOMINANCE.

Name________________________ Class________________________ Date____________

Mendel continued to cross (mate) large numbers of pure-breeding plants and repeated this procedure with all seven contrasting traits. He concluded that there were traits that *always* appeared (were expressed) when they were present in an organism. The trait that always appears when it is present is called the **dominant** trait. The trait that is hidden by the dominant trait is called the **recessive** trait. Two examples of dominant traits in humans are curly hair and the ability to roll the tongue. Dominant and recessive traits in garden pea plants are shown in Table 23-1.

TRAIT	DOMINANT FORM	RECESSIVE FORM
Stem Length	Tall	Short
Seed Color	Yellow	Green
Coat Color	Gray	White
Pod Shape	Inflated	Constricted
Pod Color	Green	Yellow
Flower Position	Axial	Terminal
Seed Shape	Round	Wrinkled

TABLE 23-1. DOMINANT AND RECESSIVE TRAITS.

Name________________________ Class________________________ Date__________

Review Questions

1. Describe Mendel's first experiment. ______________________________

____

____

2. Pure-bred plants are called the ____________________ generation and the offspring of a cross between pure-bred parents is called the ____________________ generation.

3. The ____________________ trait is the trait that appears when it is present and the ____________________ trait is the trait that doesn't appear if the dominant trait is present.

4. Name two traits that are dominant in humans. ______________________________

____

5. In a cross of a black and white guinea pigs all the offspring produced were black.

   What was the dominant trait? ____________________

   What was the recessive trait? ____________________

♦ **Segregation.** Mendel continued his experiments with pea plants by crossing members of the F_1 generation. The offspring from this cross were called the **second filial (F_2) generation.** He observed that in the F_2 generation there were some short plants. What a surprise! The trait that was hidden in the F_1 generation had reappeared in the F_2 generation (Figure 23-6). He concluded that during sexual reproduction traits must separate, or **segregate**, and then recombine randomly during fertilization. Remember, Mendel did not know about genes and chromosomes. Today we know that it is the chromosomes that are carrying genetic information for traits that separate during meiosis and recombine again during fertilization.

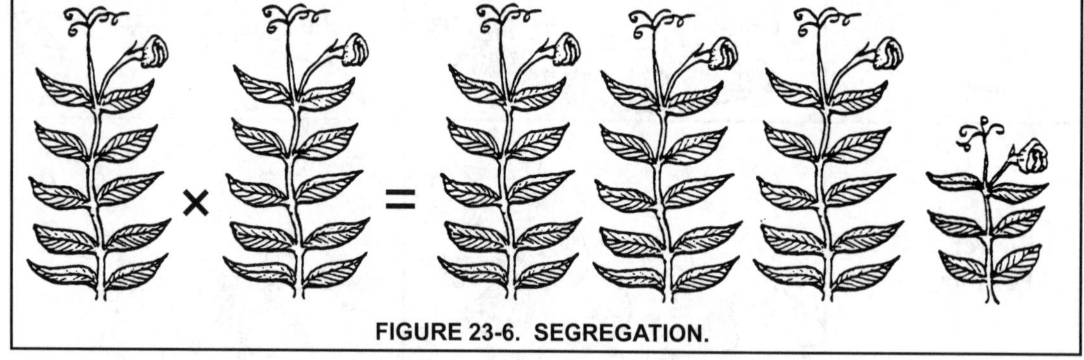

FIGURE 23-6. SEGREGATION.

Review Questions

1. The F_2 generation results from crossing two members of the ____________________ generation.

2. During sexual reproduction genes separate or ____________________.

Name______________________ Class______________________ Date______________

H. GENETIC TERMS. The language of genetics is very exact. In addition to the terms you already learned in this unit you will need to know the following terms: genotype, phenotype, homozygous, heterozygous and hybrid.

Sexually reproducing organisms *usually* have two genes for each trait. A zygote (fertilized egg) with two of the same kind of genes for a particular trait is called **pure** or **homozygous** for that trait. For example, a pea plant with two genes for tallness is said to be pure or homozygous tall. **Heterozygous** or **hybrid** organisms have two different genes for a given trait. A pea plant with one gene for tallness and one for shortness is called heterozygous or hybrid tall.

The genetic makeup of an individual is known as its **genotype.** The physical makeup (appearance) of an organism is called its **phenotype**. A tall pea plant's phenotype is said to be tall because it appears (looks) tall. A tall pea plant's genotype can be either heterozygous tall (one tall gene and one short gene) or pure tall (two tall genes). An organism can have the same phenotype but can have different genotypes. For example, an organism that looks tall can have a genotype that is pure tall or hybrid tall. This is because whenever the dominant trait is present the organism expresses (shows) the dominant trait.

REVIEW QUESTIONS

1. Sexually reproducing organisms usually have ________________ genes for each trait.
2. An organism that has two of the same kind of genes for a particular trait is called ____________________ or ____________________ for that trait.
3. ____________________ or ____________________ organisms have two different genes for a particular trait.
4. The genetic makeup of an individual is known as its ____________________ and the physical makeup of an organism is called its ____________________.
5. Explain how it is possible for two organisms to have the same phenotype but different genotypes. ____

____

____

____

____

____

I. USING GENETIC SYMBOLS. Scientists use symbols instead of words to represent genetic traits. They have agreed to represent the dominant trait (gene) by its capital letter and the recessive trait by the lower case form of the same letter. For example, in pea plants the dominant gene for tallness is represented by **T** while the recessive gene for shortness is represented by **t**. A pure or homozygous tall organism is represented as **TT.** A pure or homozygous short organism is **tt**. A hybrid or heterozygous organism is represented by **Tt**. (Remember that every organism *usually* has two genes for every trait.) Table 23-2 shows how symbols are used to represent traits of Mendel's garden pea plant.

PLANT TRAIT	DOMINANT TRAIT	RECESSIVE TRAIT	HOMOZYGOUS (PURE) PLANTS	HETEROZYGOUS (HYBRID) PLANTS
Stem Length	Tall (**T**)	Short (**t**)	Pure Tall (**TT**) Pure Short (**tt**)	Hybrid Tall (**Tt**)
Seed Color	Yellow (**Y**)	Green (**y**)	Pure Yellow (**YY**) Pure Green (**yy**)	Hybrid Yellow (**Yy**)
Coat Color	Gray (**G**)	White (**g**)	Pure Gray (**GG**) Pure White (**gg**)	Hybrid Gray (**Gg**)
Pod Shape	Inflated (**I**)	Constricted (**i**)	Pure Inflated (**II**) Pure Constricted (**ii**)	Hybrid Inflated (**Ii**)
Pod Color	Green (**G**)	Yellow (**g**)	Pure Green (**GG**) Pure Yellow (**gg**)	Hybrid Green (**Gg**)
Flower Position	Axial (**A**)	Terminal (**a**)	Pure Axial (**AA**) Pure Terminal (**aa**)	Hybrid Axial (**Aa**)
Seed Shape	Round (**R**)	Wrinkled (**r**)	Pure Round (**RR**) Pure Wrinkled (**rr**)	Hybrid Round (**Rr**)

TABLE 23-2. USING SYMBOLS TO REPRESENT TRAITS.

Review Questions

1. Scientists use ________________ instead of words to represent genetic traits.
2. By agreement scientists represent the dominant trait by with ________________ letter and the recessive trait with the ________________ of the same letter.
3. An organism usually has ________________ genes for every trait.
4. In guinea pigs, rough coat is dominant to smooth coat.
   (a) What symbol should be used to represent the gene for rough coat? ________
   (b) What symbol should be used to represent the gene for smooth coat? ________
   (c) What symbols should be used to represent a pure (homozygous) rough pig? ________
   (d) What symbols should be used to represent a pure (homozygous) smooth pig? ________
   (e) What symbols should be used to represent a hybrid (heterozygous) rough pig: ________

J. PREDICTING GENETIC RESULTS. You can predict genetic results if you understand that predicting the results of genetic crosses is based on the laws of chance or probability. **Probability** tells you how much chance there is for something to happen. For example, when you pick a playing card out of a deck of red and blue cards, the probability that it will be red is one out of two. You know that when you toss a coin, the probability that the coin will turn up heads is 50-50 or one chance out of two. However, it is necessary to toss thousands of coins to get these results. Try it yourself by tossing a coin 100 times. Did you get 50 heads and 50 tails? You probably would not because you would need to toss the coin thousands of times to get close to a 50-50 **ratio** (percentage). Probability predictions are based on *large* numbers of events.

Genetic diagrams and Punnett squares are two methods used by scientists to predict possible genotypes and phenotypes among the offspring of a particular genetic cross.

REVIEW QUESTIONS

1. Another word for probability is ________________.

2. ________________ and ________________ are two methods used to predict the offspring of genetic crosses.

♦ **Using Genetic Diagrams.** The first step in making a genetic diagram is to determine the genotype of the parent generation (P). For example, in Mendel's first experimental cross between pure tall and pure short pea plants, the genotypes of the parent generation were TT and tt. All gametes produced by the tall parent contained the gene for tallness (T) while all gametes produced by the short parent contained the gene for shortness (t). A diagram of this cross is shown in Figure 23-7.

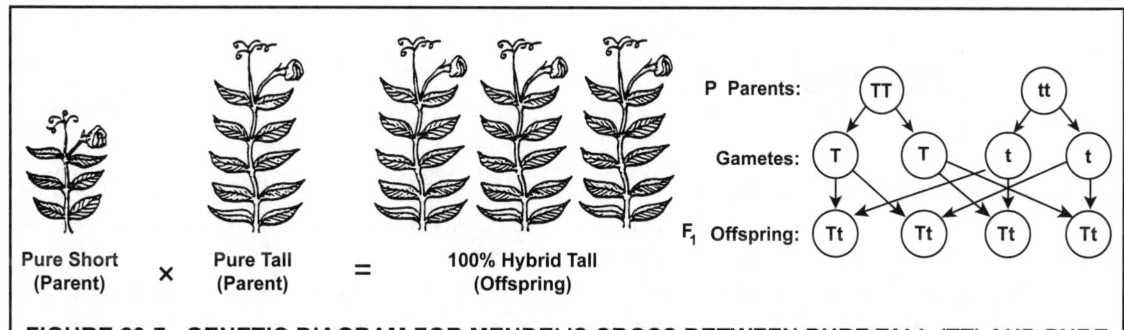

FIGURE 23-7. GENETIC DIAGRAM FOR MENDEL'S CROSS BETWEEN PURE TALL (TT) AND PURE SHORT (tt) PEA PLANTS.

The above F_1 results show that 100 percent of the offspring of the first generation are heterozygous tall or hybrid (Tt). Although they all looked tall (phenotype) they contained the gene for shortness.

Mendel's second cross between two hybrids is shown in Figure 23-8.

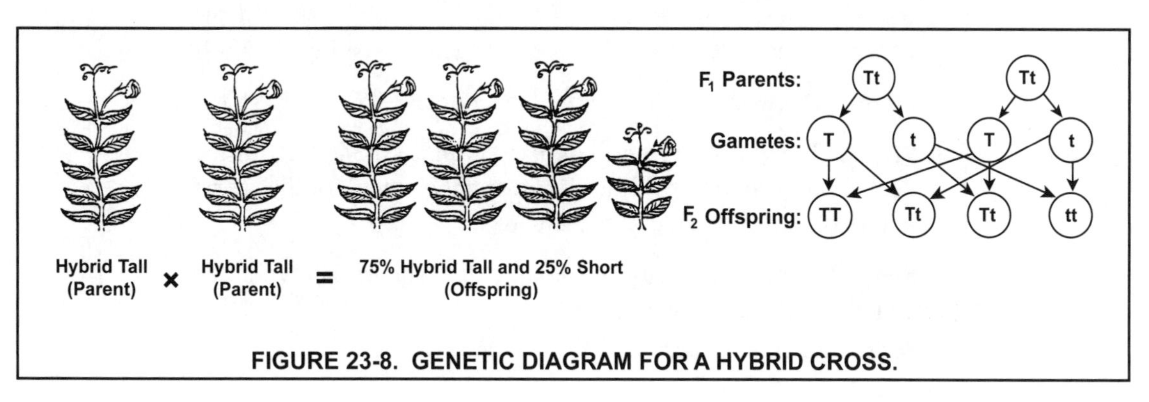

FIGURE 23-8. GENETIC DIAGRAM FOR A HYBRID CROSS.

Name________________________ Class________________________ Date____________

The results show that the phenotype ratio of a hybrid cross is 3:1 or 75% to 25% (three tall offspring to each short offspring). In actual experiments such results become clear only after many crosses that involve a large number of offspring.

The genotype ratio of a hybrid cross is 1:2:1 or 25% to 50% to 25% (one homozygous tall to two heterozygous tall to one homozygous short).

REVIEW QUESTIONS

1. What is the first step in making a genetic diagram? ______________________________

____

2. Draw a genetic diagram of a cross between a heterozygous tall pea plant (Tt) and a homozygous tall (TT) pea plant.

Parents:

Gametes:

Offspring:

♦ **Punnett Squares.** Like a genetic diagram the **Punnett square** is often used to predict the results of genetic crosses. The Punnett square is an easy way to figure out the offspring of genetic crosses because you can see all the possible genetic combinations.

The square is divided into four parts. Each part is equal to 25%. The entire square represents 100% or all possible crosses. The steps to follow when solving problems using the Punnett square method are shown below.

Using The Punnett Square

- **Step 1. State the key** by using the capital letter of the dominant trait to represent the dominant gene and the small letter of the dominant trait to represent the recessive gene. **(See Figure 23-9)**
- **Step 2. Draw the cross** to show the gametes.
- **Step 3. Draw the Punnett square** and place the letters for the egg alleles on one side of the square and the letters for the sperm alleles on the other side of the square.
- **Step 4. Write the results** next to the square showing the genotype and phenotype ratios.

Name________________________ Class________________________ Date____________

The use of the Punnett square to predict Mendel's ***purebred cross*** (pure tall crossed with pure short) is shown in Figure 23-9.

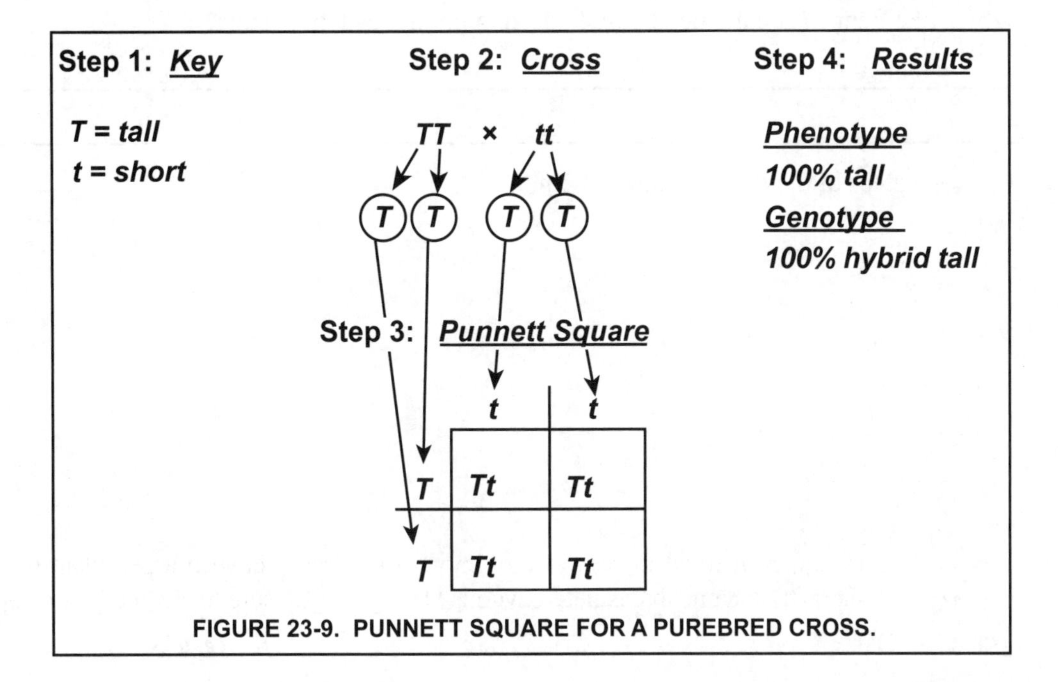

FIGURE 23-9. PUNNETT SQUARE FOR A PUREBRED CROSS.

The above results show a phenotype ratio of 100% tall and a genotype ratio of 100% hybrid tall. A Punnett square for a ***hybrid cross*** (hybrid tall crossed with hybrid tall) is shown in Figure 23-10.

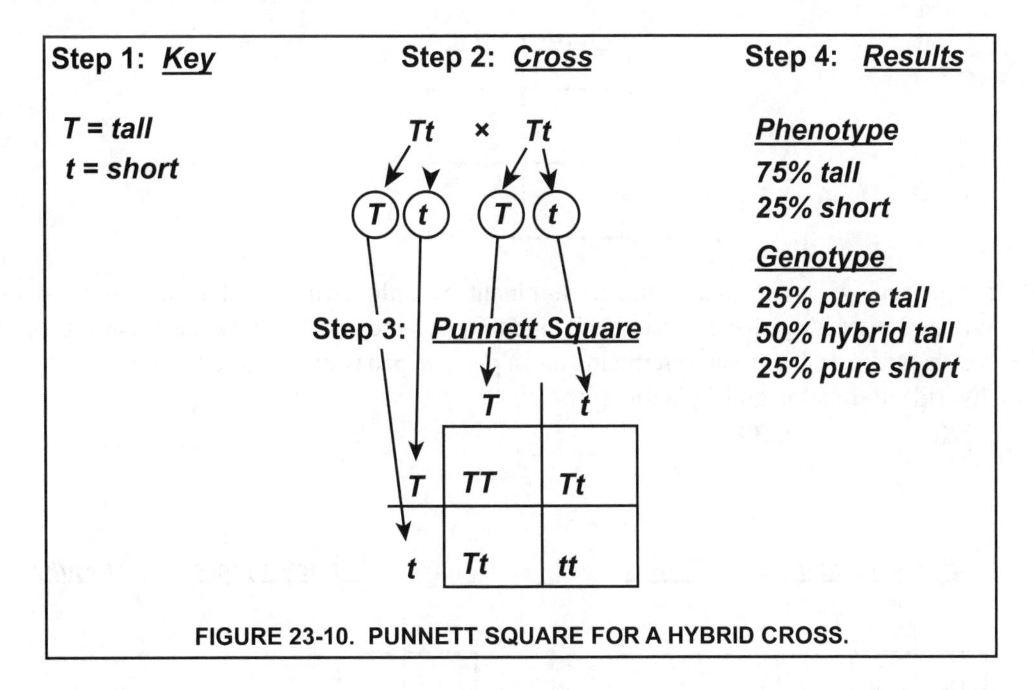

FIGURE 23-10. PUNNETT SQUARE FOR A HYBRID CROSS.

The above results show a phenotype ratio of ***3:1*** (tall to short) and a genotype ratio of ***1:2:1*** (25% homozygous or pure tall to 50% heterozygous or hybrid tall to 25% homozygous or pure short).

Name________________ Class________________ Date________

REVIEW QUESTIONS

1. Why is the Punnett square method often used to predict genetic results?

____

____

2. Show the steps of the Punnett square method.

3. Use the Punnett square method to show the offspring of a cross between a pea plant that is homozygous short (tt) and one that is heterozygous (Tt). *Note:* Be sure to show all four steps.

Key ***Cross*** ***Results***

Punnett Square

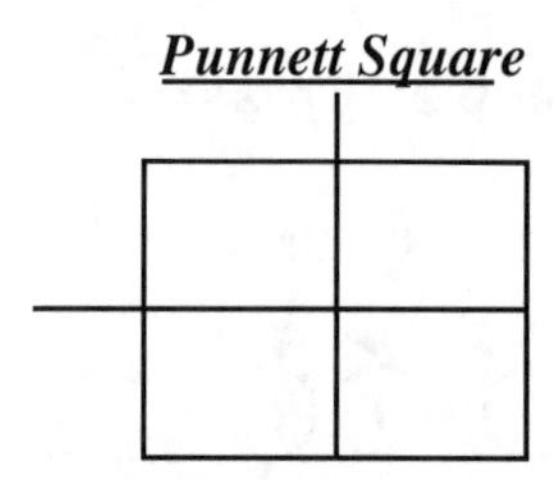

4. In watermelons, solid green color is dominant over the striped pattern and short shape is dominant over long shape. Use the Punnett square method to show the offspring of (1) a cross between a pure green watermelon and a pure striped watermelon and (2) a cross between a hybrid short melon and a pure long melon.

Key ***Cross #1*** ***Key*** ***Cross #2***

Punnett Square ***Results*** ***Punnett Square*** ***Results***

Name_________________________ Class_____________________ Date___________

LAB INVESTIGATION: TESTING PROBABILITY LAWS

Objective

Upon completion of this activity you should be able to state why the predicted genetic ratios based on the laws of probability are not always the same as the actual genetic results.

Laboratory Procedure

Materials: A penny and a pencil.

1. In this lab you will test the law of probability. *Probability* tells you how much chance there is for something to happen. For example, when you toss a coin the probability that the coin will turn up heads is 50-50 or one chance out of two. Try it yourself by tossing a coin 100 times as directed below.

2. Toss a penny 25 times and record the results in the **Observation Table** in the **Observation Section** below.

3. Repeat **Procedure 2** three more times.

4. Calculate your total number of heads and tails. Enter your results in the **Observation Section** below.

5. Report your results to your teacher so that a class record can be calculated.

6. After your teacher has calculated the total class results record them in the **Observation Section** below.

7. When you have completed your observations answer the questions in the **Conclusion Section** on the next page.

Observations

INDIVIDUAL RECORD	NUMBER OF HEADS	NUMBER OF TAILS	CLASS RECORD	NUMBER OF HEADS	NUMBER OF TAILS
TOSS NUMBER 1			TOSS NUMBER 1		
TOSS NUMBER 2			TOSS NUMBER 2		
TOSS NUMBER 3			TOSS NUMBER 3		
TOSS NUMBER 4			TOSS NUMBER 4		
INDIVIDUAL TOTALS			CLASS TOTALS		

Name_______________ Class_______________ Date_______________

CONCLUSIONS

1. What is probability? ____________________

____

____

____

____

____

2. How close were your results to the predicted 50-50 ratio? ____________________

____

____

____

____

____

3. How close were the class results to the predicted 50-50 ratio? ____________________

____

____

____

____

____

4. How do you explain any difference(s) between the individual results and the class results.

____

____

____

____

____

5. Probability predictions are based on ____________________ numbers of events.

Name________________ Class ________________ Date ____________

REVIEW ACTIVITIES

Important Terms

***DIRECTIONS:** Define the following terms in the spaces provided.*

alleles ____

contrasting traits ____

dominant trait ____

first filial generation ____

gene-chromosome theory ____

genetics ____

genotype ____

heredity ____

heterozygous ____

homozygous ____

hybrid ____

karyotype ____

phenotype ____

probability ____

Name________________ Class________________ Date________________

Punnett square ____

____

pure-breeding plants ____

____

ratio ____

____

recessive trait ____

____

second filial generation ____

____

segregate ____

____

species chromosome number ____

____

traits ____

____

variations ____

____

Name________________________ Class________________________ Date____________

Skill Practice

Part A. Use the Punnett square method to solve the following complete dominance genetic problems.

1. In pea plants, flowers located along the stem (axial) are dominant to flowers located at the end of the stem (terminal). Let **A** represent the allele for axial flowers and **a** represent the allele for terminal flowers. When plants with axial flowers are crossed with plants having terminal flowers all of the offspring have axial flowers. What were the genotypes of the parent plants?

Key ***Cross*** ***Results***

Punnett Square

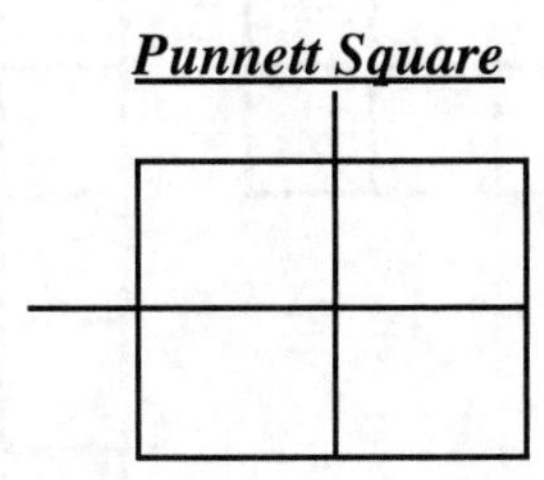

2. In fruit flies, gray body trait (**G**) is dominant over ebony body trait (**g**). Two gray fruit flies are mated and produce 174 gray-bodied and 58 ebony-bodied offspring. Use the Punnett square method to show the parental genotypes.

Key ***Cross*** ***Results***

Punnett Square

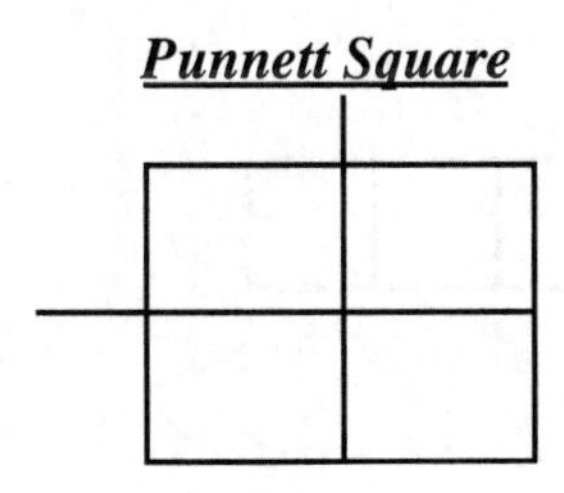

3. In humans, albinism (lack of color pigment) is recessive to normal skin pigmentation. If an albino female marries a heterozygous normal male, what percentage of their offspring would most probably be normal?

Key ***Cross*** ***Results***

Punnett Square

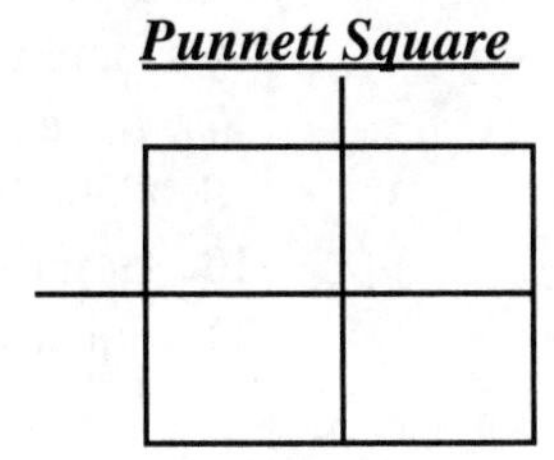

Name________________________ Class________________________ Date____________

Part B. Complete the following crossword puzzle.

Crossword Puzzle

Clues

ACROSS

1. Study of passage of traits from generation to generation
4. A percentage
5. One gene
6. Physical appearance
9. The _______ chromosomes number in humans is 46
10. Name for the *P* generation
12. Genetic makeup
13. Chromosome picture

DOWN

2. Trait that always appears when it is present
3. Basic unit of heredity
4. Trait that is sometimes "hidden"
6. Plant used in genetics
7. To segregate means to _______
8. Called the "father of genetics"
10. Homozygous
11. Square used to solve genetic problems

Name________________________ Class____________________ Date__________

CHAPTER 23: QUIZ

A. FILL-IN QUESTIONS

DIRECTIONS: ***Complete each of the following statements by writing the correct word or phrase in the space provided.***

1. ____________________ is the study of the way in which traits are passed on to offspring.

2. ____________________ is known as the "father of genetics."

3. The human species chromosome number is ____________________.

4. A hybrid organism has two ____________________ genes for a particular trait.

5. The trait that always appears when it is present is the ____________________ trait.

6. Another word for trait is ____________________.

7. Pairs of genes that carry the same traits are called ____________________.

8. A ____________________ is a photograph of chromosomes.

9. The dominant trait of an organism is represented by a/an ____________________ letter.

10. ____________________ is the science of heredity.

11. An organism that is pure for a trait is also ____________________ for that trait.

12. Mendel used the term ____________________ when referring to genes.

13. The genetic makeup of an individual is known as its ____________________.

14. A/an ____________________ is a difference in a trait within each species.

15. The physical appearance of an organism is called its ____________________.

16. ____________________ traits are two very different forms of the same trait.

17. ____________________ tells you how much chance there is for something to happen.

18. The trait that is hidden by the dominant trait is the ____________________ trait.

19. The term "segregation" means ____________________.

20. The ____________________ square is often used to predict the results of genetic crosses.

B. MULTIPLE-CHOICE QUESTIONS

DIRECTIONS: ***Circle the number of the expression that best completes each of the following statements.***

1. If a cross between a tall pea plant and a short pea plant produces all tall offspring, then tallness is most likely

(1) recessive
(2) dominant
(3) sex-linked
(4) blended

2. The offspring resulting from a cross between two pure recessives would most likely be

(1) 50% pure recessive and 50% hybrid
(2) 75% hybrid and 25% pure recessive
(3) 50% pure dominant and 50% pure recessive
(4) 100% pure recessive

Name________________________ Class________________________ Date____________

3. The biologist who studied hereditary factors in pea plants was
   (1) Darwin (2) Punnett (3) Benedict (4) Mendel

Directions (4-6): Base your answers to questions 4 through 6 on the diagram of experimental crosses of pea plants shown at the right and on your knowledge of biology.

Pure tall, Pure short → Parents → Hybrid tall, Hybrid tall → 1st Generation → Hybrid tall, Hybrid tall, Hybrid tall (3), Pure short (1) — 2nd Generation

4. Which Punnett square represents the cross that produces the first generation plants?

(1)

	T	*T*
t	*Tt*	*Tt*
t	*Tt*	*Tt*

(2)

	T	*t*
T	*TT*	*Tt*
t	*Tt*	*tt*

(3)

	T	*t*
t	*Tt*	*tt*
t	*Tt*	*tt*

(4)

	T	*T*
T	*TT*	*TT*
t	*Tt*	*Tt*

5. The geneotype of the hybrid tall plant in the second generation is best represented by
   (1) ***TT*** (2) ***T*** (3) ***tt*** (4) ***Tt***

6. The pattern of inheritance represented in the diagram is
   (1) dominance (3) mutation
   (2) multiple gene inheritance (4) sex-linked inheritance

7. Some human inherited traits are transmitted by
   (1) blood cells (2) bone cells (3) sperm cells (4) liver cells

8. Hereditary traits are controlled by the
   (1) blood (2) antibodies (3) placenta (4) genes

Directions (9-10): Base your answers to questions **9** and **10** on the diagram to the right which represents a cross between hybrid pea plants.

Tt* × *Tt

	T	*t*
T	*TT*	*Tt*
t	*Tt*	*tt*

Key
T = tall
t = short

9. In the gene pair ***Tt***, the symbol ***T*** represents a
   (1) recessive gene (3) fertilized gene
   (2) sex-linked gene (4) dominant gene

10. The percentage of offspring that shows the recessive trait in this cross is
    (1) 0% (2) 25% (3) 50% (4) 75%

C. ESSAY QUESTION

DIRECTIONS: Use complete sentences to answer the question in this part.

1. State the gene-chromosome theory. ____________________________________

____

____

____

Name________________________ Class____________________ Date____________

Chapter 24: Going Further in Genetics

A. TEST CROSS. Mendel could not tell from *just looking* at his tall pea plants whether they were pure tall (TT) or hybrid tall (Tt). He had to use a test cross to check the genotype of the tall plants. A **test cross** is a method used to determine whether an organism that exhibits the dominant trait is pure dominant for that trait or whether it is hybrid. In a test cross the organism in question is mated with an organism that is the homozygous recessive. If, after large numbers of crosses, none of the offspring show the recessive trait the test organism is considered to be pure (homozygous) dominant. If, after large numbers of crosses, even *one* of the offspring shows the recessive trait, the test organism is considered to be hybrid (heterozygous) dominant. Test crosses are used by plant and animal breeders to help them predict what kind of offspring will be produced.

REVIEW QUESTIONS

1. What is a test cross? ____

   ____

2. In a test cross the organism in question is mated with ____________________

   ____.

3. If, after large numbers of crosses, none of the offspring show the recessive trait the test organism with the dominant trait is considered to be ____________________.

4. If, after large numbers of crosses, even one of the offspring shows the recessive trait the test organism is considered to be ____________________.

5. Test crosses are used by ____________________ to help them predict what kind of offspring will be produced.

♦ **Example 1.** In pea plants tallness is dominant and shortness is recessive (tt). A breeder wishes to determine whether a tall pea plant is pure (TT) or hybrid (Tt) for tallness. If the tall pea plant is pure (TT) all of the offspring of a test cross will be tall (Figure 24-1).

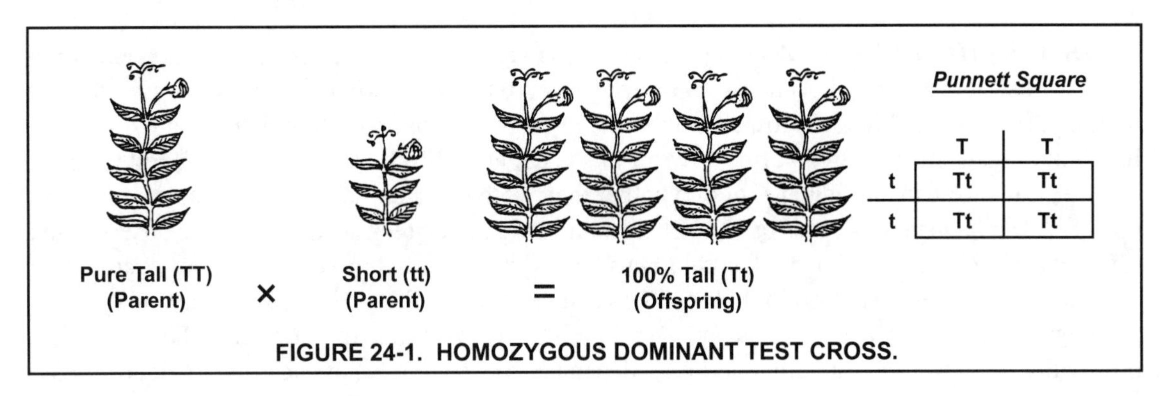

FIGURE 24-1. HOMOZYGOUS DOMINANT TEST CROSS.

Name________________________ Class________________________ Date____________

♦ **Example 2.** If the tall pea plant is hybrid (Tt), then one or more of the offspring *could* be short. If *any* offspring with the recessive trait (tt) appears the dominant-looking plant was hybrid (Tt) (Figure 24-2).

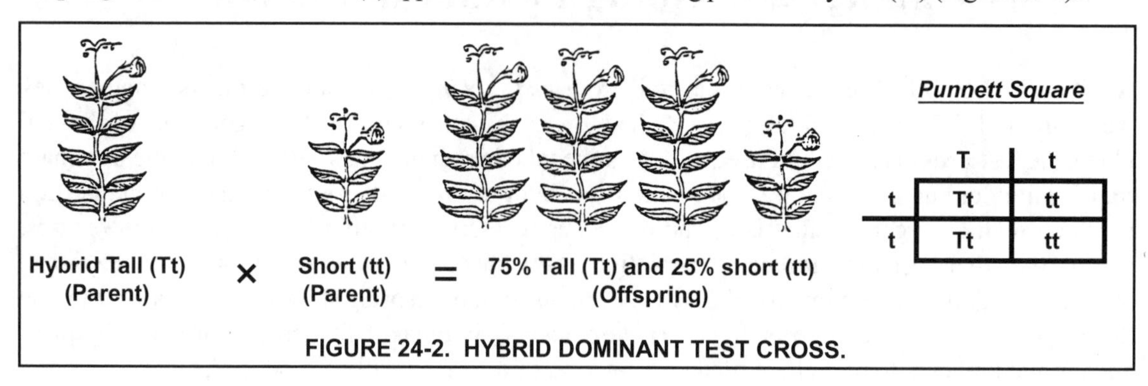

FIGURE 24-2. HYBRID DOMINANT TEST CROSS.

REVIEW QUESTIONS

1. In guinea pigs, black fur is dominant and white fur is recessive. A breeder wishes to determine whether a black guinea pig is homozygous (BB) or heterozygous (Bb) for fur color. Show, by using two punnett squares, how you would determine the genotype of the black guinea pig.

Key ***Cross #1*** ***Cross #2***

Punnett Square ***Results*** ***Punnett Square*** ***Results***

2. A test cross is done to determine whether an organism showing the dominant trait is homozygous or heterozygous for that trait. In a test cross the organism in question is mated with an organism that is

(1) homozygous dominant
(2) heterozygous
(3) hybrid
(4) homozygous recessive

B. DIHYBRID CROSS. In Mendel's first group of experiments he studied one pair of contrasting traits. This kind of cross is called a **monohybrid cross**. When Mendel finished his studies of monohybrid crosses, Mendel crossed plants that showed two pairs of contrasting traits. A cross involving organisms that are hybrid for two traits is called a **dihybrid cross**. He wanted to know whether traits were inherited together or whether they were inherited separately. That is, would tall plants *always* have yellow seeds or would they *sometimes* have green seeds. When he observed the offspring of his crosses he found that tall plants had both yellow and green seeds. For example, in a cross of plants that are hybrid for both tallness and seed color (TtYy) the offspring are tall/yellow, tall/green, short/yellow and short/green. Mendel concluded that in a dihybrid cross the factors (we now call genes) for each trait are inherited independently (separately) of each other (Figure 24-3).

Name________________________ Class________________________ Date____________

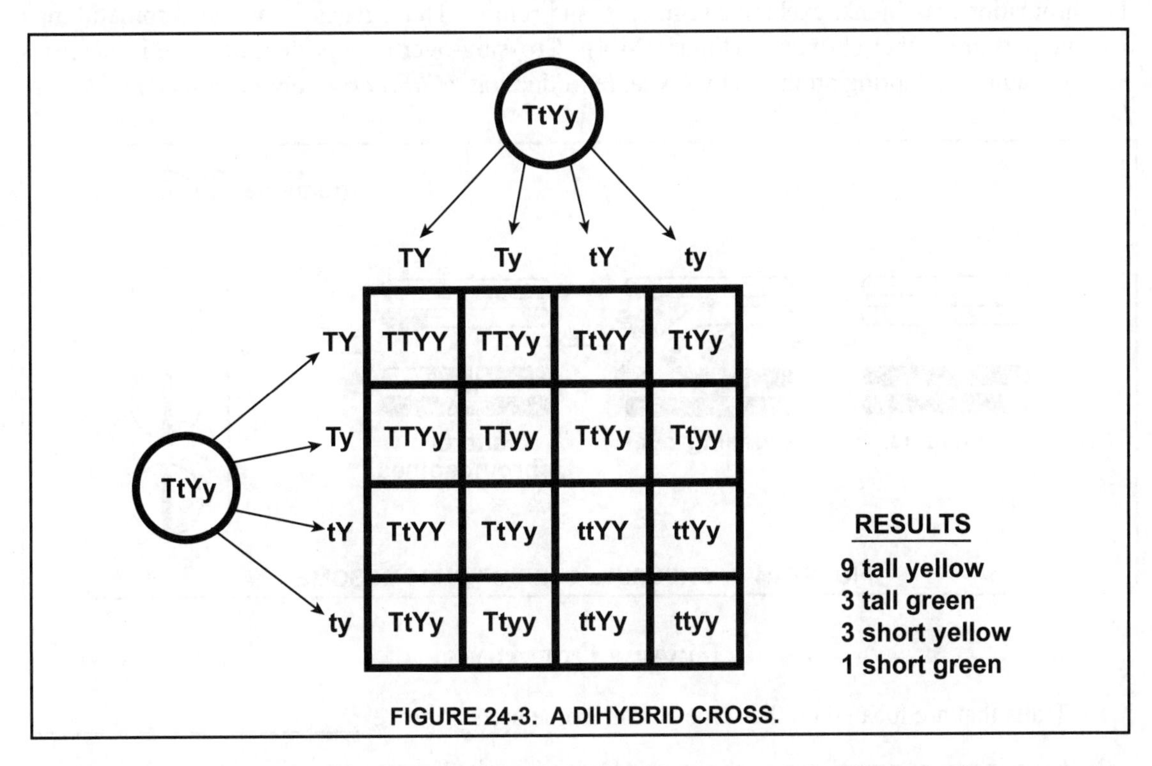

FIGURE 24-3. A DIHYBRID CROSS.

The phenotype ratio in the offspring of this dihybrid cross is 9 tall yellow: 3 tall green: 3 short yellow: 1 short green. This 9:3:3:1 ratio is called a **dihybrid phenotype ratio.**

REVIEW QUESTIONS

1. Explain the difference between a monohybrid cross and a dihybrid cross.

____

____

2. The dihybrid phenotype ratio is ______________________.

3. Mendel concluded that in a dihybrid cross the factors (now called genes) for each trait are inherited ______________________ of each other.

C. GENE LINKAGE AND CROSSING-OVER. Mendel's experiments are the basis of today's genetic studies. There are, however, exceptions to Mendel's conclusions. Because Mendel chose traits that were located on separate chromosomes they appeared to be inherited independently of each other.

We now know that traits are not all inherited independently of each other. Scientists learned that traits that are located on the same chromosome *tend* to be inherited together. Mendal thought traits were all inherited separately. Traits that are located on the same chromosome are said to show **linkage**.

Although linked genes are generally inherited together they can become separated by **crossing-over**, which may occur during a stage of meiosis called **synapsis**. During synapsis the four chromatids of a homologous chromosome pair sometimes twist around each other. As they separate the chromatids may break, exchange segments, and rejoin. Thus, genes from one chromatid may become part of another chromatid (Figure 24-4). Crossing-over is important because it increases variation among offspring produced by sexual reproduction. ***[Chromatids are described in Chapter 18.]***

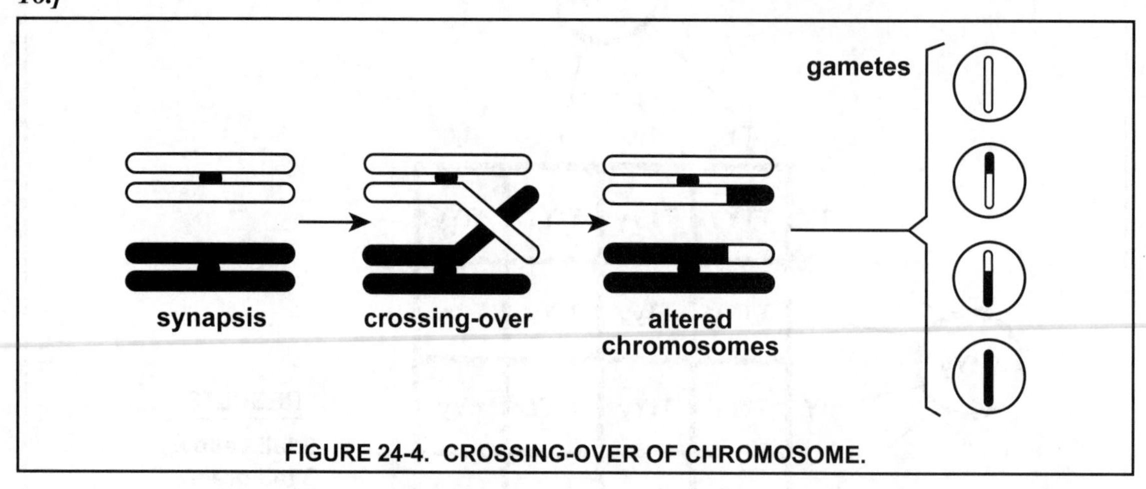

FIGURE 24-4. CROSSING-OVER OF CHROMOSOME.

REVIEW QUESTIONS

1. Traits that are located on the same chromosome are said to be ________________.
2. Crossing-over occurs during the stage of meiosis called ________________.
3. Crossing-over increases ________________ among offspring produced by sexual reproduction.

D. INCOMPLETE DOMINANCE. Incomplete dominance is another exception to Mendel's experiments. The type of inheritance he studied involved traits that had a dominant and a recessive form. This type of dominance is called **complete dominance**. There are traits that are neither dominant nor recessive and the offspring of such a cross exhibit traits that are a blend or mix of the two parents. This type of inheritance is called **incomplete dominance** or **blending inheritance**. For example, when red snapdragons (RR) are crossed with white snapdragons (WW) the offspring always have pink flowers (RW). The phenotype of the heterozygous individual is different from both its contrasting parents. Another organism that is an example of incomplete dominance is the Japanese-four o'clock. In this case there are red flowers (RR) and white flowers (WW). Mating the red and white flowered plants produces pink flowers (RW). When two hybrid plants with pink flowers (RW X RW) are crossed the offspring show a ratio of 1 red: 2 pink: 1 white. The traits red and white reappeared when the two hybrids were crossed.

REVIEW QUESTIONS

1. The type of inheritance involving traits that have a dominant and recessive form are called

____.

Name________________ Class________________ Date________________

2. Explain the meaning of incomplete dominance. ________________

____

____

3. Blending inheritance is the same as ________________.

4. When red snapdragons are crossed with white snapdragons the offspring are ________ in color.

5. What colors appear when two pink snapdragons are crossed? ________________

____

◆ **Example.** Some four-o'clock plants are pure for red flowers and some are pure for white flowers. When a plant with red flowers (RR) is crossed with a plant with white flowers (WW) the hybrid offspring produce only pink flowers (RW). If these plants are crossed the flowers of the offspring show a ratio of 1 red: 2 pink: 1 white (Figure 24-5). In all cases of incomplete dominance the offspring of a cross between heterozygous individuals show a 1:2:1 phenotype ratio.

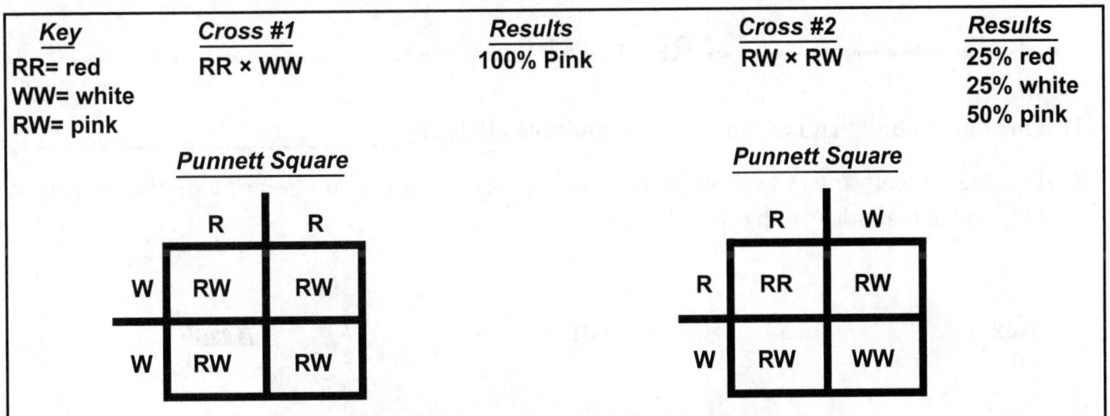

Key
RR= red
WW= white
RW= pink

Cross #1
RR × WW

Results
100% Pink

Punnett Square

	R	R
W	RW	RW
W	RW	RW

Cross #2
RW × RW

Results
25% red
25% white
50% pink

Punnett Square

	R	W
R	RR	RW
W	RW	WW

FIGURE 24-5. INCOMPLETE DOMINANCE.

REVIEW QUESTIONS

1. When a mouse with black fur is crossed with a mouse with white fur all F_1 generation offspring have gray fur. Use the Punnett square method to show the results of crossing two gray mice.

Key ***Cross*** ***Results***

Punnett Square

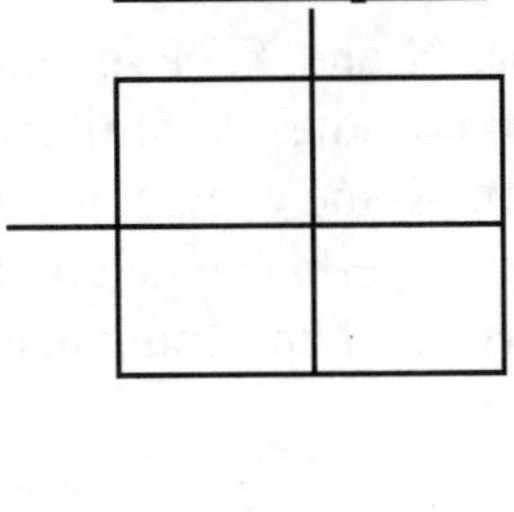

Name________________________ Class________________________ Date____________

E. MULTIPLE ALLELES. Although Mendel thought that traits were controlled by one pair of alleles (genes) this is not always the case. The inheritance of some traits is determined by more than two different alleles. This type of inheritance involves **multiple alleles**. In traits controlled by multiple alleles there may be three or more different alleles for a particular trait. The cells of any individual can contain no more than two of the alleles for the trait–one allele on each chromosome of a homologous pair.

In humans there are four possible blood types: A, B, AB, and O. The inheritance of the ABO blood group involves multiple alleles, which are represented as A, B, AB, and O. A and B are both dominant and O is recessive. When A and B come together incomplete dominance occurs. Table 24-1 shows the phenotypes (blood types) associated with each of the possible genotypes.

BLOOD TYPE	GENOTYPE
A	AA or AO
B	BB or BO
AB	AB
O	OO

TABLE 24-1. BLOOD TYPES IN HUMANS.

REVIEW QUESTIONS

1. One human trait that is determined by multiple alleles is ______________________.

2. Use the Punnett square to show all possible genotypes of the children of a mother with type O blood and a father with type AB blood.

Key ***Cross*** ***Results***

Punnett Square

F. INHERITANCE OF SEX. Your sex (male or female) was determined when your mother's egg was fertilized by your father's sperm. Humans have one pair of chromosomes, called the **sex chromosomes**, that are responsible for determining the sex of an individual. The other 22 pair of chromosomes are called **autosomes.**

Sex chromosomes are represented as **X** and **Y**. Egg cells have only X chromosomes while sperm cells carry either an X or a Y chromosome. At fertilization two X chromosomes produce a female (XX). When an X and a Y chromosome come together a male offspring is produced. In humans, and most other organisms, it is the sperm that determines the sex of the offspring. At each fertilization the offspring has a 50-50 chance of becoming male or female (Figure 24-6).

Name________________ Class________________ Date________

Key	Cross	Results
X= female chromosome	female × male	50% males
Y= male chromosome	XX × XY	50% females

Punnett Square

	X	X
X	XX	XX
Y	XY	XY

FIGURE 24-6. SEX DETERMINATION IN HUMANS.

REVIEW QUESTIONS

1. When is the sex of an individual determined? ________________________________

____

2. Sex chromosomes are represented as __________ and __________

3. The __________ chromosomes are responsible for determining the sex of an individual.

4. Two X chromosomes produce a ________________, while an X and a Y chromosome produce a ________________.

G. SEX-LINKED INHERITANCE. The Y chromosome is smaller than the X chromosome. Several of the genes found on the X chromosome *are not* found on the Y chromosome. The genes on the X chromosome that have no matching genes on the Y chromosome are called **sex-linked genes**. Sex-linked genes are usually recessive.

Two human diseases associated with sex-linked genes are hemophilia and color blindness. **Hemophilia** is a disease in which the blood does not clot properly. **Color blindness** is an inability to see certain colors—most commonly red and green. Both of these disorders (diseases) are more common in males than in females. This happens because the sex-linked recessive gene on the male's X chromosome is the *only* gene the male has for the sex-linked trait. When the sex-linked gene is present on the male's X chromosome the male *has* the sex-linked disorder. In females the recessive gene is expressed (shows) only when two recessive genes are inherited. A female will not have hemophilia, color blindness, or any other sex-linked condition as long as she has one normal gene for the trait. **Myopia**, extreme nearsightedness, is another common sex-linked trait.

Females who have one normal gene and one recessive gene for a sex-linked trait are called "**carriers**" for that trait. This means they *do not have* the disorder but they *carry* the recessive

Name________________ Class________________ Date________________

gene. Children of carriers *can inherit* the sex-linked gene. Figure 24-7 shows the inheritance of sex-linked traits.

Key

XY = normal male
X^cY = colorblind male

XX = normal female
X^cX = carrier female
X^cX^c = colorblind female

Cross #1

normal male × carrier female

Punnett Square

	X	Y
X	XX	XY
X^c	X^cX	X^cY

Results

25% normal females
25% carrier females
25% normal males
25% colorblind males

Cross #2

colorblind male × carrier female

Punnett Square

	X^c	Y
X	XX^c	XY
X^c	X^cX^c	X^cY

Results

25% carrier females
25% colorblind females
25% normal males
25% colorblind males

FIGURE 24-7. INHERITANCE OF SEX-LINKED TRAITS.

REVIEW QUESTIONS

1. What is meant by the term "sex-linked gene". ________________

____

2. Name two sex-linked diseases. ________________

____

3. Are carriers male or female? ________________. Does a carrier *have* the sex-linked disorder he or she carries? ________________.

4. Use the punnett square to show all possible genotypes of the children of a colorblind mother and a father who has normal color vision.

Key ***Cross*** ***Results***

Punnett Square

Name____________________ Class ____________________ Date __________

LAB INVESTIGATION: INHERITED HUMAN TRAITS

Objective

Upon completion of this activity, you should be able to identify some inherited human traits and state whether the traits are recessive or dominant.

Laboratory Procedure

Materials: Mirror and pencil.

1. Human inheritance follows the same genetic principles as inheritance in other organisms. In this lab you will observe several human traits that are inherited as either dominant or recessive genes. The traits that you will observe are hairline shape, earlobe position, tongue-rolling, cleft chin, and dimples.

2. Look at your hairline in the mirror. Does it come to a point or does it go straight across your forehead? If it comes to a point, called a "widow's peak", check (√) the box under ***YES*** in the **Observation Table** in the **Observation Section** on the next page. If you do not have a "widow's peak", check (√) the box under *NO*. ***[Note: The gene for a "widow's peak" is a dominant gene.]***

3. Now check your earlobes. If they are attached to the side of your head check (√) ***YES.*** If they are not attached (are free) check (√) *NO*. ***[Note: The gene for free earlobes is dominant and attached earlobes are due to a recessive gene.]***

4. Stick out your tongue and see if you can roll it up on the sides. If you can roll your tongue check (√) ***YES***. If you cannot roll your tongue check (√) *NO*. ***[Note: The ability to roll your tongue is a dominant trait and the inability to roll your tongue is a recessive trait.]***

5. Next look at your chin. Is there a cleft (dent) in your chin? If there is a cleft check (√) ***YES***. If there is no cleft check (√) ***NO. [Note: The gene for cleft chin is dominant and no cleft is recessive.]***

6. Check your face for dimples. If you have dimples check (√) ***YES.*** If you do not have dimples check (√) ***NO. [Note: Dimples is caused by a dominant gene and lack of dimples is recessive.]***

7. Report your results to your teacher so that a class record can be calculated.

8. After your teacher has calculated the total class results record them in the **Observation Section** on the next page.

9. When you have completed your observations return your mirror to the lab supply table and answer the questions in the **Conclusion Section** on the next page.

Name________________________ Class ________________________ Date ____________

OBSERVATIONS

INDIVIDUAL RECORD	YES	NO	CLASS RECORD	YES	NO	% OF CLASS WITH TRAIT	% OF CLASS LACKING TRAIT
Hairline			Hairline				
Earlobes			Earlobes				
Tongue-Rolling			Tongue-Rolling				
Chin Cleft			Chin Cleft				
Dimples			Dimples				

CONCLUSIONS

1. List five inherited human traits and state the dominant form and recessive form of each trait.

____

____

____

____

____

____

____

____

2. Was the dominant form of each trait the most common class trait? ____________.

3. In order for a recessive trait to appear in an individual, how many recessive genes must the individual inherit? Explain your answer. ________________________________

____

____

____

Name________________________ Class________________________ Date__________

REVIEW ACTIVITIES

Important Terms

DIRECTIONS: ***Define the following terms in the spaces provided.***

autosomes ____

____

blending inheritance ____

____

carrier ____

____

color blindness ____

____

complete dominance ____

____

dihybrid cross ____

____

hemophilia ____

____

incomplete dominance ____

____

linkage ____

____

monohybrid cross ____

____

multiple alleles ____

____

myopia ____

____

sex chromosomes ____

____

sex-linked genes ____

____

test cross ____

____

Name______________________ Class______________________ Date______________

Skill Practice

Part A. Use the Punnett square method to solve the following genetic problem involving test crosses. Underline the correct answer.

Problem. In guinea pigs rough coat (**R**) is dominant and smooth coat (**r**) is recessive. Show how a breeder would determine whether a rough-coated guinea pig is homozygous or heterozygous for coat type.

Key ***Cross #1*** ***Results*** ***Cross #2*** ***Results***

Punnett Square ***Punnett Square***

Question: In a test cross the organism in question is mated with an organism that is

(1) homozygous dominant
(2) heterozygous
(3) hybrid
(4) homozygous recessive

Part B. Use the Punnett square method to solve the following genetic problem involving incomplete dominance.

Problem. A gardener found that when white petunias and purple petunias were crossed only blue petunias were produced. Use the Punnett square below to show the farmer's cross.

Key ***Cross*** ***Results***

Punnett Square

Question: From which of the following crosses would the gardener most probably obtain the greatest percentage of ***white*** petunias? ***(Note: Use the squares below to work out your answer.)***

(1) white and blue petunias
(2) purple and purple petunias
(3) blue and blue petunias
(4) purple and blue petunias

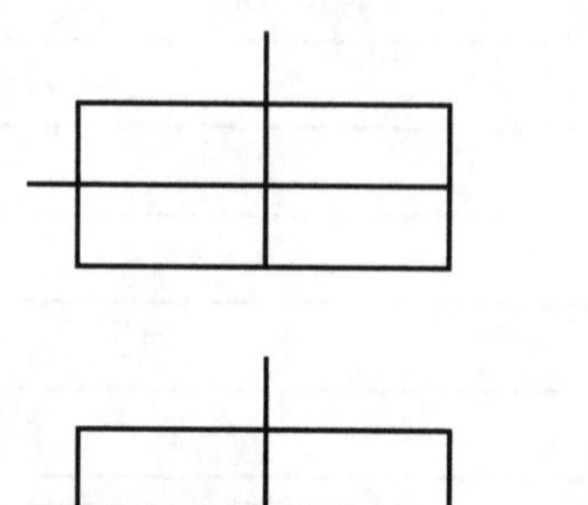

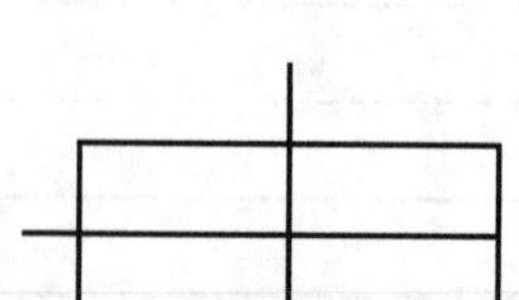

Name________________________ Class________________________ Date____________

Part C. Use the Punnett square method to solve the following genetic problems involving multiple alleles. Underline the correct answer.

Problem. Show all the possible blood types of the children of a man who is heterozygous for blood type A and a woman with blood type AB.

Key ***Cross*** ***Results***

Punnett Square

Question: The blood type of their offspring could not be (1) A (2) B (3) O (4) AB.

Problem. Show how two parents who do not have blood type O are able to produce a child with type O blood.

Key ***Cross*** ***Results***

Punnett Square

Question: People with type O blood are
(1) homozygous recessive
(2) heterozygous
(3) hybrid
(4) heterozygous dominant

Part D. Use the Punnett square method to solve the following genetic problems involving sex-linked traits.

Problem. A colorblind man marries a woman who is a carrier for color blindness. Show all the possible genotypes of their children.

Key ***Cross*** ***Results***

Punnett Square

Question: It is most probable that (1) half of their sons will be colorblind (2) all of their sons will have normal color vision (3) all of their sons will be colorblind (4) none of their children will have normal color vision

Name________________ Class________________ Date________________

Problem. A man with normal color vision married a woman with normal color vision whose father was colorblind. Show all the possible genotypes of their children.

Key ***Cross*** ***Results***

Punnett Square

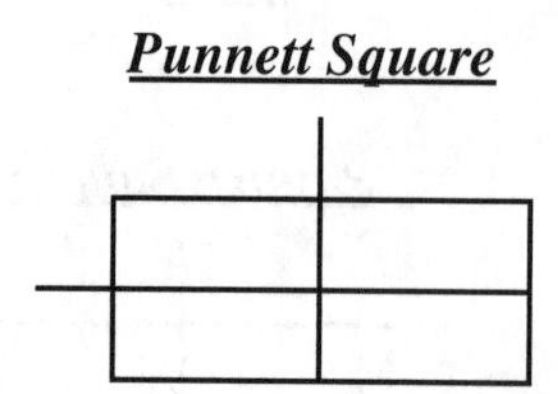

Question: What is their chance of having a colorblind daughter?

(1) 0% (3) 75%
(2) 25% (4) 100%

Problem. Complete the following Punnett square. Base your answers to questions a and b on the following diagram.

Key
X^h = X chromosome with hemophilia (h) gene
X = normal X chromosome
Y = normal Y gene

Cross
XX^h × XY

Punnett Square

	X	**X^h**
X	(1) **XX**	(3) **XX^h**
Y	(2)	(4) **X^hY**

Questions:

(a) The gene symbols of the offspring represented in box 2 should be
(1) **XX^h** (3) **XY**
(2) **XX** (4) **X^hY**

(b) Which box represents the gene type of a female carrier?
(1) 1 (3) 3
(2) 2 (4) 4

Name________________________ Class____________________ Date__________

CHAPTER 24: QUIZ

A. FILL-IN QUESTIONS

DIRECTIONS: ***Complete each of the following statements by writing the correct word or phrase in the space provided.***

1. A/an ____________________ is a method used to determine whether an organism that shows the dominant trait is pure dominant for that trait or whether it is hybrid.
2. A monohybrid cross studies ____________________ pair(s) of contrasting traits.
3. ____________________ is a disease in which the blood does not clot properly.
4. The sex of an individual is determined by the ____________________ chromosome.
5. Extreme nearsightedness is called ____________________.
6. The four types of blood are A, B, AB, and ____________________.
7. Females who have one normal gene and one recessive gene for a sex-linked trait are called ____________________.
8. Genes that are located on the same chromosome are said to show ____________________.
9. Crossing-over separates ____________________ genes.
10. Humans have ____________________ pair(s) of autosomes.
11. A dihybrid cross studies ____________________ pair of contrasting traits.
12. An organism with an *X* and a *Y* chromosome is called a ____________________.
13. In ____________________ dominance there is one dominant form and one recessive form of a certain trait.
14. A person who cannot see red and green colors is said to be ____________________.
15. Blood typing is an example of ____________________ allele inheritance.
16. When red four-o'clock flowers are mated with white four-o'clock flowers the offspring is ____________________ in color.
17. Hemophilia is a ____________________ trait.
18. Another name for incomplete dominance is ____________________ inheritance.
19. In a test cross the unknown organism is crossed with a ____________________ organism.
20. The genes on the *X* chromosome that have no matching genes on the *Y* chromosome are called ____________________.

B. MULTIPLE-CHOICE QUESTIONS

DIRECTIONS: ***Circle the number of the expression that best completes each of the following statements.***

1. A normal human female would have which combination of sex chromosomes?

   (1) XX (3) YY
   (2) XY (4) YX

Name________________________ Class________________________ Date____________

2. Parents whose blood types are AB and A could ***not*** have a child with blood type

(1) A (3) AB
(2) B (4) O

3. The chance that parents will produce a child with XY chromosomes is

(1) 100% (3) 25%
(2) 50% (4) 0%

4. Hemophilia (bleeder's disease) and red-green color blindness are examples of traits passed from generation to generation by

(1) blood cells (3) mutagenic agents
(2) sex linkage (4) pollination

Directions (5-7): Base your answers to questions **5** through **7** on the diagram below and on your knowledge of biology.

	X	*X*
X	*XX*	*XX*
Y	*XY*	*XY*

5. The diagram illustrates a cross between

(1) two hybrid individuals (3) two pure individuals
(2) male and female individuals (4) recessive and dominant individuals

6. The genetic cross illustrated would result in

(1) all males (3) 1/2 males & 1/2 females
(2) all dominant individuals (4) 1/2 dominants and 1/2 recessives

7. The presence of an abnormal gene on an ***X*** chromosome could result in

(1) color blindness (3) appendicitis
(2) diabetes (4) goiter

8. When pure black guinea pigs were mated with pure white guinea pigs all the offspring were black. The trait for whiteness would be described as

(1) dominant (3) sex linked
(2) recessive (4) hybrid

9. The ABO blood groups in humans can best be explained by

(1) sex linkage (3) multiple genes
(3) platelets (4) mitosis

10. When round squash are crossed with long squash all the offspring are oval. This illustrates

(1) dominance (3) mitosis
(2) pollination (4) blending

C. ESSAY QUESTION

DIRECTIONS: Use complete sentences to answer the question in this part.

1. Describe how it is possible for a trait to "skip" a generation.

____

____

____

____

Name________________ Class________________ Date________

Chapter 25: Modern Genetics

A. CHEMICAL BASIS FOR GENETICS. It wasn't until modern times that scientists began to understand the chemical makeup of genes and chromosomes. In the 1940's and 1950's experiments showed that genes, the basic units of heredity, are made up of the chemical compound **DNA (deoxyribonucleic acid)**. DNA is a large complex molecule found in high concentrations in the nucleus of the cell. It is responsible for passing genetic information from generation to generation. DNA also controls the manufacture of enzymes. Enzymes control cellular activity.

REVIEW QUESTIONS

1. Genes are composed of a chemical compound called ________________.
2. Name two processes for which DNA is responsible. ________________

____

____

B. NUCLEOTIDES. The DNA molecule is made up of a long chain of repeating **nucleotide** units. Nucleotides contain nitrogenous bases, a sugar, and a phosphate group. The four different nitrogenous bases in DNA nucleotides are **adenine, guanine, cytosine,** and **thymine.** The sugar in DNA is **deoxyribose,** a 5-carbon sugar. The **phosphate** group contains phosphorus and oxygen. Figure 25-1 is a model (representation) of a typical DNA nucleotide.

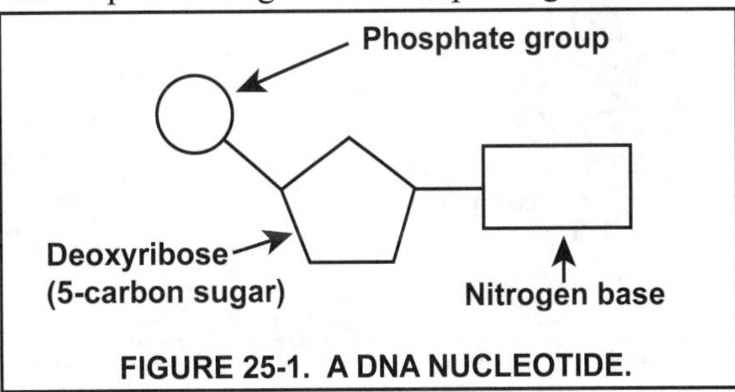

FIGURE 25-1. A DNA NUCLEOTIDE.

REVIEW QUESTIONS

1. The DNA molecule is a long chain of units known as ________________.
2. The four different nitrogenous bases in DNA nucleotides are ________________

____

3. In the space below draw and label a DNA nucleotide.

Name______________________ Class______________________ Date__________

C. DNA STRUCTURE. The structure of DNA was discovered in the 1950's by James Watson and Francis Crick. According to Watson and Crick DNA molecules are shaped like a twisted ladder. The twisted ladder structure is called a **double helix** (Figure 25-2). The DNA double helix has two strands or sides. The strands are connected at the rungs. The sides of the ladder consist of alternating sugar and phosphate molecules. The rungs are pairs of nitrogenous bases. The nitrogen bases are attached to each other by weak hydrogen bonds.

The four nitrogenous bases in DNA bond (join) together in a certain way called as base pairing. According to the DNA base pairing rule adenine **(A)** and thymine **(T)** bond together and guanine **(G)** and cytosine **(C)** bond together. No other combinations are possible. Wherever there is a **C** on one strand it is bonded to a **G** on the other strand. Wherever there is an **A** on one strand there is a **T** on the other strand. (Look at base pairing in Figure 25-2.)

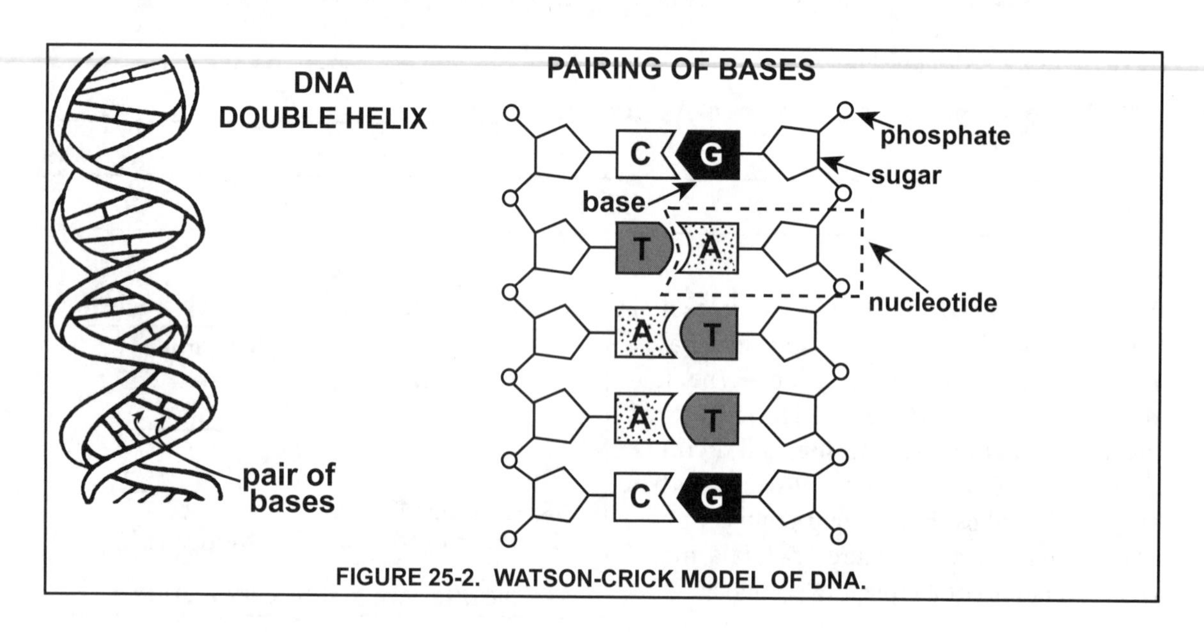

FIGURE 25-2. WATSON-CRICK MODEL OF DNA.

REVIEW QUESTIONS

1. A double helix looks like a ____________________ ladder.
2. Nitrogen bases are attached to each other by ______________________________.
3. According to the rule for DNA base pairing, adenine pairs only with ________________ and ________________ pairs only with cytosine.

D. DNA REPLICATION. As a result of reproduction daughter cells are identical to parent cells because during reproduction DNA makes exact copies of itself **(replicates)**. These exact copies are passed from parent cells to daughter cells during cell division. Replication of DNA occurs both in mitosis and meiosis. The process begins with an untwisting of the DNA helix (Figure 25-3). The two strands that make up the helix then "unzip." The bonds holding the nitrogenous bases together break and leave the molecule in the form of two nucleotide strands. Each strand is a pattern for the new nucleotide strand. Free nucleotides present in the cytoplasm pair with the free nitrogenous bases of both strands. Because nitrogenous bases can pair in only one way, two identical DNA molecules that are identical to the parent cell are produced.

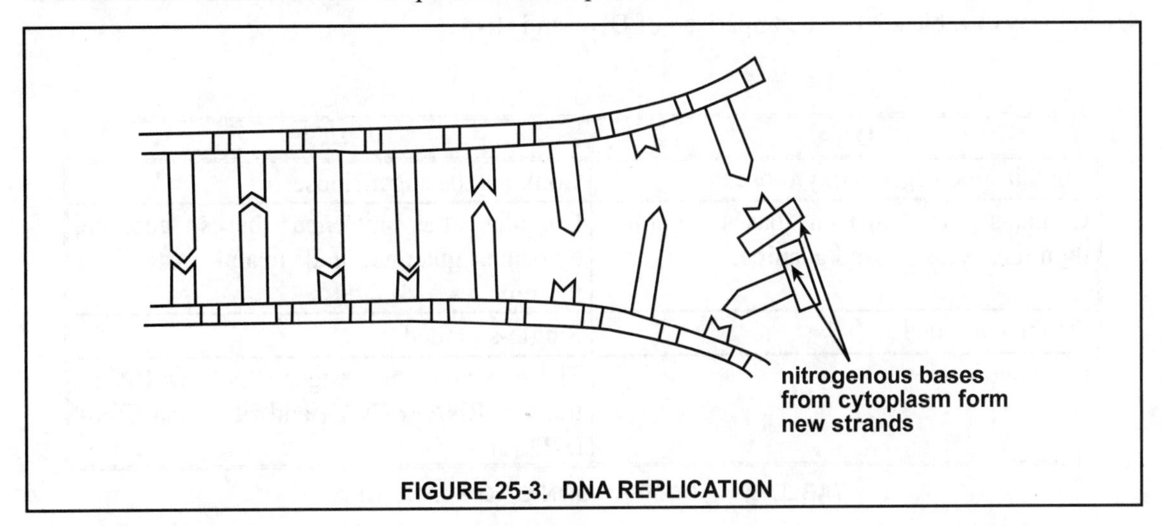

FIGURE 25-3. DNA REPLICATION

REVIEW QUESTIONS

1. When DNA replicates it makes ________________________________.
2. When does replication occur? ________________________________
3. The diagram below represents a part of a DNA molecule. Using the base pairing rule for DNA label the missing nucleotides.

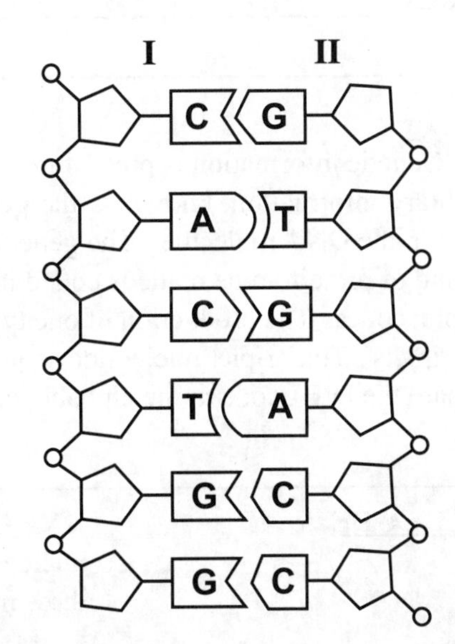

4. Which two bases are present in equal amounts in a double-stranded DNA molecule?
   (1) cytosine and thymine
   (2) adenine and guanine
   (3) adenine and thymine
   (4) cytosine and adenine

Name________________________ Class ____________________ Date __________

E. RNA. Control of cell activities involves two kinds of nucleic acids known as DNA and **RNA (ribonucleic acid)**. Both are composed of nucleotides but the two types of molecules differ in several ways. Table 25-1 is a comparison of DNA and RNA.

DNA	RNA
Contains the sugar deoxyribose.	Contains the sugar ribose.
Contains the nitrogen bases adenine, thymine, cytosine, and guanine.	Contains the nitrogen bases adenine, cytosine, guanine, and **uracil** instead of thymine.
Double-stranded.	Single-stranded.
Only one kind.	Three kinds: messenger RNA (***m*****RNA**), transfer RNA (***t*****RNA**), and ribosomal RNA (***r*****RNA**).

TABLE 25-1. COMPARISON OF DNA AND RNA.

REVIEW QUESTIONS

1. RNA contains the nitrogen base ____________________ instead of thymine.

2. DNA is ____________________-stranded, while RNA is ____________________-stranded.

3. RNA contains the sugar ____________________.

4. Name the three kinds of RNA. ____

____

F. THE GENETIC CODE. Genetic information is present in the structure and organization of the DNA molecule. This hereditary information, known as the **genetic code**, depends upon the order of the different nucleotides in the DNA molecule. The genetic code is a message to the cell to make certain proteins. The kind of protein to be made is coded in the arrangement of groups of three nucleotide bases called triplet codes. The production of one type of protein is controlled by a sequence (order) of nucleotide triplets. This triplet nucleotide sequence is called a gene. To help understand genetic coding compare the DNA code to the alphabet code.

ALPHABET CODE	DNA CODE
letters	nucleotides
words	three nucleotides
sentences	genes
chapters	chromosomes
book	nucleus

Name______________________ Class______________________ Date__________

REVIEW QUESTIONS

1. Genetic information is present in the structure and organization of the ______________.

2. What is the genetic code? ____

____

G. PROTEIN FORMATION. Proteins are made at the cell's ribosomes. Special chemical molecules, known as **messenger RNA (mRNA)**, carry the genetic code information of DNA from the nucleus to the ribosomes in the cytoplasm. The information in the genetic code of DNA is copied into molecules of messenger RNA in a process that is similar to DNA replication. RNA, however, is single-stranded. The base pairing rule for RNA is the same as for DNA except adenine pairs with uracil instead of thymine. The newly formed molecule is now called messenger RNA or mRNA. The mRNA separates from the DNA and passes out of the nucleus through the cytoplasm to the ribosome. Transfer RNA (tRNA) molecules, located in the cytoplasm, carry specific amino acids. Transfer RNA reads the message for protein formation carried by mRNA. tRNA then transfers amino acids along mRNA at the ribosome forming protein chains. Peptide bonds form between the amino acids by dehydration synthesis. The proteins then leave the ribosome and travel to wherever they are needed in the body (Figure 25-4).

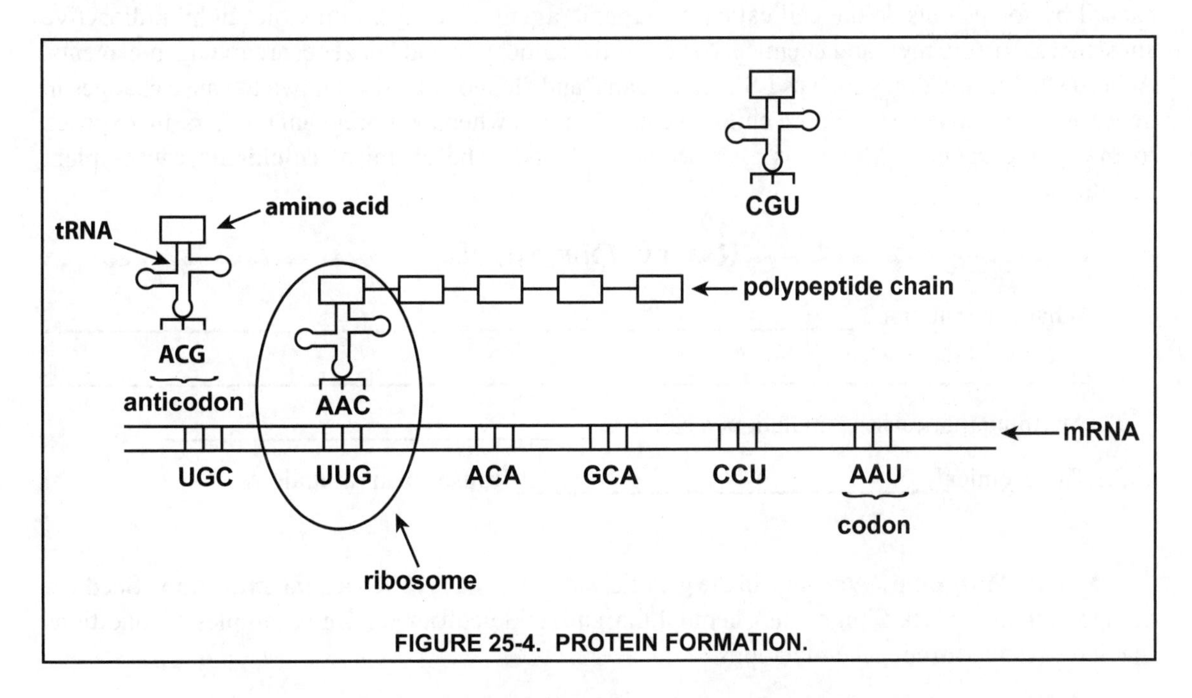

FIGURE 25-4. PROTEIN FORMATION.

At the ribosomes the messenger RNA, because of the specific information it carries, controls the making of certain proteins. Some of these proteins are enzymes. Others include the plasma membrane, chromosomes, and organelles. Enzymes control certain cellular processes and chemical reactions. Because they control certain reactions enzymes control specific traits. It is through this mechanism of enzyme production that genes control genetic traits.

Name_____________________ Class_____________________ Date__________

REVIEW QUESTIONS

1. Proteins are made at the cell's ______________________.
2. What kind of RNA carries amino acids? ______________________.
3. Name three proteins that are made at the cell's ribosomes. ______________________

____

H. MUTATIONS. A **mutation** is any change or mistake in the genes or chromosomes of an organism that can be inherited. These changes usually produce new characteristics. To be inherited the mutation *must occur* in the gamete or sex cell. When they occur in body cells they can be passed on only to other body cells. As a result of fertilization the changed gene or chromosome in the sex cell is passed on to the new organism. Most mutations are harmful because they upset normal cell functions. Fortunately, since mutations are usually recessive, they do not affect the organism as long as the dominant gene is present. A beneficial mutation is one that results in traits that make an organism better adapted to its environment. Mutations and the sorting and recombining of genes during meiosis and fertilization result in a great variety of possible gene combinations.

Mutations occur as random chance events and may happen naturally within the cell or may be caused by forces outside the cell called **mutagenic agents.** X rays, ultraviolet light, radioactive substances, cosmic rays, and chemicals, such as formaldehyde and benzene, are mutagenic agents. Asbestos fibers and drugs such as LSD, marijuana, and alcohol, are also known to cause changes in genes and chromosomes. Unborn children can be injured when their pregnant mothers are exposed to mutagenic agents. Mutations also occur in plants. The chemical **colchicine** causes plant mutations.

REVIEW QUESTIONS

1. What is a mutation? ______________________________

____

2. Anything that causes a mutation is called a ______________________.
3. The chemical ______________________ causes plant mutations.

♦ **Gene Mutations.** A change in the genetic code of DNA is called a **gene mutation**. Seedless oranges, albinism (lack of pigments), hemophilia, and sickle-cell anemia, are examples of conditions that have resulted from gene mutations.

REVIEW QUESTIONS

1. What is a gene mutation? ______________________________

____

2. Name three conditions that have resulted from gene mutations. ______________________

____

♦ **Chromosome Mutations. Chromosome mutations** occur when there is a change in the number or structure of chromosomes. Some chromosome mutations and their causes are listed in Table 25-2.

MUTATION	CAUSE
Crossing-over	Chromatids break, exchange segments, and rejoin during meiosis. Linked genes are separated resulting in variation among offspring.
Nondisjunction	Pairs of homologous chromosomes fail to separate during meiosis. Results in gametes containing 1 chromosome more or less than the monoploid chromosome number.
Down syndrome	Nondisjunction of human chromosome #21. Offspring has an extra chromosome.
Polyploidy	An entire set of chromosomes fails to separate during meiosis. The resulting gamete contains the diploid (2n) chromosome number. Fatal in animal offspring. In plants offspring often larger or more vigorous than normal diploid plants.
Deletions	A chromosome segment is lost.
Translocation	A chromosome breaks off and becomes reattached to a non-homologous chromosome.
Inversion	A chromosome segment breaks off and becomes reattached at a new point on the original chromosome.

TABLE 25-2. CHROMOSOME MUTATIONS

REVIEW QUESTIONS

1. What is a chromosome mutation? ______________________________________

____

____

2. Name three chromosome mutations. ____________________________________

____

3. What causes Down syndrome? ____

____

I. HUMAN INHERITANCE. Human inheritance follows the same genetic principles as inheritance in other organisms. However scientists who study human heredity face many difficulties that are not present when plants and lower animals are studied. Some of the problems faced by scientists who study human genetics are:

Human Genetics Problems

♦ ***Humans cannot be mated and bred as animals can.*** Humans choose their mates according to personal preferences and customs. In addition, there are laws that prevent scientists from performing human genetics experiments. Most information about human inheritance comes from people's memories of their family histories rather than from controlled experiments.

♦ ***Humans produce very few offspring.*** Scientists commonly use garden pea plants and fruit flies for genetic studies because each mating of these organisms results in large numbers of offspring. The production of many offspring over a short period of time results in large amounts of data for use in statistical studies. Because humans reproduce small numbers of offspring, even over a period of several generations, there is very little data for accurate studies.

♦ ***Humans reproduce their generations slowly.*** The average time between human generations is 20 years. This long time lapse slows down information collection and makes observation of family inheritance patterns very difficult.

Most of the information we have about human heredity comes from studies of family trees or pedigree charts. A **pedigree chart** is a diagram that traces the pattern of inheritance through many generations. Figure 25-5 traces the inheritance of sickle-cell anemia in humans through three generations.

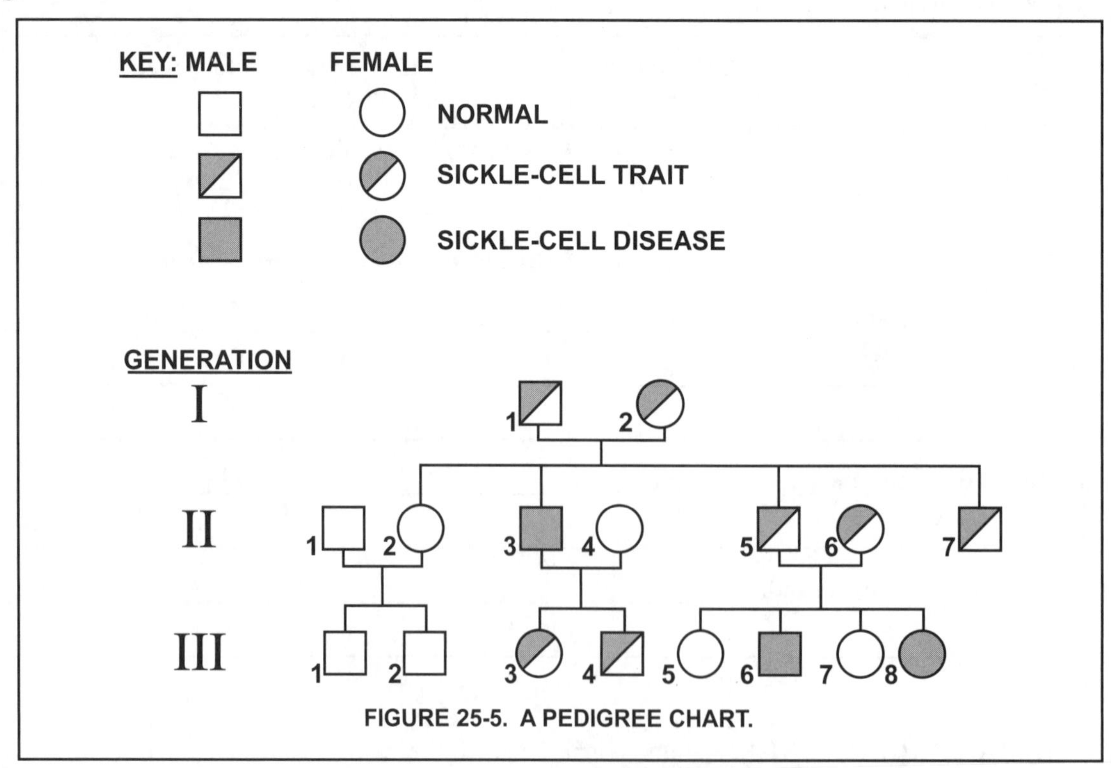

FIGURE 25-5. A PEDIGREE CHART.

Name________________________ Class________________________ Date____________

The use of pedigree charts has greatly increased our knowledge of human genetics. Scientists, called **genetic counselors**, use these charts along with other tests to study family genetic disorders. Today prospective parents can be tested for the presence of a particular gene or trait. With the help of genetic counselors they can be made aware of the chances that certain undesirable traits may appear in their offspring.

Review Questions

1. List three problems that are faced by genetic scientists.

____

____

____

____

2. What is the source of most information about human inheritance? ____________

____

____

3. What is a pedgree chart? ______________________________

____

____

4. Why would a person visit a genetic counselor? ____________________

____

____

____

J. HUMAN GENETIC DISEASES. There are over 150 known inherited genetic diseases in humans. These diseases are caused by gene or chromosome mutations. Most genetic diseases are inherited as recessive genes and involve mistakes in enzyme formation. When there is a mistake in enzyme formation the person's metabolism is flawed.

The presence of many genetic disorders can be detected either before or after birth. In some cases carriers of genetic disorders can also be identified. Screening, karyotyping, and amniocentesis are tests used to detect (identify) genetic diseases. **Screening** involves the chemical analysis of body fluids such as blood and urine. **Karyotyping** is a technique for detecting chromosomal abnormalities. In a karyotype the chromosomes from a body cell are made visible in greatly enlarged photographs and homologous pairs are matched. During **amniocentesis** a small amount of amniotic fluid is removed from around the fetus. This fluid contains some cells from the developing fetus that can be analyzed for genetic disorders either chemically or by karyotyping. Phenylketonuria, sickle-cell anemia, cystic fibrosis, and Tay-Sacs disease are examples of human genetic diseases (Table 25-3).

GENETIC DISEASE	CAUSE	DESCRIPTION	DETECTION & TREATMENT
Phenylketonuria (PKU)	Absence of an ezyme needed to metabolize an amino acid.	Mental retardation.	Detected by urine analysis of newborn infants; mental retardation can be avoided by treatment with a special diet.
Sickle-Cell Anemia	Formation of abnormal hemoglobin, which makes the red blood cells fragile and gives them a **sickle** (quarter-moon) shape.	Cells with the sickle shape tend to block small blood vessels, causing much pain. The abnormal hemoglobin cannot carry enough oxygen for the body cells. It is found most frequently among people of African descent.	Detected by blood screening. Individuals who are carriers (heterozygous) have *some* sickle-shaped cells, homozygous people have *severe* sickle-cell anemia. Analysis of the amniotic fluid can detect the condition in a fetus.
Tay-Sachs Disease	Accumulation of fatty material due to an inability to synthesize a specific enzyme.	Fatal disease characterized by an erosion of nervous tissue. Occurs most frequently among Jewish people of central European descent.	Carriers of Tay-Sacs can be detected by blood screening. Chemical analysis of amniotic fluid can detect the condition in a fetus.
Cystic Fibrosis	Nonsecretion of digestive enzymes.	Life expectancy 12-16 years (some live longer). Exists in different degrees of severity. Thick mucus interferes with lung clearance. Common in persons of northern European extraction.	Detected by examination of amniotic fluid. Symptoms are treated with digestive enzyme replacement and control of respiratory infections.

TABLE 25-3. HUMAN GENETIC DISEASES.

REVIEW QUESTIONS

1. Name three human genetic diseases. ________________________________

____

K. HEREDITY AND THE ENVIRONMENT. Most of an organism's characteristics come from the organism's genes. The development of an organism is usually controlled by its genetic makeup but sometimes the genetic makeup is also influenced by the environment. For example, in plants genes control the production of chlorophyll but light must be present for the plant to produce chlorophyll. In this way the environment (light) influenced how the genes were expressed.

Another example of the effect of environment on gene expression is shown in fur color in Himalayan rabbits. In Himalayan rabbits fur color is affected by temperature. The gene for black fur is active at low temperatures. However, when white fur on the rabbit's back is shaved and the area is covered with an ice pack the fur grows in black. In addition, Himalayan rabbits normally have black fur on the tips of their ears. When the ears are kept warm the fur grows in white (Figure 25-6).

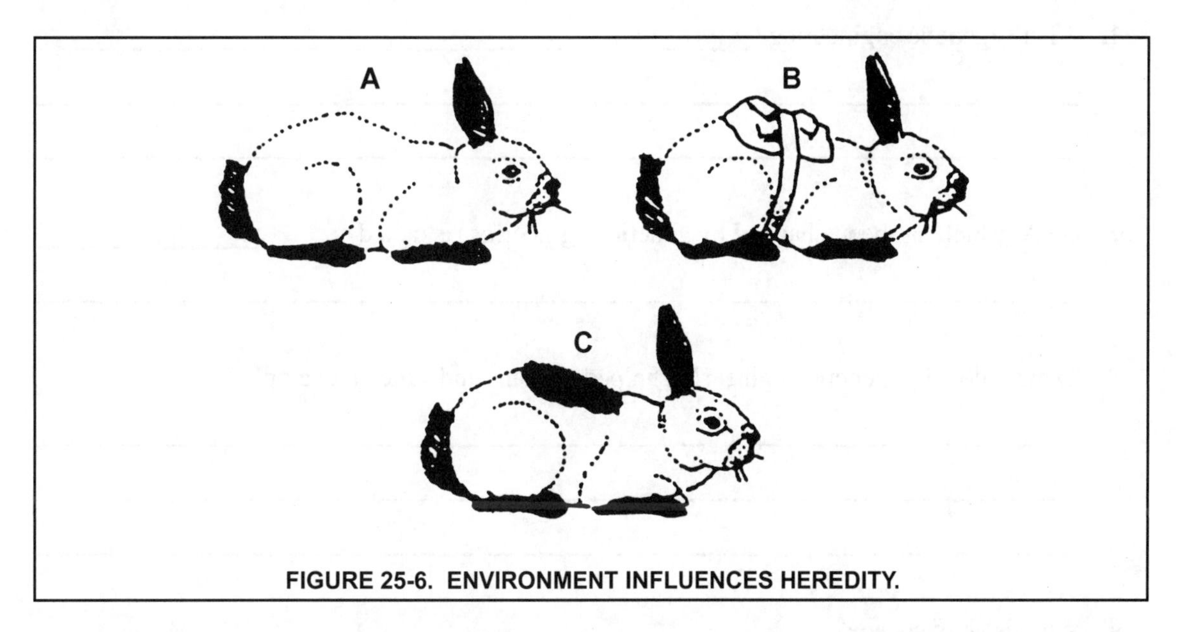

FIGURE 25-6. ENVIRONMENT INFLUENCES HEREDITY.

Studies using human identical twins have been done to learn about the relative effects of environment and heredity. Such studies involved identical twins who were raised together in the same environment and identical twins who were separated at birth. The separated twins did not eat the same kinds and amounts of food. After studying large numbers of twins scientists found that in separated indentical twins, the twin who ate more food was usually larger than the twin who ate less food.

REVIEW QUESTIONS

1. Most characteristics of an organism result from the interaction between the organism's

________________________ and the ________________________.

L. GENETIC ENGINEERING. Today scientists can deliberately remove genes from one organism and add them to the genetic material of another organism. This process, known as **genetic engineering**, alters (changes) the DNA of a cell. The changed DNA is called **recombinant DNA**. The cell that receives the recombinant DNA receives new traits such as the ability to prevent a certain disease. Genetic engineering has greatly increased our ability to treat genetically related disorders. For example, the biochemical insulin has been synthetically manufactured for the treatment of diabetes. Also, cancer scientists have already used genetic engineering techniques to show genetic links to certain types of cancer. By removing small sections of particular genes scientists have been able to pinpoint the location of genes that have the potential to cause cancer. Cancer-causing genes are known as **oncogenes.** With continued research into the use of recombinant DNA scientists hope to cure other conditions caused by genetic defects and to develop plants and animals with desirable traits. Genetic engineering, along with other types of biological research, generates knowledge used to design ways of diagnosing, preventing, treating, controlling, or curing plant and animal diseases. There is, however, concern that genetic engineering may lead to the reproduction of new forms of life potentially dangerous to humans and other organisms.

REVIEW QUESTIONS

1. What is genetic engineering? ____

____

____

2. DNA, which has been changed by genetic engineering, is called ____________________

____.

3. Explain how has genetic engineering helped humans and state an example?

____

____

____

4. What is an oncogene? ____

____

Name________________________ Class________________________ Date__________

LAB INVESTIGATION: CONSTRUCTING DNA MODELS

OBJECTIVE

Upon completion of this activity you should be able to construct a model representing a small DNA segment and identify the basic units of a nucleotide molecule.

LABORATORY PROCEDURE

Materials: DNA molecular model kit and colored pencils.

1. Pick up your laboratory materials at the supply table and carry them to your lab area. Check your DNA molecular model kit to be sure that it contains the following: *16 base pairs, 16 phosphate groups, 16 deoxyribose sugar groups, 8 hydrogen bonds and the student guide that accompanys the kit.* ***(Important: Your student guide or your teacher will explain the color-coding method for your model kit.)***

2. You will use your molecular model kit to make a model (representation) of a small part of a DNA molecule. *Genes*, the basic units of heredity, are composed of a chemical called DNA. *DNA (deoxyribonucleic acid)* is a large complex molecule found in high concentrations in the nucleus of the cell. It is responsible for passing genetic information from generation to generation. The DNA molecule is made up of a long chain of repeating nucleotide units. *Nucleotides* contain nitrogenous bases, a sugar, and a phosphate group.

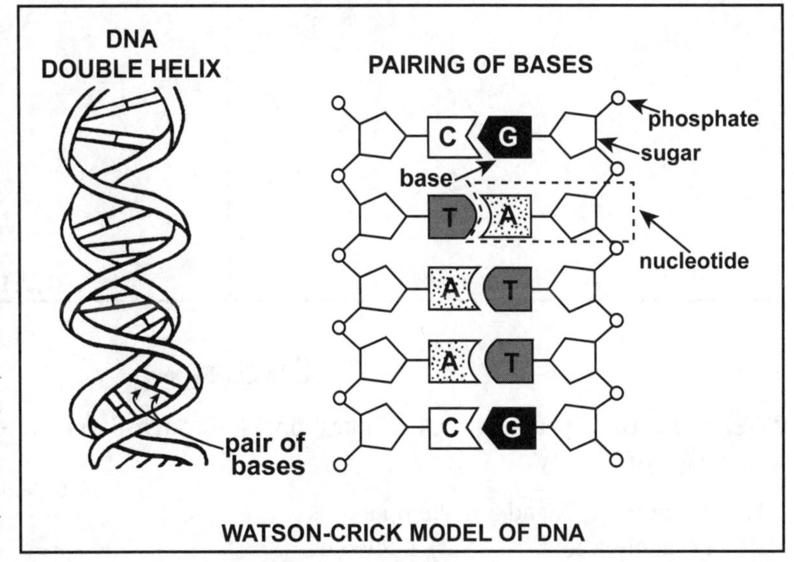

WATSON-CRICK MODEL OF DNA

The four different nitrogenous bases in DNA nucleotides are *adenine, guanine, cytosine,* and *thymine***.** The sugar in DNA is *deoxyribose***,** a 5-carbon sugar. The *phosphate group* contains phosphorus and oxygen.

3. Make a model of a nucleotide by joining a phosphate group, a deoxyribose sugar group and a nitrogen base. Have your teacher check your nucleotide model and then draw your *nucleotide model* in the space provided in **Observation (1)** on the next page. Label the *phosphate group, deoxyribose sugar group,* and *nitrogen base.* Color the parts of your model using the color-coding method for your model kit.

4. The diagram on this page is a model of a typical DNA segment (part). DNA molecules are shaped like a twisted ladder. The twisted ladder structure is called a *double helix*. The DNA double helix has two strands or sides. The strands are connected at the rungs. The sides of the ladder consist of alternating sugar and phosphate molecules. The rungs are pairs of nitrogenous bases named *adenine, thymine, cytosine,* and *guanine.* The nitrogen bases are attached each other by *weak hydrogen bonds*. The four nitrogenous bases in DNA bond (join) together in a certain way known as *base-pairing*. According to the ***DNA base-pairing rule:*** adenine ***(A)*** and thymine ***(T)*** bond together and guanine ***(G)*** and cytosine ***(C)*** bond together. No other combinations are possible. Wherever there is a **C** on one strand, it is bonded to a **G** on the other strand. Wherever there is an **A** on one strand, there is a **T** on the other strand.

5. Make a model of the DNA segment shown on the preceding page. Have your teacher check your DNA model, then draw your model in the space provided in **Observation (2)** on this page. Color the parts of your model using the color-coding method for your kit.

6. When you are finished with your lab put your model-making materials back in your kit. Clean your lab area and return your materials to the supply table.

Observations

(1) A NUCLEOTIDE.	**(2) A DNA SEGMENT.**

Conclusions

Directions: Base your answers to questions 1 through 3 on the diagram below and on your knowledge of biology.

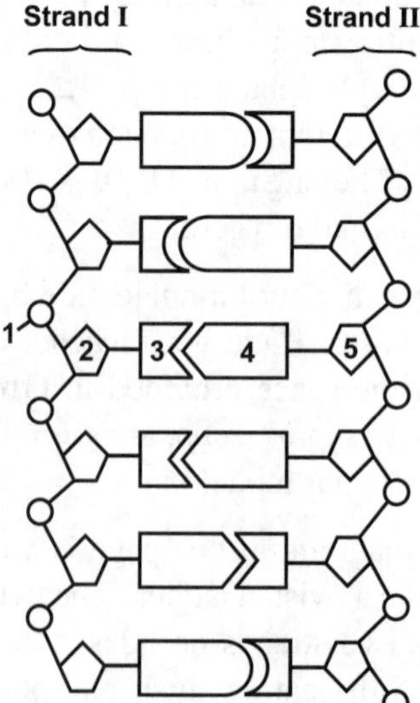

1. Structures 1, 2, and 3 make up a
(1) nucleic acid (3) nucleolus
(2) ribosome (4) nucleotide

2. If strand I represents a segment of a replicating DNA molecule with bases ***A-T-C-C-G-A,*** the complementary DNA strand would contain the bases
(1) ***T-A-G-G-C-T*** (3) ***U-A-G-G-C-U***
(2) ***T-U-G-G-C-T*** (4) ***A-T-G-G-C-T***

3. Structures 3 and 4 are held together by
(1) weak peptide bonds
(2) strong hydrogen bonds
(3) weak hydrogen bonds
(4) strong peptide bonds

Name____________________ Class ____________________ Date __________

REVIEW ACTIVITIES

Important Terms

DIRECTIONS: Define the following terms in the spaces provided.

amniocentesis ____

chromosome mutation ____

colchicine ____

crossing-over ____

cystic fibrosis ____

deoxyribose ____

DNA ____

double helix ____

Down syndrome ____

gene mutation ____

genetic code ____

genetic counselor ____

genetic engineering ____

karyotyping ____

Name______________________ Class______________________ Date__________

messenger RNA ____

____

mutagenic agent ____

____

mutation ____

____

nondisjunction ____

____

pedigree chart ____

____

PKU ____

____

polyploidy ____

____

recombinant DNA ____

____

replicate ____

____

RNA ____

____

sickle-cell anemia ____

____

Tay-Sachs disease ____

____

Name______________________ Class______________________ Date______________

Skill Practice

Part A. Solve the following genetic problems. Underline the correct answer.

1. Which is the correct identification of the parts of the DNA nucleotide in the diagram below?

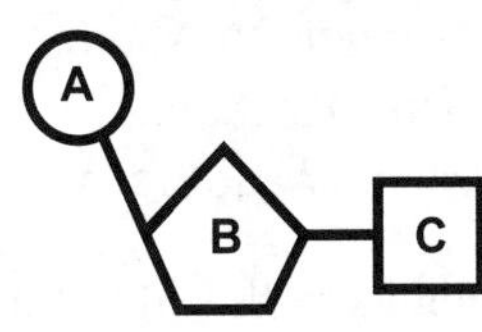

(1) A=uracil, B=deoxyribose, C=thymine
(2) A=phosphate, B=ribose, C=uracil
(3) A=thymine, B=ribose, C=uracil
(4) A=phosphate, B=deoxyribose, C=thymine

Directions (2-5): Base your answers to questions 2 through 5 on the diagram below that represents part of an organic molecule.

2. This diagram represents a molecule of
(1) DNA (3) ATP
(2) RNA (4) FSH

3. In this molecule weak hydrogen bonds connect
(1) x to y (3) G to C
(2) y to G (4) G to T

4. The structures labeled G, C, T, and A represent
(1) phosphate groups (3) ribose sugars
(2) nitrogenous bases (4) deoxyribose sugars

5. In the diagram, the letter **x** represents a group of atoms known as
(1) ribose (3) phosphate
(2) deoxyribose (4) adenine

x y G C T A A T C G C G

6. Which diagram below correctly illustrates the structure of a portion of a DNA molecule? ____

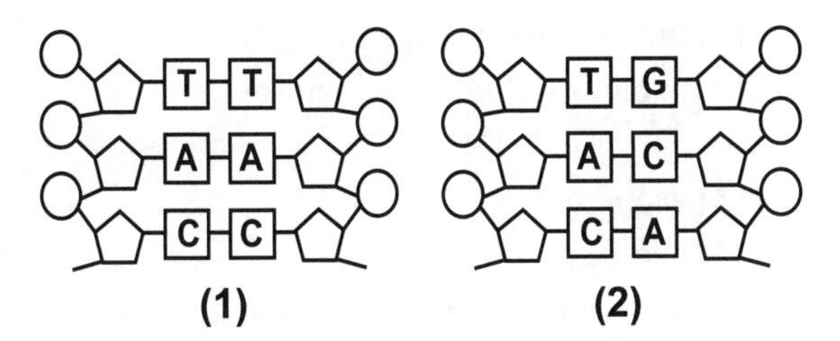

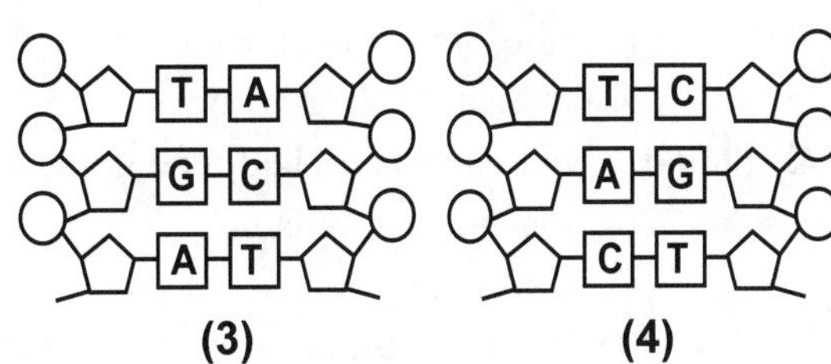

Name________________________ Class________________________ Date____________

Directions (7-10): For *each* phrase in questions 7 through 10 select the type of molecule *chosen from the list below* that most closely matches that phrase. Write its number in the space next to the question.

Molecules

(1) DNA, only
(2) Messenger RNA, only
(3) Transfer RNA, only
(4) Messenger and transfer RNA, only

7. Carries a specific code from the nucleus to the site (place) of protein synthesis. _____

8. Carries amino acids to the site of protein synthesis. _____

9. May contain the nitrogenous base uracil. _____

10. Contains the hereditary information passed on from generation to generation in humans. _____

Directions(11-14): Base your answers to questions 11 through 14 on the diagram below and on your knowledge of biology.

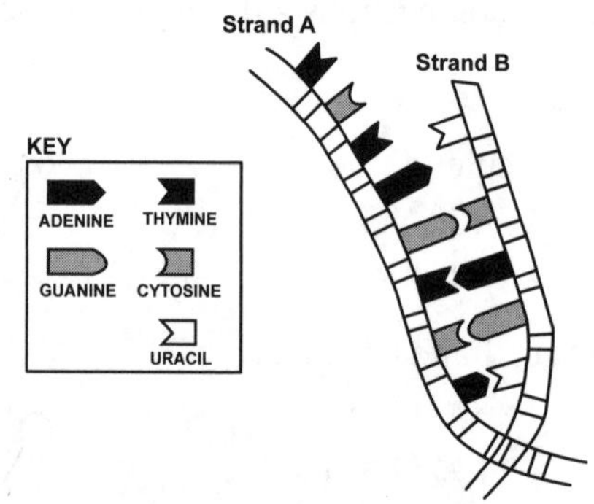

11. If the diagram represents a part of the process of protein synthesis, strand A would
(1) serve as a pattern for the synthesis (making) of messenger RNA
(2) carry a code determined by the original DNA molecule from the nucleus to the cytoplasm
(3) pick up and transfer specific amino acids to the cytoplasm
(4) pick up and transfer nucleic acids to the nucleus

12. If strand A represents a portion of a DNA molecule, its complementary sequence of nitrogenous bases on messenger RNA would normally be
(1) A-G-A-T-C-A-G-T
(2) T-C-T-A-G-T-C-T
(3) A-G-A-U-C-A-G-U
(4) U-G-U-A-G-U-C-U

13. If strand B represents messenger RNA, it would transport the genetic code from the
(1) ribosome to the nucleus
(2) nucleus to the ribosome
(3) mitochondria to the nucleus
(4) nucleus to the mitochondria

14. Strand A would normally be found in the
(1) plasma membrane
(2) ribosome
(3) vacuole
(4) nucleus

15. Which technique is used to alter bacteria in such a way that they produce human insulin?
(1) hydrolysis
(2) DNA replication
(3) recombinant DNA formation
(4) genetic screening

Name____________________ Class____________________ Date__________

CHAPTER 25: QUIZ

A. FILL-IN QUESTIONS

DIRECTIONS: Complete each of the following statements by writing the correct word or phrase in the space provided.

1. Genes are composed of the chemical compound ____________________.
2. During reproduction DNA makes an exact copy of itself by a process called __________.
3. DNA is ____________________-stranded.
4. According to the DNA base pairing rule, guanine and ____________________ bond together.
5. During protein formation, ____________________ carries information from the nucleus to the ribosome.
6. A/an ____________________ is any change or mistake in the genes or chromosomes that is inherited.
7. There are ____________________ kinds of RNA.
8. Adenine is a/an ____________________ found in both DNA and RNA.
9. Uracil is found only in ____________________.
10. ____________________ causes mutations in plants.
11. DNA contains the ____________________ deoxyribose.
12. DNA molecules are shaped like a/an ____________________ or double helix.
13. Most characteristics of an organism result from the interaction between the organism's genes and the ____________________.
14. The genetic information present in the structure and organization of the DNA molecule is known as the ____________________.
15. A process known as ____________________ changes the DNA of a cell.
16. The DNA molecule is made up of a long chain of repeating ____________________ units.
17. A/an ____________________ is a diagram that traces the pattern of inheritance through families.
18. RNA is ____________________-stranded.
19. In amniocentesis a small amount of amniotic fluid is removed from around the __________
20. Watson and Crick discovered the structure of ____________________.

B. MULTIPLE-CHOICE QUESTIONS

DIRECTIONS: Circle the number of the expression that best completes each of the following statements.

1. A complex molecule that is found in the nucleus of a cell and is important for passing on hereditary traits is

(1) DNA	(3) chlorophyll
(2) PTC	(4) starch

Name________________________ Class________________________ Date____________

2. The building blocks of DNA are units known as
   (1) amino acids (3) simple sugars
   (2) nucleotides (4) fatty acids

3. X-rays and colchicine are mutagenic agents because they may alter the structure of
   (1) DNA (3) glycerol
   (2) starch (4) glucose

4. A substance now manufactured by genetic engineering is
   (1) chlorophyll (3) hemoglobin
   (2) pepsin (4) insulin

5. Which of the following is not a genetic disease?
   (1) Tay-Sachs disease (3) malaria
   (2) sickle-cell anemia (4) Down syndrome

6. A possible danger of genetic engineering is the
   (1) treatment of genetic disorders (3) production of insulin
   (2) treatment of cancer (4) production of harmful organisms

7. Genetic information is copied in the process of
   (1) protein digestion (3) aerobic respiration
   (2) starch formation (4) DNA replication

8. Characteristics of an organism result from environmental influences and the organism's
   (1) lymph (3) blood
   (2) bile (4) genes

9. Which of the following is not a technique used in the detection of human genetic disorders?
   (1) karyotyping (3) amniocentesis
   (2) cloning (4) screening

10. A change in DNA information caused by X-rays or chemicals is known as
   (1) a mutation (3) a dominant trait
   (2) fertilization (4) a recessive trait

C. ESSAY QUESTION

DIRECTIONS: Use complete sentences to answer the question in this part.

1. Why would a person visit a genetic counselor? ________________________________

____

____

____

____

____

____

Name________________________ Class ____________________ Date __________

UNIT SIX TEST

Matching Questions

***DIRECTIONS:** In the space at the left of each item in Column A, place the letter of the term or phrase in Column B that is most closely related to that item.*

________ **1.** The physical appearance of an organism.

________ **2.** Discovered the DNA molecule shape.

________ **3.** A change in the genetic code.

________ **4.** A genetic disease.

________ **5.** Called the "father of genetics".

________ **6.** The genetic makeup of an individual.

________ **7.** Two different genes for a trait.

________ **8.** Making a copy of DNA.

________ **9.** A chromosome picture.

________ **10.** Two of the same kind of genes for a trait.

a. Gene Mutation
b. Hybrid
c. Pernicious Anemia
d. Mendel
e. Phenotype
f. Replication
g. Genotype
h. Homozygous
i. Chromosome Mutation
j. Sickle-Cell Anemia
k. Watson & Crick
l. Karyotype

True–False Questions

***DIRECTIONS:** Write TRUE before each statement that is true and FALSE before each statement that is false.*

________ **1.** The test cross is a method used to determine the genetic makeup of an organism.

________ **2.** Hemophilia is a disease in which the red blood cells do not have the correct shape.

________ **3.** Females who have one normal gene and one recessive gene for a sex-linked trait are called pure for that trait.

________ **4.** Crossing-over increases variation among sexually produced organisms.

________ **5.** How much chance there is for something to happen is called probability.

________ **6.** Adenine is a nucleotide that bonds with cytosine.

________ **7.** RNA is double-stranded.

________ **8.** Humans are good choices for genetic studies.

________ **9.** Pregnant mothers should use alcohol every day.

________ **10.** The sugar deoxyribose is found in DNA.

Name________________________________ Class ________________________ Date ______________

Fill-In Questions

***DIRECTIONS:* Complete each of the following statements by writing the correct word or phrase in the space provided.**

1. The hereditary information present in the structure and organization of the DNA molecule is called the ______________________.
2. X-rays and radioactive substances are examples of ______________________ agents.
3. ______________________ are chromosomes that do not carry information about an organism's sex.
4. The trait that always appears when it is present is called the ______________________ trait.
5. When pure tall pea plants are crossed with pure ______________________ pea plants the offspring are hybrid tall.
6. The characteristics of an organism are called ______________________.
7. A change in the genetic code of DNA is called a/an ______________________ mutation.
8. Genetic engineering changes the ______________________ of a cell.
9. There are ______________________ major human blood types.
10. Most characteristics of an organism result from the interaction between the organism's genes and the ______________________.

Multiple-Choice Questions

***DIRECTIONS:* Circle the number of the expression that best completes each of the following statements.**

1. In which molecule are human hereditary traits coded?
   (1) DNA
   (2) PTC
   (3) fat
   (4) chlorophyll
2. If one parent is a hybrid tongue roller (Tt) and the other parent is pure dominant (TT) for this trait, what is the possibility of their having a child who is a non-tongue roller (tt)?
   (1) 0%
   (2) 25%
   (3) 50%
   (4) 75%
3. Color blindness is a sex-linked disorder that is more common in males than in females. The defective gene that produces this trait is carried on
   (1) the X chromosome, only
   (2) either the X or Y chromosome
   (3) the Y chromosome, only
   (4) neither the X nor Y chromosome
4. In garden peas tall is dominant and short is recessive. If pure tall pea plants are crossed with pure short pea plants the offspring will be
   (1) 100% short
   (2) 50% tall, 50% short
   (3) 100% tall
   (4) 75% tall, 25% short
5. Exposure to radiation may cause damage to future generations because radiation
   (1) alters DNA molecules
   (2) decreases the mutation rate
   (3) increases the rate of venereal disease
   (4) damages cell walls

Name__________ Class__________ Date__________

6. The portion of a DNA molecule that controls a genetic trait is the

(1) chromosome
(2) gene
(3) nucleus
(4) nucleolus

7. In humans, if the gene for a trait is located on the Y chromosome, then the trait will

(1) be passed on only by females
(2) appear only in females
(3) appear only in males
(4) not be passed on by males

8. A disease that can be inherited by humans is

(1) food poisoning
(2) tetanus
(3) scurvy
(4) hemophilia

9. The information in a DNA molecule is determined by the arrangement of

(1) starches
(2) fatty acids
(3) amino acids
(4) nucleotides

10. After the birth of four male children, what is the probability that a fifth child will be female?

(1) 25%
(2) 50%
(3) 75%
(4) 100%

Essay Question

DIRECTIONS: Use complete sentences to answer the question in this part.

1. State one reason why pregnant women should not be exposed to mutagenic agents.

Class Notes

Name________________________ Class____________________ Date__________

UNIT SEVEN

EVOLUTION OF LIVING THINGS

LEARNING OUTCOMES: Upon completion of the study of this unit, you should be able to:

- Define organic evolution.
- Recognize the problems involved in determining the age of the earth and its fossils.
- Recognize the problems involved in formulating theories for the origin of life.
- Identify observations that support evolution.
- Contrast the theories of evolution of Charles Darwin and Jean Lamarck.
- Explain modern theories of evolution that have grown out of new research.
- Recoginze the scientific theories that humans may have evolved from ancestral organisms.

Chapter 26: Evidence for Organic Evolution

A. WHAT IS EVOLUTION? Scientists are like detectives because they search and search for information to solve science problems. They then propose (suggest) theories based on their observations. Scientists observed that the earth and its organisms have gradually changed over a long period of time. The process of gradual (slow) change through time is called **evolution**. **Geologic evolution** is the study of the changes that have occurred to the earth itself. The study of the changes in living things is called **organic evolution**. Included in organic evolution are the changes in characteristics in populations through generations. The theory of evolution helps to explain the differences in structure, function, and behavior among living things. In this unit you will investigate such problems as:

Evolution Problems

- **How life began on earth.**
- **How complex organisms developed from simpler forms of life.**
- **How organisms may have changed over long periods of time.**

Name__________ Class__________ Date__________

There are other commonly accepted solutions to evolution problems that will be discussed in this unit. The theory of evolution presented in this book is currently accepted by *most* scientists. Studies supporting the current theory of organic evolution include evidences of fossil records and similarities in the skeletons, embryos, cell structures and functions, and chemical makeup of organisms. The presence of vestigial structures is also evidence that living things have changed over time. You will study these theories and evidences in this unit. ***Remember that theories change as new evidence is discovered.***

REVIEW QUESTIONS

1. What is the meaning of the term "evolution"? __________

____

____

2. State the difference between geologic evolution and organic evolution. __________

____

____

____

B. GEOLOGIC TIME. Most people are used to thinking of time in terms of years. You probably think that 50 years is a long time and 100 years is forever! To understand evolution you have to think in very large numbers—in millions and billions of years! For example, scientists estimate the earth to be more than 4.5 billion years old. The oldest living thing, a bacteria-like organism, is estimated to be 3.4 billion years old.

To make the study of evolution easier scientists developed a time chart that divides the large numbers of years into smaller time units called **eras.** The major eras are the Cenozoic, Mesozoic, Paleozoic, and Precambrian (Figure 26-1). The Cenozoic era is the youngest era and the Precambrian is the oldest era.

Eras are further divided into units called **periods** and periods are divided into **epochs.** These time divisions are approximate and are based on noticeable differences in the earth's rock layers. These differences were thought to be caused by major climate changes. Proof of such a climate change was discovered in Pennsylvania where remains of tropical plants were found in coal deposits. This evidence proves that the climate of Pennsylvania was once very hot. Today Pennsylvania's climate is temperate with cold winters and warm summers. Tropical plants do not grow successfully in a temperate climate. Because of this, tropical plants are no longer common in Pennsylvania.

Each time period is identified by its dominant (common) animal and plant life. The **Cenozoic era,** the most recent era, began approximately 60 million years ago. It is called the "Age of Mammals" because it was during this era that mammals became the dominant form of animal life. Flowering plants were the dominant form of plant life. Man appeared late in the Cenozoic era.

The **Mesozoic era**, which began over 200 million years ago, is known as the "Age of Reptiles". During the Mesozoic era reptiles, such as dinosaurs, were the dominant animal life. The first birds were thought to appear during the Mesozoic era when fern forests were the dominant plants.

Name______________________ Class______________________ Date______________

The **Paleozoic era** was the longest era. It lasted over 400 million years and is divided into the "Age of Amphibians", the "Age of Fishes" and the "Age of Invertebrates". The first land plants developed during this time and fern trees were widespread along with swampy forests. Modern insects also appeared at this time and amphibians, giant insects, trilobites, crustaceans, and fishes were common.

The oldest time period, over 4.6 billion years ago, is called the **Precambrian era**. During this time simple multicellular organisms, such as sponges and worms, were numerous. The first protists (one-celled organisms) appeared during this time and probably bacteria and algae were dominant.

COMMON ORGANISMS				
TIME	60 Million Years Ago	200 Million Years Ago	600 Million Years Ago	4.6 (?) Billion Years Ago
ERA	CENOZOIC (Age of Mammals)	MESOZOIC (Age of Reptiles)	PALEOZOIC (Age of Amphibians, Fishes, and Invertebrates)	PRECAMBRIAN (Simple Multicellular Organisms and First Protists)

PRESENT → PAST

FIGURE 26-1. GEOLOGIC TIME.

REVIEW QUESTIONS

1. Name the four major eras into which geologic time is divided. ______________________

____

2. Which era is the most recent era? ______________________.

3. Which era is the oldest era? ______________________.

4. During which era did man first appear? ______________________.

Name________________________________ Class ____________________________ Date __________

C. FOSSIL EVIDENCE. Fossils are the remains or traces of organisms that once lived. Scientists who study fossils are called **paleontologists.** The study of fossils in the earth provides evidence to support the idea that life changed over time from simple to complex. Fossil distribution shows that life began in the sea and then moved to land. It also provides evidence for the time of origin (beginning) of various forms of life. Fossils also help scientists understand how climates and land surfaces have changed. It is through fossil evidence that we know that organisms existed over three billion years ago. Using the process of **radioactive dating** scientists can determine the age of Earth's rocks and its fossils.

Many fossils are found in sedimentary rock. In sedimentary rock, where the crust of the earth is undisturbed, the oldest rock layers are located beneath the younger layers. **Sedimentary rock** is formed from layers of slowly deposited sediments. Sediments, such as rock particles, silt, and mud, are usually deposited by water. After a long period of time and a great amount of heat and pressure, sediments harden into rock forming visible layers. In undisturbed layers the oldest layer is at the bottom layer and the youngest layer is at the top. Skeletons, imprints, shells, bones and other animal and plant remains became trapped in the sediment layers. When the sediment hardened, the remains of plants and animals became fossils. Fossils found in lower rock layers are assumed to be older than fossils found in upper layers. Generally, fossils found in upper layers look like those in the lower layers but are more complex in form. This suggests a relationship between modern forms and older forms (Figure 26-2).

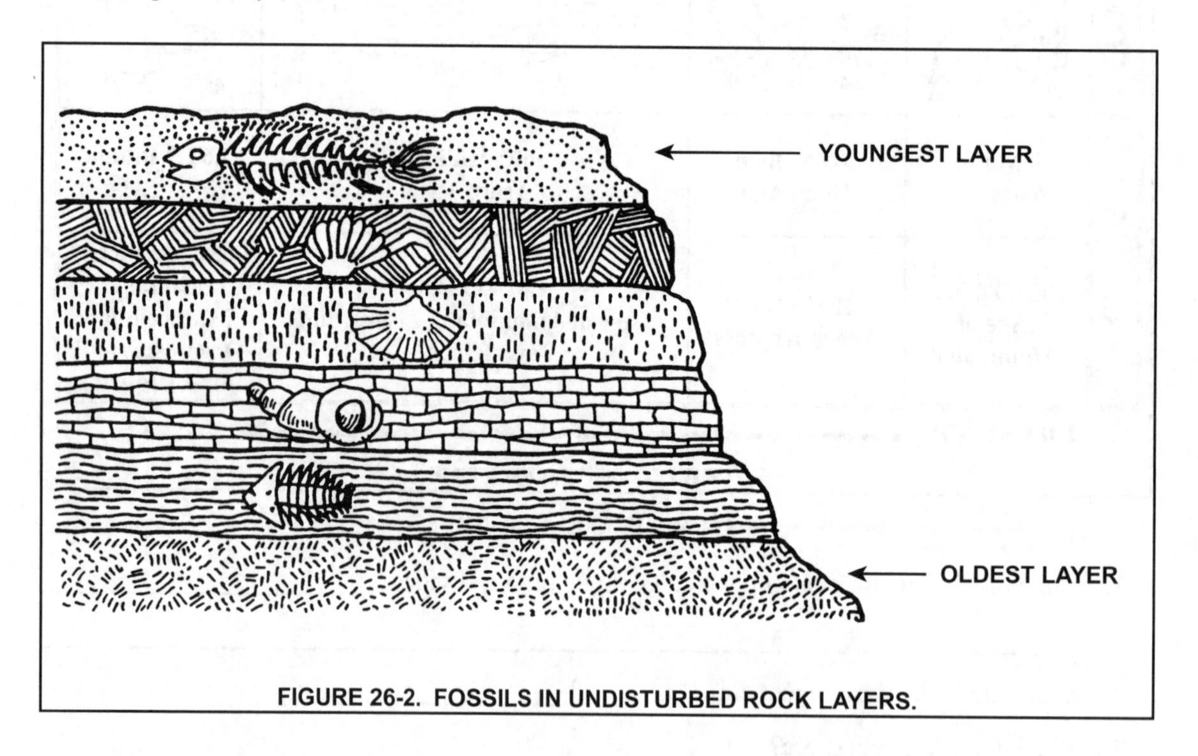

FIGURE 26-2. FOSSILS IN UNDISTURBED ROCK LAYERS.

Organisms can become fossils **(fossilization)** in a number of different ways. Whole organisms have been discovered preserved in tar, ice, and in **amber,** which is a yellowish-brown sap secreted by pine trees. By this method the entire body of an organism is preserved after death. Ancient insects have been found perfectly preserved in amber.

The soft parts of organisms usually decay but the hard parts, such as bones and teeth, may form molds or casts. A **mold** is an indentation in rock shaped like an organism. A **cast** is formed when the decayed organism forms a mold, and the mold becomes filled with a different substance.

Name________________ Class________________ Date__________

Organisms may also be preserved by petrification. During **petrification (or petrifaction)** the tissues of the organism are slowly replaced by minerals that preserve the original form of the organism. **Imprints**, such as dinosaur footprints, occur when a print is made in a soft sediment such as mud. The mud later turns into rock. Imprints of ancient ferns have been found in coal.

REVIEW QUESTIONS

1. What is a fossil? ____________________

____

2. Describe the formation of sedimentary rock. ____________________

____

____

____

3. In undisturbed layers of rock the oldest rock is found at the ____________________.

4. Name three ways that fossils are formed. ____________________

____

D. SKELETAL EVIDENCE. Comparative anatomy is the science that studies the structures (anatomy) of plants and animals. When scientists compare skeletal structures of different vertebrates they see a similar basic structure. This observation shows that organisms with similar bone structures may have evolved from a common ancestor population. Organs or structural parts that seem to have a common evolutionary origin are referred to as **homologous structures.** For example, the wing of a bat, the flipper of a whale, and a human arm are homologous structures (Figure 26-3). Although homologous structures are similar in structure they *do not always* have the same function.

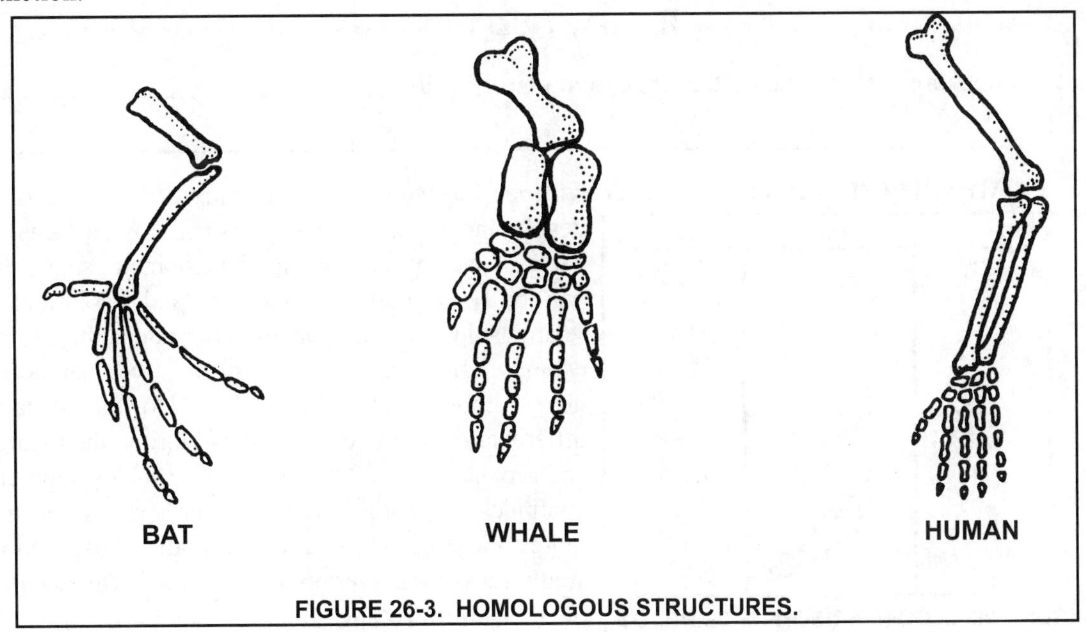

FIGURE 26-3. HOMOLOGOUS STRUCTURES.

Name________________________ Class____________________ Date__________

REVIEW QUESTIONS

1. What is comparative anatomy. ____

____

2. Organs or structural parts that appear to have a common evolutionary origin are called ____________________ structures. These structures are similar in ____________________ but are not always similar in ____________________

E. VESTIGIAL STRUCTURES. Vestigial structures are parts of an animal's body that are not used. These structures look like structures that are fully developed and used by other animals. The human appendix is an example of a vestigial structure. Scientists think that perhaps some human ancestors used their appendix and, as evolution continued, humans stopped using this organ. Other vestigial structures are human ear muscles and the leg bones of the python and porpoise. These structures provide further evidence of changing structure and function.

REVIEW QUESTIONS

1. List three vestigial structures. ____

____

2. Vestigial structures are defined as ____

____

F. COMPARING CELL STRUCTURE. Cells and cell organelles are basically alike from one group of organisms to another. For example, all cells have a nucleus, cell membrane, cytoplasm, ribosomes, mitochondria, chromosomes, and various other organelles. In terms of evolution, this is evidence that different kinds of living things *may* share a common origin.

REVIEW QUESTIONS

1. Name three cell organelles that are common to all cells. ____________________________

____

G. COMPARING EMBRYOS. Another evidence for evolution is the study of the embryonic development of different organisms. Comparisons of early stages of embryonic development show the possibility of common ancestry and evolutionary relationships. At early stages vertebrate embryos, for example, show gill slits, tails, and two-chambered hearts. Look closely at Figure 26-4. Do you see many differences among the embryos during their early embryo stages? Observe that as development continues the distinct traits of each species become more noticeable. The science that studies the structural similarities among vertebrate embryos is called **comparative embryology.**

CHICKEN | FISH | HUMAN

FIGURE 26-4. COMPARISON OF EMBRYOS

Name________________________ Class________________________ Date____________

REVIEW QUESTIONS

1. The developing organism is called an ______________________.
2. Name three vertebrate structures that are similar during early embryonic development.

____

____

H. SIMILARITIES IN BIOCHEMISTRY. Similarities in the **biochemistry** (body chemicals) of living things, such as DNA, hormones, and enzymes, show a close relationship among various forms of life. Organisms that are closely related, like the cat and the lion, have a greater similarity in their protein structure. Greater differences in cell biochemistry are thought to indicate a lesser evolutionary relationship.

Gel Electrophoresis is a complex laboratory technique that is used to analyze DNA, RNA, and proteins. A common use for this technique is DNA analysis. Complex mixtures of DNA are separated into different sized fragments by isolating the DNA to be tested and then treating it with enzymes called *restriction enzymes*. This produces small pieces that can be separated by electrophoresis. The DNA fragments are then placed in structures called *wells* at one end of a gelatinous material. In the electrophoresis chamber an electric current is applied to the gel creating an electric field inside the gel. Negatively charged DNA fragments move toward the positive pole of the chamber. Smaller fragments move faster and farther than larger ones causing separation by molecular fragment size forming a series of *bands* from one end of the gel to the other. These bands can be identified as specific fragments of DNA. Each individual has a unique banding pattern that can be used for identification purposes. Scientists also use this process to determine relationships among different organisms. They believe that organisms with similar banding patterns are more closely related than those with different banding patterns.

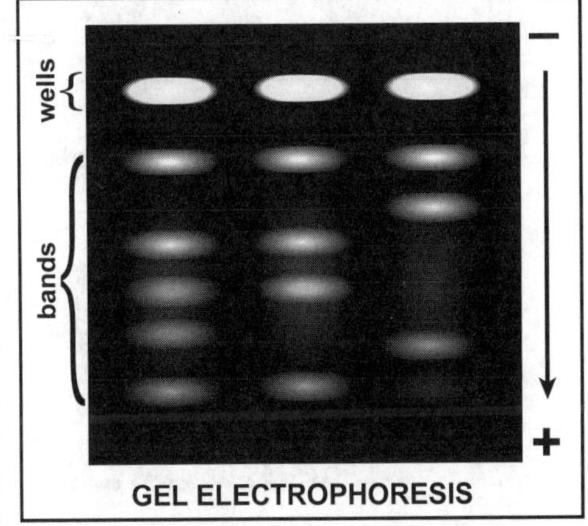

GEL ELECTROPHORESIS

REVIEW QUESTIONS

1. Organisms that are ______________ related have a greater similarity in their protein structure.
2. Name two body chemicals that are similar in living things. ______________________

____

I. EXAMPLES OF EVOLUTION. Scientists have discovered several complete series of fossil records that show gradual changes in animals through the ages. Two of the best examples of vertebrate evolution are those of the horse and the elephant (Figure 26-5).

The ancient ancestor of the horse, *Eohippus,* was about the size of a fox. It had four toes on its front feet and three toes on its hind feet. The horse gradually got bigger and the length of its feet increased. As time passed some of the toes disappeared until today the modern horse, *Equus,* is one-toed. The middle toe is the one that remains but the horse retains tiny splints of two other toes. The skull grew longer and the teeth became flat-topped.

The ancestor of the present elephant was the size of a pig and had no tusks. Over time the size of the elephant's body and head increased tremendously. The two upper incisor teeth increased in size and length and gradually developed into tusks. The early trunk was much shorter than the trunk of today's elephant.

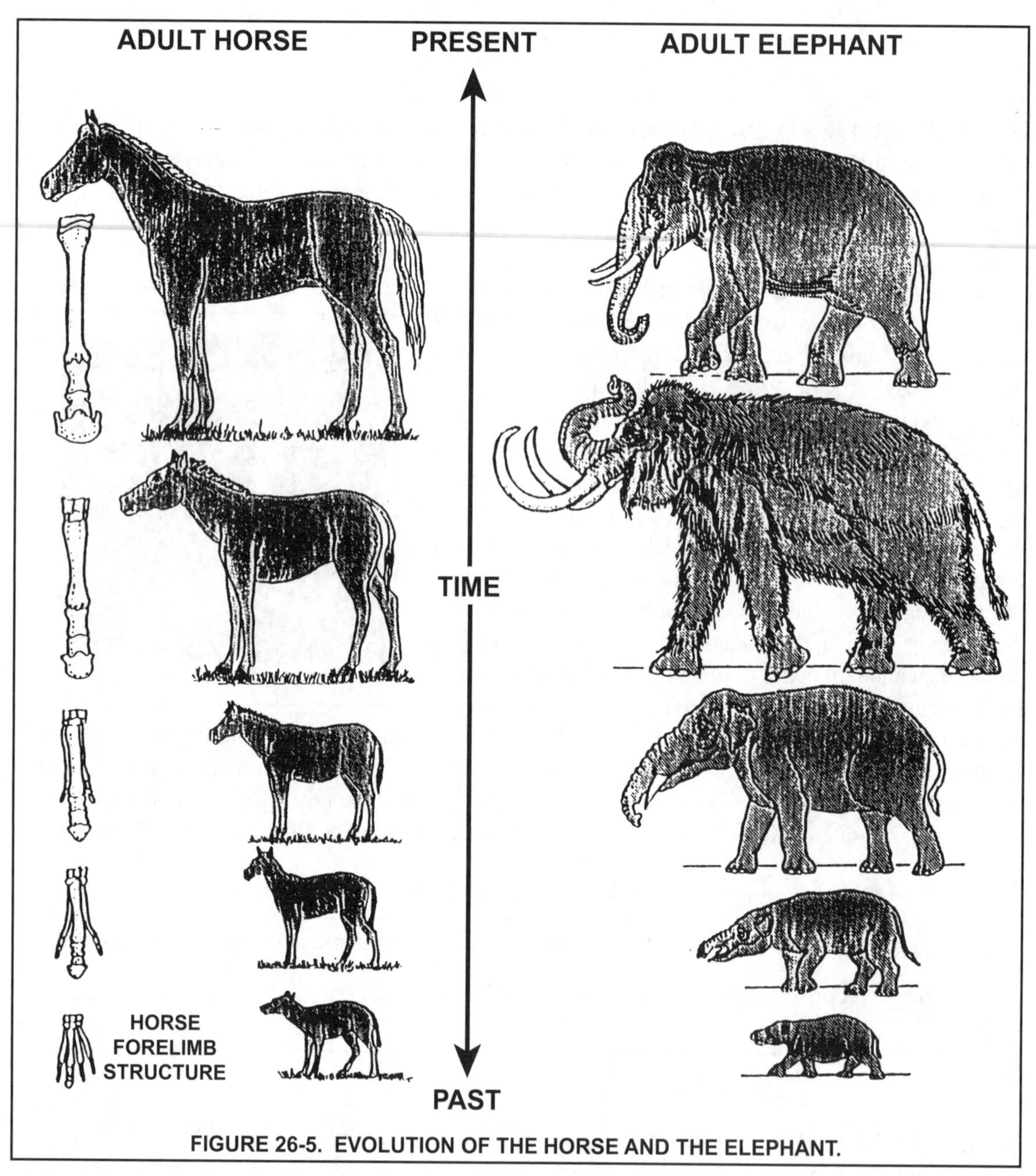

FIGURE 26-5. EVOLUTION OF THE HORSE AND THE ELEPHANT.

REVIEW QUESTIONS

1. Fossils of the ______________________ and the ______________________ show that animals have gradually changed through time.

Name________________________ Class____________________ Date__________

LAB INVESTIGATION: TYPES OF FOSSILIZATION

Objective

Upon completion of this activity you should be able to recognize several different types of fossils and name the method by which they were fossilized.

Laboratory Procedure

Materials: A variety of fossil types representing different methods of fossilization, pencil, and fossil reference books and charts.

1. Your teacher has placed a variety of fossil specimens at various locations (stations) around the room. Each specimen is labeled with a number. ***Note:*** *Fossils* are the remains or traces of organisms that once lived. *Fossilization* is the changing of organisms into fossils. Organisms can become fossils in a number of different ways such as preservation in *amber*, *molds, casts,* and by *petrification.*

2. Choose any specimen and use the reference books and charts along with your knowledge of biology to complete the observation chart below.

3. Repeat **Procedure 2** until you have identified 10 specimens.

4. When you have completed your observations answer the questions in the conclusion section.

Observations

SPECIMEN NUMBER	NAME OF FOSSIL ORGANISM	TYPE OF FOSSILIZATION	DESCRIPTION OF FOSSILIZATION METHOD

Name________________________ Class________________________ Date____________

Observations (Continued)

SPECIMEN NUMBER	NAME OF FOSSIL ORGANISM	TYPE OF FOSSILIZATION	DESCRIPTION OF FOSSILIZATION METHOD

Conclusions

1. Define the term *fossil.* ____

____

2. What occurs during fossilization? ____

____

3. Name and describe 5 methods by which organisms become fossils. ____________________

____

____

____

____

____

Name____________________ Class____________________ Date__________

REVIEW ACTIVITIES

Important Terms

***DIRECTIONS:* Define the following terms in the spaces provided.**

amber ____

cast ____

comparative anatomy ____

comparative embryology ____

Eohippus ____

epoch ____

Equus ____

era ____

evolution ____

fossil ____

geologic evolution ____

homologous structures ____

imprints ____

mold ____

Name________________________ Class________________________ Date__________

organic evolution ____
____

paleontologist ____
____

period ____
____

petrifaction ____
____

radioactive dating ____
____

sedimentary rock ____
____

vestigial structures ____
____

Name________________________ Class________________________ Date____________

Skill Practice

Part A. Complete the following chart.

ERA	YEARS AGO	IMPORTANT EVENTS
Cenozoic		
Mesozoic		
Paleozoic		
Precambrian		

Part B. Answer the following reasoning questions.

1. A geologist finds fossils in each of the undisturbed rock layers represented in the diagram below. The fossils are all structurally similar. Which is the most likely conclusion that the geologist would make.

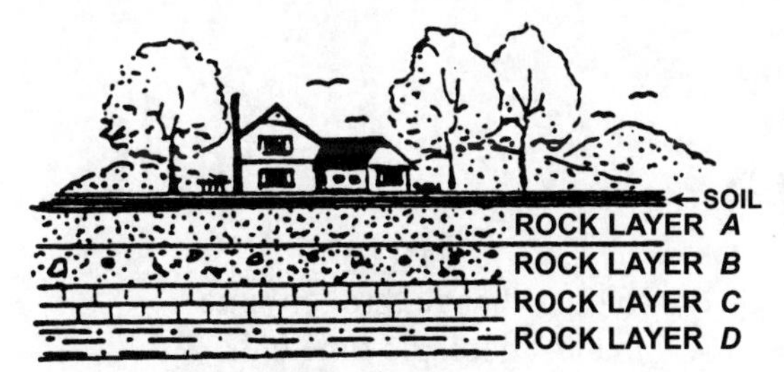

(1) All the fossils are of the same age.

(2) The relative ages of the fossils cannot be determined.

(3) The fossils in rock layer D are older than those in layer A.

(4) The fossils in rock layer B are older than those in layer C.

2. From the information given in the chart below, which two organisms are most closely related?

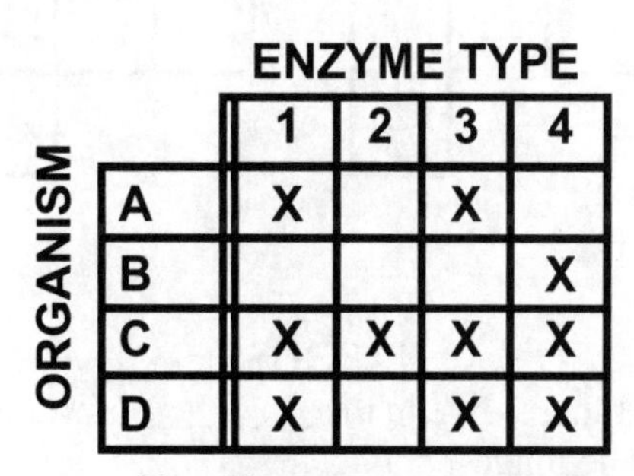

ORGANISM	ENZYME TYPE 1	2	3	4
A	X		X	
B				X
C	X	X	X	X
D	X		X	X

X = Enzyme present in organism

(1) A and B (3) C and D

(2) B and C (4) D and B

Name________________________ Class________________________ Date__________

Part C. Complete the following crossword puzzle.

Crossword Puzzle

Clues

ACROSS

1. Humans live in the _______ of Mammals
6. The longest era
7. The age of rocks is determined by _______ active dating
10. The oldest rock _______ is at the bottom
11. Fossils are found in this kind of rock
15. Structure that shows common ancestry
16. Type of evolution that studies changes in living things
18. Structure not present in early elephants

DOWN

2. Gradual change through time
3. Smallest geologic time unit
4. Remain or trace of an organism
5. Largest geologic time unit
8. Animal example of evolution
9. Structure no longer used
12. Humans no longer use these muscles
13. Yellowish-brown sap
14. Fossil indentation in rock.
17. Type of fossil

Name________________________ Class________________________ Date____________

CHAPTER 26: QUIZ

A. FILL-IN QUESTIONS

DIRECTIONS: Complete each of the following statements by writing the correct word or phrase in the space provided.

1. Fossils are found mostly in rocks known as ________________________ rocks.

2. Man appeared during the ____________________________ era.

3. An example of a vestigial organ in man is ______________________________.

4. In petrifaction, the tissues of organisms are slowly replaced by ________________________.

5. By the process of _________________________ scientists determine the age of the earth's rocks and its fossils.

6. Organs or structural parts that seem to have a common evolutionary origin are called ________________________ structures.

7. ________________________ is the process of gradual change through time.

8. An indentation in rock that is shaped like an organism is called a/an ____________________.

9. Geologic time is divided in to four smaller units called _________________________.

10. An imprint of a prehistoric living thing is called a/an ______________________________.

11. Comparisons of early stages of embryonic development show the possibility of ________________________ ancestry.

12. A structure useless in man, but similar to one useful in lower animals, is called a/an ________________________.

13. ________________________ evolution is the study of the changes in living things.

14. A yellowish-brown sap secreted by pine trees is called _________________________.

15. Paleontologists study _________________________.

16. The earliest known ancestor of the modern horse is named ________________________.

17. Gill slits are common in vertebrate ____________________________.

18. The study of the changes that have occurred to the earth itself is called __________________ evolution.

19. In undisturbed rock layers, the __________________________ is at the bottom.

20. The oldest time period was the __________________________ era.

B. MULTIPLE-CHOICE QUESTIONS

DIRECTIONS: Circle the number of the expression that best completes each of the following statements.

1. Which is a vestigial structure found in humans?

(1) toe
(2) tooth
(3) fingernail
(4) appendix

2. Evidence that suggests that the dog and cat had a common evolutionary origin is a comparison of their

(1) sizes
(2) colors
(3) diets
(4) skeletons

Name________________________ Class________________________ Date____________

3. Two animals would probably show a close evolutionary relationship if they
   (1) have a similar embryonic development
   (2) live in the same habitat
   (3) eat the same food
   (4) show the same behavior

Directions (4-6): For *each* statement in questions 4 through 6 select the term, *chosen from the list below,* that is most closely related to that statement. Then record its *number* on the line provided.

Evolutionary Terms

(1) Fossil evidence
(2) Evidence from embryology
(3) Evidence from anatomy
(4) Vestigial organs

4. The wing of a bat is similar to the flipper of a whale. _______
5. Early stages of the development of fish and amphibians show some similarities. _______
6. Insects have been found in amber. _______
7. According to the theory of evolution, with the passage of time organisms have
   (1) not changed
   (2) changed
   (3) changed for the better, only
   (4) changed for the worse, only

8. In undisturbed rock layers, the oldest rocks are located
   (1) in the top layer
   (2) in the middle layer
   (3) in the bottom layer
   (4) between the top and bottom layers

9. Digestive enzymes are similar in mammals. This evidence, which supports evolution, resulted from comparing
   (1) types of skeletons
   (2) types of cells
   (3) development of embryos
   (4) chemicals in living things

10. A structure that an animal or plant no longer used is known as a
   (1) mutation
   (2) fossil
   (3) vestigial structure
   (4) petrified structure

C. ESSAY QUESTION

DIRECTIONS: Use complete sentences to answer the question in this part.

1. How would you account for the fact that fossils of fish are not present in the older layers of rock?

____

____

____

____

____

____

____

Name________________________ Class ____________________ Date __________

Chapter 27 Theories on Origin and Change

A. CHANGE OVER TIME. Most scientists agree that organisms have changed, from simple to complex, over a long period of time. However, scientists do not know how life first began nor how evolutionary changes occurred. In an attempt to explain these events scientists have proposed various theories. Some theories have been totally rejected because of lack of supporting evidence. Other theories have been modified (changed) based on new evidence. In this chapter you will study, in historical order, some of the most important theories concerning the **origin** (beginning) of living things and how they *may* have evolved. The evolutionary tree in Figure 27-1 represents the theory that living things *may* have had a common origin and then evolved into more complex forms of life.

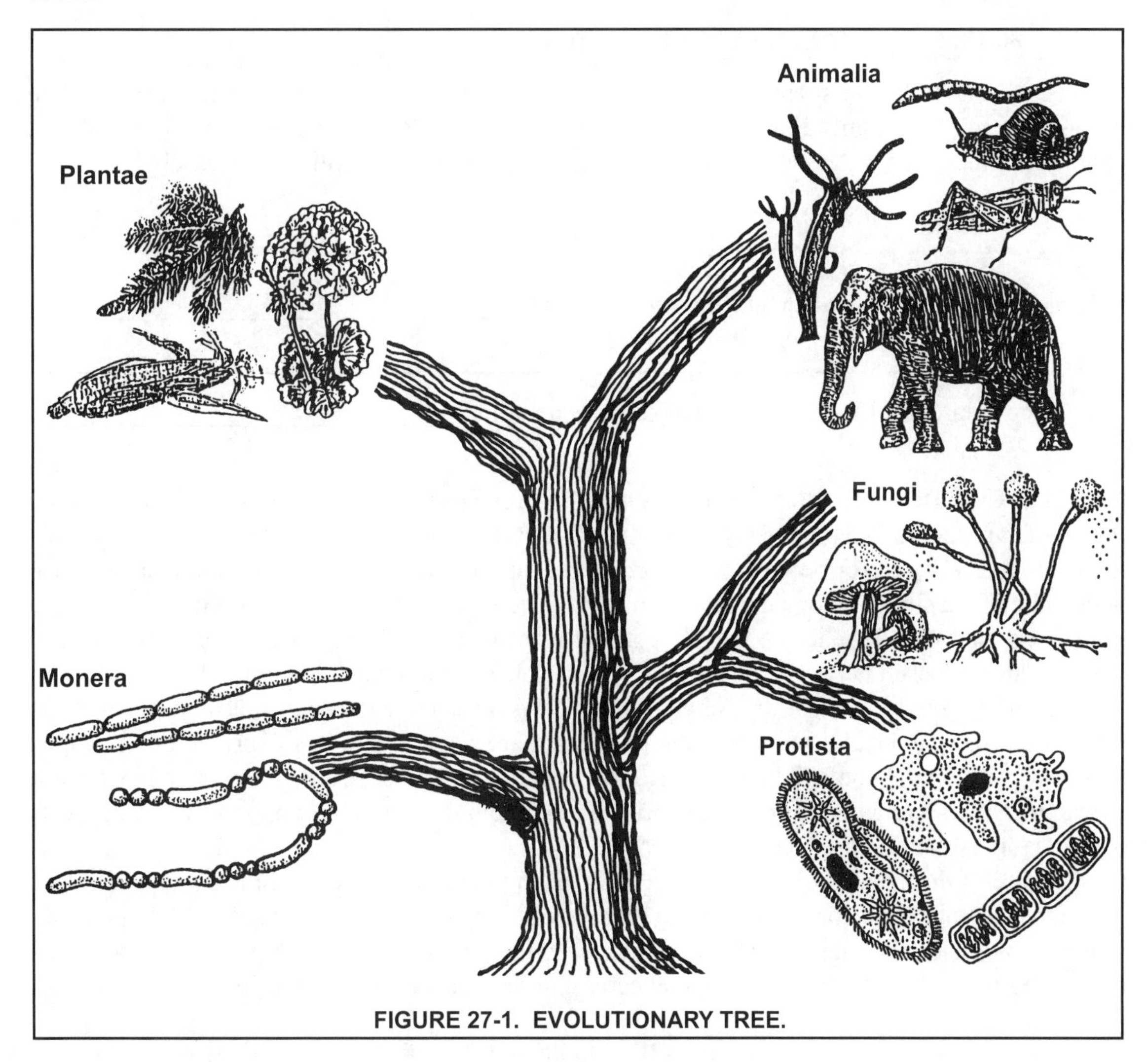

FIGURE 27-1. EVOLUTIONARY TREE.

Review Questions

1. Scientists agree that organisms have changed in form over time from ____________

to ____________.

Name__________ Class__________ Date__________

B. SPONTANEOUS GENERATION. People have always been curious about life and how it began. One of the earliest attempts to explain the origin of life was called the theory of spontaneous generation. **Spontaneous generation** is the concept that living things come from nonliving things. People believed that toads came from mud, flies came from the rotting bodies of animals, and mice were formed from cheese (Figure 27-2). This theory made sense to people because they could not see the eggs laid by the organisms, therefore, they didn't know that the organisms came from eggs. The theory of spontaneous generation was widely accepted until the late 1800's when it was disproved by **Louis Pasteur**. Today, we know that life comes from other living things although some scientists believe the first cell must have come from nonliving materials.

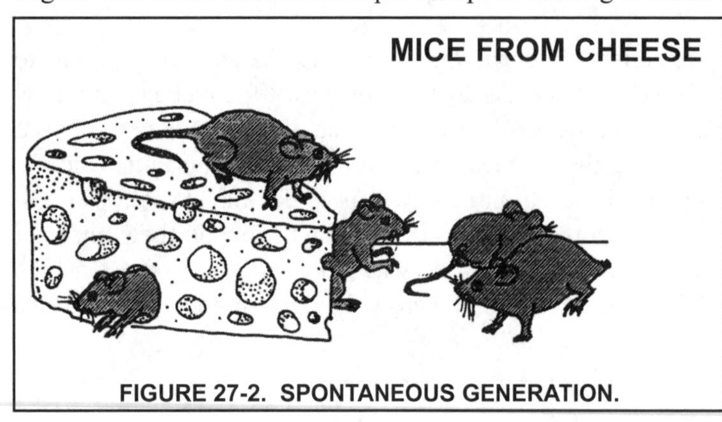

FIGURE 27-2. SPONTANEOUS GENERATION.

REVIEW QUESTIONS

1. Describe the theory of spontaneous generation. ____________________

____

2. Who disproved the theory of spontaneous generation? ____________________.

C. USE AND DISUSE. In the early 1800's the French scientist **Jean Lamarck** presented a theory of evolution called the **theory of use and disuse**. Lamarck thought that organisms were able to develop new structures because they *needed* to adapt to changes in the environment. He also believed that the size of an organ was determined by how much the organ was used. According to Lamarck's theory, ballet dancers have big strong muscles because they need strong muscles and when a dancer doesn't need a certain muscle the muscle becomes smaller and weaker.

Lamarck also believed in the **inheritance of acquired characteristics.** He stated that the useful traits an individual develops during its lifetime are passed on to its offspring. For example, according to Lamarck the children of dancers inherit their parent's strong muscles. An **acquired characteristic** is a trait that is produced during an individual's lifetime. Strong muscles in dancers is an example of an acquired characteristic.

Lamarck's theories were widely accepted for a long time. However, as time passed, scientists began to challenge his theories by showing that there was no data to support Lamarck's hypothesis. For example, scientific data proved that dancer's children are not born with big strong muscles and that strong muscles are acquired through excercise during an individual's lifetime.

REVIEW QUESTIONS

1. Lamarck believed that organisms developed new structures because they ________________ them.

2. An ________________ is a trait that is produced during an individual's lifetime.

Name______________________________ Class______________________ Date__________

D. DISPROVING LAMARCK'S THEORY. The idea that acquired traits are inherited was officially disproved in the late 1800s by the experiments of **August Weismann**. Weismann cut off the tails from mice. He then mated the tailless mice. He did this for many generations. The offspring of the tailless mice were always born with normal length tails (Figure 27-3). This experiment proved that acquired traits *are not* inherited by offspring.

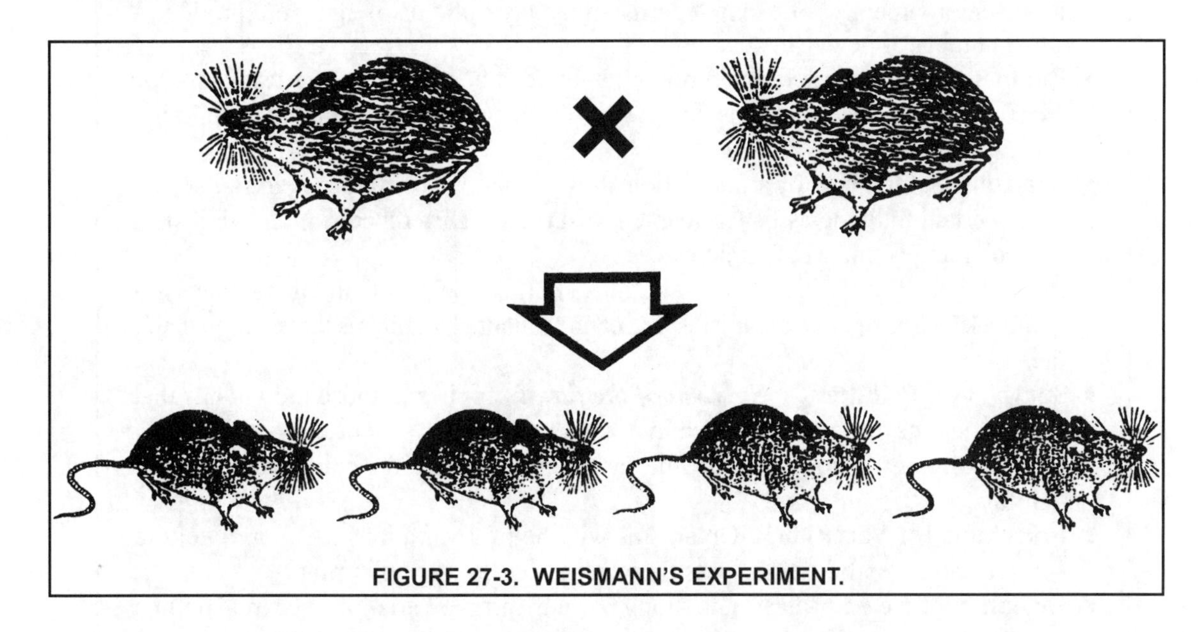

FIGURE 27-3. WEISMANN'S EXPERIMENT.

REVIEW QUESTIONS

1. The theory of acquired characteristics was disproved by ______________________.
2. Describe Weismann's experiment. ____

____

E. DARWIN'S THEORY. In the 1850's, the **theory of natural selection** was proposed by **Charles Darwin**. During his travels he noticed that a certain species in one geographic area was different from the same species in another area. His theory of evolution was developed to explain the gradual change in species. According to Darwin evolution occurs because of **natural selection.** That is, *nature (environment) acts as the selecting agent of an organism's traits*. Darwin believed organisms better adapted to the environment survive and reproduce more successfully than organisms not as well adapted. Natural selection suggests that traits that help an organism survive in a changing environment are passed on to the next generation. [Although Darwin is given credit for the theory of natural selection another scientist, Alfred Wallace, proposed a theory of evolution that was quite similar to Darwin's theory.]

The main ideas of Darwin's theory are listed on the next page. This theory is the basis for the modern theory of evolution. There were some questions that Darwin could not answer. For example, Darwin's theory of evolution did not include the genetic basis of variations. He did not know about genes, chromosomes, and mutations. He also did not know the difference between acquired variations and inherited variations.

Name______________________________ Class______________________________ Date______________

Darwin's Theory of Natural Selection

- **Overproduction:** A population generally produces more offspring than can survive in the environment. For example, a fish must lay millions of eggs to reproduce a small number of new fish.
- **Competition:** Because of overproduction there is competition, or a ***"struggle for survival,"*** between organisms for space, food, water, light, minerals, or other limited resources.
- **Variations:** Members of a population show variations (differences in traits) that make certain individuals better adapted to survive. Differences in structure, size, and color are examples of variations.
- **Natural Selection:** Since some variations are more helpful than others, there is a natural selection against organisms that cannot adapt. Organisms that cannot adapt, die.
- **Survival of the Fittest:** ***"Survival of the fittest"*** applies to those individuals that have variations that enable them to live and reproduce. In a woodland environment brown fur color would be a helpful variation and white fur color would not be helpful.
- **Inheritance of Variations:** Organisms with helpful variations are more likely to survive and to reproduce and pass these variations to their offspring.
- **Evolution of New Species:** Over long periods of time variations accumulate in a population. Eventually there are so many variations that the population becomes a new species.

Review Questions

1. Charles Darwin proposed the theory of ______________________________.

2. Darwin did not know about ______________________, ______________________,

and ______________________. He also did not know the difference between

______________________ and ______________________.

3. List the seven steps of Darwin's theory. ______________________________

____

____

F. COMPARING LAMARCK AND DARWIN. It is a fact that the ancestor of the modern long-necked giraffe had a short neck. Lamarck would have explained the change in the giraffe's neck by saying that the giraffe's ancestor was a grass-eating, short-necked animal. When the grass became scarce the giraffes needed to stretch their necks to reach for food and each generation had to stretch more and more to reach food. Because of this, each generation inherited a slightly longer neck. The longer neck was passed on to the next generation.

Darwin would have said that the giraffe's ancestors had different length necks. Through natural selection giraffes with longer necks could reach higher for food and they survived. Short-necked giraffes starved and died. Long-necked giraffes passed on their long-necked traits to their offspring (Table 27-1).

TABLE 27-1. COMPARING THE THEORIES OF LAMARCK AND DARWIN.

Name______________________________ Class______________________ Date__________

REVIEW QUESTIONS

1. How would Lamarck explain the change in the length of the giraffe's neck?

____

____

____

____

____

2. How would Darwin explain the change in the length of the giraffe's neck?

____

____

____

____

G. MUTATION THEORY. Darwin could not account for his observations that variations existed among organisms. In 1901, a scientist named **Hugo DeVries**, suggested that inherited mutations caused variations. He believed that mutations (changes in genetic material) occurred randomly and those mutations that were favorable were inherited by offspring. He would have said that the change in the length of the giraffe's neck was caused by a sudden mutation. Short-necked giraffes, according to DeVries, suddenly reproduced a mutant long-necked giraffe. It reproduced and produced more long-necked giraffes. When the ground food supply disappeared the long-necked giraffes could reach leaves in trees and were able to survive. The short-necked giraffes died and the long-necked giraffes lived, therefore, today we have a population of long-necked giraffes. DeVries based his theory on his reproduction experiments with the evening primrose plant.

REVIEW QUESTIONS

1. DeVries believed that ____________________ were responsible for variations in organisms.

H. MODERN THEORY. Modern evolutionary theory combines Darwin's ideas of variations and natural selection with studies of mutations, DNA, genes, chromosomes, and sexual reproduction and genetic recombination. The modern theory of natural selection states that:

Modern Theory of Natural Selection

- The genes of inherited variations that give an organism a better chance for survival tend to be passed on from parents to offspring.
- These favorable genes tend to increase in numbers within a population.
- Genes for traits with low survival value decrease in numbers from generation to generation.
- If the environment changes genes that previously were neutral or had low survival value may become favorable and increase in numbers.

Name____________________ Class ________________ Date __________

A scientist today might say that the evolution of the giraffe's neck started with the overproduction of short-necked, grass-eating giraffes. When the ground food supply disappeared there was no food for the short-necked giraffes. Due to random mutations some giraffes had longer necks and were able to eat tree leaves. The giraffes with the favorable long-necked mutations survived and produced more long-necked giraffes. The giraffes with short necks died. Over time other long-neck mutations occurred that had positive survival value. An accumulation of mutations with positive survival value resulted in a new long-necked giraffe species.

REVIEW QUESTIONS

1. Modern evolutionary theory combines Darwin's ideas of ____________________ and ____________________ with studies of ________________, ________________, ________________, ________________, and ________________, and ____________________.

2. List the four parts of the theory of natural selection. ____________________________

____

____

____

____

____

____

I. EVOLUTION IN OUR TIME. In modern times there have been many opportunities for scientists to observe evolution in progress. For example in some areas, such as the Adirondack Mountains in New York State, DDT was sprayed to kill a black fly insect pest. DDT is an **insecticide**–a chemical that kills insects. After a few sprayings most of the black flies disappeared but some black flies had genes that made them resistant to DDT. When the environment was free of DDT, these resistant genes did not have positive survival value. However, when the environment changed (was sprayed with DDT), the DDT-resistant gene suddenly had positive survival value. Since most of the black flies that had no resistant gene had been killed, there was little competition for food. The black flies with resistant genes rapidly increased in numbers. Within a couple of years the DDT-resistant black flies had reproduced in such large numbers that they were again pests to the inhabitants of the Adirondacks. *(DDT spraying has since been banned in New York State and a black fly population with no resistance to DDT is reappearing.)*

Another organism that evolved during modern times is the *Staphylococcus* bacteria. When antibiotics were first used some *Staphylococcus* bacteria had genes that made them resistant to antibiotics. When the use of antibiotics became widespread the bacteria with resistant genes increased in numbers producing a population of bacteria that was not killed by antibiotics. Even today scientists continuously develop new antibiotics because the bacteria population mutates and produces new antibiotic-resistant strains. ***Remember that mutations are not caused by environmental change. Mutations occur randomly.*** Mutations with positive survival value allow organisms to be better adapted to their environment. The *environment selects* those variations, or adaptations, that may have survival value. You learned in a previous chapter that an adaptation is a structure or function that enables an organism to live and successfully reproduce in a particular environment.

The **English peppered moth** is an example of an organism that adapted to a changed environment. The evolution of English peppered moth has been observed for over 100 years in Manchester, England. Peppered moths have two basic colors–light color with dark markings or dark color with light markings. Before the industrial revolution most peppered moths were light colored. This enabled them to blend with their light-colored environment such as the trunks of trees and the sides of buildings (Figure 27-4). When they blended with the environment, the light-colored moths were almost invisible and insect-eating birds could not see them.

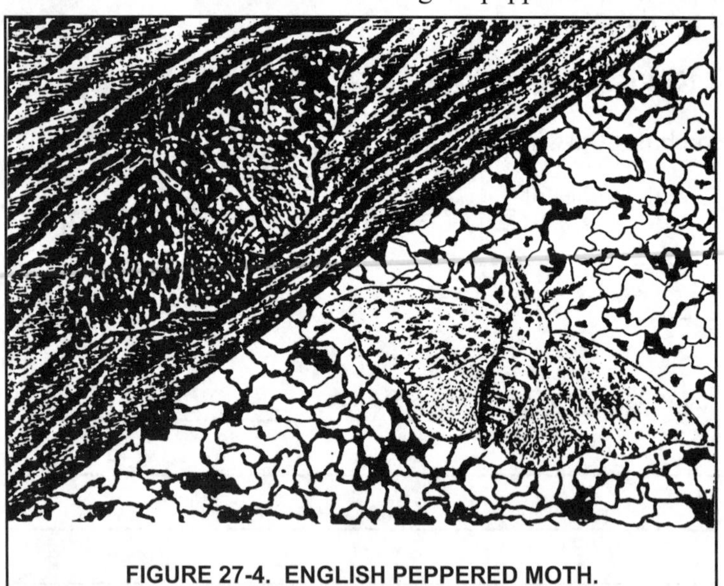

FIGURE 27-4. ENGLISH PEPPERED MOTH.

The soot and other air pollutants from the industrial revolution gradually changed the environment from light to dark. The light-colored moths became visible and were eaten by birds. The dark-colored moths could not be seen against the dark background. These moths reproduced more dark moths and the population shifted from light to dark-colored. Recently, as a result of environmental pollution laws, the moth population is slowly changing back to light-colored moths.

Sometimes plant and animal breeders purposely modify organisms by mating plants and animals that have certain desirable traits. This process is called artificial selection. **Artificial selection** involves the mating of organisms with a particular desirable trait to produce offspring with this trait. For example, racehorses and greyhounds have been produced that are faster than their predecessors. By selective breeding, man may cause evolution. In natural selection, *nature* acts as the selecting agent. In artificial selection, *humans* are the selecting agents.

Review Questions

1. Name three organisms that have evolved in modern times. ______________________________

____

2. Describe the process of artificial selection. ______________________________

____

____

____

Name________________________ Class ____________________ Date ____________

J. GEOGRAPHIC ISOLATION. Geographic isolation occurs when a population is physically separated into smaller populations by geographic barriers. **Geographic barriers** could be mountain ranges, deserts, oceans, rivers, or other bodies of water (Figure 27-5). Even humans make geographic barriers when they construct big expressways and shopping malls.

Changes may occur in these separated populations that, over a long period of time, may result in the production of different species. The production of a new species is known as **speciation.** Speciation occurs when members of the isolated population and the main populations can no longer interbreed even when the barriers are removed. This is known as **reproductive isolation**. Geographic isolation may result in reproductive isolation.

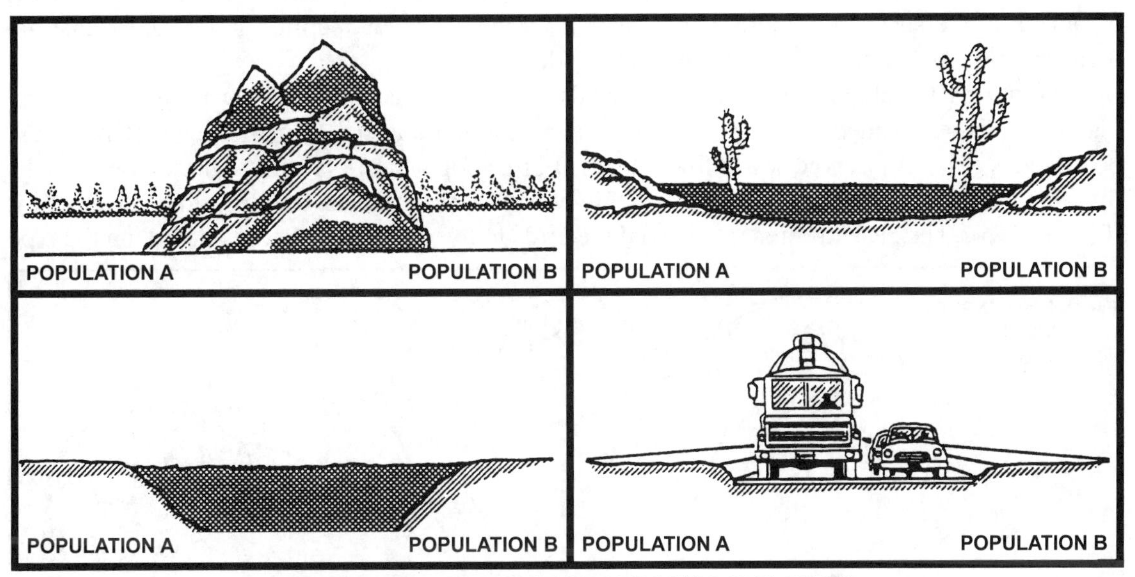

FIGURE 27-5. TYPES OF GEOGRAPHIC ISOLATION.

A common example of geographic isolation is that of the Kaibab and Abert squirrels that live in the Grand Canyon. Scientists believe that these two squirrel species developed from a single ancestral species that was separated geographically. The Kaibab squirrel lives on one side of the canyon and has a white tail, long ears, and a dark-colored body. The Abert squirrel lives on the other side of the canyon. It has a gray tail, long ears and a light-colored abdomen. The canyon is thought to be the geographic barrier that divided one squirrel species into two separate groups. One group of squirrels became isolated from the other. Over time different mutations occurred on either side of the canyon. Today the squirrels are so genetically different that they can not interbreed.

REVIEW QUESTIONS

1. Geographic isolation occurs when ____

____

2. Name three geographic barriers. ____

____

3. The production of a new species is called ____________________.

4. ______________________________ occurs when population can no longer interbreed.

K. ADAPTIVE RADIATION. **Adaptive radiation** is the process by which many new species of organisms evolve from a common ancestor. The new species evolve and fill different environmental niches where there is less competition. A **niche** is the role an organism plays in a particular environment. A niche includes an organism's feeding habits, where it lives, how it reproduces, and its other life activities. Organisms may move into new niches in the environment because of chance mutations that prove to have positive adaptive value. A positive adaptation is one that allows an organism to live successfully in a new niche. If there is little competition in the new niche the organism has a better chance to survive and reproduce.

During his travels to the Galapagos Islands, a group of islands that are isolated from the mainland of South America, Darwin saw may different and unusual animal species. One of the populations that he observed was a finch (a small bird) population. He wrote that there were 13 different finch species living on the islands. He noticed that their beak shapes were very different (Figure 27-6). The beak differences allowed the birds to live in different niches based on the type

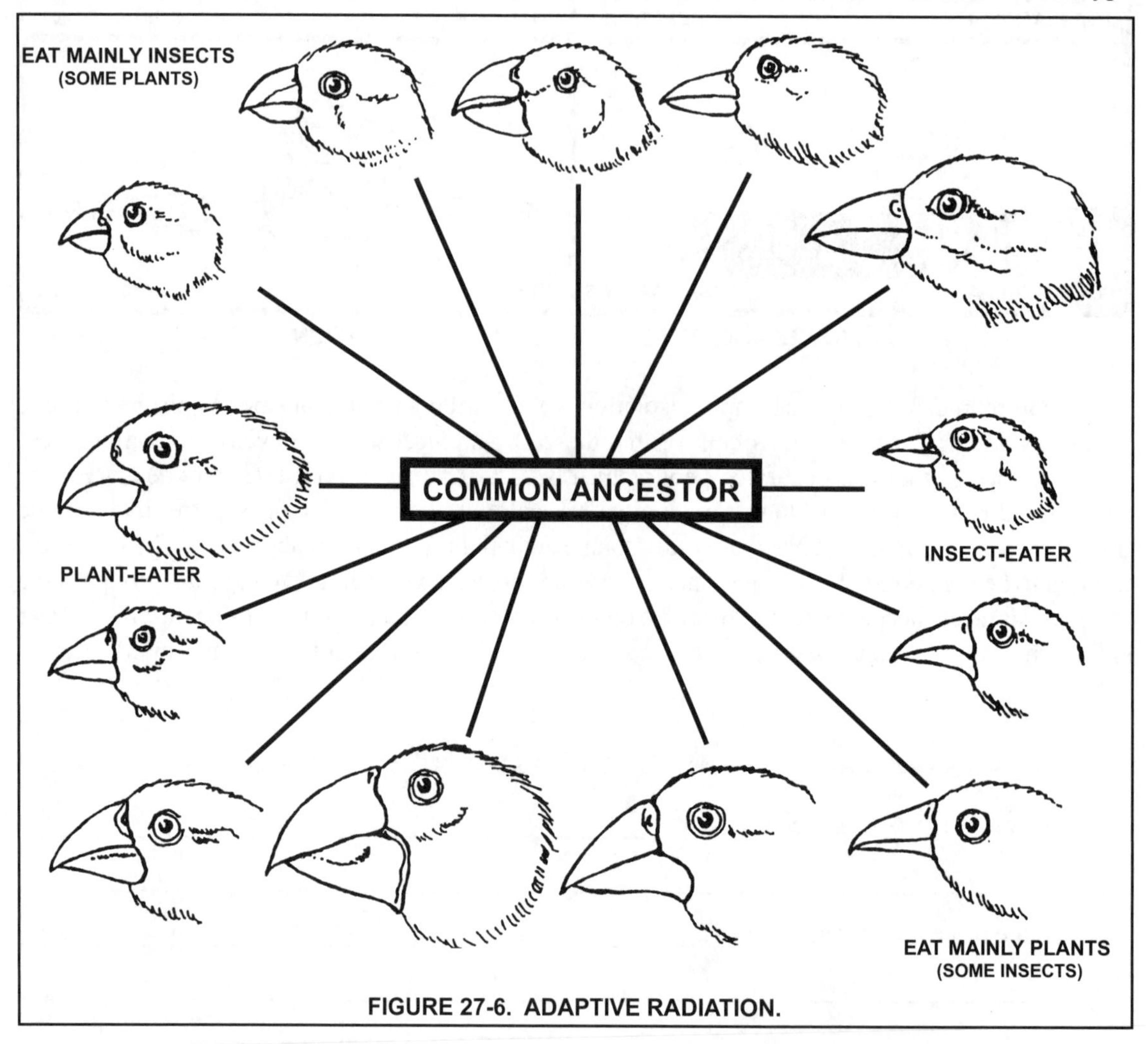

FIGURE 27-6. ADAPTIVE RADIATION.

of food they ate. Darwin thought the finches had evolved from one common ancestor. Darwin did not know why birds with beaks that were different from their parents were produced. He guessed that the new beaks gave the finches new feeding niches where there was less competition for food. For example, he saw a large ground finch with a blunt powerful beak for breaking open hard seeds. Because it could eat bigger seeds than other ground finches, it was not in direct competition with smaller birds. Therefore, the smaller birds could successfully inhabit one niche and the large birds inhabited another niche. Over time other mutations occurred and eventually many different finch species were produced.

REVIEW QUESTIONS

1. Adaptive radiation is the process by which ________________________________

____

2. Darwin's finches are an example of ______________________________.

3. A ________________________ is the role an organism plays in a particular environment.

L. RATE OF CHANGE. Although most scientists agree with the current facts of modern evolution theory, they do not agree on the time frame for evolutionary change–whether it was a slow, gradual, and continuous process or whether there were stable times interrupted by major disturbances.

The theories of **gradualism** and **punctuated equilibrium** are attempts by scientists to answer the question of the evolution rate.

Time Frame For Evolutionary Change

- **Gradualism.** A theory that proposes that evolutionary change is slow, gradual, and continuous. New species arise by the very gradual collection of minor changes in a population.
- **Punctuated Equilibrium.** A theory that proposes that species are relatively stable for long periods of time (several million years). This stability is interrupted by brief periods during which major changes occur. These changes result in the evolution of new species. According to this theory, the minor changes that occur in a population over time might produce new varieties of an existing species but not a new species.

REVIEW QUESTIONS

1. Scientists do not agree on the ____________________________ for evolution.

Name________________________ Class________________________ Date____________

2. Explain the differences between gradualism and punctuated equilibrium.

____

____

____

____

____

____

____

M. HETEROTROPH HYPOTHESIS. The **heterotroph hypothesis** is a recent attempt to explain how living things may have developed on the primitive earth. In the late 1930's experimental data was presented, by the Russian scientist **A. I. Oparin**, that showed that life could have begun in or near the ocean. The theory proposed that groups of organic molecules were formed from the chemical elements in the Earth's primitive ocean. The organic molecules combined using energy from heat, lightning, solar radiation, and radioactive materials in the rocks.

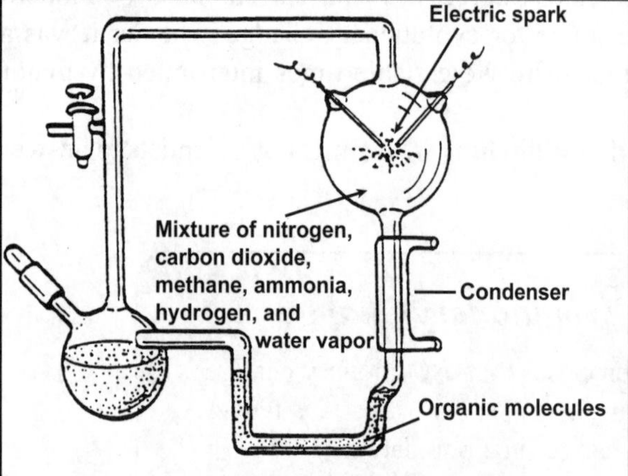

FIGURE 27-7. MILLER'S APPARATUS.

The first living things were thought to be heterotrophs (organisms that do not make their own food). They may have resembled modern anaerobic bacteria. Since no free oxygen gas existed in the atmosphere these forms of life carried on anaerobic respiration. They used the free organic molecules in the sea for food. Over time genetic changes occurred in the first organisms.

As a result of genetic changes, photosynthetic forms of life evolved. These organisms, called autotrophs (organisms that can make their own food), released oxygen into the atmosphere. Aerobic forms of life evolved from the anaerobic forms. Aerobic organisms use atmospheric oxygen for aerobic respiration.

In 1953 a graduate student, **Stanley Miller**, at the University of Chicago made amino acids in the laboratory (Figure 27-7). This data supported the heterotroph hypothesis. Today this theory is widely accepted by many scientists.

REVIEW QUESTIONS

1. The first living things were thought to be ________________________.

2. The most widely accepted theory today about the origin of life is called the

________________________.

Name________________________ Class____________________ Date__________

N. HUMAN EVOLUTION. Scientists know very little about human evolution. One reason is that there is very little fossil evidence. Some people *think* that Darwin proposed that humans evolved from apes. However Darwin only *suggested* that humans, along with other mammals, could have shared a common ancestor. There is no evidence that humans are the direct descendants of organisms living today. Some human-like fossil forms have been discovered. Their exact place in human ancestry has yet to be determined.

Scientists do agree that humans have evolved into a dominant force on Earth today. They believe that this occurred because humans have certain physical characteristics that enable them to function more efficiently than other animals. Some of these human characteristics include a superior brain that allows humans to reason, speak, and use tools, and they have a **prehensile hand** (a hand with an opposable thumb) that can be used to grasp tools, pens, and other implements. Also the upright posture of the human frees two limbs for use in activities other than support and locomotion and they have excellent vision because they are able to see things in three dimensions. Three-dimensional vision is called **stereoscopic vision.**

Modern scientists assume that human evolution, like evolution in other animals, is continuing. However, because of environment control their superior reasoning ability humans are able to control their environment. Because of this, the evolutionary effect of natural selection is not as great in humans as in other organisms. Factors that affect or may affect human evolution include:

Factors That Affect Or May Affect Human Evolution

- **Medical Knowledge.** Medical knowledge permits the survival of individualswith genetic traits such as diabetes, hemophilia, and PKU. Without medical knowledge these people would die and the genes for these diseases would decrease in number in the population. Because of modern medicine the number of genes are maintained or increased.
- **Modern Transportation.** Due to modern transportation humans are less affected by the evolutionary force of geographic isolation.
- **Advanced Technology.** Advanced technology has given humans better nutrition and greater control over their reproductive process. It has also increased the number and kinds of mutagenic agents in the environment.
- **Genetic Engineering.** Genetic engineering may possibly lead to the appearance of new traits and the elimination of others.

REVIEW QUESTIONS

1. Why do scientists know so little about human evolution? ____________________

____

2. A hand with an opposable thumb is called a ____________________.

3. Name three human characteristics that enable them to function more efficiently.

____

____

Name________________________ Class________________________ Date____________

4. List four factors that affect or may affect human evolution.

____

____

CAREER OPPORTUNITIES

PALEONTOLOGIST: Paleontologists are scientists who study fossils looking for clues to the history of the earth, its inhabitants, and past environments. To be a paleontologist you must like to travel because travel is a big part of the paleontologist's life. They go all over the world looking for fossils and acquiring other information to help them put together the pieces of the earth's puzzle.

A paleontologist usually has a Ph.D degree in paleontology or some related science such as geology, zoology, botany, or chemistry. They usually write, research and teach at universities, or work in the fuel industry for oil and gas companies.

*****

REVIEW QUESTIONS

1. What is a paleontologist?

____

____

____

____

Name________________________ Class____________________ Date__________

LAB INVESTIGATION: ADAPTATIONS

Objective

Upon completion of this activity you should be able to define the term adaptation and recognize favorable variations.

Laboratory Procedure

Materials: A plastic bag or small box containing equal amounts of *green* and four other colored toothpicks or paper clips, green artificial grass mats or green construction paper, a stop watch or other timer, and reference books. **[TEACHER'S NOTE: THIS LAB WORKS BETTER OUTDOORS ON THE LAWN.]**

1. Working with a partner pick up your laboratory materials at the supply table and carry them to your lab area. ***Note:*** The toothpicks (paper clips) represent prey and you are the predator. *Predators* are animals that kill and consume other animals called *prey*.

2. Count the number of colored toothpicks (paper clips) in your container separating them by color. Enter this number in the **Observation Section** below.

3. Scatter the toothpicks (paper clips) over the grass mat. Set the timer for one minute. ***One by one,*** pick up as many toothpicks as you can in ***1 minute*** and place them back into the container.

4. Separate the toothpicks (paper clips) by color. Count the number of toothpicks (paper clips) of each color that you picked up and enter the amounts in the **Observation Section (Trial 1)**.

5. Repeat **Procedure 3 and 4**. Enter the information in the **Observation Section (Trial 2).** (***It is important*** *that you recount your toothpicks at the beginning of Trial 2—some may have been lost in Trial 1.)*

Observations

COLOR	TRIAL 1		TRIAL 2	
	NUMBER AT START	NUMBER AT END	NUMBER AT START	NUMBER AT END
Green				

Name_______________ Class_______________ Date_______________

1. In **TRIAL 1:**

   Which color toothpicks were "captured" in the greatest numbers? _______________

   Which color toothpicks "escaped" in the greatest numbers? _______________

2. In **TRIAL 2:**

   Which color toothpicks were "captured" in the greatest numbers? _______________

   Which color toothpicks "escaped" in the greatest numbers? _______________

3. Which color would you consider to be a favorable variation? _______________

4. Define the following terms:

   Predator: _______________

   ____

   Prey: _______________

   ____

   Variations: _______________

   ____

   Adaptation: _______________

   ____

   Natural Selection: _______________

   ____

Name________________________ Class________________________ Date____________

REVIEW ACTIVITIES

Important Terms

DIRECTIONS: Define the following terms in the spaces provided.

acquired characteristic ____

____

adaptive radiation ____

____

Darwin ____

____

DeVries ____

____

geographic barriers ____

____

geographic isolation ____

____

gradualism ____

____

heterotroph hypothesis ____

____

insecticide ____

____

Lamarck ____

____

Miller ____

____

niche ____

____

Oparin ____

____

Pasteur ____

____

Name__________ **Class**__________ **Date**__________

prehensile hand ____________________

____

punctuated equilibrium ____________________

____

spontaneous generation ____________________

____

Weismann ____________________

____

Name____________________ Class____________________ Date__________

Skill Practice

Part A. Base your answers to questions 1 through 8 on the reading passages below and on your knowledge of biology. Underline the correct answer.

The Clay-Life Theory

Scientists reported a major discovery supporting the theory that life on Earth began in clay rather than in the sea. This discovery reveals that normal clay contains basic properties essential to life; the capacities to store and transfer energy. This theory was a major departure from the prevailing "hot, thin soup" hypothesis which was set forth in the 1930's by A. I. Oparin. The chemists and biologists who made the discovery, however, emphasized that their findings did not prove the clay-life theory, but did make it a more reasonable explanation worthy of further research.

The research was conducted by a team of scientists at the National Aeronautics and Space Administration. These studies of the origin of life have been under way for years. The studies have been conducted, in part, to learn how to search for life on other planets.

According to the theory, chemical evolution that led to life began in clay. The early clays could have used energy from radioactive decay and other sources to act as chemical factories for processing inorganic raw materials into complex materials from which the first life arose billions of years ago.

It has been suggested that the clay has the ability to act as a catalyst in important chemical reactions and could be capable of such life-like traits as self-replication. Scientists proposed that the inorganic "protoorganisms" in clay may have provided the intermediate evolutionary structure for the building blocks of life, such as amino acids. The synthesis of later living organisms, based on organic compounds consisting primarily of the element carbon, could have been initially directed by an inorganic pattern, or template, developed in clay.

The clay-life theory would account for the very earliest steps on the process proposed by Oparin, before the compounds got together in the hot, thin soup. This would provide an alternative to the theory of random forces of lightning acting on the right compounds at the right moment. —*New York Times* (adapted)

1. According to the reading passage, data collected on the clay-life theory.

1. prove the clay-life theory
2. support the clay-life theory
3. weaken the clay-life theory
4. disprove the clay-life theory

2. According to the clay-life theory, the original "protoorganisms" in clay were

1. organic heterotrophs
2. inorganic templates
3. unable to self-replicate
4. unable to store and transfer energy

3. According to the clay-life theory, the main role of clay in the origin of life was to

1. speed up the rate of chemical reactions
2. break down very large organic molecules
3. anchor plants in the Earth's surface
4. form fossils of new forms of life

4. Scientists at the National Aeronautics and Space Administration are researching the origin of life to learn how to

1. make amino acids from clay and lightning
2. create life on other planets
3. identify various species found in meteors
4. search for life on other planets

5. The prevailing "hot, thin soup" concept, which was set forth in the 1930's by A. I. Oparin, is known as the

1. inheritance of acquired characteristics
2. theory of natural selection
3. one-gene-one-polypeptide theory
4. heterotroph hypothesis

Name________________________ Class________________________ Date____________

Animal Modification

Humans have modified some animal species by breeding only those that possess certain desirable traits. As a result, we have racehorses and greyhounds that are faster than their predecessors. In a similar way many animals have been modified naturally. The giraffe has long forelegs and a long neck, head, and tongue which make it well adapted for browsing in the higher branches of trees. Therefore the giraffe can obtain food that is beyond the reach of other animals, especially during droughts. Ancient populations of giraffes varied in the relative length of their body parts. Those giraffes that were able to browse the highest were more likely to survive. They mated and their offspring often inherited the structural characteristics suitable for high browsing. The giraffes that could not reach the food supply most likely died of starvation and therefore did not produce as many offspring as those that could reach higher.

6. The variations to which the author refers are the direct result of
1. asexual reproduction
2. regenerative ability
3. inherent need
4. gene recombination

7. Which idea included in Darwin's theory of evolution is *not* found in the reading passage?
1. variation
2. struggle for existence
3. overproduction
4. survival of the fittest

8. The modification of some animal species by humans, as described in the reading passage, results from the process known as
1. natural selection
2. artificial selection
3. vegetative propagation
4. chromosomal mutation

Part B. Base your answer to question 1 on the reading passage below. Write your answer in complete sentences.

Time Frame for Speciation

Evolution is the process of change through time. Theories of evolution attempt to explain the diversification of species existing today. The essentials of Darwin's theory of natural selection serve as a basis for our present understanding of the evolution of species. Recently, some scientists have suggested two possible explanations for the time frame in which the evolution of species occurs.

Gradualism proposes that evolutionary change is continuous and slow, occurring over many millions of years. New species evolve thought the accumulation of many small changes. Gradualism is supported in the fossil record by the presence of transitional forms in some evolutionary pathways.

Punctuated equilibrium is another possible explanation for the diversity of species. This theory proposes that species exist unchanged for long geological periods of time, significant changes occur and new species may evolve. Some scientists use the apparent lack of transitional forms in the fossil record in many evolutionary pathways to support punctuated equilibrium.

1. Identify one major difference between gradualism and punctuated equilibrium.

____

____

____

____

____

Name____________________ Class____________________ Date__________

CHAPTER 27: QUIZ

A. FILL-IN QUESTIONS

DIRECTIONS: Complete each of the following statements by writing the correct word or phrase in the space provided.

1. Charles Darwin proposed the theory of ____________________.
2. The ____________________ theory states that living things come from nonliving things.
3. DDT is a/an ____________________.
4. Racehorses are bred by an method known as ____________________.
5. ____________________ occurs when a large population is separated by geographic barriers.
6. A trait that is produced during a person's lifetime is called a/an ____________________.
7. The process by which new species evolve from a common ancestor is ____________________.
8. Oparin proposed that life began in the ____________________.
9. According to Darwin, overproduction causes ____________________ among organisms.
10. A prehensile hand is one that has an opposing ____________________.
11. The theory of use and disuse was presented by ____________________.
12. Hugo DeVries suggested the ____________________ theory.
13. A/an ____________________ is an example of a geographic barrier.
14. Variations are ____________________ in traits.
15. A recent attempt to explain the origin of life is called the ____________________ hypothesis.
16. The theory of spontaneous generation was disproved by ____________________.
17. ____________________ observed variations in animal species in the Galapagos Islands.
18. Weismann disproved the theory of ____________________.
19. ____________________ is a theory that proposes that evolutionary change is a slow, gradual, and continuous process.
20. Scientists know very little about human evolution because there are very few ____________________.

B. MULTIPLE-CHOICE QUESTIONS

DIRECTIONS: Circle the number of the expression that best completes each of the following statements.

1. Which statement agrees with the findings of recent research into the origin of living things?
   (1) They most likely evolved from groups of organic molecules
   (2) They absorbed atmospheric carbon dioxide for their respiration.
   (3) They were green plants.
   (4) They developed inside the rock layers of the Earth.
2. In order to insure survival, salmon lay large numbers of eggs. This is an example of
   (1) use and disuse
   (2) a mutation
   (3) overproduction
   (4) isolation

Name________________ Class________________ Date________

3. One monkey gets the most food because it can climb faster than other monkeys of the same type. This is an example of
   (1) struggle for survival (3) use and disuse
   (2) protective coloration (4) geographic isolation

Directions (4-6): Base your answers to questions 4 through 6 on the information below and on your knowledge of biology.

There is a type of fish known as the pupfish. It lives only in one small pool in the Nevada desert. It has existed in this pool since the Ice Age ended.

4. Evolutionary changes in the pupfish could be possible by
   (1) asexual reproduction (3) regeneration
   (2) mutation (4) vegetative propagation
5. This fish is not found in other areas. This is an example of
   (1) use and disuse (3) geographic isolation
   (2) natural selection (4) struggle for existence
6. If the pool is destroyed by an earthquake the pupfish most likely will
   (1) become dominant (3) migrate
   (2) overpopulate (4) become extinct

---

7. Lamarck believed that new organs arise in animals
   (1) when needed (3) by chance
   (2) by gene mutation (4) from vestigial structures
8. Dogs that have had their tails clipped off by their owners continue to produce offspring with tails each time they reproduce. This fact demonstrates that
   (1) variations occur in offspring
   (2) acquired characteristics are not inherited
   (3) mutations are inherited
   (4) there is a survival of the fittest
9. The discovery of gene mutations helps to explain the
   (1) formation of fossils (3) process of sex determination
   (2) process of digestion (4) appearance of new traits
10. Much of the history of human evolution is still incomplete due to the
    (1) complete absence of human fossils (3) scarcity of human fossils
    (2) advances in technology (4) development of humans from apes

C. ESSAY QUESTION

DIRECTIONS: Use complete sentences to answer the question in this part.

1. Discuss how genetic engineering may affect the future of human evolution.

____

____

____

____

____

Name________________ Class ________________ Date ____________

UNIT SEVEN TEST

Matching Questions

DIRECTIONS: In the space at the left of each item in Column A, place the letter of the term or phrase in Column B that is most closely related to that item.

Column A	Column B
________ **1.** Theory of use and disuse.	**a.** Geologic Evolution
________ **2.** Proposed mutation theory.	**b.** August Weismann
________ **3.** Structure no longer used.	**c.** Niche
________ **4.** Study of Earth's changes.	**d.** Jean Lamarck
________ **5.** Living things came from nonliving things.	**e.** Adaptive Radiation
________ **6.** Proposed heterotroph hypothesis.	**f.** Charles Darwin
________ **7.** Evidences of evolution.	**g.** Vestigial Structure
________ **8.** Theory of natural selection.	**h.** Organic Evolution
________ **9.** Disproved Lamarck.	**i.** Spotaneous Generation
________ **10.** Study of changes in living things.	**j.** Homologous Structure
	k. Hugo DeVries
	l. A.I. Oparin

True–False Questions

DIRECTIONS: Write TRUE before each statement that is true and FALSE before each statement that is false.

________ **1.** Little is known about the evolution of man because of the lack of fossil evidence.

________ **2.** Darwin believed that overproduction caused competition among organisms.

________ **3.** Scientists agree that the *only* time frame for evolution is a process called gradualism.

________ **4.** Humans, like all animals, do not have three-dimensional vision.

________ **5.** All organisms have similar DNA.

________ **6.** The appendix is an example of a human homologous structure.

________ **7.** Man appeared on Earth late in the Paleozoic era.

________ **8.** Scientists think mutations cause variations in organisms.

________ **9.** Racehorses are bred by natural selection.

________ **10.** Variations produced from new combinations of genes occur as a result of asexual reproduction.

Name________________________ Class____________________ Date__________

Fill-In Questions

DIRECTIONS: Complete each of the following statements by writing the correct word or phrase in the space provided.

1. The role an organism plays in its environment is called its ____________________.
2. "Survival of the ____________________" applies to those organisms that have variations that enable them to live and reproduce.
3. According to modern evolutionary theory favorable genes tend to ____________________ in numbers in a population.
4. The animal used by Weismann to prove that acquired traits were not inherited was the ____________________.
5. The *Eohippus* is the ancestor of the modern ____________________.
6. Comparative ____________________ is the study of the early development of organisms.
7. The ____________________ is an example of a vestigial structure.
8. The remains or traces of organisms that once lived are called ____________________.
9. The English peppered moth is an example of adaptation to a changed ____________________.
10. Medical knowledge is a factor that affects ____________________ evolution.

Multiple-Choice Questions

DIRECTIONS: Circle the number of the expression that best completes each of the following statements.

1. A major idea in Darwin's theory of evolution, which helps explain how changes occur in organisms is known as
   (1) natural selection
   (2) mitosis
   (3) mutation
   (4) DNA replication
2. A fish may lay a thousand eggs at a given time. This is an example of
   (1) geographic distribution
   (2) overproduction
   (3) variation
   (4) survival of the fittest
3. In a region of undisturbed sedimentary rock, the oldest fossils would be found in the
   (1) top layer
   (2) upper middle layer
   (3) lower middle layer
   (4) lowest layer
4. In humans, which structure is vestigial?
   (1) heart
   (2) appendix
   (3) lungs
   (4) liver
5. A species that is most likely to survive a drastic change in the environment is one that
   (1) requires a specific environmental temperature
   (2) adapts easily and reproduces sexually
   (3) depends on only one type of food
   (4) requires a special nesting area

6. The fact that a healthy deer can outrun a timber wolf is an example of
   (1) mutation
   (2) isolation
   (3) adaptive radiation
   (4) natural selection

7. Koala bears are found only in Australia. This is most likely the result of
   (1) asexual reproduction
   (2) geographic isolation
   (3) a changing environment
   (4) overproduction

8. A single white-eyed fruit fly appears in a breeding population of red-eyed fruit flies. This is an example of
   (1) struggle for existence
   (2) overproduction
   (3) mutation
   (4) survival of the fittest

9. The skeleton of a fish becomes embedded in sediments and ultimately is a part of a rock layer. This skeleton is now
   (1) an artifact
   (2) a vestigial structure
   (3) a fossil
   (4) a remnant

10. Lamarck's theory of evolution states that
   (1) all organisms have vestigial structures
   (2) organisms do not compete for survival
   (3) all organisms survive
   (4) acquired characteristics are inherited

Essay Question

DIRECTIONS: Use complete sentences to answer the question in this part.

1. Name three evidences of organic evolution.

____

____

____

____

____

____

____

____

____

____

____

____

____

____

Class Notes

Name________________________________ Class________________________ Date______________

UNIT EIGHT

Living Things And Their Environment

LEARNING OUTCOMES: Upon completion of the study of this unit, you should be able to:

- Identify the major subdivisions of environmental organization.
- Explain the importance of preserving diversity of species and habitats.
- Describe the interactions that exist within major environmental subdivisions.
- Describe the human population in terms of its relationship to the environment.
- Relate how the need for a clean environment requires careful conservation of resources.

Chapter 28: Organization of the Environment

A. ECOLOGY. Ecology is the branch of biology that deals with the interactions between organisms and the relationships of organisms with their living and nonliving environments. An **ecologist** is a scientist who studies ecology. Ecologist study organisms and the environment at various ecological levels. Each level includes different factors. The ecological levels of environmental organization are described below.

Environmental Organization

- **Population.** A **population** includes all the members of a species found in given area. The dandelions in your lawn is an example of a population.
- **Community.** A **community** includes all the populations in a given area. Your lawn has populations of dandelions, grasses, earthworms, and other living things. These populations together make up a lawn community.
- **Ecosystem.** A community (all living things) and the physical environment (air,water, soil) interacting and functioning together make up an **ecosystem.** Examples of ecosystems include your lawn, a balanced aquarium, ponds, vacant lots, woodlots, salt marshes, and forests.
- **Biosphere.** The **biosphere** is the portion of the earth in which life exsists. It is very large and includes many complex ecosystems.

Name________________________ Class________________________ Date____________

REVIEW QUESTIONS

1. What is ecology? ____
____
____

2. A/an ____________________ includes all the members of a species found in a given area.
3. Populations make up ________________________.
4. A community and its nonliving environment make up a/an ________________________.
5. The part of the earth in which life exists is the ________________________.
6. A scientist who studies ecology is called a/an ________________________.

B. REQUIREMENTS FOR STABLE ECOSYSTEMS. Ecosystems are the basic units used by ecologists in the study of the environment. They are definite units that involve interactions between living and nonliving things. An ecosystem can support itself and is stable when the following requirements are met.

- There must be a constant supply of energy. The sun is the primary source of energy for life on Earth.
- There must be living organisms that can incorporate the energy into organic compounds.
- There must be a recycling of materials between organisms and the environment.

A balanced aquarium is an example of a very small ecosystem (Figure 28-1). It is self-supporting because the requirements for a stable ecosystem are present. Energy is supplied to the ecosystem by light. There are plants to change the light energy into the energy in the organic molecule glucose. Recycling of materials occurs during photosynthesis and respiration. During photosynthesis plants use light energy and carbon dioxide to form glucose. They give off oxygen, which is used by the fish and snail during respiration. Animals release carbon dioxide that is used by the plants.

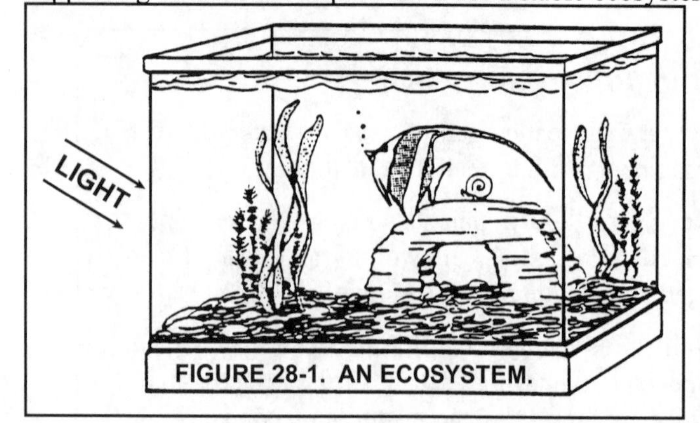

FIGURE 28-1. AN ECOSYSTEM.

REVIEW QUESTIONS

1. A balanced aquarium is an example of a/an ________________________.

2. List the three requirements for a stable ecosystem. ______________________________

____

____

____

C. ABIOTIC FACTORS. The nonliving parts of the environment are known as **abiotic** factors. They directly affect the ability of organisms to live and reproduce. These factors include soil, water, air, light, temperature, and inorganic substances such as minerals (Table 28-1). Abiotic factors vary from one place to another.

ABIOTIC FACTOR	IMPORTANCE
Soil	Types of soil include sand, clay, rock, swamp, acidic, alkaline (basic), and loam (contains organic material). Plant and animal life in an environment depends largely on the type of soil present. Examples: pine trees grow in sandy soil, lichens and mosses in rocky soil, cypress and cedar in swamps, azaleas in acid soil and peas and clover like alkaline soil.
Water	Needed in different amounts by all living things for normal functioning. Some organisms live completely in water while others need very little water. Examples: desert cactus and kangaroo rat conserve water and can live in dry environment. Water lilies and sharks live in or on water therefore require large amounts of water.
Air	Composed of gases (oxygen, nitrogen, hydrogen, carbon dioxide) used by organisms for photosynthesis and respiration. Water plants and animals used gases dissolved in water.
Light	Used in different intensities (strengths) by most living things in their life processes. Essential to green plants for photosynthesis. Examples: desert cactus requires high intensity light, underwater plants use little light.
Temperature	Organisms live in a temperature range of 0°C to 50°C. Differences in temperatures affect the kinds of organisms that can live in a particular area. Examples: Some animals, such as bears, hibernate during cold temperatures. Other animals, like birds, move to warmer climates. Certain trees lose their leaves during the winter to help them withstand the cold.
Minerals	Living things require certain minerals to survive. Some of these minerals are nitrogen, sodium, calcium carbon, iron, and potassium. The ability of green plants to live in an environment depends on the availability of soil minerals necessary for photosynthesis.

TABLE 28-1. ABIOTIC FACTORS IN THE ECOSYSTEM.

Abiotic factors may also act as limiting factors. **Limiting factors** determine the numbers and kinds of organisms that can inhabit an ecosystem. Hot temperature and little water are examples of

Name________________________ Class________________________ Date__________

limiting factors in a desert environment. For example, the species of plants and animals living in a desert environment are limited to mainly those that need very little water and can survive hot temperatures. Limiting factors also keep a population's size in check because they reduce the size of the population that would normally be expected through reproduction. Biotic factors (living things) such as food resources, disease, and predation are also limiting factors.

REVIEW QUESTIONS

1. List six abiotic factors in an ecosystem. ____

____

2. What do limiting factors determine? ____

____

D. BIOTIC FACTORS. All the living things that directly or indirectly affect the ecosystem are called **biotic factors.** Biotic factors interact with other living organisms and with the physical environment. The major divisions of biotic factors in an ecosystem are:

Biotic Factors In An Ecosystem

- **Producers.** A **producer** is any plant that manufactures food by photosynthesis. Green plants are producers.
- **Consumers. Consumers** eat producers and/or other animals. All animals are consumers.
- **Decomposers. Decomposers** break down dead organisms and make their materials available to other living things. Bacteria and saprophytic fungi are examples of decomposers.

REVIEW QUESTIONS

1. Complete the following chart.

BIOTIC FACTOR	DESCRIPTION	EXAMPLES
Producer		
Consumer		
Decomposer		

2. The living things that directly or indirectly affect the ecosystem are the ______________ factors.

Name________________________ Class________________________ Date____________

E. HABITATS AND NICHES. The place in the ecosystem where an organism lives is called its **habitat.** For example, an earthworm's habitat is moist soil. An organism's habitat is determined by abiotic and biotic factors. The factors an organism needs to survive determine where it lives.

Organisms also play a role in the ecosystem. This is called an organism's **niche**. The niche includes its feeding habits, where it lives in the ecosystem, its reproductive behavior, and what it contributes to its surroundings. In a freshwater pond community a carp (type of fish) eats decaying material from around the bases of underwater plants. In the same community snails scrape algae from the leaves and stems of the same plants. Both organisms live in the *same* pond habitat but they occupy *different* niches.

REVIEW QUESTIONS

1. What is the difference between a habitat and a niche? ________________________

____

____

F. BIOMES. The biosphere is organized into smaller parts known as biomes. A **biome** is a large geographic area of the earth identified by a particular type of dominant (most common) plant and animal life. Biomes may be **terrestrial** (land) or **aquatic** (water). This is determined by geography and climate (Figure 28-2). The major land biomes are the tundra, taiga, temperate deciduous forest, tropical rain forest, grassland, and desert biomes. The water biomes are marine (saltwater) and freshwater biomes.

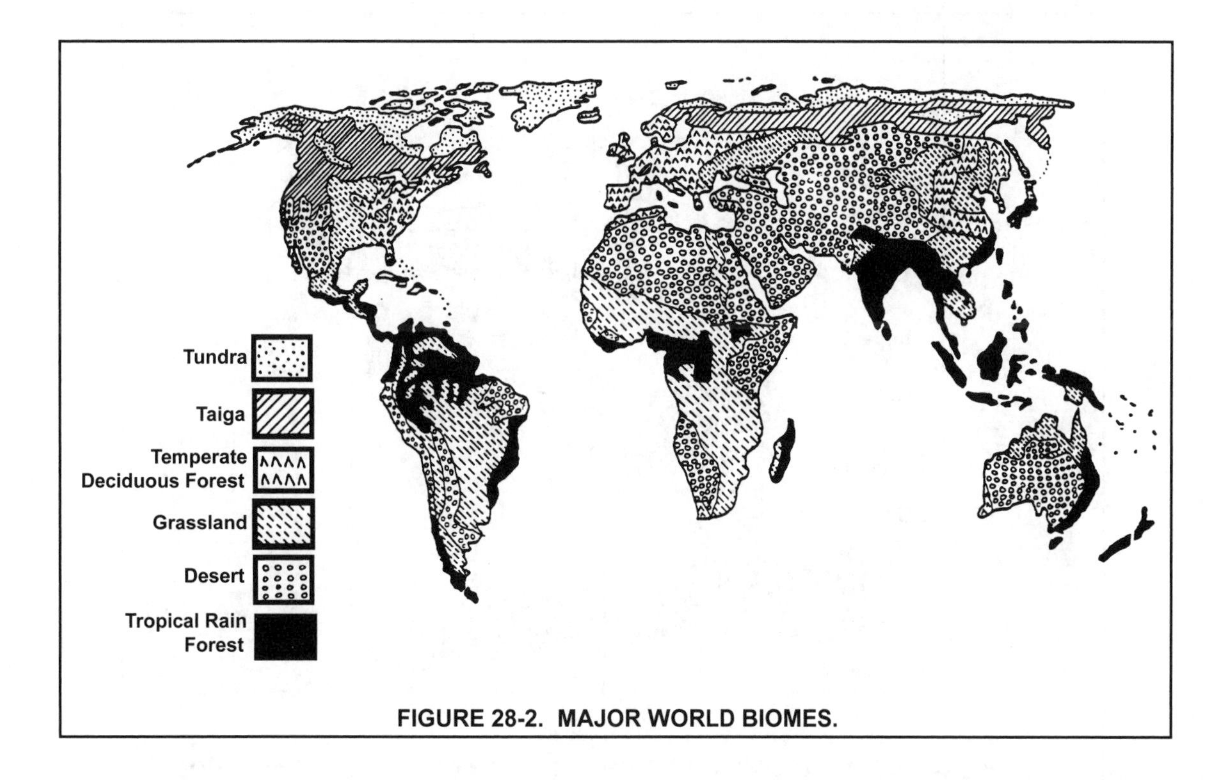

FIGURE 28-2. MAJOR WORLD BIOMES.

Name________________________ Class ________________________ Date ____________

REVIEW QUESTIONS

1. What is a biome? ____

____

2. A land biome is called a ____________________ biome and a water biome is known as a/an ____________________ biome.

3. List the major land biomes. ____

____

4. Name the two major water biomes. ____

____

G. LAND BIOMES. In land (terrestrial) biomes the major plant and animal groups are determined by the major climate zones of the earth. They are sometimes modified by local land and water conditions. Climates vary widely in temperature range, strength and duration of solar radiation, and amount of precipitation. The presence or absence of water is a major limiting factor for terrestrial biomes. Table 28-2, on the opposite page, describes the characteristics of the major land biomes.

The types of climate conditions and dominant communities present in an area are affected both by **latitude** (distance north or south of the Equator) and **altitude** (distance above or below sea level). Figure 28-3 below, shows this relationship. High up on a mountain at the Equator the climate and dominant vegetation would be similar to that of the taiga.

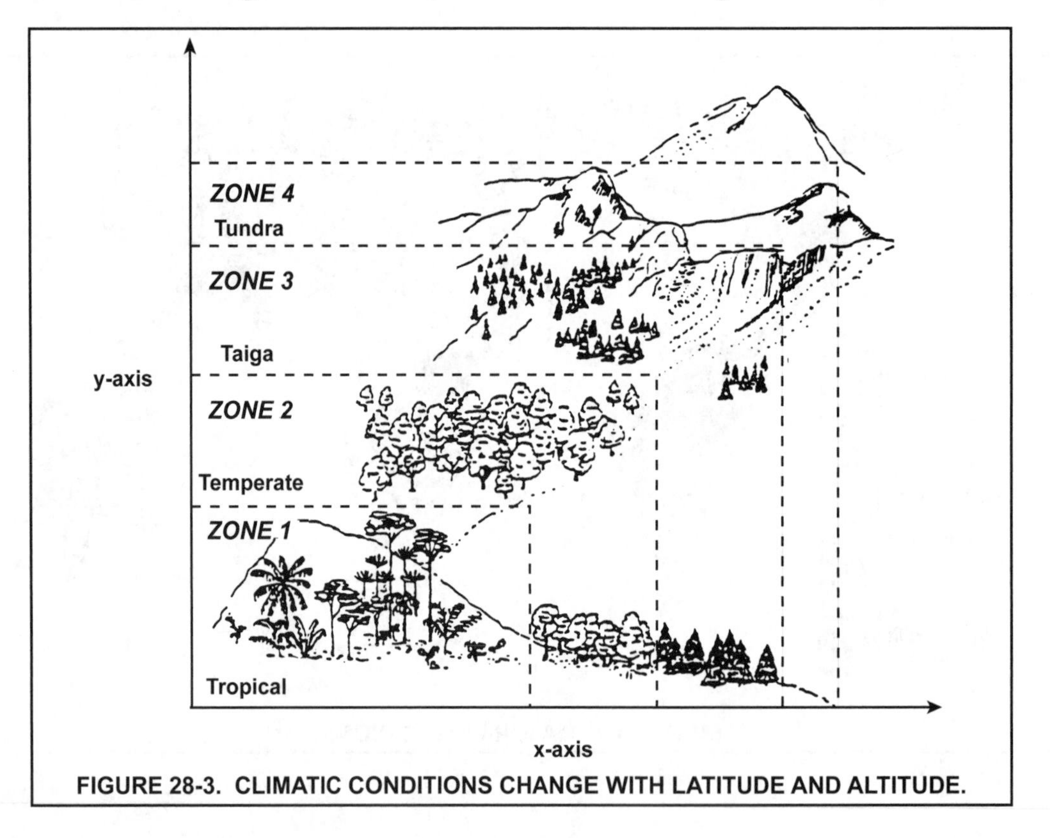

FIGURE 28-3. CLIMATIC CONDITIONS CHANGE WITH LATITUDE AND ALTITUDE.

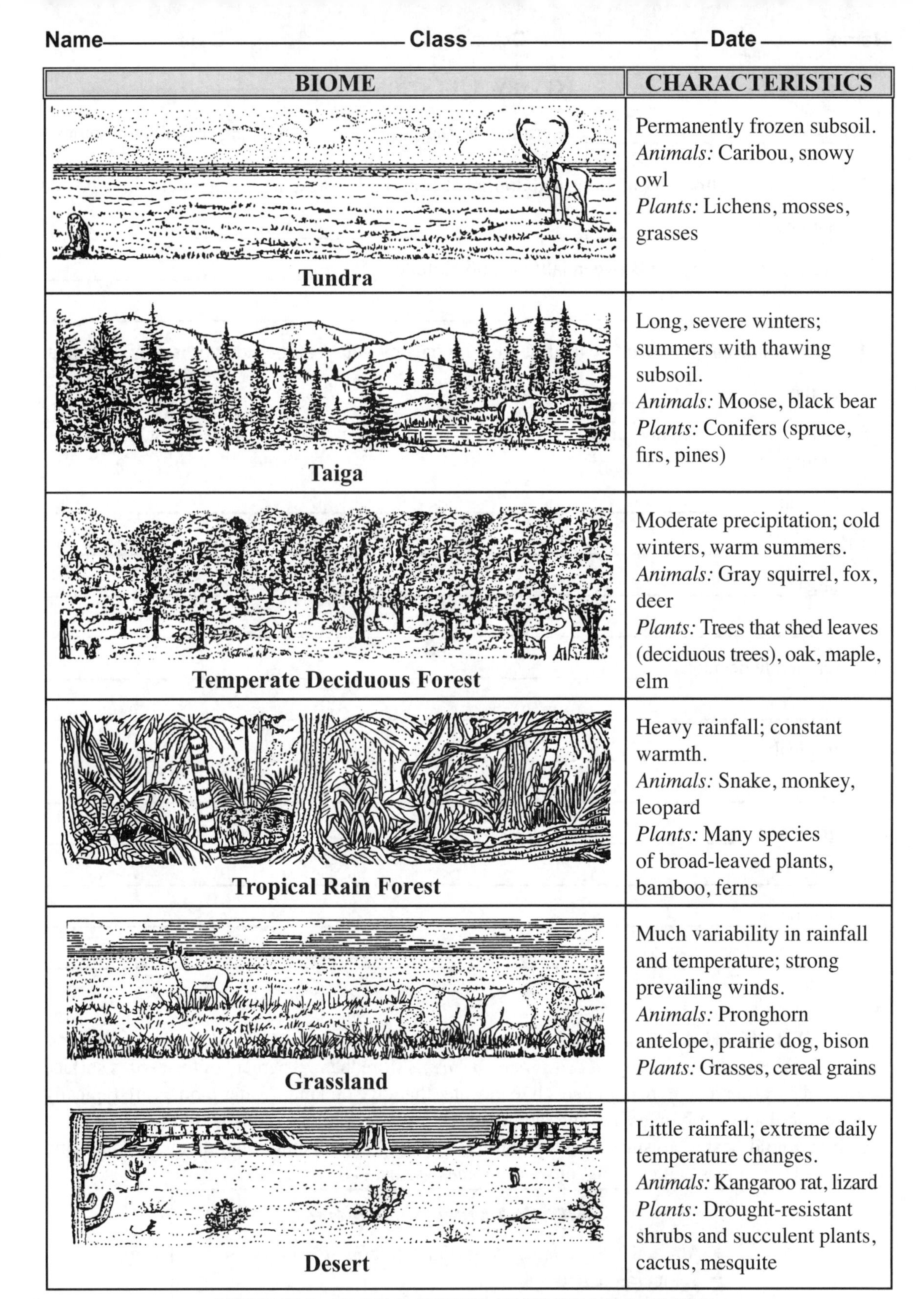

Name________________________ Class____________________ Date__________

BIOME	CHARACTERISTICS
Tundra	Permanently frozen subsoil. *Animals:* Caribou, snowy owl *Plants:* Lichens, mosses, grasses
Taiga	Long, severe winters; summers with thawing subsoil. *Animals:* Moose, black bear *Plants:* Conifers (spruce, firs, pines)
Temperate Deciduous Forest	Moderate precipitation; cold winters, warm summers. *Animals:* Gray squirrel, fox, deer *Plants:* Trees that shed leaves (deciduous trees), oak, maple, elm
Tropical Rain Forest	Heavy rainfall; constant warmth. *Animals:* Snake, monkey, leopard *Plants:* Many species of broad-leaved plants, bamboo, ferns
Grassland	Much variability in rainfall and temperature; strong prevailing winds. *Animals:* Pronghorn antelope, prairie dog, bison *Plants:* Grasses, cereal grains
Desert	Little rainfall; extreme daily temperature changes. *Animals:* Kangaroo rat, lizard *Plants:* Drought-resistant shrubs and succulent plants, cactus, mesquite

TABLE 28-2. CHARACTERISTIC OF MAJOR LAND BIOMES.

Name________________________ Class________________________ Date____________

Review Questions

1. ________________________ determine the major plant and animal groups in land biomes.

2. The types of climate conditions and dominant community present in an area are affected both by ________________________ and ________________________.

3. What is the difference between latitude and altitude? ________________________

____

4. The climate and dominant vegetation high up on a mountain at the Equator is similar to that of the ________________________ biome.

5. State the characteristics and two dominant plant and animal species of the following biomes.

tundra: ____

____

taiga: ____

____

temperate decidous: ____

____

tropical: ____

____

grassland: ____

____

desert: ____

____

H. WATER BIOMES. Water (aquatic) biomes include marine (saltwater) and freshwater biomes. *Aquatic biomes make up the largest ecosystem on earth*. More than 70 percent of the earth's surface is covered by water and more organisms live in water than live on land. Water biomes are typically more stable than land biomes and the temperature varies less because of the ability of water to absorb and hold heat. Moisture is not a limiting factor. Major factors that affect the kinds and numbers of organisms that can exist in water biomes are listed below.

Factors Affecting Water Biomes

- Amounts of available oxygen and carbon dioxide.
- Temperature and light.
- Amounts of dissolved minerals and suspended particles.

Name________________________ Class________________________ Date____________

The oceans of the earth make up **marine** (saltwater) biomes. They are continuous bodies of water that provide the most stable aquatic environment. Oceans also take in and hold large quantities of solar heat and help to stabilize the earth's atmosphere. They contain a relatively constant supply of nutrients and dissolved salts. Oceans also serve as habitats for large numbers of different organisms. Much of the photosynthesis on earth is carried on by algae near the surface of the oceans and along the edges of land masses (coastal waters). Light penetrates through water to a depth of about 30 meters (Figure 28-4). No photosynthesis occurs at greater depths.

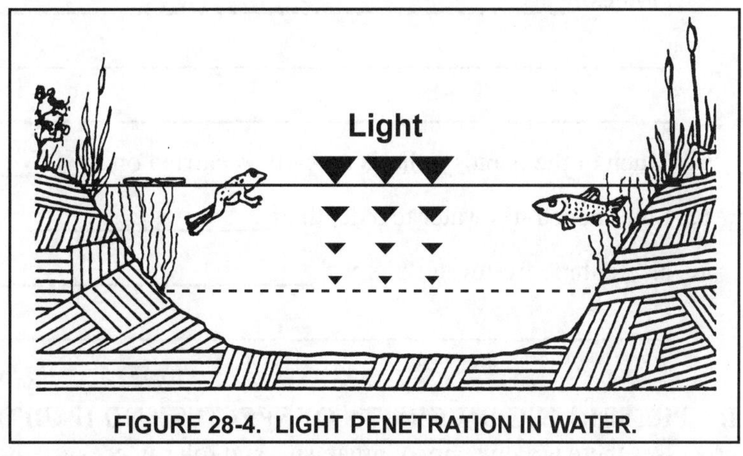

FIGURE 28-4. LIGHT PENETRATION IN WATER.

Freshwater biomes include ponds, lakes, streams, and rivers. These bodies of water show great variation in size, speed of the current, temperature, concentrations of dissolved gases and suspended particles, and rate of change.

Ponds and small lakes tend to fill in due to erosion of their banks and the gradual accumulation of sediments on the bottom formed from the remains of dead plants. Eventually the pond becomes a swamp and finally a land community develops (Figure 28-5).

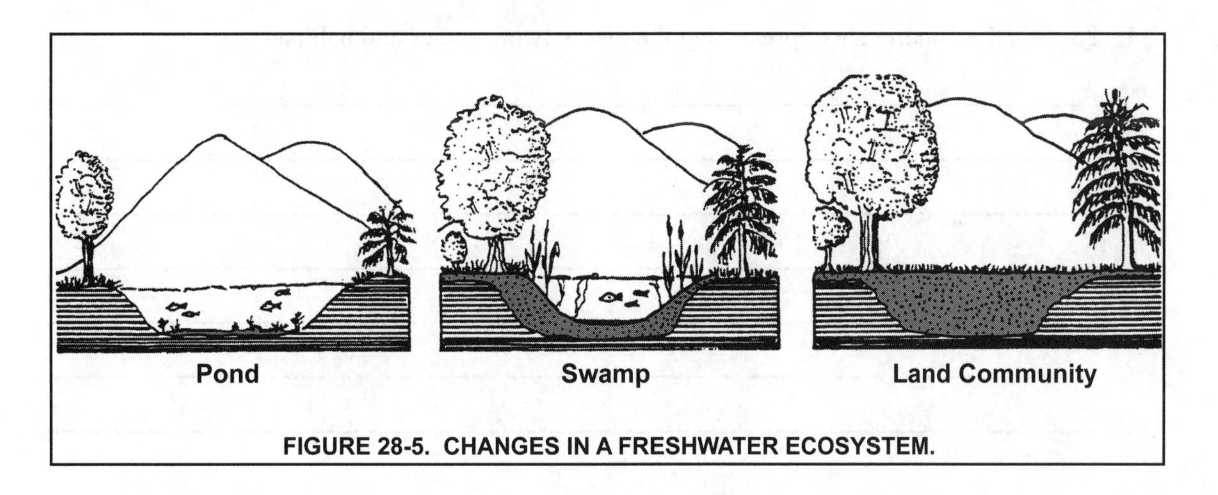

FIGURE 28-5. CHANGES IN A FRESHWATER ECOSYSTEM.

Review Questions

1. Name two types of water biomes. ____

____

2. More than 70 percent of the earth's surface is covered by ____________________.

3. ____________________ biomes are more stable than ____________________ biomes.

Name________________________Class________________________Date____________

4. List the major factors that affect the kinds and numbers of organisms that can exist in water biomes. ____

____

____

5. Much of the photosynthesis on earth is carried on by ____________________.

6. Light penetrates water to a depth of ____________________.

7. Name three freshwater biomes. ____

____

I. PRESERVING DIVERSITY OF SPECIES AND HABITATS. As a result of evolutionary processes there is a diversity of organisms and roles in ecosystems. This diversity of species, called **biodiversity**, increases the chance that at least some species will survive in the face of large environmental changes. Biodiversity also increases the stability of the ecosystem and ensures the availability of a rich variety of genetic material. This genetic variety is important because it may lead to future agricultural or medical discoveries that have significant value to the human population. As diversity is lost, potential sources of these materials may also be lost.

REVIEW QUESTIONS

1. Explain the importance of preserving the diversity of species and habitats.

____

____

____

____

____

____

____

Name________________________Class________________________Date____________

LAB INVESTIGATION: ECOSYSTEMS

Objective

Upon completion of this activity you should be able to identify the abiotic factors, biotic factors, consumers, producers, decomposers, populations, and communities that are present in an ecosystem.

Laboratory Procedure

Materials: A teacher constructed aquarium or terrarium and reference books.

1. Use either the aquarium or terrarium located in your classroom or the diagram on this page, as your teacher directs, to complete this lab investigation.

2. The aquarium or terrarium is a small ecosystem. An *ecosystem* is made up of living and nonliving things interacting and functioning together. A stable ecosystem needs a constant supply of energy such as sunlight or artificial light. There must also be living organisms that can change light energy into organic compounds. Finally, recycling of materials must take place between organisms and the environment.

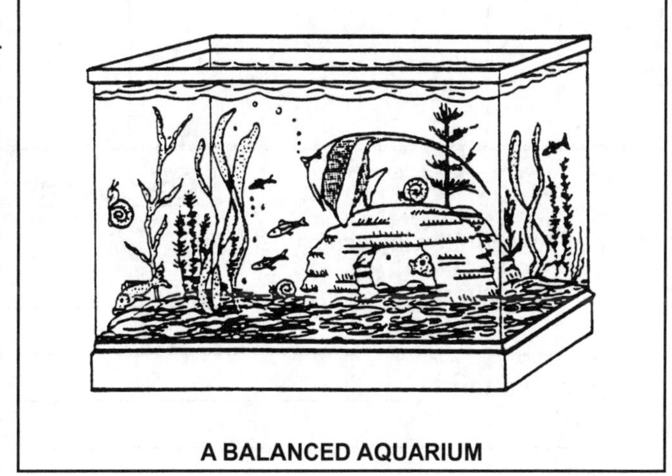

A BALANCED AQUARIUM

3. The nonliving things in the ecosystem are called the *abiotic factors*. Which abiotic factors are present in your ecosystem? Write your observations in the **Observation Table** in the **Observation Section** on the next page.

4. The living things in an ecosystem are the *biotic factors*. Which abiotic factors are present in your ecosystem? Write your observations in the **Observation Table** on the next page.

5. A *producer* is any plant that manufactures food by photosynthesis. Green plants are producers. Use your reference materials to help you identify the producers in your ecosystem. Write your observations in the **Observation Table** on the next page.

6. *Consumers* eat producers and/or other animals. All animals are consumers. Use your reference materials to help you identify the consumers in your ecosystem. Write your observations in the **Observation Table** on the next page.

7. Dead organisms are chemically broken down into simpler materials by *decomposers*. The materials are then recycled through the ecosystem for use by other organisms. Bacteria and saprophytic fungi are examples of decomposers. Use your reference materials to help you identify the decomposers in your ecosystem. Write your observations in the **Observation Table** on the next page.

Name________________________ Class________________________ Date____________

8. *Populations* include all the members of a species found in a particular location. Use your reference materials to help you identify the different populations in your ecosystem. Write your observations in the **Observation Table** on this page.

9. A *community* includes all the populations in the ecosystem. A woodland community, a saltwater community, and a freshwater community are some examples of communities. Use your reference materials to help you identify the type of community in your own ecosystem. Write your observations in the **Observation Table** on this page.

10. When you are finished with your laboratory activity, clean your lab area and return any materials to the supply table. Answer the questions in the **Conclusion Section**.

OBSERVATIONS

ABIOTIC FACTORS	BIOTIC FACTORS	PRODUCERS	CONSUMERS	DECOMPOSERS	POPULATIONS

CONCLUSIONS

1. Define the following ecological terms:

   Abiotic Factor: ____

   ____

   Biotic Factor: ____

   ____

   Producer: ____

   ____

   Consumer: ____

   ____

   Decomposer: ____

   ____

   Population: ____

   ____

   Community: ____

   ____

2. What type of a community is present in your ecosystem? ______________________

   ____

Name______________________ Class______________________ Date__________

REVIEW ACTIVITIES

Important Terms

DIRECTIONS: Define the following terms in the spaces provided.

abiotic ____

____

altitude ____

____

aquatic ____

____

biome ____

____

biosphere ____

____

biotic ____

____

community ____

____

consumer ____

____

decomposer ____

____

desert ____

____

ecology ____

____

ecosystem ____

____

freshwater biome ____

____

grassland ____

____

Name________________ Class________________ Date________

habitat ____________________

latitude ____________________

limiting factors ____________________

marine biome ____________________

niche ____________________

population ____________________

producer ____________________

taiga ____________________

temperate deciduous ____________________

terrestrial ____________________

tropical rain forest ____________________

tundra ____________________

Name________________________ Class____________________ Date__________

Skill Practice

Part A. Base your answers to questions 1 through 5 on the diagrams below that represent different land biomes and on your knowledge of biology.

A

B

C

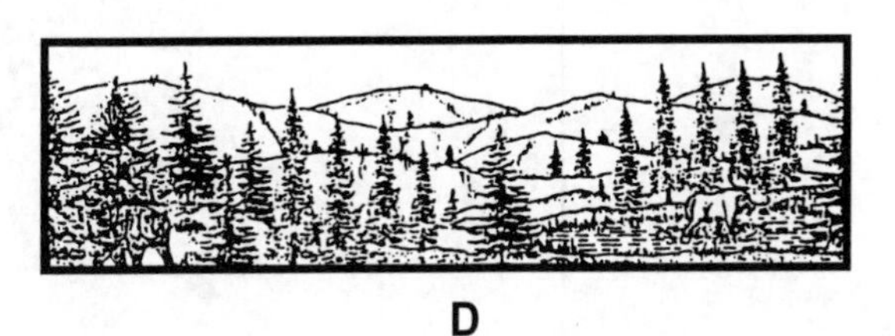
D

1. The biome represented by diagram D is known as a

(1) desert
(2) temperate deciduous forest
(3) taiga
(4) tundra

2. Which of the biomes *represented* is located at the highest altitudes and/or the highest latitudes?

(1) A
(2) B
(3) C
(4) D

3. Which biome has the greatest annual rainfall?

(1) A
(2) B
(3) C
(4) D

4. Daily changes in temperature would be greatest in the biome represented in diagram

(1) A
(2) B
(3) C
(4) D

5. Name the biome in the above diagram that is represented by each of the following letters.

A ______________________

B ______________________

C ______________________

D ______________________

Name________________________ Class____________________ Date__________

Part B. Base your answers to questions 1 through 4 on the diagram below and on your knowledge of biology. The diagram shows areas on a mountain that represent some major biomes.

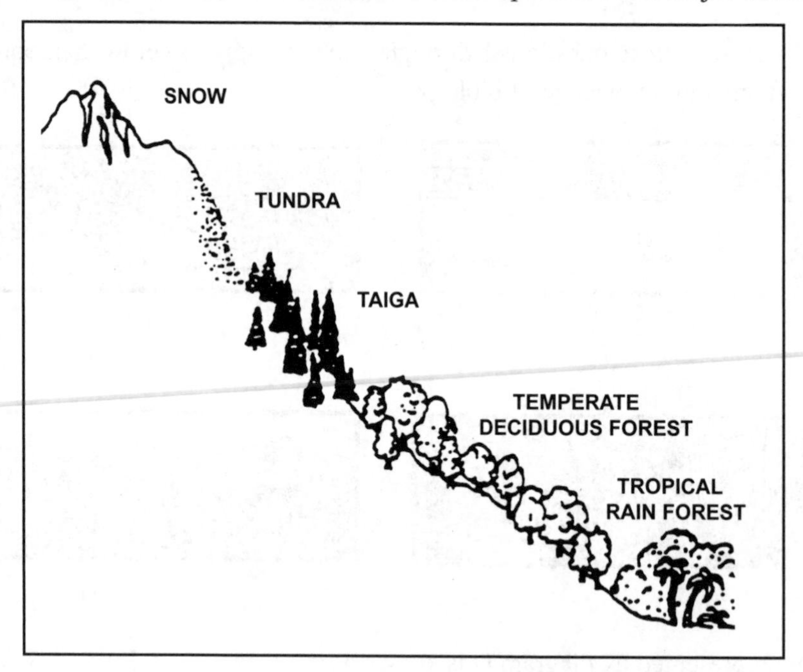

1. In which biome do lichens and mosses grow in large numbers and represent the dominant plant life?

(1) tundra
(2) taiga
(3) temperate deciduous forest
(4) tropical rain forest

2. The characteristic climax vegetation of which biome consists of coniferous (pine) trees?

(1) tundra
(2) taiga
(3) temperate deciduous forest
(4) tropical rain forest

3. Which major biome is found throughout most of New York State?

(1) tundra
(2) taiga
(3) temperate deciduous forest
(4) tropical rain forest

4. Which diagram below best shows the order of major land biomes that would be met by a person who travels north from the Equator to the polar region at a steady elevation?

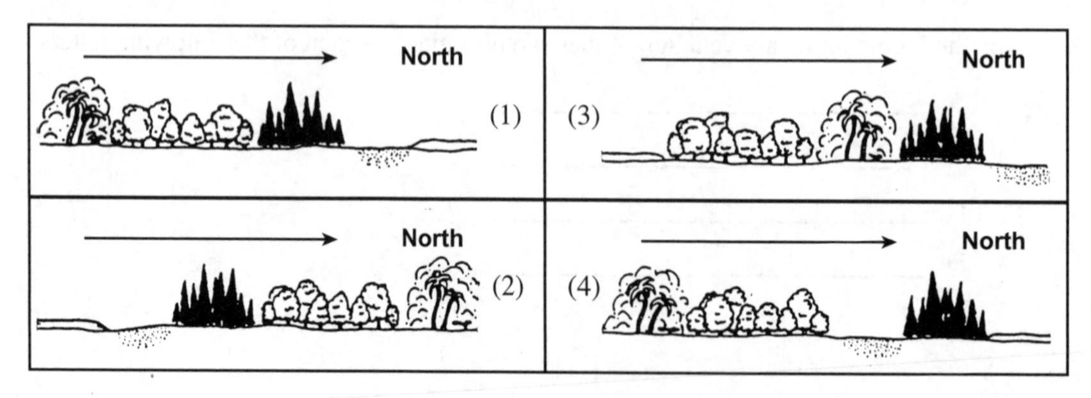

Name________________ Class________________ Date________

CHAPTER 28: QUIZ

A. FILL-IN QUESTIONS

DIRECTIONS: Complete each of the following statements by writing the correct word or phrase in the space provided.

1. A ______________ includes all the members of a species found in a given area.
2. Organisms that manufacture food are called ______________.
3. A balanced aquarium is an example of a/an ______________.
4. The place in the ecosystem where an organism lives is called its ______________.
5. All the populations in a particular area form a ______________.
6. Terrestrial biomes are ______________ biomes.
7. ______________ break down dead organisms.
8. A community and the physical environment together make up ______________.
9. ______________ is the distance above or below sea level.
10. The nonliving parts of the environment are the ______________ factors.
11. All ______________ are consumers.
12. The science that deals with organisms and their environment is called ______________.
13. ______________ is the distance north or south of the Equator.
14. Aquatic biomes are ______________ biomes.
15. The ______________ biome has permanently frozen subsoil.
16. The ______________ is the portion of the earth in which life exists.
17. ______________ trees shed their leaves in the fall.
18. The living things in the environment are the ______________ factors.
19. The biome that has little rainfall and extreme daily temperature changes is the ______________.
20. The role an organism plans in the environment is its ______________.

B. MULTIPLE-CHOICE QUESTIONS

DIRECTIONS: Circle the number of the expression that best completes each of the following statements.

1. The primary source of energy for life on Earth is
   (1) wood (3) oil
   (2) sunlight (4) coal
2. Which of the following organisms are classified as producers?
   (1) snakes and frogs (3) bacteria and molds
   (2) dogs and wolves (4) geraniums and algae
3. Decomposers are unable to break down
   (1) leaves (3) wood
   (2) plastic (4) cotton

Name________________ Class________________ Date________

Directions (4-6): Base your answers to questions 4 through 6 on your knowledge of biology and on the diagram of an aquarium containing water, soil, green plants, a snail, and a fish.

4. Which gas do the snail and fish release into the water?

(1) oxygen (3) carbon dioxide
(2) nitrogen (4) hydrogen

5. The fish in the aquarium functions as a

(1) producer (3) decomposer
(2) consumer (4) parasite

6. The gas released by the green plants is used by the snail for

(1) photosynthesis (3) excretion
(2) digestion (4) respiration

7. Which organism supplies oxygen to the others?

(1) snail (3) algae
(2) fish (4) protozoa

Directions (8-10): Base your answers to questions 8 through 10 on the information below and on your knowledge of biology.

A large bottle with a layer of mud on the bottom is filled with pond water. Several fish and some green plants are then added and the bottle is made airtight.

8. The living and nonliving contents of this bottle make up

(1) an ecosystem (3) a biome
(2) a population (4) a species

9. The green plants in this bottle are necessary as

(1) producers (3) saprophytes
(2) herbivores (4) consumers

10. When a fish in this bottle dies, the nitrogen from its body is released through the action of

(1) decomposers (3) algae
(2) producers (4) viruses

C. ESSAY QUESTION

DIRECTIONS: Use complete sentences to answer the question in this part.

1. Name two occupations where a knowledge of ecology would be useful.

____

____

____

____

____

Name________________________ Class____________________ Date__________

Chapter 29: Interactions in the Environment

A. FOOD RELATIONSHIPS. The food relationships in an ecosystem involve the interaction of organisms. In food relationships nutrients (food) are transferred from one organism to another. Nutrition is the life process by which organisms obtain and use food.

Nutritionally, organisms are either autotrophs or heterotrophs. Autotrophs can make their own food from inorganic compounds. Green plants are autotrophs. In an ecosystem autotrophs are also called producers. Heterotrophs (consumers) cannot make their own food and must obtain nutrients from the environment. Heterotrophs are classified according to the type of food they eat.

Food Relationships

- **Saprophytes. Saprophytes** include heterotrophic plants, bacteria, and fungi, that feed on dead and decaying organisms. They are also called decomposers.
- **Herbivores. Herbivores** are animals that feed on plants and plant materials. Cows, horses, and sheep are herbivores.
- **Carnivores. Carnivores** are animals that feed on other animals. Wolves, lions, and tigers are examples of carnivores.
  - **Predators** Carnivores that kill and consume their **prey** (animals killed) are called **predators.** Owls and wolves are predators.
  - **Scavengers.** Carnivores that feed on the dead animals they find are called **scavengers.** Buzzards and vultures are scavengers.
- **Omnivores. Omnivores** are animals that feed on both plants and animals. Humans are examples of omnivores.

REVIEW QUESTIONS

1. Complete the following table.

RELATIONSHIP	DESCRIPTION	EXAMPLES
Saprophytes		
Herbivores		
Carnivores		
Predators		
Scavengers		
Omnivores		

Name ______________________ Class ______________________ Date ______________

B. SYMBIOTIC RELATIONSHIPS. Another type of interaction that occurs in ecosystems is called symbiosis. **Symbiosis** involves organisms of different species living together in close association with at least one member of the association benefiting from the association. Examples of symbiotic relationships include mutualism, commensalism, and parasitism. (Figure 29-1).

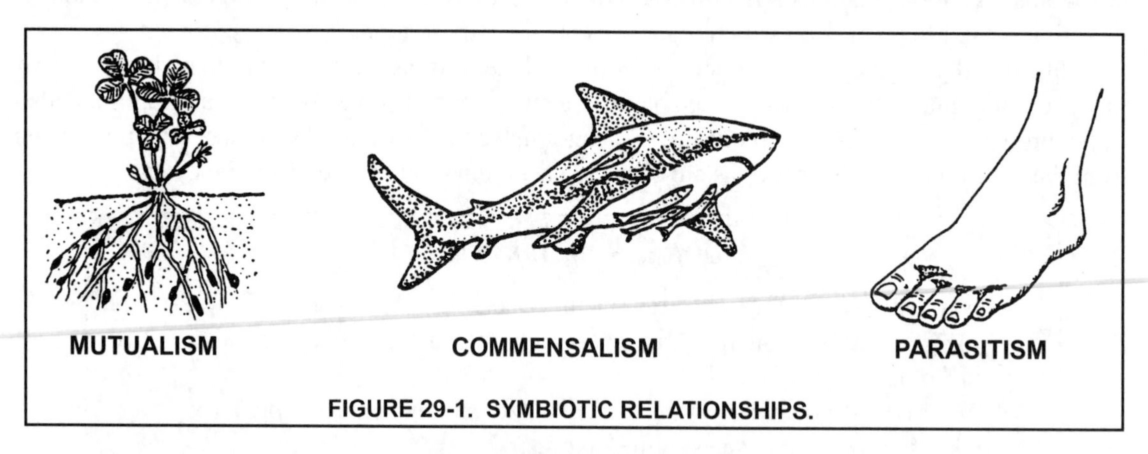

FIGURE 29-1. SYMBIOTIC RELATIONSHIPS.

Mutualism is a type of symbiotic relationship in which both organisms benefit. An example of organisms that exhibit mutualism is **nitrogen-fixing bacteria**—a type of bacteria that live in nodules (little knobs) on the roots of legumes. Legumes are plants such as peas and clover. The nitrogen-fixing bacteria make important nitrogen compounds that are used by the legumes and the legumes supply moisture and organic nutrients to the bacteria. In this way, both organisms benefit.

During **commensalism** two organisms of different species live in a relationship that is beneficial to one organism and the other organism is not affected. For example, sharks have a commensal relationship with a small fish called the remora. The remora attaches itself to the shark's body with little suction cups. The remora gets scraps of uneaten food from the shark and the shark is not harmed by the association.

During **parasitism** one organism, called the **parasite,** benefits and the other organism, called the **host**, is harmed. Athlete's foot fungus in humans and digestive tract tapeworms are examples of parasitism. The parasites (fungus and tapeworm) feed on the host organism. The host is harmed and the parasite benefits.

REVIEW QUESTIONS

1. Organisms of different species living together in close association where at least one member of the association benefits (gains) by the association is called ______________.
2. ______________ is a symbiotic relationship from which both organisms benefit.
3. During ______________ two organisms of different species live in a relationship that is beneficial to one and the other is not affected.
4. During parasitism the organism that benefits is called the ______________ and the organism that is harmed is called the ______________.

Name________________________ Class________________ Date__________

C. FOOD CHAINS. Food passes through an ecosystem in a certain path called a **food chain**. A food chain involves the transfer of food materials from producer to consumer and from one consumer to the next. The general pattern for a food chain is as follows:

PRODUCER ORGANISM → PRIMARY CONSUMER → SECONDARY CONSUMER

Green plants and other photosynthetic organisms are the producers in an ecosystem. Producers change the energy of sunlight into the chemical energy of food. Consumers eat the producers and in turn are eaten by other consumers. A series of repeated stages of eating and being eaten results a transfer of energy throughout an ecosystem.

Figure 29-2 represents a simple food chain. The producer is the green plant. Producers and other photosynthetic organisms make the organic nutrients (food) that supply energy directly or indirectly to other members of the community. In this diagram the grasshopper is eating the green plant. The grasshopper is called the first level or primary consumer. **Primary consumers** are *always* herbivores because they are animals that eat green plants.

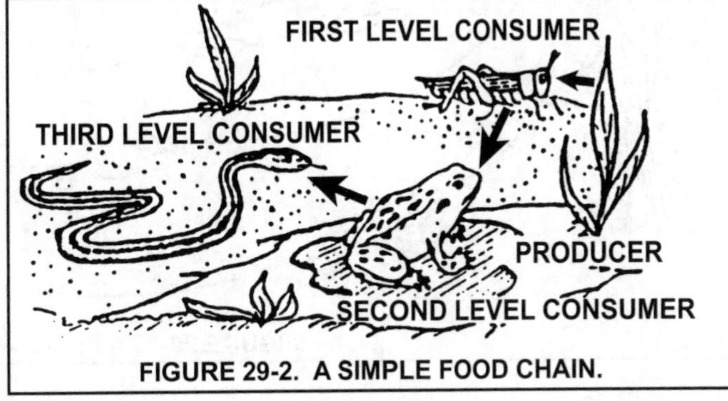

FIGURE 29-2. A SIMPLE FOOD CHAIN.

The frog in the diagram is called the secondary or second level consumer. **Secondary consumers** (carnivores) are animals that eat other animals (consumers). These include predators that kill and eat their prey, and scavengers that feed on dead animals that they find. (Omnivores can be primary or secondary consumers.) Organisms that eat secondary consumers are also called **higher-level consumers**. Because the snake is eating the frog, it is considered both a **third level consumer** and a higher-lever consumer.

Decomposers are found at all levels of a food chain. This is because all organisms eventually die and are then broken down chemically. The chemical materials formed are returned to the environment for use by other living organisms.

REVIEW QUESTIONS

1. What is a food chain? ______________________________

____

____

2. State the difference between a primary consumer and a secondary consumer.

____

____

____

3. At what level of a food chain would you find a decomposer? ______________________________

____

Name ____________ Class ____________ Date ____________

D. FOOD WEBS. In a natural community there are many interconnecting food chains. This is because most organisms eat more than one type of food, and most organisms are consumed (eaten) by more than one species of organism. The flow of energy and materials is much more complicated than a simple food chain. The interconnecting food chains of an ecosystem form a **food web** (Figure 29-3).

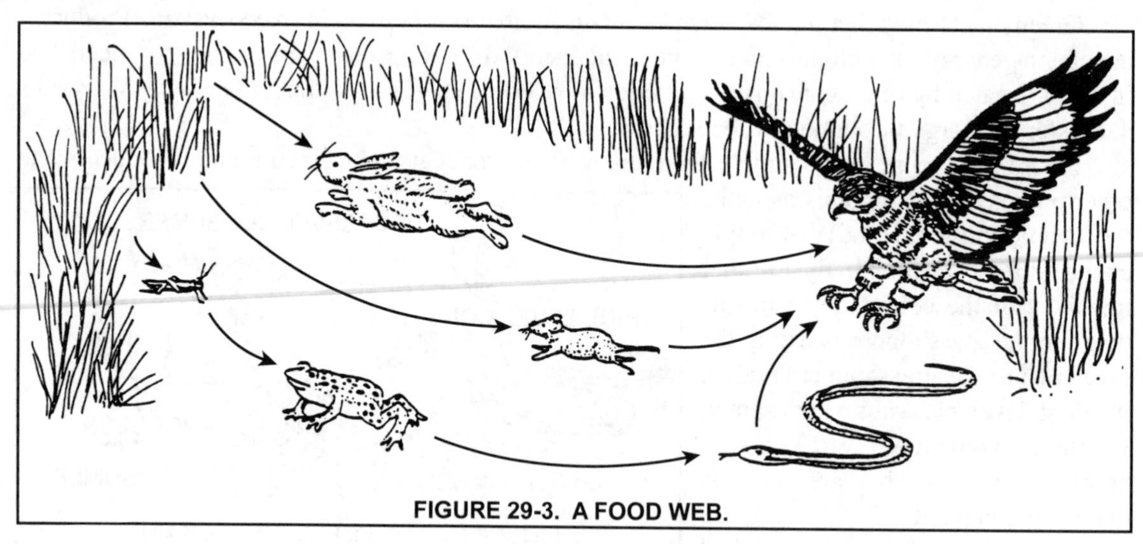

FIGURE 29-3. A FOOD WEB.

REVIEW QUESTIONS

1. What is a food web? ____________

____

2. Use the diagram of a food web above to name the following:

herbivores: ____________

____

carnivores: ____________

____

primary consumers: ____________

____

secondary consumers: ____________

____

producers: ____________

____

Name________________________ Class________________________ Date____________

E. PYRAMID OF ENERGY. An important use of food is for energy. At each step of a food web energy is transferred to the next higher level. Energy from the sun is transferred from producer to primary consumer and from primary consumer to secondary consumer. Sunlight is the original source of energy for all organisms in a food pyramid.

This energy transfer is not efficient because much of the food energy taken in by a consumer is used during the processes of metabolism. Energy is "lost" at each food level therefore less energy is available to the higher levels of the food chain than to the lower levels. At each consumer level only about 10 percent of ingested nutrients are used to make new body tissues that represent food for the next feeding level. The rest of the energy is lost as heat and unavailable chemical energy. This concept is often represented by a pyramid. In a food web the greatest amount of energy is at the producer level. This is why the producer level is shown at the bottom of the pyramid. The amount of usable energy decreases with each higher feeding level forming a **pyramid of energy** (Figure 29-4).

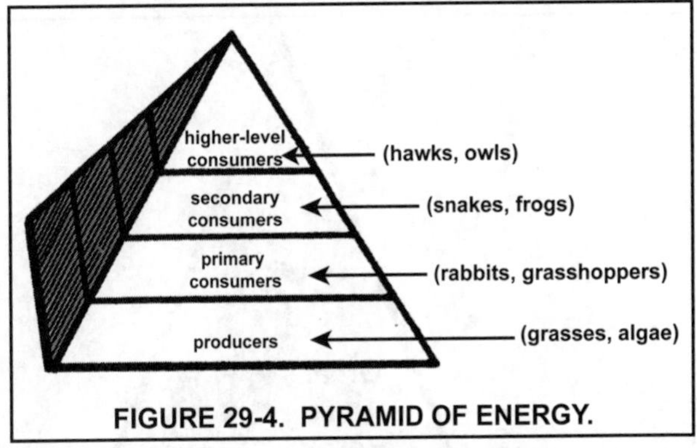

FIGURE 29-4. PYRAMID OF ENERGY.

REVIEW QUESTIONS

1. Why is the energy transfer in a food web inefficient? ________________________
____
____

2. A pyramid of energy shows usable energy ____________________ with each higher feeding level.

3. At each consumer level only about ______________ percent of ingested nutrients are used to make new body tissues. The rest of the energy is lost as ____________________ and unavailable ____________________.

Directions (4-6): Base your answers to questions 4 through 6 on the diagram at the right that represents a food pyramid of organisms living in a pond.

D
Bass
C
Minnows
B
Copepods
A
Algae

4. At which level of the food pyramid is the *smallest* percentage of total stored energy found?
   (1) A
   (2) B
   (3) C
   (4) D

5. Which organisms in the food pyramid function as primary consumers?
   (1) bass
   (2) minnows
   (3) copepods
   (4) algae

6. What is the original source of energy for all organisms in this food pyramid?
   (1) water
   (2) sunlight
   (3) the substratum
   (4) carbon dioxide

Name________________ Class________________ Date________

F. PYRAMID OF BIOMASS. The amount of organic matter in an ecosystem is called its **biomass**. This pyramid shows that the total amount of biomass that an ecosystem can support decreases at each high higher feeding level because there is less available energy at each level. The greatest amount of biomass is found at the producer level and decreases with each higher feeding level. For example, in the following simple food chain: **[GRASS⇒SHEEP⇒HUMANS]**; thousands of pounds of grass are needed to support one sheep over its lifetime and hundreds of sheep would be needed to feed one human for a lifetime.

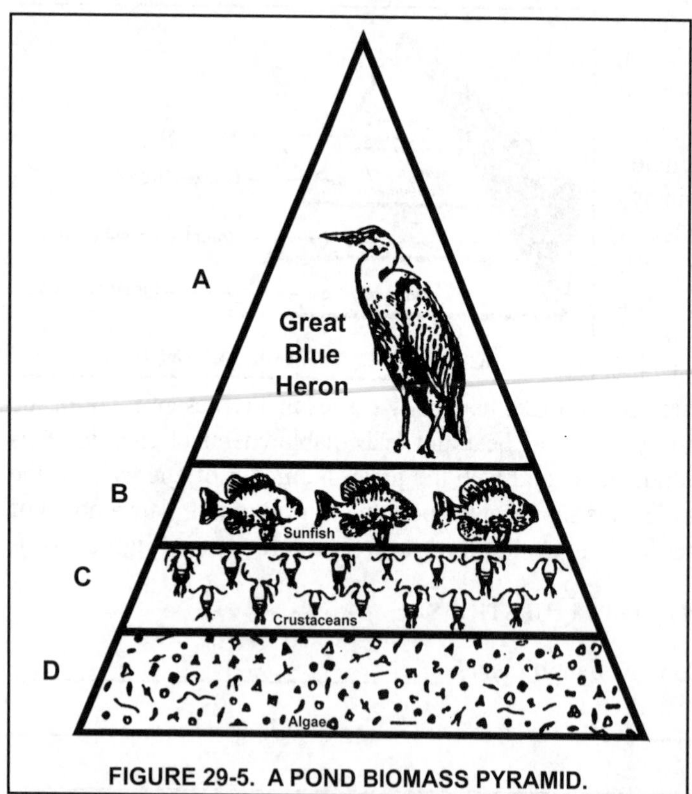

FIGURE 29-5. A POND BIOMASS PYRAMID.

Figure 29-5 represents a biomass pyramid for a pond ecosystem. Level D is the producer level. It contains the aquatic green plant algae. The crustaceans are primary consumers (herbivores). The crustaceans (small animals) feed on algae. Notice that the biomass of the algae is greater than that of the crustaceans. Sunfish are the secondary consumers because they feed on the crustaceans. Again, many crustaceans are required to support fewer sunfish. The highest level consumer in this example is the great blue heron. Many sunfish are needed to feed one heron.

REVIEW QUESTIONS

1. What is biomass? ____

____

2. Draw a pyramid of biomass using the example below. Label the producers, primary consumers, and secondary consumers.

[GRASS ⟶ SHEEP ⟶ HUMANS]

Name________________________ Class________________________ Date____________

G. MATERIAL CYCLES. In a self-supporting ecosystem, materials must be recycled between the living and nonliving environment so that they can be reused. The three major material cycles are shown in Table 29-1.

MATERIAL CYCLE	IMPORTANCE
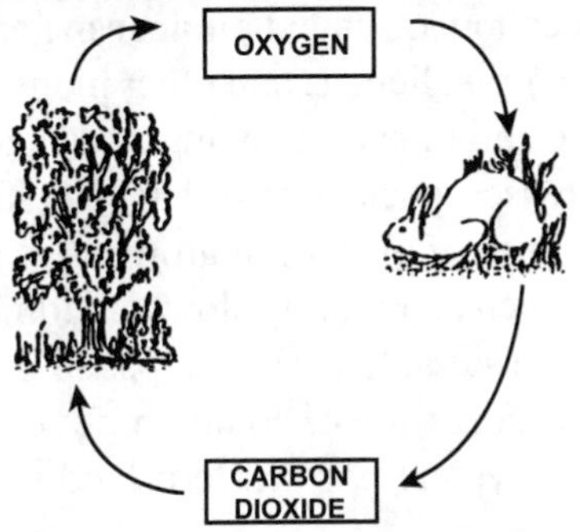 OXYGEN CARBON DIOXIDE The Carbon-Oxygen Cycle	Involves the processes of cellular respiration and photosynthesis. During photosynthesis water and carbon dioxide are used to produce carbohydrates—compounds made up of carbon, hydrogen, and oxygen. Oxygen is released as a by-product of photosynthesis. In respiration, oxygen is used for the oxidation of carbohydrates and carbon dioxide and water are released.
 The Water Cycle	Mainly a physical process involving the evaporation of water from the surface of the earth and the condensation of rain, snow, dew, etc. Water in the form of vapor is also given off by transpiration in plants and as a waste product of respiration. During **evaporation** water is changed into water vapor and during **condensation** water vapor is changed back into water.
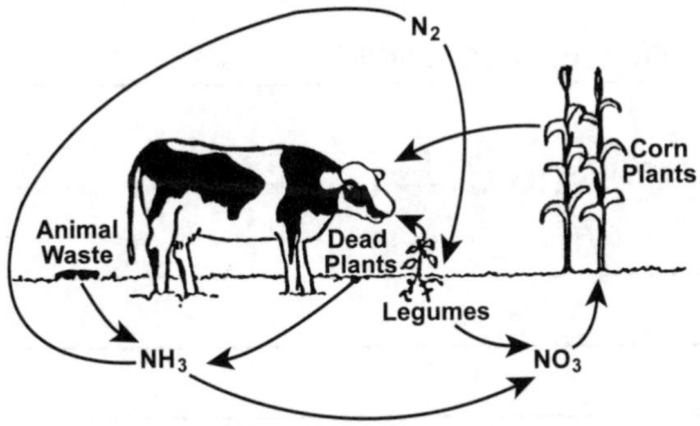 N_2 Corn Plants Animal Waste Dead Plants Legumes NH_3 NO_3 The Nitrogen Cycle	Nitrogenous wastes and the remains of dead organisms are converted by decomposers and soil bacteria into compounds that can be used by autotrophs.

TABLE 29-1. MATERIAL CYCLES.

REVIEW QUESTIONS

1. Name the three major material cycles. ____

____

Name________________ Class________________ Date__________

H. ECOLOGICAL SUCCESSION. The gradual replacement of one community by another is called **ecological succession.** Ecological succession eventually leads to the formation of a stable community. A stable community is called a **climax community**.

Ecological succession occurs in steps or stages. The first stage in a land succession usually begins with bare rock. Lichens are one of the first organisms to appear because they are able to live on bare rock. The first organisms to populate a given location are called **pioneer organisms.** Each stage in a succession *changes* the environment. For example, lichens and other pioneer organisms break off small bits of rock. These organisms die at the end of each growing season and add their remains (organic matter) to the rock particles. As time passes, pockets of soil develop from the rock particles and organic matter. When this happens other types of plants can grow in the soil pockets. The new plants form a different community. In this way each community slowly modifies (changes) the environment. The changed environment is often more suitable for new types of organisms and less suitable for the existing organisms. This process of succession of communities continues until a climax community is formed. The major stages in a typical northeastern land succession are shown in Figure 29-7.

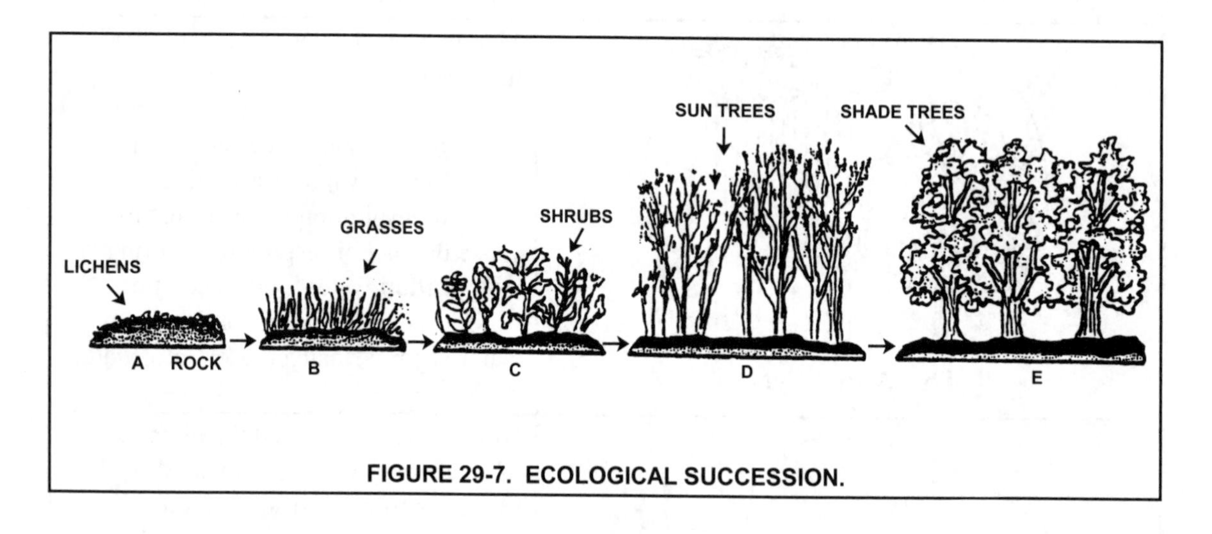

FIGURE 29-7. ECOLOGICAL SUCCESSION.

REVIEW QUESTIONS

1. What is an ecological succession? ____________________________

____

____

2. A stable community is called a ____________________ community.

3. ____________________ organisms are the first organisms to populate an area.

4. In an ecological succession the changed environment often is ____________________ suitable for new types of organisms and ____________________ suitable for the existing organisms.

Name________________________ Class________________________ Date____________

I. CLIMAX COMMUNITIES. When environmental conditions in an ecosystem remain stable over long periods of time, the same species of plants and animals that make up that ecosystem continue to live and interact together generation after generation. These permanent plant and animal species make up a stable or climax community.

A climax community is a self-perpetuating community in which the populations remain the same because they are in balance with one another and with the environment. A climax community remains the same until a drastic environmental change occurs. Such an event can involve either biotic or abiotic factors. Storm damage, forest fires, floods, and volcanic eruptions are environmental changes that can destroy a climax community. Because of environmental change, some species may be replaced by other species. These changes occur over long periods of time and cause the formation of new climax communities. The new community can be the same type or different from the last climax community.

The types of climax communities present in an ecosystem are determined by the abiotic factors of the area. They are named by the dominant plant species that develop in an the area. Because plants make up most of the biomass of the community, plants are the most abundant food source for animals. Therefore, the types of animals found in a community are, in part, determined by the types of plants present in the community. The world biomes—tundra, taiga, temperate deciduous, tropical rain forest, grasslands, and desert are examples of large climax communities. Oak-hickory, hemlock-beech-maple, pine barrens, sand dunes, and sphagnum bogs are examples of smaller climax communities.

REVIEW QUESTIONS

1. Describe a stable community. ________________________________

____

____

____

2. Name two environmental changes that can disrupt a stable community.

____

____

3. List five climax communities. ________________________________

____

____

____

____

Name________________________ Class________________________ Date__________

J. POPULATION INTERACTIONS. All the interacting individuals of the same species in a limited geographic area make up a population. The interactions that take place within a population may include those associated with individual or group survival. Food-getting, territorial defense, or reproductive behavior are examples of interactions that occur within populations.

REVIEW QUESTIONS

1. The interactions that occur within a population may include those associated with

   ____________________ and ____________________ survival.

2. Name two kinds of population interactions. ____________________

   ____

♦ **Stable Populations.** Under stable environmental conditions, the number of organisms in naturally occurring populations remains constant with only small periodic changes. A population's size is kept in check by a variety of limiting factors. These factors reduce the increase in population that would normally be expected through reproduction. Limiting factors may include food resources, water resources, disease, predation, and living space. For example, the mouse population is kept in check by the owl population. Without owls preying on mice, the mouse population would greatly increase. Instead, it remains relatively stable. Owls, as mouse predators, act as limiting factors in this example.

REVIEW QUESTIONS

1. Under stable environmental conditions, the number of organisms in naturally occurring

   populations remains ____________________.

2. Name two factors that limit population size. ____________________

   ____

3. Describe a predator-prey relationship that acts as a limiting factor.

   ____

   ____

   ____

   ____

♦ **Unstable Populations.** Though a combination of natural and human interactions, some species have been drastically reduced in number. Many such species are classified as "endangered". This means that without some form of human protection the entire species may completely disappear (become extinct). Examples of endangered species are the blue whale and timber wolf. Examples of extinct species are the great auk and the passenger pigeon. Endangered or extinct animal species are studied in the following chapter.

Name________________________ Class ______________________ Date __________

REVIEW QUESTIONS

1. A species that is endangered may become ____________________.
2. Name two endangered species. ______________________________

   ____
3. Name two extinct species. ______________________________

   ____

♦ **Exploding Populations.** Occasionally conditions may temporarily favor the rapid reproduction of a species leading to a "population explosion." Such explosions are usually followed by a rapid decline in population due to limiting factors. Examples of organisms in which exploding populations occured are algal blooms in polluted lakes, Kaibab deer in the early 1900's, and some gypsy moth populations.

REVIEW QUESTIONS

1. What is a population explosion? ______________________________

   ____
2. State an example of a population explosion. ______________________

   ____

   ____

K. COMPETITION. Competition occurs when there is a struggle for the same limited resources among organisms living in the same habitat (environment). Some of these resources are food, space, water, light, oxygen, and minerals. Competition is more intense (strong) if the needs of the organisms involved are very similar. Competition sometimes results in the elimination of one species when two different species compete for the same food or reproductive site (place). This usually establishes one species per niche in a community. *Note:* The bluebird population in New York State is close to extinction because they are competing with the starling population for reproductive sites.

REVIEW QUESTIONS

1. When does competition occur? ______________________________

   ____
2. When is competition more intense? ______________________________

   ____

Name________________ Class________________ Date________

CAREER OPPORTUNITIES

ECOLOGY CAREERS: People interested in working with plants and animals and the environment have many careers from which to choose. Some careers call for many years of education after high school and others do not. Some ecology careers, and the amount of study and/or training they require, are described below.

Aquatic biologists study the interactions of plants and animals that live in water biomes. Four to seven years of study beyond high school is required for this career. Forestry aides need only one or two years of post high school study. **Forestry aides** collect and read data, monitor instruments, stream flow, rain gauges, and do road surveys. **Physical scientists** observe environmental changes and test natural resources. This career involves four to eight years of training beyond high school. **Game wardens** need one to four years of training. They monitor animals in parks or preserves. **Park rangers** study and monitor organisms and conditions in public parks. Part of their job is to instruct the public about plants and animals. Fours years of study is needed to become a park ranger. **Wildlife attendants** need no post high school training. This job involves caring for animals in parks, hatcheries, refuges, and animal conservation areas. **Botanists, morphologists,** and **botanical pathologists** all must study and train from four to eight years after high school. These careers involve the study of the relationship between plant, environments, plant structures, and plant diseases.

All of these ecology careers have one thing in common—people who love to work out of doors with plants and animals.

*****

REVIEW QUESTIONS

1. Name five careers that are available to people who are interested in ecology.

____

____

____

____

____

____

____

Name________________________ Class________________________ Date____________

LAB INVESTIGATION: CONSTRUCTING A FOOD WEB

OBJECTIVE

Upon completion of this activity you should be able to construct a food web and identify the members of a food chain.

LABORATORY PROCEDURE

Materials: A collection of magazines containing pictures of plants and animals, scissors, glue stick, reference books, and black markers.

1. Pick up your materials at the supply table and take them to your lab area.

2. In this lab you will construct a food web using pictures of organisms that you will cut out of your magazines. A *food web* is made up of many interconnecting food chains. A *food chain* is a path through which food passes in an ecosystem. A food chain involves the transfer of food and energy from producer to consumer and from one consumer to the next. The general pattern for a food chain is as follows:

PRODUCER ORGANISM ⟶ PRIMARY CONSUMER ⟶ SECONDARY CONSUMER

3. A *producer* is any plant that manufactures food by photosynthesis. Green plants are producers. *Consumers* eat producers and/or other animals. All animals are consumers. *Primary consumers* are plant-eaters (*herbivores). Secondary consumers,* or *carnivores* eat other animals.

4. The diagram on this page represents a food web located in and around a meadow environment. There are decomposers present at every level of a food chain. A *decomposer* chemically breaks down dead organisms and returns the materials back into the environment. In this diagram the decomposers are placed around the sides.

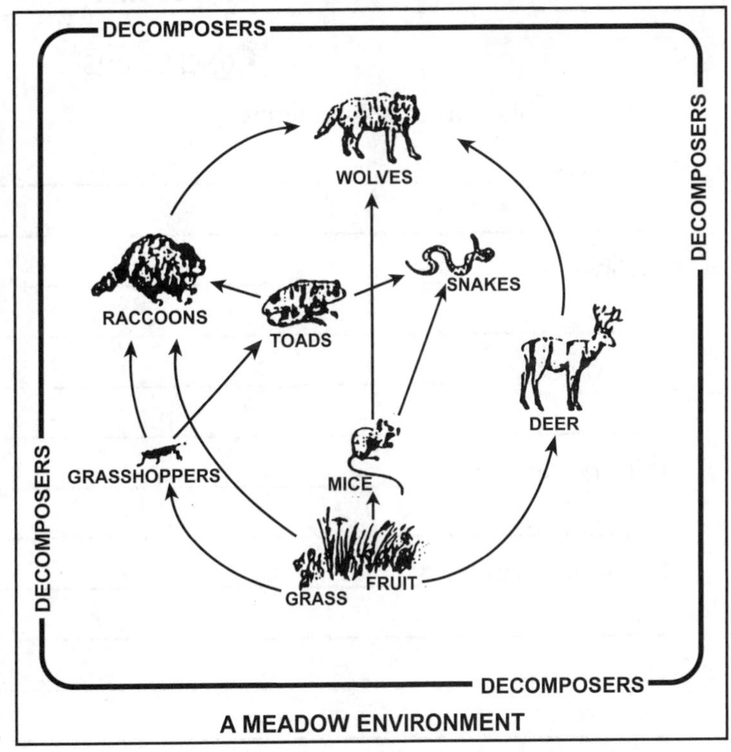

A MEADOW ENVIRONMENT

5. Use your scissors to cut out pictures of plants and animals that interact in food chains. Your reference materials will help you identify the organisms in your food chains. Construct a food web by pasting the pictures of your organisms in the **Observation Section** on the next page. Draw a line from each organism to the organism that eats it.

Name________________ Class________________ Date________

6. When you are finished with your laboratory activity clean your lab area and return any materials to the supply table. Answer the questions in the **Conclusion Section**.

Observations

A FOOD WEB

Conclusions

1. Define the following ecological terms:

   Producers: ______________________

   ____

   Herbivores: ______________________

   ____

   Carnivores: ______________________

   ____

   Primary Consumers: ______________________

   ____

   Secondary Consumers: ______________________

   ____

   Decomposers: ______________________

   ____

2. State the relationship between a food chain and a food web. ______________________

   ____

Name________________________ Class________________________ Date__________

REVIEW ACTIVITIES

Important Terms

***DIRECTIONS:** Define the following terms in the spaces provided.*

biomass ____

____

carbon-oxygen cycle ____

____

carnivores ____

____

climax community ____

____

commensalism ____

____

competition ____

____

condensation ____

____

evaporation ____

____

food chain ____

____

food web ____

____

herbivores ____

____

host ____

____

mutualism ____

____

nitrogen cycle ____

____

Name____________________ **Class**____________________ **Date**__________

omnivores ____

parasite ____

parasitism ____

pioneer organisms ____

predators ____

prey ____

primary consumer ____

saprophytes ____

scavengers ____

secondary consumer ____

succession ____

symbiosis ____

water cycle ____

Name______________________ Class______________________ Date______________

Skill Practice

Part A. Base your answers to questions 1 through 7 on the diagram below and on your knowledge of biology.

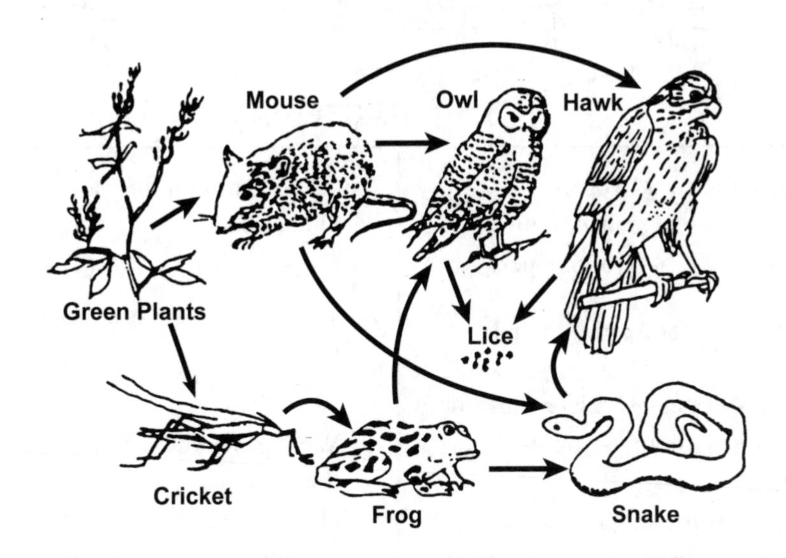

1. The diagram best represents
   (1) part of a food chain
   (2) part of a food web
   (3) ecological succession
   (4) a classification system

2. The organisms that are most likely present in the largest numbers are
   (1) green plants (3) owls
   (2) hawks (4) snakes

3. According to the diagram, the mouse is a source of food for how many different types of organisms?
   (1) 1 (3) 3
   (2) 2 (4) 4

4. Which is a parasitic relationship?
   (1) cricket⇒frog
   (2) hawk⇒lice
   (3) green plant⇒mouse
   (4) frog⇒snake

5. Which organisms are the herbivores?
   (1) cricket and mouse
   (2) frog and owl
   (3) snake and hawk
   (4) green plants and lice

6. Which food pyramid is represented in the diagram.

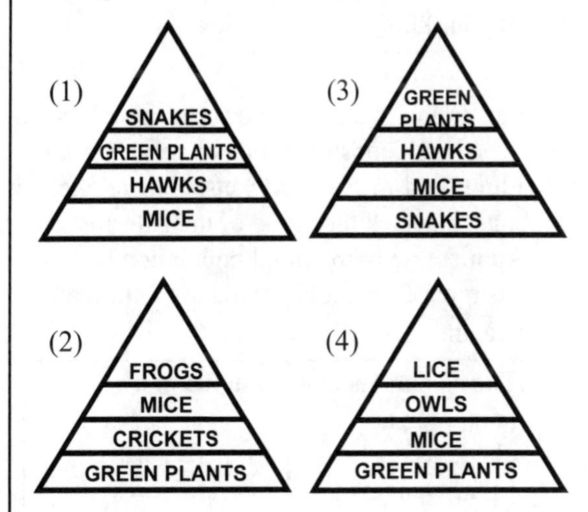

7. Which statement about the diagram is correct?
   (1) Energy is lost in each step from producer to consumer.
   (2) The greatest number of individuals in the diagram are the hawks.
   (3) Snakes are eaten by mice.
   (4) The hawks are the producers.

Name________________________ Class________________________ Date__________

Part B. Base your answers to questions 1 through 5 on the organisms represented in the diagram below.

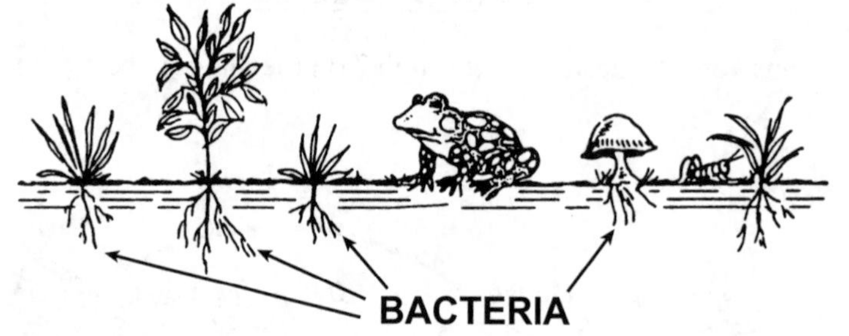

1. Which organism is a carnivore?
   (1) grass (3) mushroom
   (2) frog (4) grasshopper

2. Which is a possible food chain in this diagram?
   (1) frog→grasshopper→grass→mushroom
   (2) bacteria→mushroom→frog→grasshopper
   (3) grass→frog→grasshopper→bacteria
   (4) grass→grasshopper→frog→bacteria

3. The mushroom functions as
   (1) herbivore (3) a decomposer
   (2) a producer (4) an omnivore

4. Which organism is a producer?
   (1) grass (3) grasshopper
   (2) frog (4) mushroom

5. What gas given off by the frog is used by the grass?
   (1) carbon dioxide (3) oxygen
   (2) nitrogen (4) ammonia

Part C. Base your answers to questions 1 through 5 on the information in the following passage and on your knowledge of biology.

Life in a Cave

Bats living in a cave go outside at night to feed on flying insects and return to the cave for the day. The bats deposit mounds of solid waste on the floor of the cave. Molds grow on this waste providing food for cave crickets. The crickets, in turn, are food for the other insects and spiders. Bat bugs that suck the blood of the bats are also found in the cave.

An increase in the mold population is followed by an increase in the number of crickets. The crickets reduce the mold population until many crickets starve to death, thus allowing the molds to grow again.

1. The spiders mentioned in the first paragraph are
   (1) parasites (3) herbivores
   (2) scavengers (4) carnivores
2. An increase in the bat population would most likely result in
   (1) a decrease in mold growth
   (2) a decrease in bat bug population
   (3) an increase in cricket population
   (4) an increase in the outside insect population
3. The food relationships in this cave are best indicated by the food chain
   (1) bat→wastes→mold→crickets→bat bugs
   (2) bats→batwastes→mold crickets
   (3) insects→bat wastes→mold crickets
   (4) bats→mold spiders→crickets
4. The mold mentioned in the passage is a
   (1) parasite (3) carnivore
   (2) herbivore (4) decomposer
5. Bat bugs in the cave are
   (1) herbivores (3) parasites
   (2) carnivores (4) producers

Name__________ Class__________ Date__________

CHAPTER 29: QUIZ

A. FILL-IN QUESTIONS

DIRECTIONS: Complete each of the following statements by writing the correct word or phrase in the space provided.

1. ____________________ are animals that feed on both plants and animals.
2. Food passes through an ecosystem in a path called a ____________________.
3. Athlete's foot is an example of a ____________________ relationship.
4. In ____________________, organisms of different species live together in close association.
5. Interconnecting food chains form ____________________.
6. Primary consumers always eat ____________________.
7. Organisms that feed on dead and decaying organisms are called ____________________.
8. The amount of usable energy decreases with each higher feeding level forming a ____________________ of energy.
9. In ____________________, one organism benefits and the other is harmed by the relationship.
10. The amount of living matter in an ecosystem makes up its ____________________.
11. Carnivores feed on ____________________.
12. In the carbon-oxygen cycle, ____________________ is released as a by-product of photosynthesis.
13. Secondary consumers eat ____________________.
14. A relationship where one organism benefits and the other is not harmed is called ____________________.
15. Herbivores eat ____________________.
16. Water changes into water vapor by the process of ____________________.
17. ____________________ is a relationship in which both organisms benefit.
18. A ____________________ community is a stable community.
19. Buzzards and vultures are examples of ____________________.
20. The first organisms to populate an area are called ____________________ organisms.

B. MULTIPLE-CHOICE QUESTIONS

DIRECTIONS: Circle the number of the expression that best completes each of the following statements.

1. Animals that kill and eat other animals are known as
   (1) scavengers
   (2) herbivores
   (3) predators
   (4) decomposers
2. The species composition of a community will change over a long period of time if the
   (1) environment changes
   (2) environment remains stable
   (3) same plants remain in the community
   (4) same animals remain in the community

Name____________________ Class____________________ Date__________

3. The gradual replacement of one species by another in a natural community is known as
   (1) a food web (3) ecological succession
   (2) food chain (4) energy transfer

4. In parasitism, one organism benefits and the other is harmed. An example of this type of relationship would be
   (1) a tapeworm living in a human
   (2) nitrogen-fixing bacteria on the roots of clover
   (3) a lichen living on a tree
   (4) a bird building a nest in a bush

5. In the cycle shown at the right, which organism will best complete the cycle when placed at position **X**?
   (1) green plant (3) virus
   (2) herbivore (4) decomposer

CONSUMER
PRODUCER
X
NITRATES IN THE SOIL

Directions (6-10): Base your answers to questions 6 through 10 on the diagram below and on your knowledge of biology.

grass ⟶ field mouse ⟶ snake ⟶ hawk

6. Which organism represents a primary consumer?
   (1) grass (3) hawk
   (2) snake (4) field mouse

7. Which organism is normally present in the greatest numbers?
   (1) grass (3) snake
   (2) field mouse (4) hawk

8. This diagram represents the ecological principle known as
   (1) bacterial decomposition (3) parasitism
   (2) a food chain (4) mutualism

9. Which organism is capable of carrying on photosynthesis?
   (1) grass (3) snake
   (2) field mouse (4) hawk

10. Which organisms are known as carnivores?
   (1) grass and snake (3) snake and field mouse
   (2) snake and hawk (4) field mouse and grass

C. ESSAY QUESTION

DIRECTIONS: Use complete sentences to answer the question in this part.

1. Name and describe the two processes of the water cycle.

____

____

____

____

____

____

Name______________________ Class______________________ Date__________

Chapter 30: Humans and the Environment

A. HUMAN REQUIREMENTS. Humans differ from all other kinds of organisms in their ability to change the environment. Human activities upset various natural systems and have had negative effects on the biotic and abiotic environment. Although most ecosystems can recover from minor disruptions, some human activities cause changes that cannot be reversed.

Humans need certain things to maintain their lives. Individual human requirements are listed below. In addition, a certain amount of land must be available for growing food. When human activities pollute the environment all of their requirements are reduced in value.

Human Requirements

- Clean Air and Water
- Nutritious Food
- Fertile Soil
- Space for Shelter and Living

Review Questions

1. How do humans differ from all other kinds of organisms? ______________________

____

2. How have humans affected the environment? ______________________

____

____

3. Name four individual human requirements. ______________________

____

4. What happens to human requirements when the environment is polluted? __________

____

B. HUMAN INTERACTIONS. In order to survive as a species humans need to interact with many different forms of life as well as with the nonliving environment. Although we humans are not aware of many of these interactions they are very important for our survival because these interactions may provide us with food, clothing, oxygen, or other requirements.

Human interaction also affects the lives of other organisms. Some organisms depend on our presence for their survival while others may be affected negatively by our activities. An organism whose survival depends on humans is the English sparrow. English sparrows live independently of humans but survive better if humans live nearby. This is because human houses provide nesting space for sparrows. Mayflies indirectly interact with humans because they are an important food source for game fish such as trout and bass. Three organisms that have been negatively affected by human activities are whales, whooping cranes, and bald eagles.

The nonliving environment provides us with many essential components upon which our survival depends. Human activities are increasingly changing the nonliving environment. The burning of coal and oil has added oxides of carbon, sulfur, and nitrogen to the air in significant quantities. Water and soil are also affected. Mineral resources of many types are becoming scarce as they are used in our technological and agricultural practices. **Technology** is the use of tools, machines, inventions, and scientific principles to do work and solve problems. Acid rain and the "*greenhouse effect*" are two examples of negative environmental changes caused by human technology. The way in which we change our physical environment will ultimately determine the survival of all living things including that of our own species. We will discuss these problems in more detail later in this chapter.

REVIEW QUESTIONS

1. Name three things provided by human interactions.

____

____

____

2. Name two organisms whose survival depends on humans.

____

____

3. Name three organisms that have been negatively affected by human activities.

____

____

4. What is technology? ______________________________

____

5. Name two negative changes humans have made to the nonliving environment.

____

____

C. HUMAN POPULATION GROWTH. Unlike that of naturally occurring species human population growth is not stable. Our population around the world is growing rapidly and has been doing so for the past two centuries (Figure 30-1). This is partly the result of medical knowledge and education, which have decreased the death rate from disease. Many ecosystems are unable to produce enough food because of rapid population growth. This has resulted in starvation in many countries. In other ecosystems food production has been greatly increased by human scientific discoveries and technology.

There are both positive and negative effects of the growth in the human population. However, some scientists estimate that we are rapidly approaching the limits of our ability to increase as a species. This is because of limiting factors such as the availability of food, clean water, and clear air.

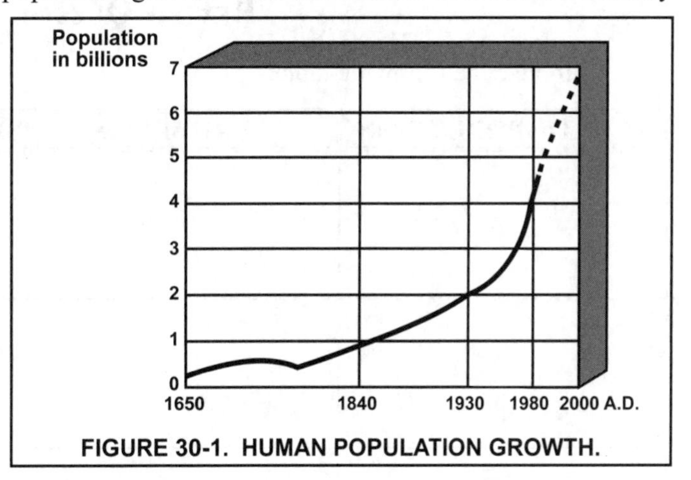

FIGURE 30-1. HUMAN POPULATION GROWTH.

REVIEW QUESTIONS

1. State two reasons why the human population is growing so rapidly. ____________________

____

D. ENVIRONMENTAL POLLUTION. One important result of the rapid growth of the human population and technology is the considerable increase in the amount of environmental pollution. A **pollutant** is something that is put into the air, water, or soil that makes it dirty and unfit for living things. Many substances become pollutants when their presence exceeds the capacity of natural systems to break them down, or they cannot be broken down, or they are toxic (poisonous). Three major types of environmental pollution are:

Major Types Of Environmental Pollution

♦ **WATER POLLUTION.** Water pollution interferes with our ability to obtain pure water for drinking, washing, recreation, and industry. Water pollutants include heat (**thermal pollution**), pesticides, sewage, heavy metals, and chemicals such as phosphates (from washing detergents) and PCB's (from industrial wastes). Phosphates are eaten by lake algae causing rapid growth known as **algal bloom.** The algae die and decompose. This uses up all the oxygen causing other aquatic organisms to suffocate and die from a lack of oxygen.

♦ **AIR POLLUTION.** Air pollution interferes with our ability to obtain clean air for breathing. It produces residues that are destructive to our buildings and machines. Smoke, ash, and soot are examples of air pollutants along with sulfur and nitrogen oxides, organic vapors, hydrocarbons, carbon monoxide, and carbon dioxide. Too much carbon dioxide in the air causes warming known as **"greenhouse effect".** Sulfur and nitrogen oxides combine with water vapor to create **acid rain**. Acid rain is harmful to organisms that live in lakes and forests. **Smog** forms when smoke, gas, and fog are warmed by sunlight.

♦ **SOIL POLLUTION.** Soil pollution interferes with our ability to obtain water from wells, reduces our enjoyment of recreational areas, and may kill soil decomposers important in the recycling of materials. Soil pollutants include organic chemicals, inorganic chemicals, solid wastes, and pesticides.

Name________________________ Class ________________________ Date ____________

REVIEW QUESTIONS

1. Complete the following table.

TYPE OF POLLUTION	PROBLEMS CAUSED	POLLUTANTS

2. What is a pollutant? ____

____

E. NEGATIVE HUMAN ACTIVITIES. Some human activities have led to the extinction or endangerment of many plant and animal species. An **endangered** species is a species that soon may completely disappear without some form of human protection. An **extinct** species has already entirely disappeared. Negative human activities include overhunting, importation of organisms, exploitation, poor land management, use of biocides, and improper waste disposal.

REVIEW QUESTIONS

1. What is the difference between an endangered species and an extinct species?

____

____

2. List five human activities that have a negative effect on plant and animal species.

____

____

F. OVERHUNTING AND EXPLOITATION. Unregulated hunting, fishing, and trapping have resulted in the extinction of species such as the dodo bird and the passenger pigeon. Many species that have been overhunted, including the blue whale, are endangered and close to extinction (Figure 30-2).

The **exploitation** (selfish use) of wild plants and animals for products and pets has disrupted ecosystems and endangered populations. The African elephant and the Pacific walrus have been hunted for their ivory tusks. The Colombian parrot has been captured for the pet trade, and the trees of the tropical rain forests have been cut for the manufacture of plywood.

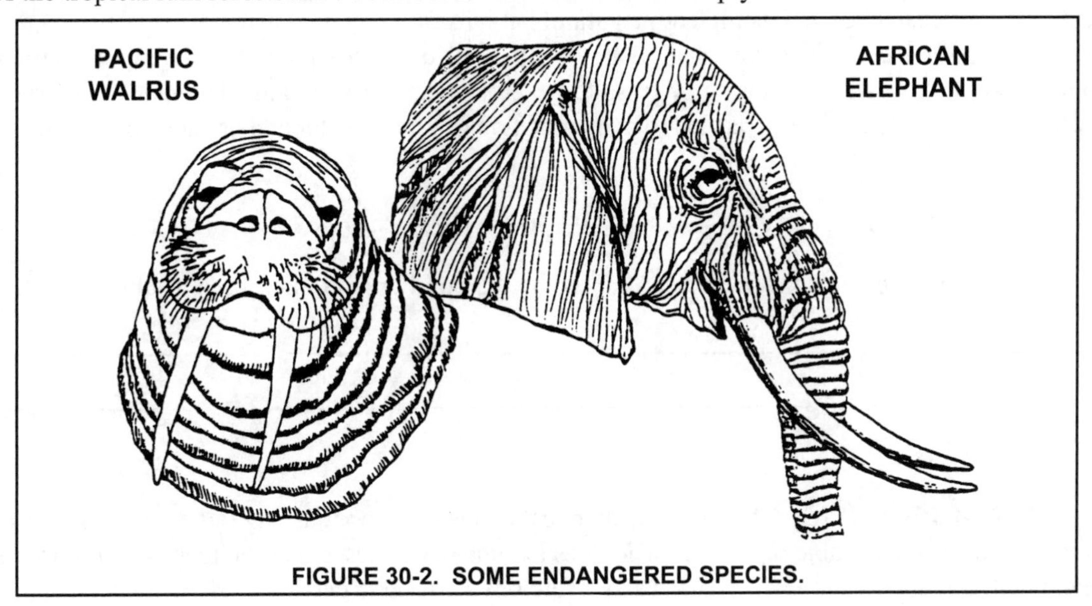

FIGURE 30-2. SOME ENDANGERED SPECIES.

REVIEW QUESTIONS

1. Name two species that have become extinct because of overhunting.

____

2. Name three endangered species and state the reason why they are endangered.

____

G. IMPORTATION OF ORGANISMS. Humans have accidentally and sometimes intentionally imported organisms into areas where they have no natural enemies. Without natural enemies organisms reproduce in large numbers. This leads to the disruption of an existing ecosystem. Examples of imported organisms that have caused extensive problems are the Japanese beetle, the gypsy moth, the starling, and the organisms that cause Dutch elm disease.

REVIEW QUESTIONS

1. What happens to organisms if they have no natural enemies?

____

____

2. Name two organisms that have no natural enemies.

____

____

H. POOR LAND MANAGEMENT. The rapid growth of cities and suburban areas around cities has reduced the land available for agriculture. It has also changed the watershed areas that replenish water supplies and disrupted the natural habitats of many organisms.

Attempts to increase agricultural productivity have led to overcropping, overgrazing, and failure to use cover crops. These, in turn, have resulted in erosion and loss of valuable topsoil. Excessive use of fertilizers and pesticides has led to contamination of groundwater and damage to wildlife.

REVIEW QUESTIONS

1. Name two problems that have been caused by the rapid growth of cities and suburban areas.

____

____

I. USE OF BIOCIDES. A **biocide** is a chemical that is used to kill living things such as insects, weeds, or other undesirable organisms. Biocides include pesticides and herbicides. **Pesticides**, for example DDT, are used to kill insect pests. **Herbicides** are used to destroy or slow down unwanted plant growth. These chemicals have, in some cases, contaminated the soil, air, and water supply. They have also disrupted food webs. This is because DDT and other chemicals are taken in by organisms at the bottom of food chains. As these organisms are eaten by larger organisms the chemicals collect in animal body tissues in increasingly greater amounts. This is harmful because DDT causes body systems to behave abnormally. Brown pelicans, peregrine falcons, and bald eagles are examples of birds that almost disappeared because of the effects of DDT. DDT spraying was banned in 1973 and these endangered birds are slowly beginning to increase in number.

Some human fat tissue has also been found to contain DDT that was at one time sprayed on grain fields to kill insects. When humans eat these grains or eat animals that have eaten these grains DDT collects in their body tissues.

REVIEW QUESTIONS

1. What is a biocide? ____

____

2. What is the difference between a pesticide and an herbicide? ____________________

____

____

3. Name three birds that have been endangered because of DDT. ____________________

____

____

Name________________________ Class______________________ Date______________

J. WASTE DISPOSAL. Modern life styles use many different kinds of products and require large amounts of energy. These needs create many wastes in the form of solids, chemicals, and nuclear materials. Disposing of these wastes has become a major pollution problem.

Solid wastes are biodegradable or nonbiodegradable. **Biodegradable** wastes can be broken down naturally by microorganisms into harmless materials and then recycled and reused by other organisms. Paper and cotton are biodegradable. **Nonbiodegradable** wastes such as plastics, aluminum, glass and disposable diapers, cannot be broken down.

REVIEW QUESTIONS

1. Name three types of wastes that have become a pollution problem. ____________________

____

2. ____________________ are wastes that can be broken down naturally into harmless materials.

3. Wastes that cannot be broken down are known as ________________________.

K. IMPROVING THE ENVIRONMENT. If population growth and environmental pollution are not slowed down they will probably become limiting factors for our species as well as other species. Through education humans are becoming better aware of their ecological interactions with the environment. This has resulted in changes in human attitudes and behavior. Individual understanding of ecological interactions is an important step toward improving the environment.

Scientists are constantly at work trying to increase our understanding of the natural world. Public support for environmental research will further the goal of improving the environment. Other attempts to correct problems caused by past negative activities include environmental laws for pollution controls, wildlife preservation, biological pest controls, and improvement in the conservation of resources.

REVIEW QUESTIONS

1. Why must we slow down population growth and environmental pollution?

____

____

____

2. List three ways that humans are trying to correct environmental problems.

____

____

____

3. What effect does education have on human behavior toward the environment.

____

____

____

Name________________________ Class ____________________ Date __________

L. ENVIRONMENTAL LAWS. Governmental agencies have begun to take responsibility for environmental protection by passing laws to stop the pollution of land, air, and water. They have also encouraged the development of new techniques for handling sanitation. These federal, state, and local laws regulate the use of natural resources and land development. Some environmental laws that will help improve the quality of our environment include:

Environmental Laws

- Freshwater Wetlands Act
- Hazardous Waste Disposal Regulations
- Air Pollution Control Laws
- State Environmental Quality Review (SEQR) Act
- Returnable Container Law
- Endangered Species Act

REVIEW QUESTIONS

1. List six environmental laws that will help improve the environment.

____

____

____

M. CONSERVATION OF NATURAL RESOURCES. Conservation involves the protection and wise use of our natural resources. **Natural resources** include the basic things in the natural world such as soil, water, air, energy, wildlife, and open space. Some resources such as water, air, soil, and wildlife are **renewable resources**. This means they can be reused or replaced. Other resources, for example fuels like gas, coal, and oil, cannot be replaced. Resources that cannot be replaced are known as **nonrenewable resources**.

The conservation of the limited natural resources available to us is necessary for the survival of the environment. Today communities are encouraging individuals to **recycle** (reuse) nonrenewable resources in an effort to conserve them.

Much soil is lost through **erosion** (wearing away by wind and water). Even though soil is a renewable resource it takes thousands of years to rebuild land so that it can be used for farming. Soil is conserved by reforestation (replanting forests) and growing cover crops. Alfalfa and clover are good cover crops because they can be planted close together to keep the soil from eroding. **Strip cropping**, **terracing**, and **contour plowing** are other methods of soil conservation (Figure 30-3).

Other efforts that are being made to conserve our natural resources include building **watersheds** to control the wasteful runoff of rain water. Also big water users, such as farms and industries, are being encouraged to conserve water, as much as possible, along with other natural resources. Communities in some areas have started discouraging overbuilding in an effort to preserve large open spaces.

Name________________________ Class________________________ Date________

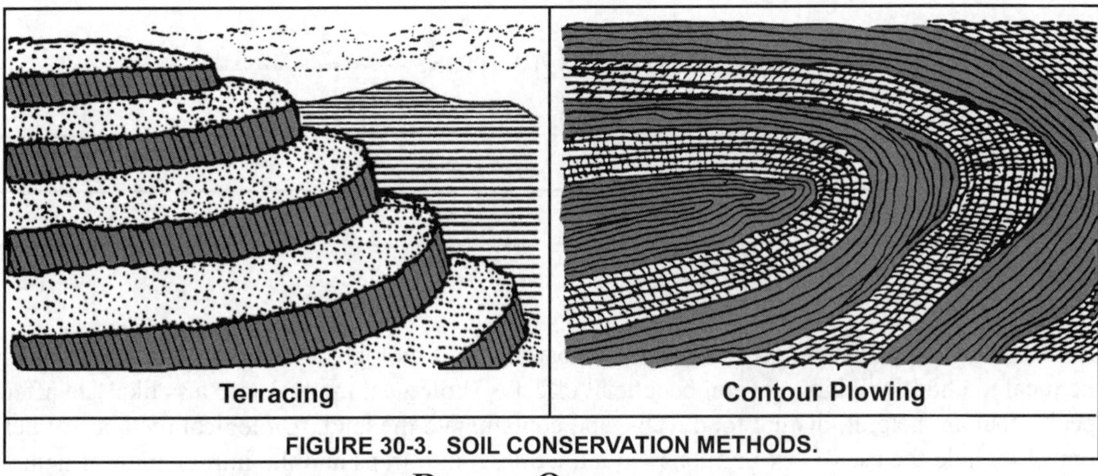

FIGURE 30-3. SOIL CONSERVATION METHODS.

REVIEW QUESTIONS

1. The protection and wise use of our natural resources is called ________________.
2. What is the difference between a renewable resource and a nonrenewable resource?

____

____

3. Name two renewable resources and two nonrenewable resources. ________________

____

4. ________________ control the wasteful runoff of rain water.

N. WILDLIFE PRESERVATION. Efforts are being made to help endangered species and to protect other forms of wildlife. In 1993, for example, a Georgia timber company signed an agreement with our Government to protect the red cockaded woodpecker that lives in its Southern forest lands (Figure 30-4) and the California gnatcatcher was declared a threatened species and their living areas are now under protection. Endangered species also have protected habitats provided by wildlife refuges and national parks. In addition, laws have been passed regulating overhunting and overfishing help to protect various species.

FIGURE 30-4. RED COCKADED WOODPECKER.

As a result of the laws, bisons and egrets that were once endangered are now increasing in number. The whooping crane, bald eagle, brown pelican, and peregrine falcon are just beginning to make a comeback, but still require careful protection.

Name__________ Class__________ Date__________

REVIEW QUESTIONS

1. Describe one wildlife preservation method. __________

____

____

O. BIOLOGICAL PEST CONTROLS. Substitution of biological methods of pest control for chemical methods will have several beneficial effects. Biological methods are less likely to affect species that are helpful, disrupt food webs, and contaminate the land. Biological methods of pest control include the use of sex hormones to attract pests into traps and the introduction of natural parasites of pests.

REVIEW QUESTIONS

1. Why are biological control methods better for the environment than chemical methods?

____

____

Name________________________ Class________________ Date__________

LAB INVESTIGATION: SOIL CONSERVATION

OBJECTIVE

Upon completion of this activity you should be able to state why soil conservation is important.

LABORATORY PROCEDURE

Materials: Two plants of the same species (e.g. ivy plants) that are identical in size and shape and planted in the same kind of soil. Distilled water, a "soil enricher" such as Miracle-Gro dissolved in water, labels, and marking pencils.

1. In this lab you will set up a controlled experiment to determine whether soil conditions affect plant growth.

2. Your teacher has provided you with two identical plants. Label one plant the **CONTROL PLANT** and the other plant the **EXPERIMENTAL PLANT.**

3. Place the plants near a window or in a lighted area. Water the *control plant* with a small amount of water once a week. Water the *experimental plant* with water containing Miracle-Gro once a week.

4. Observe the growth of your plants once a week for four weeks and write your observations in the **Observation Table** in the following section.

OBSERVATIONS

WEEK	OBSERVATIONS
1	
2	
3	
4	

Name________________ Class________________ Date________

CONCLUSIONS

1. State the problem for your experiment. ________________

2. What was the variable in your experiment? ________________

3. What was the control in your experiment? ________________

4. In a controlled experiment, you should test only ________ factor.

5. Describe how your plants changed over the four week period. ________________

6. What is your conclusion in this experiment? ________________

7. Name four soil conservation methods. ________________

8. Why is it important for humans to conserve soil? ________________

Name____________________ Class____________________ Date__________

REVIEW ACTIVITIES

Important Terms

DIRECTIONS: *Define the following terms in the spaces provided.*

algal bloom ____

biocide ____

biodegradable ____

conservation ____

contour plowing ____

endangered species ____

erosion ____

exploitation ____

extinct species ____

herbicide ____

natural resources ____

nonbiodegradable ____

nonrenewable resources ____

pesticide ____

Name____________________ Class____________________ Date__________

pollutant ____

recycle ____

renewable resources ______________________________________

smog ____

strip cropping ____

technology ____

terracing ____

thermal pollution ____

watersheds ____

Name________________________ Class________________________ Date________________

Skill Practice

Part A. Base your answers to questions 1 through 3 on the graph below and on your knowledge of biology. The graph illustrates a comparison between pH (acid/base) conditions and species survival rates in certain Adirondack lakes.

The Effect of pH on Survival Rates of Selected Species in Certain Adirondack Lakes

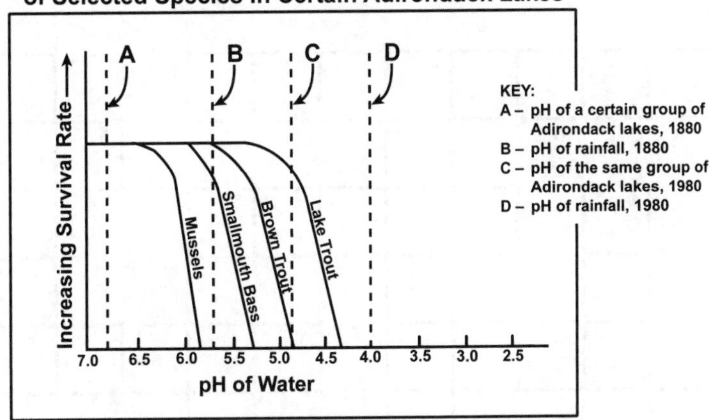

– *National Geographic (adapted)*

1. Which species can tolerate the highest level of acidity in its water environment?

(1) mussels (3) brown trout
(2) smallmouth bass (4) lake trout

2. In the years between 1880 and 1980, which species would most likely have been eliminated first due to the gradual acidification (to get more acid) of the Adirondack lakes?

(1) mussels (3) brown trout
(2) smallmouth bass (4) lake trout

3. What is the total change in the pH value of rainwater from 1880 to 1980?

(1) 1.3 (3) 5.3
(2) 1.7 (4) 9.7

Part B. Base your answers to questions 4 and 5 on the information below and on your knowledge of biology.

There is an urgent need to preserve the quality of the air, water, and land for the survival of future generations. The quality of these resources for future generations should be at least as good as, and possibly better than, it is now. Because of a rapid increase in the number of people in the world, it will be necessary to use materials over and over again to make sure that they are available for the people who come after us. Materials such as wood, paper, and cardboard may be broken down by decomposers and reused, but metal, glass, and plastic must be changed by industrial processes in order to be used again.

4. In the paragraph, the phrase "use materials over and over again" refers to

(1) pollution (3) diffusion
(2) parasitism (4) recycling

5. Which substance mentioned in the paragraph is biodegradable?

(1) paper (3) plastic
(2) glass (4) metal

Name________________________ Class________________________ Date__________

Part C. Complete the following crossword puzzle.

Crossword Puzzle

Clues

ACROSS

1. The wise use of natural resources
3. Plants and animals that will disappear without human protection
5. Water pollution interferes with our ability to obtain ________ water
7. _______ cropping is done to save soil
9. Kind of pollution caused by smog
11. Wearing away of soil
12. _______ bloom uses up oxygen in water
14. Kind of rain that harms lakes and forests
15. Elephants are hunted for their ______
16. Wastes that cannot be broken down
17. Hormones used for pest control
18. Selfish use of resources

DOWN

1. Type of plowing
2. ______ resources are air, water, and soil
4. Organisms that have already disappeared from Earth
6. Chemicals used to kill insect pests
8. Makes air, water, or oil dirty and unfit for living things
10. Watersheds control the wasteful runoff of ______ water
13. Organisms killed by herbicides

Name________________________ Class________________________ Date____________

CHAPTER 30: QUIZ

A. FILL-IN QUESTIONS

DIRECTIONS: Complete each of the following statements by writing the correct word or phrase in the space provided.

1. ________________________ pollution is the pollution of water by heat.
2. DDT is an example of a chemical compound called a/an ________________________.
3. If population growth is not slowed down it may become a/an ____________________ factor.
4. Sulfur and nitrogen oxides combine with water vapor to make ________________________.
5. A/an ________________________ species is one that may soon completely disappear without some human protection.
6. ________________________ wastes can be broken down naturally.
7. The bald eagle is an example of a/an ________________________ species.
8. Air, soil, and wildlife are ____________________________ resources.
9. ________________________ is the use of tools, machines, invention, and scientific principles to do work and solve problems.
10. ______________________ pest control methods are better for the environment than chemical methods.
11. Herbicides are used to destroy or slow down unwanted ______________________ growth.
12. Exploitation is the ________________ use of wild plants and animals for products and pets.
13. Recycling means the ________________________ of natural resources.
14. Imported organisms become pests if they have no ________________________.
15. ________________________ make the air, water, or soil dirty and unfit for living things.
16. Gas, oil, and coal are ________________________ resources.
17. A/an ________________________ species is one that has already disappeared from the earth.
18. ______________________ wastes cannot be broken down naturally.
19. Areas that control the wasteful runoff of rain water are called ________________________.
20. The passenger pigeon is an example of a/an ________________________ species.

B. MULTIPLE-CHOICE QUESTIONS

DIRECTIONS: Circle the number of the expression that best completes each of the following statements.

1. When pollutants in moist air are acted upon by sunlight, there is a greater chance of forming
   (1) fog (3) smog
   (2) soot (4) smoke
2. Which of the following substances does *not* decrease the quality of the air?
   (1) nitrogen dioxide (3) smoke
   (2) oxygen (4) carbon monoxide

Name________________________ Class________________________ Date ____________

3. The operation of modern sewage plants helps to decrease
   (1) water pollution
   (2) farmland runoff
   (3) noise pollution
   (4) radioactive contamination
4. Due to the rapid growth of the human population, certain animal and plant species have been classified as endangered. This means that certain animal and plant species
   (1) are causing the rapid growth of the human population
   (2) are becoming dangerous to humans
   (3) are overproducing
   (4) may become extinct
5. Humans had a negative influence on the quality of the environment by
   (1) contributing to the causes of acid rain
   (2) regulating hazardous waste disposal
   (3) regulating natural resource use
   (4) building sewage treatment plants
6. Major sources of air pollutants are
   (1) boats
   (2) trains
   (3) automobiles
   (4) oil spills
7. Thermal pollution would most likely be caused by
   (1) waste from sewers reaching groundwater
   (2) detergents being discharged into a lake
   (3) chemical pesticides being washed into a river
   (4) nuclear power plants discharging heated water into a river
8. The large number of active decay bacteria in Lake Erie has resulted in
   (1) an increase in food production
   (2) an increase in the fish population
   (3) a decrease in oxygen in the water
   (4) a decrease in evaporation of the water
9. The process of recycling involves the
   (1) oxidation of food
   (2) movement of animals from place to place
   (3) use and reuse of materials
   (4) oxidation of food
10. Which substance is biodegradable?
    (1) aluminum cans
    (2) glass bottles
    (3) disposable diapers
    (4) cotton rags

C. ESSAY QUESTION

DIRECTIONS: Use complete sentences to answer the question in this part.

1. State two ways humans have attempted to protect the environment.

____

____

____

____

____

____

Name________________________ Class ________________________ Date ____________

UNIT EIGHT TEST

Matching Questions

***DIRECTIONS:** In the space at the left of each item in Column A, place the letter of the term or phrase in Column B that is most closely related to that item.*

Column A	Column B
_________ **1.** All the populations in a given area.	**a.** Brown Pelican
_________ **2.** Combination of smoke, gas, and fog.	**b.** Carnivores
_________ **3.** Feed on dead organisms.	**c.** Biosphere
_________ **4.** An endangered species.	**d.** Evaporation
_________ **5.** Animals that eat only plants.	**e.** Acid Rain
_________ **6.** Water is changed into water vapor.	**f.** Condensation
_________ **7.** An extinct species.	**g.** Saprophytes
_________ **8.** Formed from sulfur and nitrogen oxides.	**h.** Community
_________ **9.** Animals that eat other animals.	**i.** Dodo Bird
_________**10.** The portion of the Earth on which life exsists.	**j.** Smog
	k. Herbivores
	l. Ecosystem

True–False Questions

***DIRECTIONS:** Write TRUE before each statement that is true and FALSE before each statement that is false.*

_________ **1.** The living things in the environment are the abiotic factors.

_________ **2.** Animals that feed on the dead animals they find are known as scavengers.

_________ **3.** Interconnecting food chains are called food webs.

_________ **4.** In parasitism the host organism benefits from the relationship.

_________ **5.** A marine biome is a freshwater biome.

_________ **6.** Little rain and extreme daily temperature changes are typical of the taiga biome.

_________ **7.** Green plants are classified as producers.

_________ **8.** A balanced aquarium is an example of an ecosystem.

_________ **9.** Disposable diapers are nonbiodegradable materials.

_________**10.** The wearing away of soil by wind and water is called exploitation.

Name________________________ Class____________________ Date__________

Fill-In Questions

DIRECTIONS: Complete each of the following statements by writing the correct word or phrase in the space provided.

1. The nonliving parts of the environment are known as ____________________ factors.
2. Carnivores are animals that feed on ____________________.
3. A/an ____________________ includes all the members of the same species that are found in a certain area.
4. In a food chain, the amount of usable energy ____________________ with each higher feeding level.
5. A stable community is called a ____________________ community.
6. The living and nonliving environments interacting together make up a/an ____________________.
7. ____________________ occurs when there is a struggle for limited resources among organisms living the same habitat.
8. The use of tools, machines, inventions, and scientific principles to do work and solve problems is called ____________________
9. An ____________________ species is one that may soon disappear with human protection.
10. ____________________ resources cannot be replaced.

Multiple-Choice Questions

DIRECTIONS: Circle the number of the expression that best completes each of the following statements.

1. Water pollution may be decreased by all the following *except*
   (1) proper treatment of sewage
   (2) use of biodegradable detergents
   (3) the addition of insecticides
   (4) building more sewage disposal plants
2. Thermal pollution of river water is most closely associated with
   (1) phosphate runoff
   (2) sewage plants
   (3) power plants
   (4) algae decay
3. Grizzly bears include meat as well as plant material in their diet. The grizzly bear can then be called
   (1) an herbivore
   (2) a carnivore
   (3) a vegetarian
   (4) an omnivore
4. Which material cannot be broken down by decomposers?
   (1) sewage
   (2) wood
   (3) cotton
   (4) glass
5. The primary source of energy for life on Earth is
   (1) wood
   (2) sunlight
   (3) oil
   (4) coal

Name________________________ Class________________________ Date____________

Directions (6-10): Base your answers to questions 6 through 10 on the diagram below that illustrates certain relationships among living things and on your knowledge of biology.

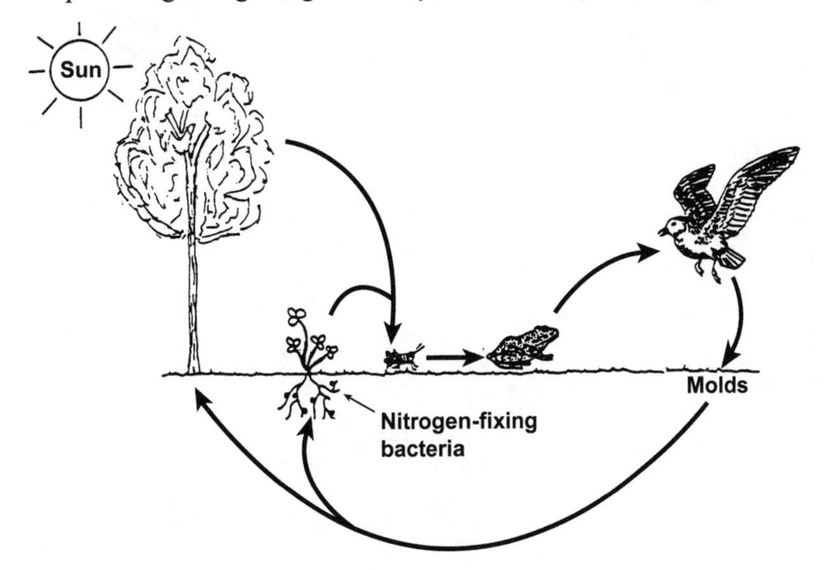

6. Which organism is classified as a herbivore?

(1) clover
(2) frog
(3) hawk
(4) insect

7. The molds are examples of organisms that are

(1) producers
(2) consumers
(3) predators
(4) decomposers

8. The relationship between the nitrogen-fixing bacteria and the clover plant is known as

(1) parasitism
(2) mutualism
(3) a food web
(4) a food pyramid

9. What gas produced by the tree is used by the frog for respiration?

(1) carbon dioxide
(2) nitrogen
(3) oxygen
(4) hydrogen

10. The diagram best illustrates

(1) a food chain
(2) a biome
(3) parasitism
(4) a population

Essay Question

DIRECTIONS: Use complete sentences to answer the question in this part.

1. Give two reasons why pesticide use should be controlled.

____

____

____

____

____

Class Notes

Index

A

B

C

D

E

F

G

H

O

P

R

S

T

U

V

W

X

Y

Z

Notes

Notes

Notes

Notes

Notes

Notes

Notes